Introduction to Organic Laboratory Techniques

Boston University

D1304763

Custom Edition

Donald L. Pavia | George S. Kriz | Gary M. Lampman
Randall G. Engel

CENGAGE
Learning

Australia • Brazil • Japan • Korea • Mexico • Singapore • Spain • United Kingdom • United States

CENGAGE
Learning·

Introduction to Organic Laboratory Techniques: Boston University, Custom Edition

Donald L. Pavia | George S. Kriz
Gary M. Lampman | Randall G. Engel

Senior Project Development Manager:
Linda deStefano

Market Development Manager:
Heather Kramer

Senior Production/Manufacturing Manager:
Donna M. Brown

Production Editorial Manager:
Kim Fry

Sr. Rights Acquisition Account Manager:
Todd Osborne

A Microscale Approach to Organic Laboratory Techniques, 5th Edition
Donald L. Pavia | George S. Kriz | Gary M. Lampman | Randall G. Engel
© 2013, 2007, 1999 and 1995 Cengage Learning. All rights reserved.

For product information and technology assistance, contact us at
Cengage Learning Customer & Sales Support, 1-800-354-9706
For permission to use material from this text or product,
submit all requests online at **cengage.com/permissions**
Further permissions questions can be emailed to
permissionrequest@cengage.com

This book contains select works from existing Cengage Learning resources and was produced by Cengage Learning Custom Solutions for collegiate use. As such, those adopting and/or contributing to this work are responsible for editorial content accuracy, continuity and completeness.

Compilation © 2013 Cengage Learning
ISBN-13: 978-1-285-91530-2

ISBN-10: 1-285-91530-5

Cengage Learning
5191 Natorp Boulevard
Mason, Ohio 45040
USA
Cengage Learning is a leading provider of customized learning solutions with office locations around the globe, including Singapore, the United Kingdom, Australia, Mexico, Brazil, and Japan. Locate your local office at:
international.cengage.com/region.

Cengage Learning products are represented in Canada by Nelson Education, Ltd.
For your lifelong learning solutions, visit **www.cengage.com/custom.**
Visit our corporate website at **www.cengage.com.**

Printed in the United States of America

Brief Contents

Excerpted from:

A Microscale Approach to Organic Laboratory Techniques,
5th Edition
Pavia | Kriz | Lampman | Engel

Excerpted from:
Introduction to Organic Laboratory Techniques: A Microscale Approach,
4th Edition
Pavia | Lampman | Kriz | Engel

Excerpted from:
Introduction to Organic Laboratory Techniques, A Microscale Approach
Second Edition
Pavia | Lampman | Kriz | Engel

Excerpted from:
A Microscale Approach to Organic Laboratory Techniques
5/e
Pavia | Lampman | Kriz | Engel

Excerpted from:
A Microscale Approach to Organic Laboratory Techniques
2nd Edition
Pavia | Lampman | Kriz | Engel

Acetylsalicylic Acid

Crystallization
Vacuum filtration
Melting point
Esterification

Aspirin (acetylsalicylic acid) can be prepared by the reaction between salicylic acid and acetic anhydride:

Salicylic acid   Acetic anhydride   Acetylsalicylic acid   Acetic acid

In this reaction, the **hydroxyl group** (—OH) on the benzene ring in salicylic acid reacts with acetic anhydride to form an **ester** functional group. Thus, the formation of acetylsalicylic acid is referred to as an **esterification** reaction. This reaction requires the presence of an acid catalyst, indicated by the H^+ above the equilibrium arrows.

When the reaction is complete, some unreacted salicylic acid and acetic anhydride will be present, along with acetylsalicylic acid, acetic acid, and the catalyst. The technique used to purify the acetylsalicylic acid from the other substances is called **crystallization.** This technique, which was introduced in Experiment 3, will be studied in more detail in Experiment 11. The basic principle is quite simple. At the end of this reaction, the reaction mixture will be hot, and all substances will be in solution. As the solution is allowed to cool, the solubility of acetylsalicylic acid will decrease, and it will gradually come out of solution, or crystallize. Because the other substances are either liquids at room temperature or are present in much smaller amounts, the crystals formed will be composed mainly of acetylsalicylic acid. Thus, a separation of acetylsalicylic acid from the other materials will have been accomplished. The purification process is facilitated by the addition of water after the crystals have formed. The water decreases the solubility of acetylsalicylic acid and dissolves some of the impurities.

The most likely impurity in the final product is salicylic acid itself, which can arise from incomplete reaction of the starting materials or from **hydrolysis** (reaction with water) of the product during the isolation steps. The hydrolysis reaction of acetylsalicylic acid produces salicylic acid. Salicylic acid and other compounds that contain a hydroxyl group on the benzene ring are referred to as **phenols.** Phenols form a highly colored complex with ferric chloride (Fe^{3+} ion). Aspirin is not a phenol, because it does not possess a hydroxyl group directly attached to the ring.

Because aspirin will not give the color reaction with ferric chloride, the presence of salicylic acid in the final product is easily detected. The purity of your product will also be determined by obtaining the melting point.

REQUIRED READING

Review: Introduction to Microscale Laboratory (Experiment 1)

	Technique 8	Filtration, Sections 8.1–8.6
	Technique 9	Physical Constants, Melting Points
New:	Technique 5	Measurement of Volume and Weight
	Technique 6	Heating and Cooling Methods
	Technique 7	Reaction Methods, Sections 7.1–7.4
	Essay	Aspirin

SPECIAL INSTRUCTIONS

This experiment involves concentrated phosphoric acid, which is highly corrosive. It will cause burns if it is spilled on the skin. Exercise care in handling it. The acetylsalicylic acid crystals should be allowed to air-dry overnight after filtration on the Hirsch funnel.

SUGGESTED WASTE DISPOSAL

Dispose of the aqueous filtrate in the container for aqueous waste.

PROCEDURE

Preparation of Acetylsalicylic Acid (Aspirin)

Prepare a hot water bath using a 250-mL beaker and a hot plate. Use about 100 mL of water and adjust the temperature to about 50°C. Weigh 0.210 g of salicylic acid ($MW = 138.1$) and place this in a **dry** 5-mL conical vial. It is not necessary for you to weigh exactly 0.210 g of salicylic acid. Try to obtain a weight within about 0.005 g of the indicated weight without spending excessive time at the balance. Record the actual weight in your notebook, and use this weight in any subsequent calculations. Using an automatic pipette or a dispensing pump, add 0.480 mL of acetic anhydride ($MW = 102.1$, $d = 1.08$ g/mL), followed by exactly one drop of concentrated phosphoric acid from a Pasteur pipette.

> **CAUTION**
>
> **Concentrated phosphoric acid is highly corrosive. You must handle it with great care.**

Add a magnetic spin vane (Technique 7, Figure 7.8A) and attach an air condenser to the vial. Clamp this assembly so that the vial is partially submerged in the hot water bath (Technique 6, Figure 6.6). Stir the mixture with the spin vane until the salicylic acid dissolves. (If the spin vane becomes stuck in the solid salicylic acid, insert a microspatula through the air condenser into the conical vial and gently push the spin vane until it begins spinning.) Heat the mixture for 8–10 minutes after the solid dissolves to complete the reaction.

Crystallization of Acetylsalicylic Acid

Remove the vial from the water bath and allow it to cool. After the vial has cooled enough for you to handle it, detach the air condenser and remove the spin vane with forceps or a magnetic stirring bar. (If you use forceps, be sure to clean them.) Place the conical vial in a small beaker and allow the vial to cool to room temperature, during which time the acetylsalicylic acid should begin to crystallize from the reaction mixture. If it does not crystallize, scratch the walls of the vial with a glass rod (not fire-polished) and cool the mixture slightly in an ice-water bath (Technique 11, Section 11.3C) until crystallization has occurred. (Scratching the inside walls of the container often helps to initiate crystallization.) After crystal formation is complete (usually when the product appears as a solid mass), add 3.0 mL of water (measured with a 10-mL graduated cylinder) and stir thoroughly with a microspatula.

Vacuum Filtration

Set up a Hirsch funnel for vacuum filtration (see Technique 8, Section 8.3, and Figure 8.5). Moisten the filter paper with a few drops of water and turn on the vacuum (or aspirator) to the fullest extent. Transfer the mixture in the conical vial to the Hirsch funnel. When you have removed as much product as possible from the vial, add about 1 mL of cold water to the vial using a calibrated Pasteur pipette. Stir the mixture and transfer the remaining crystals and water to the Hirsch funnel. When all the crystals have been collected in the funnel, rinse them with several 0.5-mL portions of cold water. Continue drawing air through the crystals on the Hirsch funnel by suction until the crystals are nearly dry (5–10 minutes). Remove the crystals for air-drying on a watch glass or clay plate. It is convenient to hold the filter paper disc with forceps while *gently* scraping the crystals off the filter paper with a microspatula. If the paper is scraped too hard, small pieces of paper will be removed along with the crystals. To dry the crystals completely, you must set the crystals aside overnight. Weigh the dry product and calculate the percentage yield of acetylsalicylic acid (*MW* = 180.2).

Ferric Chloride Test

Test for Purity

You can perform this test on a sample of your product that is not completely dry. To determine if there is any salicylic acid remaining in your product, carry out the following procedure. Obtain three small test tubes. Add 0.5 mL of water to each test tube. Dissolve a small amount of salicylic acid in the first tube. Add a similar amount of your product to the second tube. The third test tube, which contains only solvent, will serve as the control. Add one drop of 1% ferric chloride solution to each tube and note the color after shaking. Formation of an iron–phenol complex with Fe(lll) gives a definite color ranging from red to violet, depending on the particular phenol present.

Melting Point

As an additional test for purity, determine the melting point of your product (see Technique 9, Sections 9.5–9.8). The melting point must be obtained with a completely dried sample. Pure aspirin has a melting point of 135–136°C.

Place your product in a small vial, label it properly (Technique 2, Section 2.4), and submit it to your instructor.

Aspirin Tablets   Aspirin tablets are acetylsalicylic acid pressed together with a small amount of inert binding material. Common binding substances include starch, methylcellulose, and microcrystalline cellulose. You can test for the presence of starch by boiling approximately one-fourth of an aspirin tablet with 2 mL of water. Cool the liquid and add a drop of iodine solution. If starch is present, it will form a complex with the iodine. The starch–iodine complex is deep blue-violet. Repeat this test with a commercial aspirin tablet and with the acetylsalicylic acid prepared in this experiment.

QUESTIONS

1. What is the purpose of the concentrated phosphoric acid used in the first step?

2. What would happen if the phosphoric acid were left out?

3. If you used 250 mg of salicylic acid and excess acetic anhydride in the preceding synthesis of aspirin, what would be the theoretical yield of acetylsalicylic acid in moles? In milligrams?

4. What is the equation for the decomposition reaction that can occur with aspirin in water?

5. Most aspirin tablets contain five grains of acetylsalicylic acid. How many milligrams is this? (*Hint*: See the essay "Aspirin.")

6. A student performed the reaction in this experiment using a water bath at 90°C instead of 50°C. The final product was tested for the presence of phenols with ferric chloride. This test was negative (no color observed); however, the melting point of the dry product was 122–125°C. Explain these results as completely as possible.

7. If the aspirin crystals were not completely dried before the melting point was determined, what effect would this have on the observed melting point?

Analgesics

Acylated aromatic amines (those having an acyl group, $R-\overset{\overset{\displaystyle O}{\|}}{C}-$, substituted on nitrogen) are important in over-the-counter headache remedies. Over-the-counter drugs are those you may buy without a prescription. Acetanilide, phenacetin, and acetaminophen are mild analgesics (relieve pain) and antipyretics (reduce fever) and are important, along with aspirin, in many nonprescription drugs.

Acetanilide   **Phenacetin**   **Acetaminophen**

© Cengage Learning 2013

The discovery that acetanilide was an effective antipyretic came about by accident in 1886. Two doctors, Cahn and Hepp, had been testing naphthalene as a possible **vermifuge** (an agent that expels worms). Their early results on simple worm cases were very discouraging, so Dr. Hepp decided to test the compound on a patient with a larger variety of complaints, including worms—a sort of shotgun approach. A short time later, Dr. Hepp excitedly reported to his colleague, Dr. Cahn, that naphthalene had miraculous fever-reducing properties.

In trying to verify this observation, the doctors discovered that the bottle they thought contained naphthalene apparently did not. In fact, the bottle brought to them by their assistant had a label so faint as to be illegible. They were sure that the sample was not naphthalene, because it had no odor. Naphthalene has a strong odor reminiscent of mothballs. So close to an important discovery, the doctors were nevertheless stymied. They appealed to Hepp's cousin, who was a chemist in a nearby dye factory, to help them identify the unknown compound. This compound turned out to be acetanilide, a compound with a structure not at all like that of naphthalene. Certainly, Hepp's unscientific and risky approach would be frowned on by doctors today; and to be sure, the Food and Drug Administration (FDA) would never allow human testing before extensive animal testing (consumer protection has greatly progressed). Nevertheless, Cahn and Hepp made an important discovery.

Naphthalene

© Cengage Learning 2013

5

In another instance of serendipity, Cahn and Hepp's publication, describing their experiments with acetanilide, caught the attention of Carl Duisberg, director of research at the Bayer Company in Germany. Duisberg was confronted with the problem of how to profitably get rid of nearly 50 tons of *p*-aminophenol, a by-product of the synthesis of one of Bayer's other commercial products. He immediately saw the possibility of converting *p*-aminophenol to a compound similar in structure to acetanilide by putting an acyl group on the nitrogen. It was then believed, however, that all compounds having a hydroxyl group on a benzene ring (that is, phenols) were toxic. Duisberg devised a scheme of structural modification of *p*-aminophenol to synthesize the compound phenacetin. The reaction scheme is shown here.

Phenacetin turned out to be a highly effective analgesic and antipyretic. A common form of combination pain reliever called an APC tablet was once available. An APC tablet contained **A**spirin, **P**henacetin, and **C**affeine (hence, **APC**). Phenacetin is no longer used in commercial pain-relief preparations as it was discovered that not all aromatic hydroxyl groups lead to toxic compounds. Today the compound acetaminophen is very widely used as an analgesic in place of phenacetin.

Another analgesic, structurally similar to aspirin, that has found some application is **salicylamide.** Salicylamide is a n ingredient in some pain-relief preparations, although its use is declining.

Upon continued or excessive use, acetanilide can cause a serious blood disorder called **methemoglobinemia**. In this disorder, the central iron atom in hemoglobin is converted from Fe(II) to Fe(III) to give methemoglobin. Methemoglobin will not function as an oxygen carrier in the bloodstream. The result is a type of anemia (deficiency of hemoglobin or lack of red blood cells). Phenacetin and acetaminophen cause the same disorder, but to a much lesser degree. Because they are also more effective as antipyretic and analgesic drugs than acetanilide, they are preferred remedies. Acetaminophen is marketed under a variety of trade names, including Tylenol, Datril, and Panadol, and is often successfully used by people who are allergic to aspirin.

Heme portion of blood-oxygen carrier, hemoglobin.

© Cengage Learning 2013

More recently, a new drug has appeared in over-the-counter preparations. This drug is **ibuprofen,** which was initially marketed as a prescription drug in the United States under the name Motrin. Ibuprofen was first developed and patented in England in 1961. The United States obtained marketing rights in 1974. Ibuprofen is now sold without a prescription under several brand names, which include Advil, Motrin, and Nuprin. Ibuprofen is principally an anti-inflammatory drug, but it is also effective as an analgesic and an antipyretic. It is particularly effective in treating the symptoms of rheumatoid arthritis and menstrual cramps. Ibuprofen appears to control the production of prostaglandins, which parallels aspirin's mode of action. An important advantage of ibuprofen is that it is a very powerful pain reliever. One 200-mg tablet is as effective as two tablets (650 mg) of aspirin. Furthermore, ibuprofen has a more advantageous dose–response curve, which means that taking two tablets of this drug is approximately twice as effective as one tablet for certain types of pain. Aspirin and acetaminophen reach their maximum effective dose at two tablets. Little additional relief is gained at doses above that level. Ibuprofen, however, continues to increase its effectiveness up to the 400-mg level (the equivalent of four tablets of aspirin or acetaminophen). Ibuprofen is a relatively safe drug, but its use should be avoided in cases of aspirin allergy, kidney problems, ulcers, asthma, hypertension, or heart disease.

Analgesics and caffeine in some common preparations

	Aspirin	*Acetaminophen*	*Caffeine*
Aspirin*	0.325 g	—	—
Anacin	0.400 g	—	0.032 g
Bufferin	0.325 g	—	—
Cope	0.421 g	—	0.032 g
Excedrin (Extra-Strength)	0.250 g	0.250 g	0.065 g
Tylenol	—	0.325 g	—
B. C. Tablets	0.325 g	—	0.016 g
Advil	—	—	—
Aleve	—	—	—
Orudis	—	—	—

Note: Nonanalgesic ingredients (e.g., buffers) are not listed.

*5-grain tablet (1 grain = 0.0648 g).

© Cengage Learning 2013

$$CH_3 - CH - CH_2 - \text{(ring)} - CH - COOH$$

(with CH₃ branch on the left carbon and CH₃ above the right CH)

Ibuprofen

© Cengage Learning 2013

The Food and Drug Administration has also approved two other drugs with similar structures to ibuprofen for over-the-counter use as pain relievers. These new drugs are known by their generic names, **naproxen** and **ketoprofen.** Naproxen is often administered in the form of its sodium salt. Naproxen and ketoprofen can be used to alleviate the pain of headaches, toothaches, muscle aches, backaches, arthritis, and menstrual cramps, and they can also be used to reduce fever. They appear to have a longer duration of action than the older analgesics.

Naproxen

Ketoprofen

© Cengage Learning 2013

Salicylamide	Ibuprofen	Ketoprofen	Naproxen
—	—	—	—
—	—	—	—
—	—	—	—
—	—	—	—
—	—	—	—
—	—	—	—
0.095 g	—	—	—
—	0.200 g	—	—
—	—	—	0.220 g
—	—	0.0125 g	—

REFERENCES

Barr, W. H.; Penna, R. P. O-T-C Internal Analgesics. In *Handbook of Non-Prescription Drugs*, 7th ed.; Griffenhagen, G. B., Ed.; American Pharmaceutical Association: Washington, DC, 1982.

Bugg, C. E.; Carson, W. M.; and Montgomery, J. A. Drugs by Design. *Sci. Am.* **1993,** *269* (Dec), 92.

Flower, R. J.; Moncada, S.; and Vane, J. R. Analgesic-Antipyretics and Anti-inflammatory Agents; Drugs Employed in the Treatment of Gout. In *The Pharmacological Basis of Therapeutics*, 7th ed.; Gilman, A. G., Goodman, L. S., Rall, T. W., and Murad, F., Eds.; Macmillan: New York **1985.**

Hansch, C. Drug Research or the Luck of the Draw. *J Chem. Educ.* **1974,** *51,* 360.

The New Pain Relievers. *Consum. Rep.* **1984,** *49* (Nov), 636–638.

Ray, O. S. Internal Analgesics. *Drugs, Society, and Human Behavior*, 2nd ed.; C. V. Mosby: St. Louis, 1978.

Senozan, N. M. Methemoglobinemia: An Illness Caused by the Ferric State. *J. Chem. Educ.* **1985,** *62* (Mar), 181.

Isolation of the Active Ingredient in an Analgesic Drug

Extraction
Filtration
Melting point

Most analgesic (pain-relieving) drugs found on the shelves of any drug or grocery store generally fall into one of four categories. These drugs may contain **acetylsalicylic acid, acetaminophen,** or **ibuprofen** as the active ingredient, or some **combination** of these compounds may be used in a single preparation. All tablets, regardless of type, contain a large amount of starch or other inert substance. This material acts as a binder to keep the tablet from falling apart and to make it large enough to handle. Some analgesic drugs also contain caffeine or buffering agents. In addition, many tablets are coated to make them easier to swallow and to prevent users from experiencing the unpleasant taste of the drugs.

Acetylsalicylic acid

Acetaminophen

Ibuprofen

© Cengage Learning 2013

The three drugs, along with their melting points (MP) and common brand names, follow:

Drug	MP	Brand Names
Acetylsalicylic acid	135–136°C	Aspirin, ASA, acetylsalicylic acid, generic aspirin, Empirin
Acetaminophen	169–170.5°C	Tylenol, Datril, Panadol, nonaspirin pain reliever (various brands)
Ibuprofen	75–77°C	Advil, Brufen, Motrin, Nuprin

© Cengage Learning 2013

The purpose of this experiment is to demonstrate some important techniques that are applied throughout this textbook and to allow you to become accustomed to working in the laboratory at the microscale level. More specifically, you will extract

9

(dissolve) the active ingredient of an analgesic drug by mixing the powdered tablet with a solvent, methanol. Two steps are required to remove the fine particles of binder, which remain suspended in the solvent. First, you will use centrifugation to remove most of the binder. The second step will be a filtration technique using a Pasteur pipette packed with alumina (finely ground aluminum oxide). The solvent will then be evaporated to yield the solid analgesic, which will be collected by filtration on a Hirsch funnel. Finally, you will test the purity of the drug by doing a melting-point determination.

REQUIRED READING

Review: Experiment 1   Introduction to Microscale Laboratory

New: Technique 7   Reaction Methods, Section 7.9

Technique 8   Filtration, Sections 8.1–8.6

Technique 9   Physical Constants of Solids: The Melting Point

SPECIAL INSTRUCTIONS

You will be allowed to select an analgesic that is a member of one of the categories described previously. You should use an uncoated tablet that contains only a single ingredient analgesic and binder. If it is necessary to use a coated tablet, try to remove the coating when the tablet is crushed. To avoid decomposition of aspirin, it is essential to minimize the length of time that it remains dissolved in methanol. Do not stop this experiment until after the drug is dried on the Hirsch funnel.

SUGGESTED WASTE DISPOSAL

Dispose of any remaining methanol in the waste container for nonhalogenated organic solvents. Place the alumina in the container designated for wet alumina.

PROCEDURE

Extraction of Active Ingredient

If you are isolating aspirin or acetaminophen, use *one* tablet in this procedure. If you are isolating ibuprofen, use *two* tablets. Using a pestle, crush the tablet (or tablets) between two pieces of weighing paper. If the tablet is coated, try to remove fragments of the coating material with forceps after the tablet is first crushed. Add all the powdered material to a 3-mL conical vial. Using a calibrated Pasteur pipette, add about 2 mL of methanol to the vial. Cap the vial and mix thoroughly by shaking. Loosen the cap at least once during the mixing process to release any pressure that may build up in the vial.

Allow the undissolved portion of the powder to settle in the vial. A cloudy suspension may remain even after 5 minutes or more. You should wait only until it is obvious that the larger particles have settled completely. Using a filter-tip pipette (Technique 8, Figure 8.9), transfer the liquid phase to a centrifuge tube. Add a second 2-mL portion of methanol to the conical vial and repeat the shaking process described previously. After the solid has settled, transfer the liquid phase to the centrifuge tube containing the first extract.

Place the tube in a centrifuge along with another centrifuge tube of equal weight on the opposite side. Centrifuge the mixture for two to three minutes. The suspended solids should collect on the bottom of the tube, leaving a clear or nearly clear **supernatant liquid,** the liquid above the solid. If the liquid is still quite cloudy, repeat the centrifugation for a longer period or at a higher speed. Being careful not to disturb the solid at the bottom of the tube, transfer the supernatant liquid with a Pasteur pipette to a test tube or small beaker.

Column Chromatography

2.0 cm — Alumina
— Cotton

Column for purifying an analgesic drug.

Prepare an alumina column using a Pasteur pipette, as shown in the figure. Insert a small ball of cotton into the top of the column. Using a long, thin object such as a glass stirring rod or a wooden applicator stick, push the cotton down so that it fits into the Pasteur pipette where the constriction begins. Add about 0.5 g of alumina to the pipette and tap the column with your finger to pack the alumina. Clamp the pipette in a vertical position so that the liquid can drain from the column into a small beaker or a 5-mL conical vial. Place a small beaker under the column. With a calibrated Pasteur pipette, add about 2 mL of methanol to the column and allow the liquid to drain until the level of the methanol just reaches the top of the alumina. Once methanol has been added to the alumina, the top of the alumina in the column should not be allowed to run dry. If necessary, add more methanol.

NOTE: It is essential that the methanol not be allowed to drain below the surface of the alumina.

When the level of the methanol reaches the surface of the alumina, transfer the solution containing the drug from the beaker or test tube to the column using a Pasteur pipette. Collect the liquid that passes through the column into a 5-mL conical vial. When all the liquid from the beaker has been added to the column and has penetrated the alumina, add an additional 1 mL of methanol to the column and allow it to drain. This ensures that all the analgesic drug has been eluted from the column.

Evaporation of Solvent

If you are isolating aspirin, it is essential that the following evaporation procedure be completed in 10–15 minutes. Otherwise, the aspirin may partially decompose. Using a Pasteur pipette, transfer about half the liquid in the 5-mL conical vial to another small container. Evaporate the methanol in the 5-mL conical vial using a water bath at about 50°C (Technique 7, Section 7.10).[1] To speed evaporation, direct a gentle stream of dry air or nitrogen into the vial containing the liquid. Evaporate the solvent until the volume is less than about 1 mL. Then add the remainder of the liquid and continue evaporation.

When the solvent has completely evaporated or it is apparent that the remaining liquid is no longer evaporating, remove the vial from the water bath (or sand bath) and allow it to cool to room temperature. (The volume of liquid should be less than 0.5 mL when you discontinue evaporation.) If liquid remains, which is likely with the ibuprofen- or acetaminophen-containing analgesics, place the cool vial in an ice-water bath for 10–15 minutes. Prepare the ice-water bath in a small beaker, using both ice and water. Be sure that the vial cannot tip over. Crystallization of the product may occur more readily if you scrape the inside of the vial with a microspatula or a glass rod (not fire-polished). If the solid is hard and clumped,

---

[1] As an alternative, you may use a sand bath at about 50°C.

you should use a microspatula to break up the solid as much as possible before going on to the next step.

Vacuum Filtration

Set up a Hirsch funnel for vacuum filtration (see Technique 8, Section 8.3, and Figure 8.5). Moisten the filter paper with a few drops of methanol and turn on the vacuum (or aspirator) to the fullest extent. Use a microspatula to transfer the material in the conical vial to the Hirsch funnel. The vacuum will draw any remaining solvent from the crystals. Allow the crystals to dry for 5–10 minutes while air is drawn through the crystals in the Hirsch funnel.

Carefully scrape the dried crystals from the filter paper onto a tared (previously weighed) watch glass. If necessary, use a spatula to break up any remaining large pieces of solid. Allow the crystals to air-dry on the watch glass. To determine when the crystals are dry, move them around with a dry spatula. When the crystals no longer clump or cling to the spatula, they should be dry. If you are working with ibuprofen, the solid will be slightly sticky even when it is completely dried. Weigh the watch glass with the crystals to determine the weight of analgesic drug that you have isolated. Use the weight of the active ingredient specified on the label of the container as a basis for calculating the weight percentage recovery.

Use a small sample of the crystals to determine the melting point (see Technique 9, Sections 9.5–9.8). Crush the crystals into a powder, using a stirring rod, in order to determine their melting point. You may observe some "sweating" or shrinkage (see Technique 9, Section 9.7) before the substance actually begins to melt. The beginning of the melting-point range is when actual melting is observed, not when the solid takes on a slightly wet or shiny appearance or when shrinkage occurs. If you have isolated ibuprofen, the melting point may be somewhat lower than that given at the beginning of this experiment.

At the instructor's option, place your product in a small vial, label it properly (Technique 2, Section 2.4), and submit it to your instructor.

QUESTIONS

1. Why was the percentage recovery less than 100%? Give several reasons.
2. Why was the tablet crushed?
3. What was the purpose of the centrifugation step?
4. What was the purpose of the alumina column?
5. If 185 mg of acetaminophen were obtained from a tablet containing 350 mg of acetaminophen, what would be the weight percentage recovery?
6. A student who was isolating aspirin stopped the experiment after the filtration step with alumina. One week later, the methanol was evaporated and the experiment was completed. The melting point of the aspirin was found to be 110–115°C. Explain why the melting point was low and why the melting range was so wide.

Acetaminophen

Decolorization

Filtration

Crystallization

Use of a Craig tube or Hirsch funnel

Preparation of an amide

Preparation of acetaminophen involves treating an amine with an acid anhydride to form an amide. In this case, *p*-aminophenol, the amine, is treated with acetic anhydride to form acetaminophen (*p*-acetamidophenol), the amide.

© Cengage Learning 2013

The crude solid acetaminophen contains dark impurities carried along with the *p*-aminophenol starting material. These impurities, which are dyes of unknown structure, are formed from oxidation of the starting phenol. Although the amount of the dye impurity is small, it is intense enough to impart color to the crude acetaminophen. Most of the colored impurity is destroyed by heating the crude product with sodium dithionite (sodium hydrosulfite $Na_2S_2O_4$). The dithionite reduces double bonds in the colored dye to produce colorless substances.

The decolorized acetaminophen is collected on a Hirsch funnel. It is further purified by crystallization from a methanol/water mixture. There are two procedures given in this experiment. Experiment 11A involves crystallization using a Craig tube, whereas Experiment 11B is a larger-scale reaction involving an Erlenmeyer flask and Hirsch funnel for crystallization.

REQUIRED READING

Review: Experiment 1   Introduction to Microscale Laboratory
                                            (Experiment 1)

              Techniques 5 and 6

              Technique 7   Reaction Methods, Sections 7.1–7.3

	Technique 8	Filtration, Sections 8.1–8.6
	Technique 9	Physical Constants, Melting Points
New:	Technique 8	Filtration, Section 8.7
	Technique 11	Crystallization
	Essay	Analgesics

SPECIAL INSTRUCTIONS

Acetic anhydride can cause irritation of tissue, especially in nasal passages. Avoid breathing the vapor, and avoid contact with skin and eyes. *p*-Aminophenol is a skin irritant and is toxic.

WASTE DISPOSAL

Aqueous solutions obtained from filtration operations should be poured into the container designated for aqueous wastes. This includes the filtrates from the methanol and water crystallization steps.

NOTES TO THE INSTRUCTOR

The *p*-aminophenol acquires a black color on standing due to air oxidation. It is best to use a recently purchased sample, which usually is gray. If necessary, black material can be decolorized by heating it in a 10% aqueous solution of sodium dithionite (sodium hydrosulfite) prior to starting the experiment.

 EXPERIMENT 11A

Acetaminophen (Microscale Procedure)

PROCEDURE

Reaction Mixture

Weigh about 0.150 g of *p*-aminophenol (*MW* = 109.1) and place this in a 5-mL conical vial. Using an automatic pipette (or a dispensing pump or a graduated pipette), add 0.450 mL of water and 0.165 mL of acetic anhydride (*MW* = 102.1, *d* = 1.08 g/mL). Place a spin vane in the conical vial and attach an air condenser.

Heating

Heat the reaction mixture with an aluminum block or sand bath at about 120°C (see inset in Technique 6, Figure 6.2A) and stir gently. If you are using a sand bath, the conical vial should be partially buried in the sand so that the vial is nearly at the bottom of the sand bath. After the solid has dissolved (it may dissolve, precipitate, and redissolve), heat the mixture for an additional 20 minutes to complete the reaction.

Isolation of Crude Acetaminophen

Remove the vial from the heat and allow it to cool. When the vial has cooled to the touch, detach the air condenser and remove the spin vane with clean forceps or a magnet. Rinse the spin vane with two or three drops of warm water, allowing the water to drop into the conical vial. Place the conical vial in a small beaker and let it cool to room temperature. If crystallization has not occurred, scratch the inside of the vial with a glass stirring rod to initiate crystallization. Cool the mixture thoroughly in an ice bath for 15–20 minutes and collect the crystals by vacuum filtration on a Hirsch funnel (see Technique 8, Section 8.3, and Figure 8.5). Rinse the vial with about 0.5 mL of ice water and transfer this mixture to the Hirsch funnel. Wash the crystals on the funnel with two additional 0.5-mL portions of ice water. Dry the crystals for 5–10 minutes by allowing air to be drawn through them while they remain on the Hirsch funnel. Transfer the product to a watch glass or clay plate and allow the crystals to dry in air. It may take several hours for the crystals to dry completely, but you may go on to the next step before they are totally dry. Weigh the crude product and set aside a small sample for a melting-point determination and a color comparison after the next step. Calculate the percentage yield of crude acetaminophen ($MW = 151.2$). Record the appearance of the crystals in your notebook.

Decolorization of Crude Acetaminophen

Dissolve 0.2 g of sodium dithionite (sodium hydrosulfite) in 1.5 mL of water in a 5-mL conical vial. Add your crude acetaminophen to the vial. Heat the mixture at about 100°C for 15 minutes, with occasional stirring with a microspatula. Some of the acetaminophen will dissolve during the decolorization process. Cool the mixture thoroughly in an ice bath for about 10 minutes to reprecipitate the decolorized acetaminophen (scratch the inside of the vial, if necessary, to induce crystallization). Collect the purified material by vacuum filtration on a Hirsch funnel, using small portions (about 0.5 mL total) of ice water to aid the transfer. Dry the crystals for 5–10 minutes by allowing air to be drawn through them while they remain on the Hirsch funnel. You may go on to the next step before the material is totally dry. Weigh the purified acetaminophen and compare the color of the purified material to that obtained in the preceding paragraph.

Crystallization of Acetaminophen

Place the purified acetaminophen in a Craig tube. Crystallize the material from a solvent mixture composed of 50% water and 50% methanol by volume (aluminum block or sand bath set at about 100°C). Follow the crystallization procedure described in Technique 11, Section 11.4, and Figure 11.6. The solubility of acetaminophen in this hot (nearly boiling) solvent is about 0.2 g/mL. Although you can use this as a rough indication of how much solvent is required to dissolve the solid, you should still use the technique shown in Figure 11.6 to determine how much solvent to add. Add small portions (several drops) of hot solvent until the solid dissolves. Step 2 in Figure 11.6 (removal of insoluble impurities) should not be required in this crystallization. When the solid has dissolved, place the Craig tube in a 10-mL Erlenmeyer flask, insert the inner plug of the Craig tube, and let the solution cool.

When the mixture has cooled to room temperature, place the Craig tube in an ice-water bath for several minutes. If necessary, induce crystallization by gently scratching the inside of the Craig tube with your microspatula (Technique 11, Section 11.8B). Because acetaminophen may crystallize *slowly* from the solvent, continue to cool the Craig tube in an ice bath for at least 10 minutes. Collect the crystals using the apparatus shown in Technique 8, Figure 8.11. Place the assembly in a centrifuge (be sure it is balanced by a centrifuge tube filled with water so that both tubes contain the same weight) and turn on the centrifuge for several minutes. Collect the crystals on a watch glass or piece of smooth paper, as shown in Technique 11, Figure 11.6. Set the crystals aside to air-dry. Very little additional time should be required to complete the drying.

Yield Calculation and Melting-Point Determination

Weigh the crystallized acetaminophen ($MW = 151.2$) and calculate the percentage yield. This calculation should be based on the number of moles of the limiting reagent used at the beginning of this procedure. Determine the melting point of the product. Compare the melting point of the final product with that of the crude acetaminophen. Also compare the colors of the crude, decolorized, and pure acetaminophen. Pure acetaminophen melts at 169.5–171°C. Place your product in a properly labeled vial and submit it to your instructor.

 EXPERIMENT 11B

Acetaminophen (Semimicroscale Procedure)

PROCEDURE

Reaction Mixture

Weigh about 0.400 g of *p*-aminophenol ($MW = 109.1$) and place this in a 5-mL conical vial. Using an automatic pipette (or a dispensing pump or a graduated pipette), add 1.20 mL of water and 0.450 mL of acetic anhydride ($MW = 102.1$, $d = 1.08$ g/mL). Place a spin vane in the conical vial and attach an air condenser.

Heating

Heat the reaction mixture with an aluminum block or a sand bath at about 120°C (see inset in Technique 7, Figure 7.6A) and stir gently. If you are using an aluminum block, position the vial so that it is touching the surface of the hot plate and place aluminum collars around the vial. If you are using a sand bath, the conical vial should be partially buried in the sand so that the vial is nearly at the bottom of the sand bath. After the solid has dissolved (it may dissolve, precipitate, and redissolve), heat the mixture for an additional 20 minutes to complete the reaction.

Isolation of the Crude Acetaminophen

Remove the vial from the heat and allow it to cool. When the vial has cooled to the touch, detach the air condenser and remove the spin vane with clean forceps or a magnet. Rinse the spin vane with two or three drops of warm water, allowing the water to drop into the conical vial. Place the conical vial in a small beaker and let it cool to room temperature. If crystallization has not occurred, scratch the inside of the vial with a glass stirring rod to initiate crystallization. Cool the mixture thoroughly in an ice bath for 15–20 minutes and collect the crystals by vacuum filtration on a Hirsch funnel (see Technique 8, Section 8.3, and Figure 8.5). Rinse the vial with about 0.5 mL of ice-cold water and transfer this mixture to the Hirsch funnel.

Repeat this rinsing with two additional 0.5-mL portions of ice-cold water. Dry the crystals for 5–10 minutes by allowing air to be drawn through them while they remain on the Hirsch funnel. Transfer the product to a watch glass or a clay plate and allow the crystals to dry in air. It may take several hours for the crystals to dry completely, but you may go on to the next step before they are totally dry. Weigh the crude product and set aside a small sample for a melting point determination and a color comparison after the next step. Calculate the percentage yield of crude acetaminophen ($MW = 151.2$). Record the appearance of the crystals in your notebook.

Decolorization of Crude Acetaminophen

Dissolve 0.5 g of sodium dithionite (sodium hydrosulfite) in 4.0 mL of water in a small Erlenmeyer flask. Add your crude acetaminophen to the flask. Heat the mixture at about 100°C for 15 minutes, with occasional swirling. Some of the acetaminophen will dissolve during the decolorization process. Cool the mixture thoroughly in an ice-water bath for about 10 minutes to reprecipitate the decolorized acetaminophen (scratch the inside of the flask, if necessary, to induce crystallization). Collect the purified material by vacuum filtration on a Hirsch funnel using small portions (about 1.0 mL total) of ice-cold water to aid the transfer. Dry the crystals for 5–10 minutes by allowing air to be drawn through them while they remain on the Hirsch funnel. You may go on to the next step before the material is totally dry. Weigh the purified acetaminophen and compare the color of the purified material to that obtained earlier.

Crystallization of Acetaminophen

Follow the semimicroscale crystallization procedure described in Technique 11, Section 11.3, and shown in Figure 11.4. Step 2 in Figure 11.4 (removal of insoluble impurities) will not be required in this crystallization.

Place all your acetaminophen in a 10-mL Erlenmeyer flask. In another flask, place about 3 mL of a solvent mixture composed of 50% water and 50% methanol, *with a boiling stone,* and put it on the hot plate. When the solvent begins to boil, start adding the hot solvent slowly to the acetaminophen using a Pasteur pipette. At this point, place both flasks on the hot plate to keep them hot. Continue to add the boiling solvent to the flask containing the acetaminophen until the solid *just dissolves.* Because the solubility of acetaminophen in this nearly boiling solvent is only about 0.2 g/mL, you will likely not use all the boiling solvent. The idea is to add the *minimum* amount of boiling solvent that *just dissolves* the solid.

Once the solid is dissolved, cork the flask and allow the contents of the flask to cool slowly to room temperature. Pure acetaminophen should crystallize out of the solvent. If solid does not form, scratch the inside of the flask with your microspatula. Place the flask in an ice bath to complete the crystallization for at least 10 minutes. Transfer the solid from the flask to a Hirsch funnel (Technique 8, Section 8.3, and Figure 8.5). Rinse the flask with about 0.5 mL of ice-cold solvent (50% methanol/50% water) and transfer this mixture to the Hirsch funnel. Repeat this rinsing with an additional 0.5-mL portion of ice-cold solvent. Dry the crystals for 5–10 minutes by allowing air to be drawn through them while they remain on the Hirsch funnel. Transfer the product to a watch glass or a clay plate and allow the crystals to dry in air. Let the crystals dry until the next laboratory period.

Yield Calculation and Melting Point Determination

Weigh the crystallized acetaminophen and calculate the percentage yield ($MW = 151.2$). This calculation should be based on the number of moles of the limiting reagent used at the beginning of this procedure. Determine the melting point of the product.

Compare the melting point of the final product with that of the crude acetaminophen. Also compare the colors of the crude, decolorized, and pure acetaminophen. Pure acetaminophen melts at 169.5–171°C. Place your product in a properly labeled vial and submit it to your instructor.

QUESTIONS

1. During the crystallization of acetaminophen, why was the mixture cooled in an ice bath?

2. In the reaction between *p*-aminophenol and acetic anhydride to form acetaminophen, 0.450 mL of water was added. What was the purpose of the water?

3. Why should you use a minimum amount of water to rinse the conical vial while transferring the purified acetaminophen to the Hirsch funnel?

4. If 0.130 g of *p*-aminophenol is allowed to react with excess acetic anhydride, what is the theoretical yield of acetaminophen in moles? In grams?

5. Give two reasons, discussed in Experiments 9 and 11, why the crude product in most reactions is not pure.

6. Phenacetin has the structure shown. Write an equation for its preparation, starting from 4-ethoxyaniline.

Identification of Drugs

Frequently, a chemist is called on to identify a particular unknown substance. If there is no prior information to work from, this can be a formidable task. There are several million known compounds, both inorganic and organic. For a completely unknown substance, the chemist must often use every available method. If the unknown substance is a mixture, then the mixture must be separated into its components and each component identified separately. A pure compound can often be identified from its physical properties (melting point, boiling point, density, refractive index, and so on) and a knowledge of its functional groups. These groups can be identified by the reactions that the compound is observed to undergo or by spectroscopy (infrared, ultraviolet, nuclear magnetic resonance, and mass spectroscopy). The techniques necessary for this type of identification are introduced in a later section.

A somewhat simpler situation often arises in drug identification. The scope of drug identification is more limited, and the chemist working in a hospital trying to identify the drug in an overdose or the law enforcement officer trying to identify a suspected illicit drug or a poison usually has some prior clues to work from. So does the medicinal chemist working for a pharmaceutical manufacturer who might be trying to discover why a competitor's product may be better.

Consider a drug overdose case as an example. The patient is brought into the emergency ward of a hospital. This person may be in a coma or a hyperexcited state, have an allergic rash, or clearly be hallucinating. These physiological symptoms are themselves a clue to the nature of the drug. Samples of the drug may be found in the patient's possession. Correct medical treatment may require a rapid and accurate identification of a drug powder or capsule. If the patient is conscious, the necessary information can be elicited orally; if not, the drug must be examined. If the drug is in the form of a tablet or capsule, the process is often simple because many drugs are coded by a manufacturer's trademark or logo, by shape (round, oval, or bullet shape), by formulation (tablet, gelatin capsule, or time-release microcapsule), and by color. Some drugs also bear an imprinted number or code.

It is more difficult to identify a powder, but such identification may be easy under some circumstances. Plant drugs are often easily identified because they contain microscopic bits and pieces of the plant from which they are obtained. This cellular debris is often characteristic for certain types of drugs, and they can be identified on this basis alone. A microscope is all that is needed. Sometimes chemical color tests can be used as confirmation. Certain drugs give rise to characteristic colors when treated with special reagents. Other drugs form crystalline precipitates of characteristic color and crystal structure when treated with appropriate reagents.

If the drug itself is not available and the patient is unconscious (or dead), identification may be more difficult. It may be necessary to pump the stomach or bladder contents of the patient (or corpse) or to obtain a blood sample. These samples of stomach fluid, urine, or blood would be extracted with an appropriate organic solvent, and the extract would be analyzed.

Often the final identification of a drug, as extracted from stomach fluid, urine, or blood hinges on some type of **chromatography.** Thin-layer chromatography (TLC) is often used. Under specified conditions, many drug substances can be identified by their R_f values and by the colors that their TLC spots turn when treated with various reagents or when observed under certain visualization methods. In the experiment that follows, TLC is applied to the analysis of an unknown analgesic drug.

REFERENCES

Keller, E. Origin of Modern Criminology. *Chemistry* **1969**, *42*, 8.

Keller, E. Forensic Toxicology: Poison Detection and Homicide. *Chemistry* **1970**, *43*, 14.

Lieu, V. T. Analysis of APC Tablets. *J. Chem. Educ.* **1971**, *48*, 478.

Neman, R. L. Thin Layer Chromatography of Drugs. *J. Chem. Educ.* **1972**, *49*, 834.

Rodgers, S. S. Some Analytical Methods Used in Crime Laboratories. *Chemistry* **1969**, *42*, 29.

Tietz, N. W. *Fundamentals of Clinical Chemistry*; W. B. Saunders: Philadelphia, **1970**.

Walls, H. J. *Forensic Science*; Praeger: New York, **1968**.

A collection of articles on forensic chemistry can be found in

Berry, K., and Outlaw, H. E., Eds. Forensic Chemistry—A Symposium Collection. *J. Chem. Educ.* **1985**, *62* (Dec), 1043–1065.

TLC Analysis of Analgesic Drugs

Thin-layer chromatography

In this experiment, thin-layer chromatography (TLC) will be used to determine the composition of various over-the-counter analgesics. If the instructor chooses, you may also be required to identify the components and actual identity (trade name) of an unknown analgesic. You will be given two commercially prepared TLC plates with a flexible backing and a silica-gel coating with a fluorescent indicator. On the first TLC plate, a reference plate, you will spot five standard compounds often used in analgesic formulations. In addition, a standard reference mixture containing four of these same compounds will be spotted. Ibuprofen is omitted from this standard mixture because it would overlap with salicylamide after the plate is developed. On the second plate (the sample plate), you will spot Naproxen sodium as an additional standard and four commercial analgesic preparations in order to determine their composition. At your instructor's option, one or more of these may be an unknown.

The standard compounds will all be available as solutions of 1 g of each dissolved in 20 mL of a 50:50 mixture of methylene chloride and ethanol. The purpose of the first reference plate is to determine the order of elution (R_f values) of the known substances and to index the standard reference mixture. Several of the substances have similar R_f values, but you will note a different behavior for each spot with the visualization methods. On the sample plate, the standard reference mixture will be spotted, along with Naproxen sodium and several solutions that you will prepare from commercial analgesic tablets. These tablets will each be crushed and dissolved in a 50:50 methylene chloride–ethanol mixture for spotting.

Reference Plate		Sample Plate	
Acetaminophen	(Ac)	Naproxen sodium	(Nap)
Aspirin	(Asp)	Sample 1*	(1)
Caffeine	(Cf)	Sample 2*	(2)
Ibuprofen	(Ibu)	Sample 3*	(3)
Salicylamide	(Sal)	Sample 4*	(4)
Reference mixture	(Ref)	Reference mixture	(Ref)

© Cengage Learning 2013

*At the instructor's option, one or more of the samples may be an unknown.

Two methods of visualization will be used to observe the positions of the spots on the developed TLC plates. First, the plates will be observed while under illumination from a short-wavelength ultraviolet (UV) lamp. This is best done in a darkened room or in a fume hood that has been darkened by taping butcher paper or aluminum foil over the lowered glass cover. Under these conditions, some of the spots will appear as dark areas on the plate, while others will fluoresce brightly. This difference in appearance under UV illumination will help to distinguish the substances from one another. You will find it convenient to outline very lightly in *pencil* the spots observed and to place a small **x** inside those spots that fluoresce. For a second means of visualization, iodine vapor will be used. Not all the spots will become visible when treated with iodine, but some will develop yellow, tan, or deep brown colors. The differences in the behaviors of the various spots with iodine can be used to further differentiate among them.

It is possible to use several developing solvents for this experiment, but ethyl acetate with 0.5% glacial acetic acid added is preferred. The small amount of glacial acetic acid supplies protons and suppresses ionization of aspirin, ibuprofen, and naproxen sodium, allowing them to travel upward on the plates in their protonated form. Without the acid, these compounds do not move.

In some analgesics, you may find ingredients besides the five mentioned previously. Some include an antihistamine and some contain a mild sedative. For instance, Midol contains N-cinnamylephedrine (cinnamedrine), an antihistamine, and Excedrin PM contains the sedative methapyrilene hydrochloride. Cope contains the related sedative methapyrilene fumarate. Some tablets may be colored with a chemical dye.

REQUIRED READING

Review: Essay   Analgesics
New: Technique 19   Column Chromatography, Sections 19.1–19.3
         Technique 20   Thin-Layer Chromatography
         Essay   Identification of Drugs

SPECIAL INSTRUCTIONS

You must first examine the developed plates under ultraviolet light. After comparisons of *all* plates have been made with UV light, iodine vapor can be used. The iodine permanently affects some of the spots, making it impossible to go back and repeat the UV visualization. Take special care to notice those substances that have similar R_f values; these spots each have a different appearance when viewed under UV illumination or a different staining color with iodine, allowing you to distinguish among them.

Aspirin presents some special problems because it is present in a large amount in many of the analgesics and because it hydrolyzes easily. For these reasons, the aspirin spots often show excessive tailing.

SUGGESTED WASTE DISPOSAL

Dispose of all development solvent in the container for nonhalogenated organic solvents. Dispose of the ethanol–methylene chloride mixture in the container for halogenated organic solvents. The micropipettes used for spotting the solution should be placed in a special container labeled for that purpose. The TLC plates should be stapled in your lab notebook.

NOTES TO THE INSTRUCTOR

If you wish, students may work in pairs on this experiment, each one preparing one of the two plates.

Perform the thin-layer chromatography with flexible Silica Gel 60 F-254 plates (EM Science, No. 5554-7). If the TLC plates have not been purchased recently, you should place them in an oven at 100°C for 30 minutes and store them in a desiccator until used. If you use different thin-layer plates, try out the experiment before using them with a class. Other plates may not resolve all five substances.

Ibuprofen and salicylamide have approximately the same R_f value, but they show up differently under the detection methods. For reasons that are not yet clear, ibuprofen sometimes gives two or even three spots. Naproxen sodium has approximately the same R_f as aspirin. Once again, however, these analgesics show up differently under the detection methods. Fortunately, naproxen sodium is not combined with aspirin or ibuprofen in any current commercial product.

PROCEDURE

Initial Preparations

You will need at least 12 capillary micropipettes to spot the plates. The preparation of these pipettes is described and illustrated in Technique 20, Section 20.4. A common error is to pull the center section out too far when making these pipettes, with the result that too little sample is applied to the plate. If this happens, you won't see *any* spots. Follow the directions carefully.

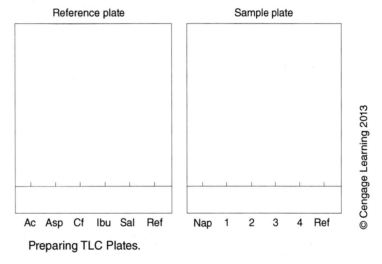

Preparing TLC Plates.

After preparing the micropipettes, obtain two 100-cm × 6.6-cm TLC plates (EM Science Silica Gel 60 F-254, No. 5554-7) from your instructor. These plates have a flexible backing, but they should not be bent excessively. Handle them carefully or the adsorbent may flake off. Also, you should handle them only by the edges; the surface should not be touched. Using a lead pencil (not a pen), *lightly* draw a line across the plates (short dimension) about 1 cm from the bottom. Using a centimeter ruler, move its index about 0.6 cm in from the edge of the plate and lightly mark off six 1-cm intervals on the line (see figure above). These are the points at which the samples will be spotted. If you are preparing two reference plates, it would be a good idea to mark a small number **1** or **2** in the upper right-hand corner of each plate to allow easy identification.

Spotting the First Reference Plate

On the first plate, starting from left to right, spot acetaminophen, then aspirin, caffeine, ibuprofen, and salicylamide. This order is alphabetic and will avoid any further memory problems or confusion. Solutions of these compounds will be found in small bottles on the supply shelf. The standard reference mixture (Ref) also found on the supply shelf, is spotted in the last position. The correct method of spotting a TLC plate is described in Technique 20, Section 20.4. It is important that the spots be made as small as possible (ca. 1–2 mm in diameter). With too much sample, the spots will tail and will overlap one another after development. With too little sample, no spots will be observed after development. The optimum applied spot should be about 1–2 mm (1/6 in.) in diameter. If scrap pieces of the TLC plates are available, it would be a good idea to practice spotting on these before preparing the actual sample plates.

Preparing the Development Chamber

When the reference plate has been spotted, obtain a 16-oz wide-mouth, screw-cap jar (or other suitable container) for use as a development chamber. The preparation of a development chamber is described in Technique 20, Section 20.5. Because the backing on the TLC plates is very thin, if they touch the filter paper liner of the development chamber *at any point,* solvent will begin to diffuse onto the absorbent surface at that point. To avoid this, you may either omit the liner or make the following modification.

If you wish to use a liner, use a very narrow strip of filter paper (approximately 5 cm wide). Fold it into an L shape that is long enough to traverse the bottom of the jar and extend up the side to the top of the jar. TLC plates placed in the jar for development should *straddle* this liner strip, but not touch it.

When the development chamber has been prepared, obtain a small amount of the development solvent (0.5% glacial acetic acid in ethyl acetate). Your instructor should prepare this mixture; it contains such a small amount of acetic acid that small individual portions are difficult to prepare. Fill the chamber with the development solvent to a depth of about 0.5–0.7 cm. If you are using a liner, be sure it is saturated with the solvent. Recall that the solvent level must not be above the spots on the plate or the samples will dissolve off the plate into the reservoir instead of developing.

Development of the Reference TLC Plate

Place the spotted plate (or plates) in the chamber (straddling the liner if one is present) and allow the spots to develop. If you are doing two reference plates, both plates may be placed in the same development jar. Be sure the plates are placed in the developing jar so that their bottom edge is parallel to the bottom of the jar (straight, not tilted); if not, the solvent front will not advance evenly, increasing the difficulty of making good comparisons. The plates should face each other and slant or lean back in opposite directions. When the solvent has risen to a level about 0.5 cm from the top of the plate, remove each plate from the chamber (in the hood) and, using a lead pencil, mark the position of the solvent front. Set the plate on a piece of paper towel to dry. It may be helpful to place a small object under one end to allow optimum air flow around the drying plate.

UV Visualization of the Reference Plate

When the plate is dry, observe it under a short-wavelength UV lamp, preferably in a darkened hood or a darkened room. Lightly outline all of the observed spots with a pencil. Carefully notice any differences in behavior between the spotted substances. Several compounds have similar R_f values, but the spots have a different appearance under UV illumination or iodine staining. Currently, there are no commercial analgesic preparations containing any compounds that have the same R_f values, but you will need to be able to distinguish them from one another to identify which one is present. Before proceeding, make a sketch of the plates in your notebook and note the differences in appearance that you observed. Using a ruler marked in millimeters, measure the distance that each spot has traveled relative to the solvent front. Calculate R_f values for each spot (see Technique 20, Section 20.9).

Analysis of Commercial Analgesics or Unknowns (Sample Plate)

Next, obtain half a tablet of each of the analgesics to be analyzed on the final TLC plate. If you were issued an unknown, you may analyze four other analgesics of your choice; if not, you may analyze five. The experiment will be most interesting if you make your choices in a way that gives a wide spectrum of results. Try to pick at least one analgesic each containing aspirin, acetaminophen, ibuprofen, a newer analgesic, and, if available, salicylamide. If you have a favorite analgesic, you may wish to include it among your samples. Take each analgesic half-tablet, place it on a smooth piece of notebook paper, and crush it well with a spatula. Transfer each crushed half-tablet to a labeled test tube or a small Erlenmeyer flask. Using a graduated cylinder, mix 15 mL of absolute ethanol and 15 mL of methylene chloride. Mix the solution well. Add 5 mL of this solvent to each of the crushed half-tablets and then heat each of them *gently* for a few minutes on a steam bath or sand bath at about 100°C. Not all of the tablet material will dissolve, because the analgesics usually contain an insoluble binder. In addition, many of them contain inorganic buffering agents or coatings that are insoluble in this solvent mixture. After heating the samples, allow them to settle and then spot the clear liquid extracts (1–4) on the sample plate. Spot the standard solution of naproxen on the left-hand edge, and spot the standard reference solution (Ref) on the right-hand edge of the plate (see figure above). Develop the plate in 0.5% glacial acetic acid–ethyl acetate as before. Observe the plate under UV illumination and mark the visible spots as you did for the first plate. Sketch the plate in your notebook and record your conclusions about the contents of each tablet. This can be done by directly comparing your plate to the reference plate(s)—they can all be placed under the UV light at the same time. If you were issued an unknown, try to determine its identity (trade name).

Iodine Analysis

Do not perform this step until UV comparisons of all the plates are complete. When ready, place the plates in a jar containing a few iodine crystals, cap the jar, and warm it gently on a steam bath or warm hot plate until the spots begin to appear. Notice which spots become visible and note their relative colors. You can directly compare colors of the reference spots to those on the unknown plate(s). Remove the plates from the jar and record your observations in your notebook.

QUESTIONS

1. What happens if the spots are made too large when preparing a TLC plate for development?
2. What happens if the spots are made too small when preparing a TLC plate for development?
3. Why must the spots be above the level of the development solvent in the developing chamber?
4. What would happen if the spotting line and positions were marked on the plate with a ball-point pen?
5. Is it possible to distinguish two spots that have the same R_f value but represent different compounds? Give two different methods.
6. Name some advantages of using acetaminophen (Tylenol) instead of aspirin as an analgesic.

Caffeine

The origins of coffee and tea as beverages are so old that they are lost in legend. Coffee is said to have been discovered by an Abyssinian goatherd who noticed an unusual friskiness in his goats when they consumed a certain little plant with red berries. He decided to try the berries himself and discovered coffee. The Arabs soon cultivated the coffee plant, and one of the earliest descriptions of its use is found in an Arabian medical book circa AD 900. The great systematic botanist Linnaeus named the plant *Coffea arabica*.

One legend of the discovery of tea—from the Orient, as you might expect—attributes the discovery to Daruma, the founder of Zen. Legend has it that he inadvertently fell asleep one day during his customary meditations. To be assured that this indiscretion would not recur, he cut off both eyelids. Where they fell to the ground, a new plant took root that had the power to keep a person awake. Although some experts assert that the medical use of tea was reported as early as 2737 BC in the pharmacopeia of Shen Nung, an emperor of China, the first indisputable reference is from the Chinese dictionary of Kuo P'o, which appeared in AD 350. The nonmedical, or popular, use of tea appears to have spread slowly. Not until about AD 700 was tea widely cultivated in China. Tea is native to upper Indochina and upper India, so it must have been cultivated in these places before its introduction to China. Linnaeus named the tea shrub *Thea sinensis*; however, tea is more properly a relative of the camellia, and botanists have renamed the shrub *Camellia thea*.

The active ingredient that makes tea and coffee valuable to humans is caffeine. Caffeine is an **alkaloid**, a class of naturally occurring compounds containing nitrogen and having the properties of an organic amine base (alkaline, hence, *alkaloid*). Tea and coffee are not the only plant sources of caffeine. Others include kola nuts, maté leaves, guarana seeds, and, in small amount, cocoa beans. The pure alkaloid was first isolated from coffee in 1821 by the French chemist Pierre Jean Robiquet.

XANTHINES
Xanthine R = R' = R" = H
Caffeine R = R' = R" = CH_3
Theophylline R = R" = CH_3, R' = H
Theobromine R = H, R' = R" = CH_3

© Cengage Learning 2013

Caffeine belongs to a family of naturally occurring compounds called **xanthines**. The xanthines, in the form of their plant progenitors, are possibly the oldest known stimulants. They all, to varying extents, stimulate the central nervous system and the skeletal muscles. This stimulation results in an increased alertness, the ability to put off sleep, and an increased capacity for thinking. Caffeine is the most powerful xanthine in this respect. It is the main ingredient of the popular No-Doz keep-alert tablets. Although caffeine has a powerful effect on the central nervous system, not all xanthines are as effective. Thus, theobromine, the xanthine found in cocoa, has fewer central

26

nervous system effects. It is, however, a strong **diuretic** (induces urination) and is useful to doctors in treating patients with severe water-retention problems. Theophylline, a second xanthine found in tea, also has fewer central nervous system effects but is a strong **myocardial** (heart muscle) stimulant; it **dilates** (relaxes) the coronary artery that supplies blood to the heart. Its most important use is in the treatment of bronchial asthma, because it has the properties of a **bronchodilator** (relaxes the bronchioles of the lungs). Because it is also a **vasodilator** (relaxes blood vessels), it is often used in treating hypertensive headaches. It is also used to alleviate and to reduce the frequency of attacks of **angina pectoris** (severe chest pain). In addition, it is a more powerful diuretic than theobromine.

One can develop both a tolerance for the xanthines and a dependence on them, particularly caffeine. The dependence is real, and a heavy user (>5 cups of coffee per day) will experience lethargy, headache, and perhaps nausea after about 18 hours of abstinence. An excessive intake of caffeine may lead to restlessness, irritability, insomnia, and muscular tremor. Caffeine can be toxic, but to achieve a lethal dose of caffeine, one would have to drink about 100 cups of coffee over a relatively short period.

Caffeine is a natural constituent of coffee, tea, and kola nuts (*Kola nitida*). Theophylline is found as a minor constituent of tea. The chief constituent of cocoa is theobromine. The amount of caffeine in tea varies from 2% to 5%. In one analysis of black tea, the following compounds were found: caffeine, 2.5%; theobromine, 0.17%; theophylline, 0.013%; adenine, 0.014%; and guanine and xanthine, traces. Coffee beans can contain up to 5% by weight of caffeine, and cocoa contains around 5% theobromine. Commercial cola is a beverage based on a kola nut extract. We cannot easily get kola nuts in this country, but we can get the ubiquitous commercial extract as a syrup. The syrup can be converted into "cola." The syrup contains caffeine, tannins, pigments, and sugar. Phosphoric acid is added, and caramel is added to give the syrup a deep color. The final drink is prepared by adding water and carbon dioxide under pressure, to give the bubbly mixture. Before decaffeination, the Food and Drug Administration required a "cola" to contain some caffeine (about 0.2 mg per ounce). In 1990, when new nutrition labels were adopted, this requirement was dropped. The Food and Drug Administration again currently requires that a "cola" contain *some* caffeine, but limits this amount, to a maximum of 5 milligrams per ounce. To achieve a regulated level of caffeine, most manufacturers remove all caffeine from the kola extract and then re-add the correct amount to the syrup. The caffeine content of various beverages is listed in the accompanying table.

Given the recent popularity of gourmet coffee beans and espresso stands, it is interesting to consider the caffeine content of these specialty beverages. Gourmet coffee certainly has more flavor than the typical ground coffee you may find on any grocery store shelf, and the concentration of brewed gourmet coffee tends to be higher than ordinary drip-grind coffee. Brewed gourmet coffee probably contains something on the order of 20–25 mg of caffeine per ounce of liquid. Espresso coffee is a very concentrated, dark-brewed coffee. Although the darker roasted beans used for espresso actually contain less caffeine per gram than regularly roasted beans, the method of preparing espresso (extraction using pressurized steam) is more efficient, and a higher percentage of the total caffeine in the beans is extracted. The caffeine content per ounce of liquid, therefore, is substantially higher than in most brewed coffees. The serving size for espresso coffee, however, is much smaller than for ordinary coffee (about 1.5–2 oz per serving), so the total caffeine available in a serving of espresso turns out to be about the same as in a serving of ordinary coffee.

Amount of Caffeine (mg/oz) Found in Beverages

Brewed coffee	12–30	Tea	4–20
Instant coffee	8–20	Cocoa (but 20 mg/oz theobromine)	0.5–2
Espresso (1 serving = 1.5–2 oz)	50–70	Coca-Cola	3.75
Decaffeinated coffee	0.4–1.0		

© Cengage Learning 2013

Note: The average cup of coffee or tea contains about 5–7 ounces of liquid. The average bottle of cola contains about 12 ounces of liquid.

Because of the central nervous system effects from caffeine, many people prefer **decaffeinated** coffee. The caffeine is removed from coffee by extracting the whole beans with an organic solvent. Then the solvent is drained off, and the beans are steamed to remove any residual solvent. The beans are dried and roasted to bring out the flavor. Decaffeination reduces the caffeine content of coffee to the range of 0.03% to 1.2%. The extracted caffeine is used in various pharmaceutical products, such as APC tablets.

Among coffee lovers there is some controversy about the best method to remove the caffeine from coffee beans. **Direct contact** decaffeination uses an organic solvent (usually methylene chloride) to remove the caffeine from the beans. When the beans are subsequently roasted at 200°C, virtually all traces of the solvent are removed, because methylene chloride boils at 40°C. The advantage of direct contact decaffeination is that the method removes only the caffeine (and some waxes), but leaves the substances responsible for the flavor of the coffee intact in the bean. A disadvantage of this method is that all organic solvents are toxic to some extent.

Water process decaffeination is favored among many drinkers of decaffeinated coffee because it does not use organic solvents. In this method, hot water and steam are used to remove caffeine and other soluble substances from the coffee. The resulting solution is then passed through activated charcoal filters to remove the caffeine. Although this method does not use organic solvents, the disadvantage is that water is not a very selective decaffeinating agent. Many of the flavor oils in the coffee are removed at the same time, resulting in a coffee with a somewhat bland flavor.

A third method, the **carbon dioxide decaffeination process**, is being used with increasing frequency. The raw coffee beans are moistened with steam and water, and they are then placed into an extractor where they are treated with carbon dioxide gas under very high temperature and pressure. Under these conditions, the carbon dioxide gas is in a **supercritical** state, which means that it takes on the characteristics of both a liquid and a gas. The supercritical carbon dioxide acts as a selective solvent for caffeine, thus extracting it from the beans.

There are, however, benefits to ingesting caffeine. Small amounts of caffeine have been found to be helpful in controlling weight, alleviating pain, and reducing the symptoms of asthma and other breathing problems. Recently, studies on mice indicate that caffeine may help to reverse or slow the development of Alzheimer's disease in mice. Other studies on humans indicate that caffeine may reduce the likelihood of developing Parkinson's disease and reduce the risk of colon cancer.

Another problem, posed by the beverage tea, is that in some cases persons who consume high quantities of tea may show symptoms of Vitamin B1 (thiamine) deficiency. It is suggested that the tannins in the tea may complex with the thiamine, rendering it unavailable for use. An alternative suggestion is that caffeine may reduce the levels of the enzyme transketolase, which depends on the presence of thiamine for its activity. Lowered levels of transketolase would produce the same symptoms as lowered levels of thiamine.

REFERENCES

Emboden, W. The Stimulants. *Narcotic Plants*, rev. ed.; Macmillan: New York, 1979.

Ray, O. S. Caffeine. *Drugs, Society, and Human Behavior*, 7th ed.; C. V. Mosby: St. Louis, 1996.

Hart, C.; Ksir, C.; and Ray, O. Caffeine. *Drugs, Society, and Human Behavior*, 13th ed.; C. V. Mosby: St. Louis, 2008.

Ross, G. W.; Abbott, R. D.; Petrovich, H.; Morens, D. M.; Grandinetti, A.; Tung, K-H.; Tanner, C. M.; Masaki, K. H.; Blanchette, P. L.; and Curb J. D.; et al. Association of Coffee and Caffeine Intake with the Risk of Parkinson Disease. *J. Am. Med. Assoc.* **2000**, *283* (May 24), 2674–2679.

Arendash, G. W.; Mori, T.; Cao, C.; Mamcarz, M.; Runfeldt, M.; Dickson, A.; Rezai-Zadeh, K.; Tan, J.; Citron, B. A.; and Lin, X.; et al. Caffeine Reverses Cognitive Impairment and Decreases Brain Amyloid-β, Levels in Aged Alzheimer's Disease. Micc. *J. Alzheim. Dis.* **2009**, *17*, 661–680.

Ritchie, J. M. Central Nervous System Stimulants. II: The Xanthines. In The *Pharmacological Basis of Therapeutics*, 8th ed.; Goodman L. S., Gilman, A., Eds.; Macmillan: New York, 1990.

Taylor, N. *Plant Drugs That Changed the World*; Dodd Mead: New York, 1965; pp. 54–56.

Taylor, N. Three Habit-Forming Nondangerous Beverages. In *Narcotics—Nature's Dangerous Gifts*; Dell: New York, 1970. (Paperbound revision of Flight from Reality.)

Isolation of Caffeine from Tea or Coffee

Isolation of a natural product

Extraction

Sublimation

Green chemistry

Solid phase extraction (optional)

Gas chromatography (optional)

Infrared spectroscopy (optional)

In Experiment 13A, caffeine is isolated from tea leaves. The chief problem with the isolation is that caffeine does not exist alone in tea leaves but is accompanied by other natural substances from which it must be separated. The main component of tea leaves is cellulose, which is the principal structural material of all plant cells. Cellulose is a polymer of glucose. Because cellulose is virtually insoluble in water, it presents no problems in the isolation procedure. Caffeine, on the other hand, is water soluble and is one of the main substances extracted into the solution called tea. Caffeine constitutes as much as 5% by weight of the leaf material in tea plants.

Tannins also dissolve in the hot water used to extract tea leaves. The term **tannin** does not refer to a single homogeneous compound or even to substances that have similar chemical structure. It refers to a class of compounds that have certain properties in common. Tannins are phenolic compounds having molecular weights between 500 and 3000. They are widely used to tan leather. They precipitate alkaloids and proteins from aqueous solutions. Tannins are usually divided into two classes: those that can be **hydrolyzed** (react with water) and those that cannot. Tannins of the first type that are found in tea generally yield glucose and gallic acid when they are hydrolyzed. These tannins are esters of gallic acid and glucose. They represent structures in which some of the hydroxyl groups in glucose have been esterified by digalloyl groups. The nonhydrolyzable tannins found in tea are condensation polymers of catechin. These polymers are not uniform in structure; catechin molecules are usually linked at ring positions 4 and 8.

Glucose if R = H
A tannin if some R = Digalloyl

A digalloyl group

© Cengage Learning 2013

Catechin

When tannins are extracted into hot water, some of these compounds are partially hydrolyzed to form free gallic acid. The tannins, because of their phenolic groups, and gallic acid, because of its carboxyl groups, are both acidic. If sodium carbonate, a base, is added to tea water, these acids are converted to their sodium salts that are highly soluble in water.

Although caffeine is soluble in water, it is much more soluble in the organic solvent methylene chloride. Caffeine can be extracted from the basic tea solution with methylene chloride, but the sodium salts of gallic acid and the tannins remain in the aqueous layer.

The brown color of a tea solution is due to flavonoid pigments and chlorophylls and to their respective oxidation products. Although chlorophylls are soluble in methylene chloride, most other substances in tea are not. Thus, the methylene chloride extraction of the basic tea solution removes nearly pure caffeine. The methylene chloride is easily removed by evaporation (bp 40°C) to leave the crude caffeine. The caffeine is then purified by sublimation at reduced pressure to prevent decomposition.

R = digalloyl

Glucose   Gallic acid

The methylene chloride solvent used in Experiment 13A is toxic and a suspected carcinogen, but it remains as one of the best solvents for extracting caffeine from aqueous tea and coffee solutions. Other solvents simply do not do as good a job of extracting caffeine. Besides being toxic, chlorinated solvents are also environmental pollutants (see the "Green Chemistry" essay). This solvent must be disposed of correctly to avoid environmental problems. Ethyl acetate is "more Green" than methylene chloride, but unfortunately it does not extract caffeine from aqueous solutions nearly as efficiently as methylene chloride.

Solid phase extraction (SPE), described in Technique 12, Section 12.14, avoids the use of methylene chloride, and the technique will be employed in Experiment 13B for extracting caffeine from tea or coffee. The material used in this SPE procedure is prepared by alkylating silica with 18-carbon chains. This process changes the silica from a polar substance to a relatively nonpolar one. The resulting material, called C-18 silica, is placed in a tube that resembles a syringe body. Because the silica is now nonpolar, water and other polar substances such as tannins and gallic acid will pass through the column, whereas the C-18 silica retains caffeine. To remove the caffeine from the column, ethyl acetate is added.

REQUIRED READING

Review:	Techniques 5 and 6	
	Technique 7	Reaction Methods, Section 7.10
	Technique 9	Physical Constants of Solids: The Melting Point
New:	Technique 12	Extractions, Separations, and Drying Agents
	Technique 17	Sublimation
	Essay	Caffeine
	Essay	Green Chemistry
	Technique 22	Gas Chromatography (optional)
	Technique 25	Infrared Spectroscopy (optional)
	Technique 28	Mass Spectrometry (optional)

SPECIAL INSTRUCTIONS

Be careful when handling methylene chloride. It is a toxic solvent and suspected carcinogen. You should not breathe it or spill it on yourself. Wear gloves and work in a fume hood. It is recommended that you use glass centrifuge tubes with screw caps. Check them first with water to make sure that they will not leak while you shake them. Plastic centrifuge tubes with screw caps can be used instead of glass ones. However, there is some tendency for the plastic to dissolve in methylene chloride, and they should not be in contact with methylene chloride for long periods (more than 1 hour).

SUGGESTED WASTE DISPOSAL

You must dispose of methylene chloride in a waste container marked for the disposal of halogenated organic waste. Dispose of the tea bag in a trash can. The aqueous solutions obtained after the extraction steps must be disposed of in a waste container labeled for aqueous waste.

13A EXPERIMENT 13A

Extraction of Caffeine from Tea with Methylene Chloride

PROCEDURE

Preparing the Tea Solution

Place 20 mL of water in a 50-mL beaker. Cover the beaker with a watch glass and heat the water on a hot plate until it is almost boiling. From information provided by your instructor, determine the weight of the tea present in the tea bag.[1] Place the tea bag into the hot water so that it lies flat on the bottom of the beaker and is covered as completely as possible with water. Replace the watch glass and continue heating for about 15 minutes. During this heating period, it is important to push down *gently* on the tea bag with a test tube so that all the tea leaves are in constant contact with water. As the water evaporates during this heating step, replace it by adding water from a Pasteur pipette.

Using the Pasteur pipette, transfer the concentrated tea solution to two centrifuge tubes fitted with screw caps. Try to keep the liquid volume in each centrifuge tube approximately equal. To squeeze additional liquid out of the tea bag, hold the tea bag on the inside wall of the beaker and roll a test tube back and forth while exerting *gentle* pressure on the tea bag. Press out as much liquid as possible without breaking the bag. Combine this liquid with the solution in the centrifuge tubes. Place the tea bag on the bottom of the beaker again and pour 2 mL of hot water over the bag. Squeeze the liquid out, as just described, and transfer this liquid to the centrifuge tubes. Add 0.5 g of sodium carbonate to the hot liquid in each centrifuge tube. Cap the tubes and shake the mixture until the solid dissolves.

Extraction and Drying

Cool the tea solution to room temperature. Using a calibrated Pasteur pipette, add 3 mL of methylene chloride to each centrifuge tube to extract the caffeine (Technique 12, Section 12.4). Cap the centrifuge tubes and gently shake the mixture for several seconds. Vent the tubes to release the pressure, being careful that the liquid does not squirt out toward you. Shake the mixture for an additional 30 seconds with occasional venting. To separate the layers and break the emulsion (see Technique 12, Section 12.10), centrifuge the mixture for several minutes (be sure to balance the centrifuge by placing the two centrifuge tubes on opposite sides). If an emulsion still remains (indicated by a green-brown layer between the clear methylene chloride layer and the top aqueous layer), centrifuge the mixture again.

Remove the lower organic layer with a Pasteur pipette and transfer it to a dry 25-mL Erlenmeyer flask. Be sure to squeeze the bulb before placing the tip of the Pasteur pipette into the liquid and try not to transfer any of the dark aqueous

---

[1] The weight of the tea in the bag varies, whereas the weight of the bag, string, and tag are relatively constant. Your instructor may provide you with the weight of everything except the tea itself. You can then determine the weight of the tea by directly weighing the tea bag provided you and subtracting the weight of the empty bag, string, and tag to determine the weight of the tea in the bag.

solution along with the methylene chloride layer. Add a fresh 3-mL portion of methylene chloride to the aqueous layer remaining in each centrifuge tube, cap the centrifuge tubes, and shake the mixture in order to carry out a second extraction. Separate the layers by centrifugation, as described previously. Combine the organic layers from each extraction into the flask containing the first extraction. If there are visible drops of the dark aqueous solution in the flask, transfer the methylene chloride solution to another flask using a clean, dry Pasteur pipette. If necessary, leave a small amount of the methylene chloride solution behind in order to avoid transferring any of the aqueous mixture. Add granular anhydrous sodium sulfate to dry the organic layer (Technique 12, Section 12.9). If all the sodium sulfate clumps together when the mixture is stirred with a spatula, add some additional drying agent. Allow the mixture to stand for 10–15 minutes. Stir occasionally with a spatula.

Evaporation

Transfer the dry methylene chloride solution with a Pasteur pipette to a dry, pre-weighed 25-mL Erlenmeyer flask, while leaving the drying agent behind. Evaporate the methylene chloride by heating the flask in a hot water bath (Technique 7, Section 7.10). This should be done in a hood and can be accomplished more rapidly if a stream of dry air or nitrogen gas is directed at the surface of the liquid. When the solvent is evaporated, the crude caffeine will coat the bottom of the flask. Do not heat the flask after the solvent has evaporated or you may sublime some of the caffeine. Weigh the flask and determine the weight of crude caffeine. Calculate the weight percentage recovery (see Technique 2, Section 2.2C) of caffeine from tea leaves, using the weight of tea that you started with. You may store the caffeine by simply placing a stopper firmly into the flask.

Sublimation of Caffeine

Caffeine can be purified by sublimation (Technique 17, Section 17.5). Assemble a sublimation apparatus as shown in Figure 17.2A.[2] Add approximately 0.5 mL of methylene chloride to the Erlenmeyer flask and transfer the solution to a clean, 5-mL, thin-walled, conical vial, using a clean and dry Pasteur pipette. Add a few more drops of methylene chloride to the flask in order to rinse the caffeine out completely. Transfer this liquid to the conical vial. Evaporate the methylene chloride from the conical vial by gentle heating in a warm water bath under a stream of dry air or nitrogen.

Insert the cold finger into the sublimation apparatus. If you are using the sublimator with the multipurpose adapter, adjust it so that the tip of the cold finger will be positioned about 1 cm above the bottom of the conical vial. Be sure that the inside of the assembled apparatus is clean and dry. If you are using an aspirator, install a trap between the aspirator and the sublimation apparatus. Turn on the vacuum and check to make sure that all joints in the apparatus are sealed tightly. Place *ice-cold* water in the inner tube of the apparatus. Heat the sample gently and carefully with a microburner to sublime the caffeine. Hold the burner in your hand (hold it at its base, *not* by the hot barrel), and apply the heat by moving the flame back and forth under the conical vial and up the sides. If the sample begins to melt, remove the flame for a few seconds before you resume heating. When sublimation is complete, discontinue heating. Remove the cold water and remaining ice from the inner tube and allow the apparatus to cool while continuing to apply the vacuum.

---

[2] If you are using another type of sublimation apparatus, your instructor will provide you with specific instructions on how to assemble it correctly.

When the apparatus is at room temperature, remove the vacuum and *carefully* remove the inner tube. If this operation is done carelessly, the sublimed crystals may be dislodged from the inner tube and fall back into the conical vial. Scrape the sublimed caffeine onto a tared piece of smooth paper and determine the weight of caffeine recovered. Calculate the weight percentage recovery (see Technique 2, Section 2.2C) of caffeine after the sublimation. Compare this value to the percentage recovery determined after the evaporation step. Determine the melting point of the purified caffeine. The melting point of pure caffeine is 236°C; however, the observed melting point will be lower. Submit the sample to the instructor in a labeled vial.

13B EXPERIMENT 13B (OPTIONAL)

Extraction of Caffeine from Tea or Coffee Using Solid Phase Extraction (SPE)

In this experiment, caffeine is isolated from brewed tea or coffee using solid phase extraction (Technique 12, Section 12.14). It is offered as a Green Chemistry alternative to the procedure given in Experiment 13A in which methylene chloride is used for the extraction of caffeine from tea.

The solid phase extraction (SPE) columns may be obtained commercially.[3] The manufacturers covalently bond nonpolar alkyl groups to silica. This process converts the polar silica to a relatively nonpolar material. Often, 18-carbon alkyl groups are bonded to the silica creating a material that is referred to as C-18 silica.

In "normal" chromatography using nontreated silica, one expects polar substances to be attracted to the polar surface and to move more slowly through the column compared to nonpolar substances. This more traditional form of chromatography is referred to as **normal phase chromatography.** With C-18-treated silica, however, the polar substances will come off first, and the relatively nonpolar substance will be retained. This type of chromatography is referred to as **reverse phase chromatography.**

Experiment 12B makes use of reverse phase chromatography to remove caffeine from a tea or coffee solution. The technique is simple. See Technique 12, Figure 12.14, for a diagram of the apparatus that you will use. The procedure involves the following steps:

1. Condition the SPE reverse phase column with methanol and water.

2. Use a vacuum to draw an aqueous solution of brewed tea or coffee through the SPE reverse phase column.

3. Caffeine is retained by the solid phase column.

4. Water, tannins, gallic acid, and other polar substances pass through the column.

5. Remove the caffeine from the column with ethyl acetate.

6. Evaporate the ethyl acetate to yield the crude caffeine.

7. Purify the caffeine by sublimation.

---

[3] We recommend a 6-mL column with 1000 mg of C18E sorbent (No. 8B-S001-JCH-S) for Experiment 13B. These columns are available from Phenomenex, 411 Madrid Avenue, Torrance, CA 90501-1430, phone: (310) 212-0555. About 25 mg of caffeine can be isolated from one batch of tea or coffee solution.

SUGGESTED WASTE DISPOSAL

This experiment approaches closely a high Green standard. Get into the spirit of the Green movement! Throw the tea bag into a trash can. Pour the aqueous solution from the column down the drain in a sink. Any remaining ethyl acetate should be given to another student who needs it or, as a last resort, poured into a nonhalogenated waste container. Remove the traces of ethyl acetate from the sodium sulfate drying agent with a blast of air and then dissolve the remaining solid inorganic material with water and pour it into an aqueous waste container (or pour it down the sink drain). Place the SPE column into a beaker that has been supplied for your use. Eventually, the tubes will be emptied and reused.

PROCEDURE

Preparing the Tea or Coffee Solution

Prepare a tea solution as described in Experiment 13A (first paragraph) and footnote 1. (If you desire to extract caffeine from coffee, dissolve about 1.5 g of instant coffee in 20 mL of boiling water.[4]) Using the Pasteur pipette, transfer the concentrated tea solution into two centrifuge tubes fitted with screw caps. Try to keep the liquid volume in each centrifuge tube approximately equal. To squeeze additional liquid out of the tea bag, hold the tea bag on the inside wall of the beaker and roll a test tube back and forth while exerting gentle pressure on the tea bag. Press out as much liquid as possible without breaking the bag. Combine this liquid with the solution in the centrifuge tubes. Place the tea bag on the bottom of the beaker again and pour 2 mL of hot water over the tea bag. Squeeze the liquid out as just described and transfer this liquid to the centrifuge tubes. Let the solution in the centrifuge tube cool to room temperature. When the solution is room temperature, cap the centrifuge tubes and centrifuge the samples for 4 to 5 minutes. When the centrifugation step is complete, a solid will be present at the bottom of the tubes. Transfer the solution with a Pasteur pipette into a small beaker so that the thick solid is left behind in the centrifuge tubes.

Preparing the SPE Column

The apparatus is shown in Technique 12, Figure 12.14. Insert a No. 1 neoprene adapter inside a No. 2 neoprene adapter and place both adapters in the top of a 50-mL filter flask. Clamp the flask securely and then apply a vacuum source. Place the SPE column[5] inside the No. 1 neoprene adapter and condition the column under vacuum in the following way. Add 2 mL of methanol to the column, 1 mL at a time. Wait for the methanol to draw through the column completely before adding the second mL. Next, add 2 mL of room-temperature de-ionized (DI) water, 1 mL at a time. Proceed to the next step as quickly as possible. Don't let the column dry out.

Filtering the Tea Solution

While still drawing a vacuum, transfer the tea (or coffee) solution in the small beaker to the SPE column in approximately 1-mL portions, using a Pasteur pipette. If some solid is present in the beaker, be careful to avoid drawing up this solid at the bottom of the beaker (this solid will plug the SPE column). The SPE column should

---

[4] Tea yields better-quality caffeine than that obtained from coffee. Caffeine from tea is relatively colorless, whereas the caffeine extracted from coffee is highly colored. About 25 mg of caffeine is isolated in either case. Sublimation removes much of the color from the tea and coffee samples.

[5] See footnote 3 for the SPE column required for this experiment.

still be under vacuum. When all the solution has been drawn through the column, add 3 mL of room-temperature DI water in 1-mL portions. Continue applying the vacuum for 1 minute to remove as much water from the column as possible. Much of the caffeine is retained in the SPE column.

Removing the Caffeine from the SPE Column

Turn off the vacuum and carefully and slowly remove the hose from the side arm of the filter flask so that the liquid in the flask will not bump up onto the adapters and SPE column. Discard the filtrate in the filter flask. Clean and dry the filter flask that you used. Reconnect the SPE column to the apparatus and reapply the vacuum. Add a total of 7 mL of ethyl acetate to the column in approximately 1-mL portions. When all the ethyl acetate has been added, turn off the vacuum source and carefully remove the hose from the filter flask. Place the SPE column in the beaker supplied by the instructor.[6] Add 1.6 g of granular anhydrous sodium sulfate to the ethyl acetate solution in the filter flask. This drying operation removes any remaining water from the ethyl acetate solution. Allow the mixture to stand for 15 minutes. Stir the solution occasionally with a spatula to complete the drying step (Technique 12, Section 12.9).

Isolation of the Caffeine

Transfer the dry ethyl acetate solution with a Pasteur pipette to a *dry, preweighed* 25-mL Erlenmeyer flask while leaving the drying agent behind. Rinse the drying agent with about 1 mL of fresh ethyl acetate and transfer it to the flask with your Pasteur pipette. Evaporate the ethyl acetate by heating the solution on a hot plate. This must be done in a hood and can be accomplished more rapidly if a stream of dry air or nitrogen gas is *carefully* directed at the surface of the liquid. Take the flask off the hot plate while some liquid remains and then use a gentle stream of air to remove the remaining traces of ethyl acetate from your sample. When the solvent has evaporated, crude solid caffeine will coat the bottom of the flask. Reweigh the flask to determine the weight of crude caffeine. Calculate the weight percentage recovery of caffeine obtained from your tea or coffee sample.[7] You may store the caffeine by placing a stopper firmly into the flask.

Sublimation of Caffeine

The caffeine obtained from tea or coffee can be purified by sublimation using the procedure described in Experiment 13A. At your instructor's option, you may combine your sample with another student's sample for sublimation. After sublimation, determine the weight of caffeine recovered and calculate the weight percentage recovery of the caffeine. Compare this value to the amount of crude sample obtained. At the instructor's option, determine the melting point of the purified caffeine. The melting point of pure caffeine is 236°C; however, the observed melting point will be lower. Submit the sample to the instructor in a labeled vial unless it is to be used for infrared spectroscopy (recommended) or mass spectroscopy (also recommended).

Analysis of Caffeine

At the option of your instructor, obtain the infrared spectrum of the caffeine as a dry film by dissolving a sample in *dry* acetone (Technique 25, Section 25.4). Alternatively, a KBr pellet of the caffeine can be prepared to obtain the spectrum (Technique 25, Section 25.5). Include the infrared spectrum with your laboratory report, along with an interpretation of the principal peaks. A spectrum is included for comparison purposes.

---

[6] *Note to the instructor:* It is recommended that the C-18 silica in the SPE columns not be reused.

[7] See footnote 3 for information on the expected yield of caffeine from tea and coffee.

At the instructor's option, you may determine the mass spectrum of the caffeine by gas chromatography/mass spectrometry (GC-MS) (Technique 28). At the same time, you can determine the purity of your sample.[8]

Report

Attach your infrared spectra to your report and label the major peaks. If you determined the mass spectrum, try to identify the important fragment ion peaks (Technique 28). Include the melting point, if it was required. Report the weight percentage of the caffeine recovered from the tea or coffee sample before and after sublimation.

Spectrum of caffeine in KBr.

QUESTIONS

1. Outline a separation scheme for isolating caffeine from tea. Use a flowchart similar in format to that shown in Technique 2, Section 2.2.

2. Why was the sodium carbonate added in Experiment 13A?

3. The crude caffeine isolated from tea often has a green tinge. Why?

4. What are some possible explanations for why the melting point of your isolated caffeine was lower than the literature value (236°C)?

5. An alternative procedure for removing the tannins and gallic acid is to heat the tea leaves in an aqueous mixture containing calcium carbonate. Calcium carbonate reacts with the tannins and gallic acid to form insoluble calcium salts of these acids. If this procedure were used, what additional step (not done in this experiment) would be needed in order to obtain an aqueous tea solution?

6. What would happen to the caffeine if the sublimation step were performed at atmospheric pressure?

---

[8] The GC/MS may be obtained on the caffeine sample using a Varian 3800 GC with Saturn 2000 MS equipped with a capillary column that is 30 m long and 0.25 mm ID containing a 0.25-μm film of Varian CP-Sil 8CB. The injector was set at 275°C, with He gas flow at 1 mL/min. The temperature of the oven was increased from 75 to 280°C at 20%/min and held at 280°C for 1 minute. The retention time for the caffeine is about 10 minutes under these conditions. No impurities were detected.

Esters—Flavors and Fragrances

Esters are a class of compounds widely distributed in nature. They have the general formula

$$R - \overset{\overset{\textstyle O}{\|}}{C} - OR'$$

The simple esters tend to have pleasant odors. In many cases, although not exclusively so, the characteristic flavors and fragrances of flowers and fruits are due to compounds with the ester functional group. An exception is the case of the essential oils. The **organoleptic** qualities (odors and flavors) of fruits and flowers may often be due to a single ester, but more often, the flavor or the aroma is due to a complex mixture in which a single ester predominates. Some common flavor principles are listed in Table 1. Food and beverage manufacturers are familiar with these esters and often use them as additives to spruce up the flavor or odor of a dessert or beverage. Many times, such flavors or odors do not even have a natural basis, as is the case with the "juicy fruit" principle, isopentenyl acetate. An instant pudding that has the flavor of rum may never have seen its alcoholic namesake; this flavor can be duplicated by the proper admixture, along with other minor components, of ethyl formate and isobutyl propionate. The natural flavor and odor are not exactly duplicated, but most people can be fooled. Often, only a trained person with a high degree of gustatory perception, a professional taster, can tell the difference.

A single compound is rarely used in good-quality imitation flavoring agents. A formula for an imitation pineapple flavor that might fool an expert is listed in Table 2. The formula includes 10 esters and carboxylic acids that can easily be synthesized in the laboratory. The remaining seven oils are isolated from natural sources.

Flavor is a combination of taste, sensation, and odor transmitted by receptors in the mouth (taste buds) and nose (olfactory receptors). The stereochemical theory of odor is discussed in the essay that precedes Experiment 16. The four basic tastes (sweet, sour, salty, and bitter) are perceived in specific areas of the tongue. The sides of the tongue perceive sour and salty tastes, the tip is most sensitive to sweet tastes, and the back of the tongue detects bitter tastes. The perception of flavor, however, is not so simple. If it were, it would require only the formulation of various combinations of four basic substances—a bitter substance (a base), a sour substance (an acid), a salty substance (sodium chloride), and a sweet substance (sugar)—to duplicate any flavor! In fact, we cannot duplicate flavors in this way. The human possesses 9,000 taste buds. The combined response of these taste buds is what allows perception of a particular flavor.

Although the "fruity" tastes and odors of esters are pleasant, they are seldom used in perfumes or scents that are applied to the body. The reason for this is chemical. The ester group is not as stable under perspiration as the ingredients

Table 1 Ester Flavors and Fragrances

Isoamyl acetate
(banana)
(alarm pheromone of honeybee)

Ethyl butyrate
(pineapple)

Isobutyl propionate
(rum)

Octyl acetate
(oranges)

Methyl anthranilate
(grape)

Isopentenyl acetate
("Juicy Fruit")

Benzyl acetate
(peach)

***n*-Propyl acetate**
(pear)

Methyl butyrate
(apple)

Ethyl phenylacetate
(honey)

© Cengage Learning 2013

of the more expensive essential-oil perfumes. The latter are usually hydrocarbons (terpenes), ketones, and ethers extracted from natural sources. Esters, however, are used only for the cheapest toilet waters because on contact with sweat they undergo hydrolysis, giving organic acids. These acids, unlike their precursor esters, generally do not have a pleasant odor.

Butyric acid, for instance, has a strong odor like that of rancid butter (of which it is an ingredient) and is a component of what we normally call body odor. It is this substance that makes foul-smelling humans so easy for an animal to detect when downwind of them. It is also of great help to the bloodhound, which is trained to follow small traces of this odor.

$$\underset{\text{O}}{\overset{\text{O}}{\text{R}-\text{C}-\text{OR}'}} + H_2O \longrightarrow \underset{\text{O}}{\overset{\text{O}}{\text{R}-\text{C}-\text{OH}}} + R'OH$$

Table 2 Artificial pineapple flavor

Pure Compounds	%	Essential Oils	%
Allyl caproate	5	Oil of sweet birch	1
Isoamyl acetate	3	Oil of spruce	2
Isoamyl isovalerate	3	Balsam Peru	4
Ethyl acetate	15	Volatile mustard oil	1
Ethyl butyrate	22	Oil cognac	5
Terpinyl propionate	3	Concentrated orange oil	4
Ethyl crotonate	5	Distilled oil of lime	2
Caproic acid	8		19
Butyric acid	12		
Acetic acid	5		
	81		

© Cengage Learning 2013

Ethyl butyrate and methyl butyrate, however, which are the *esters* of butyric acid, smell like pineapple and apple, respectively.

A sweet, fruity odor also has the disadvantage of possibly attracting fruit flies and other insects in search of food. Isoamyl acetate, the familiar solvent called banana oil, is particularly interesting. It is identical to a component of the alarm **pheromone** of the honeybee. Pheromone is the name applied to a chemical secreted by an organism that evokes a specific response in another member of the same species. This kind of communication is common among insects who otherwise lack means of intercourse. When a honeybee worker stings an intruder, an alarm pheromone, composed partly of isoamyl acetate, is secreted along with the sting venom. This chemical causes aggressive attack on the intruder by other bees, who swarm after the intruder. Obviously, it wouldn't be wise to wear a perfume compounded of isoamyl acetate near a beehive. Pheromones are discussed in more detail in the essay preceding Experiment 45.

REFERENCES

Bauer, K., and Garbe, D. *Common Fragrance and Flavor Materials.* Weinheim: VCH Publishers, 1985.

The Givaudan Index. New York: Givaudan-Delawanna, 1949. (Gives specifications of synthetics and isolates for perfumery.)

Gould, R. F., ed. *Flavor Chemistry, Advances in Chemistry,* No. 56. Washington, DC: American Chemical Society, 1966.

Layman, P. L. Flavors and Fragrances Industry Taking on New Look. *Chemical and Engineering News* (July 20, 1987): 35.

Moyler, D. Natural Ingredients for Flavours and Fragrances. *Chemistry and Industry* (January 7, 1991): 11.

Rasmussen, P. W. Qualitative Analysis by Gas Chromatography—G.C. versus the Nose in Formulation of Artificial Fruit Flavors. *Journal of Chemical Education, 61* (January 1984): 62.

Shreve, R. N., and Brink, J. *Chemical Process Industries,* 4th ed. New York: McGraw-Hill, 1977.

Welsh, F. W., and Williams, R. E. Lipase Mediated Production of Flavor and Fragrance Esters from Fusel Oil. *Journal of Food Science, 54* (November/December 1989): 1565.

Isopentyl Acetate (Banana Oil)

Esterification
Heating under reflux
Extraction
Simple distillation
Microscale boiling point

In this experiment you will prepare an ester, isopentyl acetate. This ester is often referred to as banana oil because it has the familiar odor of this fruit.

© Cengage Learning 2013

Isopentyl acetate is prepared by the direct esterification of acetic acid with isopentyl alcohol. Because the equilibrium does not favor the formation of the ester, it must be shifted to the right, in favor of the product, by using an excess of one of the starting materials. Acetic acid is used in excess because it is less expensive than isopentyl alcohol and more easily removed from the reaction mixture.

In the isolation procedure, much of the excess acetic acid and the remaining isopentyl alcohol are removed by extraction with sodium bicarbonate and water. After drying with anhydrous sodium sulfate, the ester is purified by distillation. The purity of the liquid product is analyzed by performing a microscale boiling point determination or infrared spectroscopy.

REQUIRED READING

Review:	Experiment 1	Introduction to Microscale Laboratory
	Techniques 5 and 6	
New:	Technique 7	Reaction Methods, Sections 7.2–7.4 and 7.6
	Technique 13	Physical Constants, Boiling Points
	Technique 12	Extractions, Separations, and Drying Agents
	Technique 14	Simple Distillation
	Essay	Esters—Flavors and Fragrances

If performing the optional infrared spectroscopy, also read:

Technique 25   Preparation of Samples for Spectroscopy

SPECIAL INSTRUCTIONS

Be careful when dispensing sulfuric and glacial acetic acids. They are corrosive and will attack your skin if you make contact with them. If you get one of these acids on your skin, wash the affected area with copious quantities of running water for 10–15 minutes.

Because a 1-hour reflux is required, you should start the experiment at the beginning of the laboratory period. During the reflux period, you may perform other work.

SUGGESTED WASTE DISPOSAL

Any aqueous solutions should be placed in a container specially designated for dilute aqueous waste. Place any excess ester in the nonhalogenated organic waste container.

NOTES TO THE INSTRUCTOR

Choose either Experiment 14A or Experiment 14B, but not both. The semimicroscale procedure requires the use of equipment not found in the typical microscale kit: a 20-mL round-bottom flask, a distillation head, and a vacuum takeoff adapter. The purpose of Experiment 14B is to allow an alternative to the use of a Hickman head for the distillation step.

This experiment has been carried out successfully using Dowex 50 × 2-100 ion-exchange resin instead of the sulfuric acid. Amberlyst-15 resin will also work.

  EXPERIMENT 14A

Isopentyl Acetate (Microscale Procedure)

PROCEDURE

Apparatus

Using a 5-mL conical vial, assemble a reflux apparatus using a water-cooled condenser (Technique 7, Figure 7.2A). Top the condenser with a drying tube (Technique 7, Figure 7.10B) that contains a loose plug of glass wool. The purpose of the drying tube is to control odors rather than to protect the reaction from water. Use a hot plate and an aluminum block for heating.

Preparation

Remove the empty 5-mL conical vial, weigh it, and record its weight. Place approximately 1.0 mL of isopentyl alcohol ($MW = 88.2$, $d = 0.813$ g/mL) in the vial using an automatic pipette or a dispensing pump. Reweigh the vial containing the alcohol and subtract the tare weight to obtain an accurate weight for the alcohol. Add 1.5 mL of glacial acetic acid ($MW = 60.1$, $d = 1.06$ g/mL) using an automatic pipette or dispensing pump. Using a disposable Pasteur pipette, add two to three drops of concentrated sulfuric acid. Swirl the liquid to mix. Add a small boiling stone (or a magnetic spin vane) and reattach the vial to the apparatus.

Reflux

Bring the mixture to a boil (aluminum block at about 150–160°C). Be sure to stir the mixture if you are using a spin vane instead of a boiling stone. Continue heating under reflux for 60–75 minutes. Remove the heating source and allow the mixture to cool to room temperature.

Workup

Disassemble the apparatus and, using a forceps, remove the boiling stone (or spin vane). Using a calibrated Pasteur pipette, slowly add 1.0 mL of 5% aqueous sodium bicarbonate to the cooled mixture in the conical vial. Stir the mixture in the vial with a microspatula until carbon dioxide evolution is no longer vigorous. Then cap the vial and shake *gently* with venting until the evolution of gas is complete. Using a Pasteur pipette, remove the lower aqueous layer and discard it. Repeat the extraction two more times, as outlined previously, using a fresh 1.0-mL portion of 5% sodium bicarbonate solution each time.

If droplets of water are evident in the vial containing the ester, transfer the ester to a dry conical vial using a dry Pasteur pipette. Dry the ester over granular anhydrous sodium sulfate (see Technique 12, Section 12.9). Allow the capped solution to stand for 10–15 minutes. Transfer the dry ester with a Pasteur pipette into a 3-mL conical vial while leaving the drying agent behind. If necessary, pick out any granules of sodium sulfate with the end of a spatula.

Distillation

Add a boiling stone (or a magnetic spin vane) to the dry ester. Clamping the glassware, assemble a distillation apparatus using a Hickman still and a water-cooled condenser on top of a hot plate with an aluminum heating block (Technique 14, Figure 14.5). In order to control odors, rather than to keep the reaction dry, top the apparatus with a drying tube packed loosely with a small amount of calcium chloride held in place by bits of cotton or glass wool. Begin the distillation by turning on the hot plate (about 180°C). Stir the mixture if you are using a spin vane instead of a boiling stove. Continue the distillation until only one or two drops of liquid remain in the distilling vial. If the Hickman head fills before the distillation is complete, it may be necessary to empty it using a Pasteur pipette (see Technique 14, Figure 14.6A) and transfer the distillate to a tared (preweighed) conical vial. Unless you have a sideported Hickman still, it will be necessary to remove the condenser in order to perform the transfer. When the distillation is complete, transfer the final portion of the distillate to this same vial.

Determination of Yield

Weigh the product and calculate the percentage yield of the ester. Determine its boiling point (bp 142°C) using a microscale boiling-point determination (Technique 13, Section 13.2). See the end of Experiment 14B for a spectral analysis.

14B   **EXPERIMENT 14B**

Isopentyl Acetate (Semimicroscale Procedure)

PROCEDURE

Apparatus

Assemble a reflux apparatus on top of your hot plate using a 20- or 25-mL round-bottom flask and a water-cooled condenser (refer to Technique 7, Figure 7.6A but use a round-bottom flask instead of the conical vial). To control vapors, place a drying tube packed with calcium chloride on top of the condenser. Use a hot plate and the aluminum block with the larger set of holes for heating.

Reaction Mixture

Weigh (tare) an empty 10-mL graduated cylinder and record its weight. Place approximately 2.5 mL of isopentyl alcohol in the graduated cylinder and reweigh it to determine the weight of the alcohol. Disconnect the round-bottom flask from the reflux apparatus and transfer the alcohol into it. Do not clean or wash the graduated cylinder. Using the same graduated cylinder, measure approximately 3.5 mL of glacial acetic acid ($MW = 60$, $d = 1.06$ g/mL) and add it to the alcohol already in the flask. Using a calibrated Pasteur pipette, add 0.5 mL of concentrated sulfuric acid, mixing *immediately* (swirl), to the reaction mixture contained in the flask. Add a corundum (black) boiling stone or stirring bar and reconnect the flask. Do not use a calcium carbonate (white, marble) boiling stone, because it will dissolve in the acidic medium.

Reflux

Start water circulating in the condenser and bring the mixture to a boil. Continue heating under reflux for at least 60 minutes. Be sure to stir the mixture if you are using a stirring bar instead of a boiling stone. When the reflux period is complete, disconnect or remove the heating source and let the mixture cool to room temperature.

Extractions

Disassemble the apparatus and transfer the reaction mixture to a 15-mL capped centrifuge tube. Avoid transferring the boiling stone or stirring bar. Add 5 mL of water, cap the centrifuge tube, and mix the phases by careful shaking and venting. Allow the phases to separate and then open the cap and remove the lower aqueous layer (see a similar procedure for a conical vial in Workup). Next, extract the organic layer with 2.5 mL of aqueous sodium bicarbonate, just as you did previously with water. Extract the organic layer once again, this time with 2.5 mL of saturated aqueous sodium chloride.

Drying

Transfer the crude ester to a clean, dry, 25-mL Erlenmeyer flask and add approximately 0.5 g of anhydrous sodium sulfate. Cork the mixture and let it stand for about 10 minutes while you prepare the apparatus for distillation. If the mixture does not appear dry (the drying agent clumps and does not "flow," the solution is cloudy, or drops of water are obvious), transfer the ester to a new, clean, dry, 25-mL Erlenmeyer flask and add a new 0.25-g portion of anhydrous sodium sulfate to complete the drying.

Infrared spectrum of isopentyl acetate (neat).

Distillation

Assemble a distillation apparatus using your smallest round-bottom flask to distill from (Technique 14, Figure 14.10, but insert a water condenser as shown in Experiment 7A). Use a hot plate with an aluminum block to heat. Preweigh (tare) and use a 5-mL conical vial to collect the product. Immerse the collection vial in a beaker of ice to ensure condensation and to reduce odors. Distill your ester and record its boiling-point *range* in your notebook.

Yield Determination

Weigh the product and calculate the percentage yield of the ester. At the option of your instructor, determine the boiling point using one of the methods described in Technique 13, Section 13.2. See below for a spectral analysis.

Infrared Spectroscopy

At your instructor's option, obtain an infrared spectrum using salt plates (Technique 25, Section 25.2). Compare the spectrum with the one reproduced in this experiment and include it with your report to the instructor. If any of your sample remains after performing the determination of the infrared spectrum, submit it in a properly labeled vial along with your report.

QUESTIONS

1. One method for favoring the formation of an ester is to add excess acetic acid. Suggest another method, involving the right-hand side of the equation, that will favor the formation of the ester.

2. Why is it easier to remove excess acetic acid from the products than excess isopentyl alcohol?

3. Why is the reaction mixture extracted with sodium bicarbonate? Give an equation and explain its relevance.

4. Which starting material is the limiting reagent in this procedure? Which reagent is used in excess? How great is the molar excess (how many times greater)?

5. How many grams are there in 1.00 mL of isopentyl acetate? You will need to look up the density of isopentyl acetate in a handbook.

6. How many moles of isopentyl acetate are there in 1.00 g of isopentyl acetate? You will need to calculate the molecular weight of isopentyl acetate.

7. Suppose that 1.00 mL of isopentyl alcohol was reacted with excess acetic acid and that 1.00 g of isopentyl acetate was obtained as product. Calculate the percentage yield.

8. Outline a separation scheme for isolating pure isopentyl acetate from the reaction mixture.

9. Interpret the principal absorption bands in the infrared spectrum of isopentyl acetate. (Technique 25 may be of some help in answering this question.)

10. Write a mechanism for the acid-catalyzed esterification of acetic acid with isopentyl alcohol. You may need to consult the chapter on carboxylic acids in your lecture textbook.

Terpenes and Phenylpropanoids

Anyone who has walked through a pine or cedar forest, or anyone who loves flowers and spices, knows that many plants and trees have distinctively pleasant odors. The essences or aromas of plants are due to volatile or **essential oils,** many of which have been valued since antiquity for their characteristic odors (frankincense and myrrh, for example). A list of the commercially important essential oils would run to more than 200 entries. Allspice, almond, anise, basil, bayberry, caraway, cinnamon, clove, cumin, dill, eucalyptus, garlic, jasmine, juniper, orange, peppermint, rose, sandalwood, sassafras, spearmint, thyme, violet, and wintergreen are some of the familiar examples of such valuable essential oils. Essential oils are used for their pleasant odors in perfumes and incense. They are also used for their taste appeal as spices and flavoring agents in foods. A few are valued for antibacterial and antifungal action. Some are used medicinally (camphor and eucalyptus) and others as insect repellents (citronella). Chaulmoogra oil is one of the few known curative agents for leprosy. Turpentine is used as a solvent for many paint products.

Essential oil components are often found in the glands or intercellular spaces in plant tissue. They may exist in all parts of the plant but are often concentrated in the seeds or flowers. Many components of essential oils are steam-volatile and can be isolated by steam distillation. Other methods of isolating essential oils include solvent extraction and pressing (expression) methods. Esters (see the essay "Esters-Flavors and Fragrances") are frequently responsible for the characteristic odors and flavors of fruits and flowers, but other types of substances may also be important components of odor or flavor principles. Besides the esters, the ingredients of essential oils may be complex mixtures of hydrocarbons, alcohols, and carbonyl compounds. These other components usually belong to one of the two groups of natural products called **terpenes** or **phenylpropanoids.**

Terpenes

Chemical investigations of essential oils in the 19th century found that many of the compounds responsible for the pleasant odors contained exactly 10 carbon atoms. These 10-carbon compounds came to be known as terpenes if they were hydrocarbons and as **terpenoids** if they contained oxygen and were alcohols, ketones, or aldehydes.

Eventually, it was found that there are also minor and less volatile plant constituents containing 15, 20, 30, and 40 carbon atoms. Because compounds of 10 carbons were originally called terpenes, they came to be called **monoterpenes.** The other terpenes were classified in the following way.

Class	No. of Carbons	Class	No. of Carbons
Hemiterpenes	5	Diterpenes	20
Monoterpenes	10	Triterpenes	30
Sesquiterpenes	15	Tetraterpenes	40

© Cengage Learning 2013

Further chemical investigations of the terpenes, all of which contain multiples of five carbons, showed them to have a repeating structural unit based on a five-carbon pattern. This structural pattern corresponds to the arrangement of atoms in the simple five-carbon compound isoprene. Isoprene was first obtained by the thermal "cracking" of natural rubber.

Natural rubber   Isoprene

© Cengage Learning 2013

As a result of this structural similarity, a diagnostic rule for terpenes, called the **isoprene rule,** was formulated. This rule states that a terpene should be divisible, at least formally, into **isoprene units.** The structures of a number of terpenes, along with a diagrammatic division of their structures into isoprene units, is shown in the figure on the next page that accompanies this essay. Many of these compounds represent odors or flavors that should be familiar to you.

Mevalonic acid

$$\text{Glucose} \longrightarrow \text{Acetyl Co-A} \longrightarrow$$

Isopentenyl pyrophosphate

© Cengage Learning 2013

Modern research has shown that terpenes do not arise from isoprene; it has never been detected as a natural product. Instead, the terpenes arise from an important biochemical precursor compound called **mevalonic acid** (see above). This compound arises from acetyl coenzyme A, a product of the biological degradation of glucose (glycolysis), and is converted to a compound called isopentenyl pyrophosphate. Isopentenyl pyrophosphate and its isomer 3,3-dimethylallyl pyrophosphate (double bond moved to the second position) are the five-carbon building blocks used by nature to construct all the terpene compounds.

Selected terpenes.

Phenylpropanoids

Aromatic compounds, those containing a benzene ring, are also a major type of compound found in essential oils. Some of these compounds, like *p*-cymene, are actually cyclic terpenes that have been aromatized (had their ring converted to a benzene ring), but most are of a different origin.

CH_3 structures

| Benzene | *p*-Cymene | Phenylpropane | Phenylalanine & Tyrosine (R = H) (R = OH) |

© Cengage Learning 2013

Many of these aromatic compounds are **phenylpropanoids,** compounds based on a phenylpropane skeleton. Phenylpropanoids are related in structure to the common amino acids phenylalanine and tyrosine, and many are derived from a biochemical pathway called the **shikimic acid pathway.**

| Caffeic acid (coffee) | Eugenol (cloves) | Vanillin (vanilla) |

© Cengage Learning 2013

It is also common to find compounds of phenylpropanoid origin that have had the three-carbon side chain cleaved. As a result, phenylmethane derivatives, such as vanillin, are also common in plants.

REFERENCES

Cane, D. E., ed. Isoprenoids Including Carotenoids and Steroids. In Barton, D., Nakanishi, K., and Meth-Cohn, O., eds. *Comprehensive Natural Products Chemistry.* New York: Elsevier, 1999. Vol. 2.

Cornforth, J. W. Terpene Biosynthesis. *Chemistry in Britain, 4* (1968): 102.

Geissman, T. A., and Crout, D. H. G. *Organic Chemistry of Secondary Plant Metabolism.* San Francisco: Freeman, Cooper and Co., 1969.

Hendrickson, J. B. *The Molecules of Nature.* New York: W. A. Benjamin, 1965.

Leeper, F. J., and Vederas, J. C., eds. *Biosynthesis: Aromatic Polyketides, Isoprenoids, Alkaloids.* New York: Springer, 2000.

Newman, A. A. *Chemistry of Terpenes and Terpenoids: A Survey for Advanced Students and Research Workers.* New York: Academic Press, 1972.

Pinder, A. R. *The Terpenes.* New York: John Wiley & Sons, 1960.

Ruzicka, L. History of the Isoprene Rule. *Proceedings of the Chemical Society (London)* (1959): 341.

Sterret, F. S. The Nature of Essential Oils, Part I. Production. *Journal of Chemical Education, 39* (1962): 203.

Sterret, F. S. The Nature of Essential Oils, Part II. Chemical Constituents. Analysis. *Journal of Chemical Education, 39* (1962): 246.

Isolation of Chlorophyll and Carotenoid Pigments from Spinach

Isolation of a natural product
Extraction
Column chromatography
Thin-layer chromatography

Photosynthesis in plants takes place in organelles called **chloroplasts.** Chloroplasts contain a number of colored compounds (pigments) that fall into two categories, **chlorophylls** and **carotenoids.**

Chlorophyll *a*

$$\text{Phytyl} = -CH_2-CH=\overset{\overset{\textstyle CH_3}{|}}{C}-CH_2-(CH_2-CH_2-\overset{\overset{\textstyle CH_3}{|}}{CH}-CH_2)_2-CH_2-CH_2-\overset{\overset{\textstyle CH_3}{|}}{CH}-CH_3$$

© Cengage Learning 2013

Carotenoids are yellow pigments that are also involved in the photosynthetic process. The structures of α- and β-**carotene** are given in the essay preceding this experiment. In addition, chloroplasts also contain several oxygen-containing derivatives of carotenes, called **xanthophylls.**

In this experiment, you will extract the chlorophyll and carotenoid pigments from spinach leaves using acetone as the solvent. The pigments will be separated by column chromatography using alumina as the adsorbent. Increasingly polar solvents will be used to elute the various components from the column. The colored fractions collected will then be analyzed using thin-layer chromatography. It should be possible for you to identify most of the pigments already discussed on your thin-layer plate after development.

Chlorophylls are the green pigments that act as the principal photoreceptor molecules of plants. They are capable of absorbing certain wavelengths of visible light that are then converted by plants into chemical energy. Two forms of these pigments found in plants are **chlorophyll *a*** and **chlorophyll *b*.** The two forms are identical, except that the methyl group that is shaded in the structural formula of chlorophyll *a* is replaced by a —CHO group in chlorophyll *b*. **Pheophytin *a*** and **pheophytin *b*** are identical to chlorophyll *a* and chlorophyll *b*, respectively, except that in each case the magnesium ion mg^{2+} has been replaced by two hydrogen ions 2H^{+}.

REQUIRED READING

Review:	Techniques 5 and 6	
	Technique 7	Reaction Methods, Section 7.9
	Technique 12	Extractions, Separations, and Drying Agents, Sections 12.5 and 12.9
	Technique 20	Thin-Layer Chromatography
New:	Technique 19	Column Chromatography
	Essay	The Chemistry of Vision

SPECIAL INSTRUCTIONS

Hexane and acetone are both highly flammable. Avoid using flames while working with these solvents. Perform the thin-layer chromatography in the hood. The procedure calls for a centrifuge tube with a tight-fitting cap. If this is not available, you can use a vortex mixer for mixing the liquids. Another alternative is to use a cork to stopper the tube; however, the cork will absorb some liquid.

Fresh spinach is preferable to frozen spinach. Because of handling, frozen spinach contains additional pigments that are difficult to identify. Because the pigments are light-sensitive and can undergo oxidation, you should work quickly. Samples should be stored in closed containers and kept in the dark when possible. The column chromatography procedure takes less than 15 minutes to perform and cannot be stopped until it is completed. It is important, therefore, that you have all the materials needed for this part of the experiment prepared in advance and that you be thoroughly familiar with the procedure before running the column. If you need to prepare the 70% hexane–30% acetone solvent mixture, be sure to mix it thoroughly before using.

SUGGESTED WASTE DISPOSAL

Dispose of all organic solvents in the container for nonhalogenated organic solvents. Place the alumina in the container designated for wet alumina.

NOTES TO THE INSTRUCTOR

The column chromatography should be performed with activated alumina from EM Science (No. AX0612-1). The particle sizes are 80–120 mesh, and the material is Type F-20. Dry the alumina overnight in an oven at 110°C and store it in a tightly sealed bottle. Alumina older than several years may need to be dried for a longer time at a higher temperature. Depending on how dry the alumina is, solvents of different polarity will be required to elute the components from the column.

For thin-layer chromatography, use flexible silica gel plates from Whatman with a fluorescent indicator (No. 4410 222). If the TLC plates have not been purchased recently, place them in an oven at 100°C for 30 minutes and store them in a desiccator until use.

If you use different alumina or different thin-layer plates, try the experiment before using it in class. Materials other than those specified here may give different results than indicated in this experiment.

PROCEDURE

Part A. Extraction of the Pigments

— Anhydrous sodium sulfate

— Cotton

Column for drying extract.

Weigh about 0.5 g of fresh (or 0.25 g of frozen) spinach leaves (avoid using stems or thick veins). Fresh spinach is preferable, if available. If you must use frozen spinach, dry the thawed leaves by pressing them between several layers of paper towels. Cut or tear the spinach leaves into small pieces and place them in a mortar along with 1.0 mL of cold acetone. Grind with a pestle until the spinach leaves have been broken into particles too small to be seen clearly. If too much acetone has evaporated, you may need to add an additional portion of acetone (0.5–1.0 mL) to perform the following step. Using a Pasteur pipette, transfer the mixture to a centrifuge tube. Rinse the mortar and pestle with 1.0 mL of cold acetone and transfer the remaining mixture to the centrifuge tube. Centrifuge the mixture (be sure to balance the centrifuge). Using a Pasteur pipette, transfer the liquid to a centrifuge tube with a tight-fitting cap (see "Special Instructions" if one is not available).

Add 2.0 mL of hexane to the tube, cap the tube, and shake the mixture thoroughly. Then add 2.0 mL of water and shake thoroughly with occasional venting. Centrifuge the mixture to break the emulsion, which usually appears as a cloudy green layer in the middle of the mixture. Remove the bottom aqueous layer with a Pasteur pipette. Using a Pasteur pipette, prepare a column containing anhydrous sodium sulfate to dry the remaining hexane layer, which contains the dissolved pigments. Put a plug of cotton into a Pasteur pipette (5¾-inch) and tamp it into position using a glass rod. The correct position of the cotton is shown in the figure. Add about 0.5 g of powdered or granular anhydrous sodium sulfate and tap the column with your finger to pack the material.

Clamp the column in a vertical position and place a dry test tube (13 × 100-mm) under the bottom of the column. Label this test tube with an *E* for *extract* so that you don't confuse it with the test tubes you will be working with later in this experiment. With a Pasteur pipette, transfer the hexane layer to the column. When all the solution has drained, add 0.5 mL of hexane to the column to extract all the pigments from the drying agent. Evaporate the solvent by placing the test tube in a warm water bath (40–60°C) and directing a stream of nitrogen gas (or dry air) into the test tube. Dissolve the residue in 0.5 mL of hexane. Stopper the test tube and place it in your drawer until you are ready to run the alumina chromatography column.

Part B. Column Chromatography

Introduction

The pigments are separated on a column packed with alumina. Although there are many components in your sample, they usually separate into two main bands on the column. The first band to pass through the column is yellow and consists of the carotenes. This band may be less than 1 mm wide and it may pass through the column rapidly. It is easy to miss seeing the band as it passes through the alumina. The second band consists of all the other pigments discussed in the introduction to this experiment. Although it consists of both green and yellow pigments, it appears as a green band on the column. The green band spreads out on the column more than the yellow band, and it moves more slowly. Occasionally, the yellow and green components in this band will separate as the band moves down the column. If this begins to occur, you should change to a solvent of higher polarity so that they come out as one band. As the samples elute from the column, collect the yellow band (carotenes) in one test tube and the green band in another test tube.

Because the moisture content of the alumina is difficult to control, different samples of alumina may have different activities. The activity of the alumina is an important factor in determining the polarity of the solvent required to elute each band of pigments. Several solvents with a range of polarities are used in this experiment. The solvents and their relative polarities follow:

Hexane	increasing
70% hexane–30% acetone	polarity
Acetone	
80% acetone–20% methanol	

A solvent of lower polarity elutes the yellow band; a solvent of higher polarity is required to elute the green band. In this procedure, you first try to elute the yellow band with hexane. If the yellow band does not move with hexane, you then add the next more polar solvent. Continue this process until you find a solvent that moves the yellow band. When you find the appropriate solvent, continue using it until the yellow band is eluted from the column. When the yellow band is eluted, change to the next more polar solvent. When you find a solvent that moves the green band, continue using it until the green band is eluted. Remember that occasionally a second yellow band will begin to move down the column before the green band moves. This yellow band will be much wider than the first one. If this occurs, change to a more polar solvent. This should bring all the components in the green band down at the same time.

Advance Preparation

Before running the column, assemble the following glassware and liquids. Obtain five dry test tubes (16 × 100-mm), and number them 1 through 5. Prepare two dry Pasteur pipettes with bulbs attached. Calibrate one of them to deliver a volume of about 0.25 mL. Place 10.0 mL hexane, 6.0 mL 70% hexane–30% acetone solution (by volume), 6.0 mL acetone, and 6.0 mL 80% acetone–20% methanol (by volume) into four separate containers. Clearly label each container.

Prepare a chromatography column packed with alumina. Place a *loose* plug of cotton in a Pasteur pipette (5¾-inch), and push it *gently* into position using a glass rod (see the figure for the correct position of the cotton). Add 1.25 g of alumina (EM Science, No. AX0612-1) to the pipette[1] while tapping the column gently with your finger. When all the alumina has been added, tap the column with your finger for several seconds to ensure that the alumina is tightly packed. Clamp the column in a vertical position so that the bottom of the column is just above the height of the test tubes you will be using to collect the fractions. Place test tube 1 under the column.

---

[1] As an option, students may prepare a microfunnel from a 1-mL disposable plastic pipette. The microfunnel is prepared by (1) cutting the bulb in half with a scissors and (2) cutting the stem at an angle about ½-inch below the bulb. This funnel can be placed in the top of the column (Pasteur pipette) to aid in filling the column with alumina or with the solvents.

NOTE: Read the following procedure on running the column. The chromatography procedure takes less than 15 minutes, and you cannot stop until all the material is eluted from the column. You must have a good understanding of the whole procedure before running the column.

Running the Column

Using a Pasteur pipette, slowly add about 3.0 mL of hexane to the column. The column must be completely moistened by the solvent. Drain the excess hexane until the level of hexane reaches the top of the alumina. Once you have added hexane to the alumina, the top of the column must not be allowed to run dry. If necessary, add more hexane.

NOTE: It is essential that the liquid level not be allowed to drain below the surface of the alumina at any point during the procedure.

When the level of the hexane reaches the top of the alumina, add about half (0.25 mL) of the dissolved pigments to the column. Leave the remainder in the test tube for the thin-layer chromatography procedure. (Put a stopper on the tube and place it back in your drawer.) Continue collecting the eluent in test tube 1. Just as the pigment solution penetrates the column, add 1 mL of hexane and drain until the surface of the liquid has reached the alumina.

Add about 4 mL of hexane. If the yellow band begins to separate from the green band, continue to add hexane until the yellow band passes through the column. If the yellow band does not separate from the green band, change to the next more polar solvent (70% hexane–30% acetone). When changing solvents, do not add the new solvent until the last solvent has nearly penetrated the alumina. When the appropriate solvent is found, add this solvent until the yellow band passes through the column. Just before the yellow band reaches the bottom of the column, place test tube 2 under the column. When the eluent becomes colorless again (the total volume of the yellow material should be less than 2 mL), place test tube 3 under the column.

Add several mL of the next more polar solvent when the level of the last solvent is almost at the top of the alumina. If the green band moves down the column, continue to add this solvent until the green band is eluted from the column. If the green band does not move or if a diffuse yellow band begins to move, change to the next more polar solvent. Change solvents again if necessary. Collect the green band in test tube 4. When there is little or no green color in the eluent, place test tube 5 under the column and stop the procedure.

Using a warm water bath (40–60°C) and a stream of nitrogen gas, evaporate the solvent from the tube containing the yellow band (tube 2), the tube containing the green band (tube 4), and the tube containing the original pigment solution (tube E). As soon as all the solvent has evaporated from each of the tubes, remove them from the water bath. Do not allow any of the tubes to remain in the water bath after the solvent has evaporated. Stopper the tubes and place them in your drawer.

Part C. Thin-Layer Chromatography

Preparing the TLC Plate

Technique 20 describes the procedures for thin-layer chromatography. Use a 10-cm × 3.3-cm TLC plate (Whatman Silica Gel Plates No. 4410 222). These plates have a flexible backing but should not be bent excessively. Handle them carefully or the adsorbent may flake off them. Also, you should handle them only by the edges; the surface

Preparing the TLC plate.

should not be touched. Using a lead pencil (not a pen), *lightly* draw a line across the plate (short dimension) about 1 cm from the bottom (see figure). Using a centimeter ruler, move its index about 0.6 cm in from the edge of the plate and lightly mark off three 1-cm intervals on the line. These are the points at which the samples will be spotted.

Prepare three micropipettes to spot the plate. The preparation of these pipettes is described and illustrated in Technique 20, Section 20.4. Prepare a TLC development chamber with 70% hexane–30% acetone (see Technique 20, Section 20.5). A beaker covered with aluminum foil or a wide-mouth screw-cap bottle is a suitable container to use (see Technique 20, Figure 20.5). The backing on the TLC plates is thin, so if they touch the filter paper liner of the development chamber *at any point*, solvent will begin to diffuse onto the absorbent surface at that point. To avoid this, be sure that the filter paper liner does not go completely around the inside of the container. A space about 2 inches wide must be provided.

Using a Pasteur pipette, add two drops of 70% hexane–30% acetone to each of the three test tubes containing dried pigments. Swirl the tubes so that the drops of solvent dissolve as much of the pigments as possible. The TLC plate should be spotted with three samples: the extract, the yellow band from the column, and the green band. For each of the three samples, use a different micropipette to spot the sample on the plate. The correct method of spotting a TLC plate is described in Technique 20, Section 20.4. Take up part of the sample in the pipette (don't use a bulb; capillary action will draw up the liquid). For the extract (tube labeled E) and the green band (tube 4), touch the plate once *lightly* and let the solvent evaporate. The spot should be no larger than 2 mm in diameter and should be a fairly dark green. For the yellow band (tube 2), repeat the spotting technique 5–10 times until the spot is a definite yellow. Let the solvent evaporate completely between successive applications and spot the plate in exactly the same position each time. Save the liquid samples in case you need to repeat the TLC.

Developing the TLC Plate

Place the TLC plate in the development chamber, making sure that the plate does not come in contact with the filter paper liner. Remove the plate when the solvent front is 1–2 cm from the top of the plate. Using a lead pencil, mark the position of the solvent front. As soon as the plates have dried, outline the spots with a pencil and indicate the colors. This is important to do soon after the plates have dried because some of the pigments will change color when exposed to the air.

Analysis of the Results

In the crude extract, you should be able to see the following components (in order of decreasing R_f values):

Carotenes (1 spot) (yellow-orange)

Pheophytin *a* (gray, may be nearly as intense as chlorophyll *b*)

Pheophytin *b* (gray, may not be visible)

Chlorophyll *a* (blue-green, more intense than chlorophyll *b*)

Chlorophyll *b* (green)

Xanthophylls (possibly three spots: yellow)

Depending on the spinach sample, the conditions of the experiment, and how much sample was spotted on the TLC plate, you may observe other pigments. These additional components can result from air oxidation, hydrolysis, or other chemical reactions involving the pigments discussed in this experiment. It is common to observe other pigments in samples of frozen spinach. It is also common to observe components in the green band that were not present in the extract.

Identify as many of the spots in your samples as possible. Determine which pigments were present in the yellow band and which were present in the green band. Draw a picture of the TLC plate in your notebook. Label each spot with its color and its identity, where possible. Calculate the *Rf* values for each spot produced by chromatography of the extract (see Technique 20, Section 20.9). At the instructor's option, submit the TLC plate with your report.

QUESTIONS

1. Why are the chlorophylls less mobile on column chromatography, and why do they have lower R_f values than the carotenes?

2. Propose structural formulas for pheophytin *a* and pheophytin *b*.

3. What would happen to the R_f values of the pigments if you were to increase the relative concentration of acetone in the developing solvent?

4. Using your results as a guide, comment on the purity of the material in the green and yellow bands; that is, did each band consist of a single component?

Ethanol and Fermentation Chemistry

The fermentation processes involved in making bread, making wine, and brewing are among the oldest chemical arts. Even though fermentation had been known as an art for centuries, it was not until the nineteenth century that chemists began to understand this process from the point of view of science. In 1810, Gay-Lussac discovered the general chemical equation for the breakdown of sugar into ethanol and carbon dioxide. The manner in which the process took place was the subject of much conjecture until Louis Pasteur began his thorough examination of fermentation. Pasteur demonstrated that yeast was required in the fermentation. He was also able to identify other factors that controlled the action of the yeast cells. His results were published in 1857 and 1866.

For many years, scientists believed that the transformation of sugar into ethanol and carbon dioxide by yeasts was inseparably connected with the life process of the yeast cell. This view was abandoned in 1897, when Büchner demonstrated that yeast extract would bring about alcoholic fermentation in the absence of any yeast cells. The fermenting activity of yeast is due to a remarkably active catalyst of biochemical origin, the enzyme zymase. It is now recognized that most of the chemical transformations that occur in living cells of plants and animals are brought about by enzymes. These enzymes are organic compounds, generally proteins, and establishment of the structures and reaction mechanisms of these compounds is an active field of present-day research. Zymase is now known to be a complex of at least 22 separate enzymes, each of which catalyzes a specific step in the fermentation reaction sequence.

Enzymes display an extraordinary specificity—a given enzyme acts on a specific compound or a closely related group of compounds. Thus, zymase acts on only a few select sugars and not on all carbohydrates; the digestive enzymes of the alimentary tract are equally specific in their activity.

The chief sources of sugars for fermentation are the various starches and the molasses residue obtained from refining sugar. Corn (maize) is the chief source of starch in the United States, and ethyl alcohol made from corn is commonly known as **grain alcohol**. In preparing alcohol from corn, the grain, with or without the germ, is ground and cooked to give the **mash**. The enzyme diastase is added in the form of **malt** (sprouted barley that has been dried in air and ground to a powder) or of a mold such as *Aspergillus oryzae*. The mixture is kept at 40°C until all the starch has been converted to the sugar **maltose** by hydrolysis of ether and acetal bonds. This solution is known as the **wort**.

Starch

This is a glucose polymer with 1,4- and
1,6- glycosidic linkages. The linkages
at C-1 are α.

$+ H_2O \xrightarrow[\text{in malt}]{\text{diastase}}$

Maltose (C$_{12}$H$_{22}$O$_{11}$)

The α linkage still exists at C-1.
The —OH is shown α at the 1′ postion
(axial), but it can also be ß (equatorial).

The wort is cooled to 20°C and diluted with water to 10% maltose, and a pure yeast culture is added. The yeast culture is usually a strain of *Saccharomyces cerevisiae* (or *ellipsoidus*). The yeast cells secrete two enzyme systems: maltase, which converts the maltose into glucose, and zymase, which converts the glucose into carbon dioxide and alcohol. Heat is liberated, and the temperature must be kept below 35°C by cooling to prevent destruction of the enzymes. Oxygen in large amounts is initially necessary for the optimum reproduction of yeast cells, but the actual production of alcohol is anaerobic. During fermentation, the evolution of carbon dioxide soon establishes anaerobic conditions. If oxygen were freely available, only carbon dioxide and water would be produced.

After 40–60 hours, fermentation is complete, and the product is distilled to remove the alcohol from solid matter. The distillate is fractionated by means of an efficient column. A small amount of acetaldehyde (bp 21°C) distills first and is followed by 95% alcohol. Fusel oil is contained in the higher-boiling fractions. The fusel oil consists of a mixture of higher alcohols, chiefly 1-propanol, 2-methyl-1-propanol, 3-methyl-1-butanol, and 2-methyl-1-butanol. The exact composition of fusel oil varies considerably; it particularly depends on the type of raw material that is fermented. These higher alcohols are not formed by fermentation of glucose. They arise from certain amino acids derived from the proteins present in the raw material and the yeast. These fusel oils cause the headaches associated with drinking alcoholic beverages.

Industrial alcohol is ethyl alcohol used for nonbeverage purposes. Most commercial alcohol is denatured to avoid payment of taxes, the biggest cost in the price of liquor. The denaturants render the alcohol unfit for drinking. Methanol, aviation fuel, and

$$\text{Maltose} + H_2O \xrightarrow{\text{maltase}} 2$$

β-D-(+)-Glucose
(α-D-(+)-Glucose, with an axial
—OH, is also produced.)

$$\text{Glucose} \xrightarrow{\text{zymase}} 2\ CO_2 + 2\ CH_3CH_2OH + 26\ \text{Kcal}$$
$$C_6H_{12}O_6$$

other substances are used for this purpose. The difference in price between taxed and nontaxed alcohol is more than $20 a gallon. Before efficient synthetic processes were developed, the chief source of industrial alcohol was fermented blackstrap molasses, the noncrystallizable residue from refining cane sugar (sucrose). Most industrial ethanol in the United States is now manufactured from ethylene, a product of the "cracking" of petroleum hydrocarbons. By reaction with concentrated sulfuric acid, ethylene becomes ethyl hydrogen sulfate, which is hydrolyzed to ethanol by dilution with water. The alcohols 2-propanol, 2-butanol, 2-methyl-2-propanol, and higher secondary and tertiary alcohols are also produced on a large scale from alkenes derived from cracking.

Yeasts, molds, and bacteria are used commercially for the large-scale production of various organic compounds. An important example, in addition to ethanol production, is the anaerobic fermentation of starch by certain bacteria to yield 1-butanol, acetone, ethanol, carbon dioxide, and hydrogen.

For additional information on the production of ethanol, see the essay Biofuels that precedes Experiment 27. In this essay, the production of ethanol from corn for use in automobiles is discussed, along with the production of ethanol from other sources such as plant cellulose.

REFERENCES

Amerine, M. A. Wine. *Sci. Am.* **1964**, *211* (Aug), 46.

Hallberg, D. E. Fermentation Ethanol. *ChemTech* **1984**, *14* (May), 308.

Ough, C. S. Chemicals Used in Making Wine. *Chem. Eng. News* **1987**, *65* (Jan 5), 19.

Van Koevering, T. E.; Morgan, M. D.; and Younk, T. J. The Energy Relationships of Corn Production and Alcohol Fermentation. *J. Chem. Educ.* **1987**, *64* (Jan), 11.

Webb, A. D. The Science of Making Wine. *Am. Sci.* **1984**, *72* (Jul–Aug), 360.

Students wanting to investigate alcoholism and possible chemical explanations for alcohol addiction may consult the following references:

Cohen, G.; and Collins, M. Alkaloids from Catecholamines in Adrenal Tissue: Possible Role in Alcoholism. *Science* **1970**, *167*, 1749.

Davis, V. E.; and Walsh, M. J. Alcohol Addiction and Tetrahydropapaveroline. *Science* **1970**, *169*, 1105.

Davis, V. E.; and Walsh, M. J. Alcohols, Amines, and Alkaloids: A Possible Biochemical Basis for Alcohol Addiction. *Science* **1970**, *167*, 1005.

Seevers, M. H.; Davis, V. E.; and Walsh, M. J. Morphine and Ethanol Physical Dependence: A Critique of a Hypothesis. *Science* **1970**, *170*, 1113.

Yamanaka, Y.; Walsh, M. J.; and Davis, V. E. Salsolinol, an Alkaloid Derivative of Dopamine Formed in Vitro during Alcohol Metabolism. *Nature* **1970**, *227*, 1143.

4-Methylcyclohexene

Preparation of an alkene
Dehydration of an alcohol
Distillation
Bromine and permanganate tests for unsaturation

4-Methylcyclohexanol → (H₃PO₄/H₂SO₄, Δ) → 4-Methylcyclohexene + H_2O

© Cengage Learning 2013

Alcohol dehydration is an acid-catalyzed reaction performed by strong, concentrated mineral acids such as sulfuric and phosphoric acids. The acid protonates the alcoholic hydroxyl group, permitting it to dissociate as water. Loss of a proton from the intermediate (elimination) brings about an alkene. Because sulfuric acid often causes extensive charring in this reaction, phosphoric acid, which is comparatively free of this problem, is a better choice. To make the reaction proceed faster, however, a minimal amount of sulfuric acid will also be used.

The equilibrium that attends this reaction will be shifted in favor of the product by distilling it from the reaction mixture as it is formed. The 4-methylcyclohexene (bp 101–102°C) will codistill with the water that is also formed. By continuously removing the products, one can obtain a high yield of 4-methylcyclohexene. Because the starting material, 4-methylcyclohexanol, also has a somewhat low boiling point (bp 171–173°C), the distillation must be done carefully so that the alcohol does not also distill.

Unavoidably, a small amount of phosphoric acid codistills with the product. It is removed by washing the distillate mixture with a saturated sodium chloride solution. This step also partially removes the water from the 4-methylcyclohexene layer; the drying process will be completed by allowing the product to stand over anhydrous sodium sulfate.

Compounds containing double bonds react with a bromine solution (red) to decolorize it. Similarly, they react with a solution of potassium permanganate (purple) to discharge its color and produce a brown precipitate (MnO_2). These reactions are often used as qualitative tests to determine the presence of a double bond in an organic molecule (see Experiment 53). Both tests will be performed on the 4-methylcyclohexene formed in this experiment.

← (Br₂ (red)) — CH₃ cyclohexene — (KMnO₄ (purple)) → + MnO_2 (brown)

Br Br (colorless)   HO OH (colorless)

© Cengage Learning 2013

REQUIRED READING

Review: Techniques 1, 2, 3, 5, and 6

Technique 12   Extractions, Separations, and Drying Agents, Sections 12.5 and 12.9

New: Technique 14   Simple Distillation

If performing the optional boiling point or infrared spectroscopy, also read:

Technique 13   Physical Constants of Liquids: The Boiling Point and Density

Technique 25   Infrared Spectroscopy

SPECIAL INSTRUCTIONS

Phosphoric and sulfuric acids are corrosive. Do not allow either acid to touch your skin.

If you must store the 4-methylcyclohexene, it is essential that the sample be stored in leak-proof vials. We have found that GC-MS vials work much better for this purpose than a conical vial with a septum liner and cap.

SUGGESTED WASTE DISPOSAL

Any organic residues should be discarded in an organic waste container designated for the disposal of *nonhalogenated* wastes. Discard the solutions that remain after the bromine test for unsaturation in an organic waste container designated for the disposal of *halogenated* wastes. The solutions that remain after the potassium permanganate test should be discarded into a waste container specifically marked for the disposal of heavy-metal wastes. Aqueous solutions should be placed in the container designated for that purpose.

NOTE TO THE INSTRUCTOR

Amberlyst-15 ion exchange resin (sulfonic acid groups) may be used in place of the phosphoric and sulfuric acids.[1] There is less charring with the resin. Use 0.2 g of the resin and heat more slowly, increasing the reaction time to about 45 minutes. When measuring the resin (little balls), use a measuring spoon with a depression; the spheres roll off a flat spatula, and static charges sometimes complicate the weighing problem. Provide a waste container for the spent resin.

The temperature during the distillation in Experiment 24B may be monitored with either a thermometer or a stainless steel temperature probe. If a stainless steel probe is used, it must be used in conjunction with either a digital thermometer or one of the Vernier devices (see Technique 13, Section 13.4, and Technique 14, Figure 14.12).

---

[1] Moeur, H. P., Swatik, S. A., and Pinnell, R. P. Microscale Dehydration of Cyclohexanol Using a Macroreticular Cation Exchange Resin. *Journal of Chemical Education*, 74 (July 1997): 833.

For the boiling point determination, we prefer the Semimicroscale Direct Method described in Technique 13, Section 13.2. The best way to perform this method is to use a digital thermometer with a stainless steel probe (see Technique 13, Section 13.4 and Figure 13.7).

24A   EXPERIMENT 24A

4-Methylcyclohexene (Microscale Procedure)

PROCEDURE

Apparatus Assembly

Place 1.5 mL of 4-methylcyclohexanol ($MW = 114.2$) in a tared 5-mL conical vial and reweigh the vial to determine an accurate weight for the alcohol. Add 0.40 mL of 85% phosphoric acid and six drops of concentrated sulfuric acid to the vial. Mix the liquids thoroughly using a glass stirring rod and add a boiling stone. Assemble a distillation apparatus as shown in Figure 14.5 and use a water-cooled condenser. It is recommended that you include the drying tube, filled with calcium chloride, as an odor-control measure.

Dehydration

Start circulating the cooling water in the condenser and heat the mixture until the product begins to distill (aluminum block or sand bath set to about 160–180°C). If you use an aluminum block for heating, place aluminum collars around the conical vial. The heating should be regulated so that the distillation requires about 30–45 minutes, heating slowly at the beginning.

During the distillation, use a Pasteur pipette to remove the distillate from the well of the Hickman head when necessary. You must remove the condenser when performing this experiment, unless you have a Hickman head with a side port. In that case, you can remove the distillate through the side port without removing the condenser. Transfer the distillate to a clean, dry, 3-mL conical vial, which should be capped except when liquid is being added. Continue the distillation until no more liquid is being distilled. This can be best determined by observing when boiling in the conical vial has ceased. Also, the volume of liquid remaining in the vial should be about 0.5 mL when distillation is complete.

When distillation is complete, remove as much distillate as possible from the Hickman head and transfer it to the 3-mL conical vial. Then, using a Pasteur pipette with the tip slightly bent, rinse the sides of the inside wall of the Hickman head with 1.0 mL of saturated sodium chloride. Do this thoroughly so that as much liquid as possible is washed down into the well of the Hickman head. Transfer this liquid to the 3-mL conical vial.

Isolation and Drying of Product

Allow the layers to separate and remove the bottom aqueous layer. Using a dry Pasteur pipette, transfer the organic layer to a small test tube, and dry it over granular anhydrous sodium sulfate (Technique 12, Section 12.9). Place a stopper in the test tube and set it aside for 10–15 minutes to remove the last traces of water. Carefully transfer as much distillate as possible to a small tared conical vial with a cap or a GC-MS vial. Weigh the product (*MW* = 96.2) and calculate the percentage yield.

Boiling-Point Determination and Spectroscopy[2]

At the instructor's option, determine an accurate boiling point on your sample using the microboiling-point method (Technique 13, Section 13.2), and obtain the infrared spectrum of 4-methylcyclohexene (Technique 25, Section 25.2 or Section 25.3). Because 4-methylcyclohexene is so volatile, you must work quickly to obtain a good spectrum using sodium chloride plates. A better method is to use silver chloride plates with the orientation shown in Figure 25.3B. Compare the spectrum with the one shown in this experiment. After performing the tests at the end of this experiment, submit your sample, along with the report, to the instructor.

EXPERIMENT 24B

4-Methylcyclohexene (Semimicroscale Procedure)

PROCEDURE

Apparatus Assembly

Assemble a distillation apparatus as shown in Figure 14.10, but insert a water condenser as shown in Figure 14.11 and insert the thermometer or temperature probe a bit lower than shown so that the mercury bulb or end of the temperature probe is inside the ground-glass joint. Place 4.0 mL of 4-methylcyclohexanol (*MW* = 114.2) in a 10-mL graduated cylinder and weigh it. Transfer the alcohol to the 10-mL round-bottom flask and reweigh the graduated cylinder to determine an accurate weight for the alcohol. Add 1.0 mL of 85% phosphoric acid and 16 drops of concentrated sulfuric acid to the alcohol already in the round-bottom flask. Without delay, mix the contents of the round-bottom flask thoroughly by swirling the liquids in the flask. Add a corundum (black) boiling stone and reconnect the flask to the distillation apparatus.

Dehydration

Start circulating cooling water in the condenser and heat the mixture until the product begins to distill (aluminum block approximately 180°C). The heating should be regulated so that the distillation requires about 45 minutes to be completed. Distill slowly and monitor (record) the temperature while the liquid distills; the products should distill over a range of about 90–105°C. Continue distillation until no more liquid is collected. This can best be determined by observing when the temperature drops. You should collect about 3mL of distillate. Approximately 1 mL of a dark brown liquid will remain undistilled in the round-bottom flask when the distillation is complete.

---

[2] An option is to submit the student samples to analysis by gas chromatography–mass spectrometry. If GC-MS is used, students can observe that several products besides 4-methylcyclohexene are formed in the reaction. Discussion of the mechanism of rearrangement should then be included.

When the distillation is complete, open the joint between the distillation head and the condenser, and then tilt the condenser so that any liquid trapped in the joints of the condenser will drip into the collection vial. If droplets of distillate are evident clinging to the inside tube of the condenser, wash them down with a small amount of saturated aqueous sodium chloride solution.

Isolation and Drying of the Product

Using a Pasteur pipette, transfer the distillate from the conical vial to a 15-mL capped centrifuge tube, and add approximately 2.0 mL of a saturated sodium chloride solution. Cap the tube and gently invert it several times with venting. Allow the layers to separate and remove the lower aqueous layer with a Pasteur pipette. Transfer the organic layer to a small test tube or Erlenmeyer flask, and dry it over granular anhydrous sodium sulfate (Technique 12, Section 12.9). Place a stopper in the test tube (or Erlenmeyer flask), and set it aside for 10–15 minutes to remove the last traces of water. Transfer the dry distillate to a small tared conical vial with a cap or a GC-MS vial. Weigh the product ($MW = 96.2$) and calculate the percentage yield.

Boiling-Point Determination and Spectroscopy[3]

At the instructor's option, determine a more accurate boiling point on your sample using the micro boiling-point method (Technique 13, Section 13.2) and obtain the infrared spectrum of 4-methylcyclohexene (Technique 25, Section 25.2 or Section 25.3). Because 4-methylcyclohexene is so volatile, you must work quickly to obtain a good spectrum using sodium chloride plates. A better method is to use silver chloride plates with the orientation shown in Figure 25.3B. Compare the spectrum with the one shown in this experiment. After performing the following tests, submit your sample, along with the report, to the instructor.

Infrared spectrum of 4-methylcyclohexene (neat).

---

[3] See footnote 2 in Experiment 24A.

Infrared spectrum of 4-methylcyclohexanol (neat).

UNSATURATION TESTS

Place four to five drops of 4-methylcyclohexanol in each of two small test tubes. In each of another pair of small test tubes, place four to five drops of the 4-methylcyclohexene you prepared. Do not confuse the test tubes. Take one test tube from each group, and add a solution of bromine in carbon tetrachloride or methylene chloride, drop by drop, to the contents of the test tube, until the red color is no longer discharged or until you have added 20 drops. Record the result in each case, including the number of drops required. Test the remaining two test tubes in a similar fashion with a solution of potassium permanganate. Because aqueous potassium permanganate is not miscible with organic compounds, you will have to add about 0.3 mL of 1,2-dimethoxyethane to each test tube before making the test. Record your results and explain them.

QUESTIONS

1. Outline a mechanism for the dehydration of 4-methylcyclohexanol catalyzed by phosphoric acid.

2. What major alkene product is produced by dehydrating the following alcohols?
   a. Cyclohexanol
   b. 1-Methylcyclohexanol
   c. 2-Methylcyclohexanol
   d. 2,2-Dimethylcyclohexanol
   e. 1,2-Cyclohexanediol (*Hint:* Consider keto–enol tautomerism.)

3. Compare and interpret the infrared spectra of 4-methylcyclohexene and 4-methylcyclohexanol.

4. Identify the C-H out-of-plane bending vibrations in the infrared spectrum of 4- methylcyclohexene. What structural information can be obtained from these bands?

5. In this experiment, 1.0 mL of saturated sodium chloride is used to rinse the Hickman head after the initial distillation. Why is saturated sodium chloride, rather than pure water, used for this procedure and the subsequent washing of the organic layer?

Fats and Oils

In the normal human diet, about 25% to 50% of the caloric intake consists of fats and oils. These substances are the most concentrated form of food energy in our diet. When metabolized, fats produce about 9.5 kcal of energy per gram. Carbohydrates and proteins produce less than half this amount. For this reason, animals tend to build up fat deposits as a reserve source of energy. They do this, of course, only when their food intake exceeds their energy requirements. In times of starvation, the body metabolizes these stored fats. Even so, some fats are required by animals for bodily insulation and as a protective sheath around some vital organs.

The constitution of fats and oils was first investigated by the French chemist Chevreul from 1810 to 1820. He found that when fats and oils were hydrolyzed, they gave rise to several "fatty acids" and the trihydroxylic alcohol glycerol. Thus, fats and oils are **esters** of glycerol, called **glycerides** or **acylglycerols**. Because glycerol has three hydroxyl groups, it is possible to have mono-, di-, and triglycerides. Fats and oils are predominantly triglycerides (triacylglycerols), constituted as follows:

3 Fatty acids + glycerol = A triglyceride

© Cengage Learning 2013

Thus, most fats and oils are esters of glycerol, and their differences result from the differences in the fatty acids with which glycerol may be combined. The most common fatty acids have 12, 14, 16, or 18 carbons, although acids with both lesser and greater numbers of carbons are found in several fats and oils. These common fatty acids are listed in Table 1 along with their structures. As you can see, these acids are both saturated and unsaturated. The saturated acids tend to be solids, whereas the unsaturated acids are usually liquids. This circumstance also extends to fats and oils. Fats are made up of fatty acids that are most saturated, whereas oils are primarily composed of fatty acid portions that have greater numbers of double bonds. In other words, unsaturation lowers the melting point. Fats (solids) are usually obtained from animal sources, whereas oils (liquids) are commonly obtained from vegetable sources. Therefore, vegetable oils usually have a higher degree of unsaturation.

About 20 to 30 fatty acids are found in fats and oils, and it is not uncommon for a given fat or oil to be composed of as many as 10 to 12 (or more) fatty acids. Typically, these fatty acids are randomly distributed among the triglyceride molecules, and the chemist cannot identify anything more than an average composition for a given fat or oil. The average fatty acid composition of some selected fats and oils is given in

Table 1 Common Fatty Acids

C_{12} Acids	Lauric	$CH_3(CH_2)_{10}COOH$
C_{14} Acids	Myristic	$CH_3(CH_2)_{12}COOH$
C_{16} Acids	Palmitic	$CH_3(CH_2)_{14}COOH$
	Palmitoleic	$CH_3(CH_2)_5CH{=}CH{-}CH_2(CH_2)_6COOH$
C_{18} Acids	Stearic	$CH_3(CH_2)_{16}COOH$
	Oleic	$CH_3(CH_2)_7CH{=}CH{-}CH_2(CH_2)_6COOH$
	Linoleic	$CH_3(CH_2)_4(CH{=}CH{-}CH_2)_2(CH_2)_6COOH$
	Linolenic	$CH_3CH_2(CH{=}CH{-}CH_2)_3(CH_2)_6COOH$
	Ricinoleic	$CH_3(CH_2)_5CH(OH)CH_2CH{=}CH(CH_2)_7COOH$

© Cengage Learning 2013

Table 2. As indicated, all the values in the table may vary in percentage, depending, for instance, on the locale in which the plant was grown or on the particular diet on which the animal subsisted. Thus, perhaps there is a basis for the claims that corn-fed hogs or cattle taste better than animals maintained on other diets.

Vegetable fats and oils are usually found in fruits and seeds and are recovered by three principal methods. In the first method, **cold pressing,** the appropriate part of the dried plant is pressed in a hydraulic press to squeeze out the oil. The second method is **hot pressing,** which is the same as the first method but done at a higher temperature. Of the two methods, cold pressing usually gives a better grade of product (more bland); the hot pressing method gives a higher yield, but with more undesirable constituents (stronger odor and flavor). The third method is **solvent extraction.** Solvent extraction gives the highest recovery of all and can now be regulated to give bland, high-grade food oils.

Animal fats are usually recovered by **rendering,** which involves cooking the fat out of the tissue by heating it to a high temperature. An alternative method involves placing the fatty tissue in boiling water. The fat floats to the surface and is easily recovered. The most common animal fats, lard (from hogs) and tallow (from cattle), can be prepared in either way.

Many triglyceride fats and oils are used for cooking. We use them to fry meats and other foods and to make sandwich spreads. Almost all commercial cooking fats and oils, except lard, are prepared from vegetable sources. Vegetable oils are liquids at room temperature. If the double bonds in a vegetable oil are hydrogenated, the resultant product becomes solid. In making commercial cooking fats (Crisco, Spry, Fluffo, etc.), manufacturers hydrogenate a liquid vegetable oil until the desired degree of consistency is achieved. This makes a product that still has a high degree of unsaturation (double bonds) left. The same technique is used for margarine. "Polyunsaturated" oleomargarine is produced by the partial hydrogenation of oils from corn, cottonseed, peanut, and soybean sources. The final product has a yellow dye (β-carotene) added to make it look like butter; milk, about 15% by volume, is mixed into it to form the final emulsion. Vitamins A and D are also commonly added. Because the final product is tasteless (try Crisco), salt, acetoin, and biacetyl are often added. The latter two additives mimic the characteristic flavor of butter.

$$
\begin{array}{cc}
\overset{\displaystyle HO}{\underset{\displaystyle H}{\underset{|}{\overset{|}{CH_3{-}C}}}}\overset{\displaystyle O}{\overset{\|}{-C}}{-}CH_3 &
CH_3{-}\overset{\displaystyle O}{\overset{\|}{C}}{-}\overset{\displaystyle O}{\overset{\|}{C}}{-}CH_3 \\
\textbf{Acetoin} & \textbf{Biacetyl}
\end{array}
$$

© Cengage Learning 2013

Many producers of margarine claim it to be more beneficial to health because it is "high in polyunsaturates." Animal fats are low in unsaturated fatty acid content and

Table 2 Average Fatty Acid Composition (by Percentage) of Selected Fats and Oils

	Saturated Fatty Acids (No Double Bonds)						Unsaturated (1 Double Bond)			Unsaturated (>1 Double Bond)			
	C_{10} C_8 C_6 C_4	C_{12} Lauric	C_{14} Myristic	C_{16} Palmitic	C_{18} Stearic	C_{20} C_{22} C_{24}	C_{16} Palmitoleic	C_{18} Oleic	C_{18} Ricinoleic	C_{18} Linoleic (2)	C_{18} Linolenic (3)	C_{18} Eleostearic (3)	C_{20} C_{22} C_{24} Unsaturated
Animal fats													
Tallow			2–3	24–32	14–32		1–3	35–48		2–4			
Butter	7–10	2–3	7–9	23–26	10–13		5	30–40		4–5			2
Lard			1–2	28–30	12–18		1–3	41–48		6–7			2
Animal oils													
Neat's foot				17–18	2–3		13–18	74–77					
Whale			4–5	11–18	2–4		6–15	33–38					17–31
Sardine			6–8	10–16	1–2								12–19
Vegetable oils													
Corn			0–2	7–11	3–4		0–2	43–49		34–42			
Olive			0–1	5–15	1–4		0–1	69–84		4–12			
Peanut				6–9	2–6	3–10	0–1	50–70		13–26			
Soybean			0–1	6–10	2–6			21–29		50–59	4–8		
Safflower				6–10	1–4			8–18		70–80	2–4		
Castor bean				0–1				0–9	80–92	3–7			
Cottonseed			0–2	19–24	1–2		0–2	23–33		40–48			
Linseed				4–7	2–5			9–38		3–43	25–58		
Coconut	10–22	45–51	17–20	4–10	1–5			2–10		0–2			
Palm			1–3	34–43	3–6			38–40		5–11			
Tung				3–6				4–16		0–1		74–91	

Note: A bracket value "2–6" spans the Palmitic/Stearic columns in the vegetable oils section; a bracket value "24–30" spans the Oleic (Unsaturated, 1 Double Bond) region.

are generally excluded from the diets of people who have high cholesterol levels. Such people have difficulty in metabolizing saturated fats correctly and should avoid them because they encourage cholesterol deposits to form in the arteries. This ultimately leads to high blood pressure and heart trouble. People who pay close attention to their intake of fats tend to avoid consuming large quantities of saturated fats, knowing that eating these fats increases the risk of heart disease. Diet-conscious people try to limit their fat consumption to unsaturated fats, and they make use of the current mandatory food labeling to obtain information on the fat content of the food they eat.

Unfortunately, not all of the unsaturated fats appear to be equally safe. When we eat partially hydrogenated fats, we increase our consumption of ***trans*-fatty acids.** These acids, which are isomers of the naturally occurring *cis*-fatty acids, have been implicated in a variety of conditions, including heart disease, cancer, and diabetes. The strongest evidence that *trans*-fatty acids may be harmful comes in studies of the incidence of coronary heart disease. Ingestion of *trans*-fatty acids appears to increase blood cholesterol levels, in particular the ratio of low-density lipoproteins (LDL, or "bad" cholesterol) to high-density lipoproteins (HDL, or "good" cholesterol). The *trans*-fatty acids appear to exhibit harmful effects on the heart that are similar to those shown by saturated fatty acids.

The *trans*-fatty acids do not occur naturally to any significant extent. Rather, they are formed during the partial hydrogenation of vegetable oils to make margarine and solid forms of shortening. For a small percentage of *cis*-fatty acids subjected to hydrogenation, only one hydrogen atom is added to the carbon chain. This process forms an intermediate free radical, which is able to rotate its conformation by 180 degrees before it releases the extra hydrogen atom back to the reaction medium. The result is an isomerization of the double bond.

Concern over the health and nutrition of the public, particularly over the average fat intake of most Americans, has prompted food chemists and technologists to develop a variety of **fat replacers.** The objective has been to discover substances that have the taste and mouth-feel of a real fat, but do not have deleterious effects on the cardiovascular system. One product that has recently appeared in certain snack foods is **olestra** (marketed under the trade name **Olean,** by the Procter and Gamble Company). Olestra is not an acylglycerol; rather, it is composed of a molecule of **sucrose** that has been substituted by long-chain fatty acid residues. It is a **polyester,** and the body's enzyme systems are not capable of attacking it and catalyzing its breakdown into smaller molecules.

Because the body's enzyme systems are unable to break this molecule down, it does not contain any usable dietary calories. Furthermore, it is heat stable, which makes it ideal for frying and other cooking. Unfortunately, for some individuals there may be harmful or unpleasant side effects. The use of olestra has been reported to deplete certain fat-soluble vitamins, particularly Vitamins A, D, E, and K. For this reason, products prepared with olestra have these vitamins added to offset this effect. Also, some people have reported diarrhea and abdominal cramps.

Is the development of fat replacers such as olestra part of the wave of the future? As the average American's appetite for snack foods continues to grow and as health problems arising from obesity also increase, the demand for satisfying foods that are less fattening will always be strong. In the long run, however, it would probably be better if we all learned to curtail our appetite for fatty foods and, instead, tried to increase our intake of fruits, vegetables, and other healthful foods.

Olestra

At the same time, a change from a sedentary lifestyle to one that include regular exercise would also be much more beneficial to our health.

REFERENCES

Dawkins, M. J. R.; Hull, D. The Production of Heat by Fat. *Sci. Am.* **1965,** *213* (Aug), 62.

Dolye, E. Olestra? The Jury's Still Out. *J. Chem. Educ.* **1997,** *74* (Apr), 370.

Eckey, E. W.; Miller, L. P. *Vegetable Fats and Oils;* ACS Monograph 123; Reinhold: New York, 1954.

Farines, M.; Soulier, F.; Soulier, J. Analysis of the Triglycerides of Some Vegetable Oils. *J. Chem. Educ.* **1988,** *65* (May), 464.

Gunstone, F. D. The Composition of Hydrogenated Fats Determined by High Resolution 13C NMR Spectroscopy. *Chem. Ind.* **1991,** (Nov 4), 802.

Heinzen, H.; Moyna, P.; Grompone, A. Gas Chromatographic Determination of Fatty Acid Compositions. *J. Chem. Educ.* **1985,** *62* (May), 449.

Jandacek, R. J. The Development of Olestra, a Noncaloric Substitute for Dietary Fat. *J. Chem. Educ.* **1991,** *68* (Jun), 476.

Kalbus, G. E.; Lieu, V. T. Dietary Fat and Health: An Experiment on the Determination of Iodine Number of Fats and Oils by Coulometric Titration. *J. Chem. Educ.* **1991,** *68* (Jan), 64.

Lemonick, M. D. Are We Ready for Fat-Free Fat? *Time* **1996,** *147* (Jan 8), 52.

Martin, C. TFA's—a Fat Lot of Good? *Chem. Brit.* **1996,** *32* (Oct), 34.

Nawar, W. W. Chemical Changes in Lipids Produced by Thermal Processing. *J. Chem. Educ.* **1984,** *61* (Apr), 299.

Shreve, R. N.; Brink, J. Oils, Fats, and Waxes. *The Chemical Process Industries,* 4th ed.; McGraw-Hill: New York, 1977.

Thayer, A. M. Food Additives. *Chem. Eng. News* **1992,** *70* (Jun 15), 26.

Wootan, M.; Liebman, B.; Rosofsky, W. *trans:* The Phantom Fat. *Nutr. Action Health Lett.* **1996,** *23* (Sep), 10.

4. Identify the C-H out-of-plane bending vibrations in the infrared spectrum of 4-methylcyclohexene. What structural information can be obtained from these bands?

5. In this experiment, 1.0 mL of saturated sodium chloride is used to rinse the Hickman head after the initial distillation. Why is saturated sodium chloride, rather than pure water, used for this procedure and the subsequent washing of the organic layer?

26 **EXPERIMENT 26**

Phase-Transfer Catalysis: Addition of Dichlorocarbene to Cyclohexene

Carbene formation

Phase-transfer catalysis

It has long been known that a haloform CHX_3 will react with a strong base to give a highly reactive carbene species CX_2 by Reactions 1 and 2. In the presence of an alkene, this carbene adds to the double bond to produce a cyclopropane ring (Reaction 3).

$$X-\underset{X}{\overset{X}{C}}-H + {}^{-}:\ddot{O}-H \rightleftharpoons X-\underset{X}{\overset{X}{C}}:{}^{-} + H\ddot{O}H \qquad [1]$$

$$X-\underset{X}{\overset{X}{C}}:{}^{-} \xrightarrow{\text{slow}} X-\underset{X}{C}: + :\ddot{X}:{}^{-} \qquad [2]$$

$$X-\underset{X}{C}: + {\overset{\diagdown}{\diagup}}C=C{\overset{\diagup}{\diagdown}} \longrightarrow -\underset{\underset{X}{\diagdown}\underset{X}{\diagup}C}{\overset{|}{C}}-\overset{|}{C}- \qquad [3]$$

Traditionally, the reaction has been carried out in *one homogeneous phase* in anhydrous *t*-butyl alcohol solvent, using *t*-butoxide ion as the base [*t*-Bu = $C(CH_3)_3$].

$$HCX_3 + {}^{-}Ot\text{-}Bu + {\overset{\diagdown}{\diagup}}C=C{\overset{\diagup}{\diagdown}} \xrightarrow[\text{(solvent)}]{t\text{-BuOH}} -\overset{|}{\underset{\underset{X}{\diagdown}\underset{X}{\diagup}C}{C}}-\overset{|}{C}- + HOt\text{-}Bu + X^{-}$$

Haloform

Unfortunately, this technique requires time and effort to give good results. In addition, water must be avoided to prevent conversion of the haloform and carbene to formate ion and carbon monoxide by the undesirable base-catalyzed Reactions 4 and 5.

$$
\underset{\underset{X}{|}}{\overset{\overset{X}{|}}{H-C-X}} + 2\ H_2O \longrightarrow H-\overset{\overset{\|}{O}}{C}-OH + 3\ HX \qquad [4]
$$

$$
H-\overset{\overset{\|}{O}}{C}-OH + {}^-OH \longrightarrow H-\overset{\overset{\|}{O}}{C}-O^- + H_2O
$$

$$
:CX_2 + H_2O \xrightarrow{\ {}^-OH\ } :C{\equiv}O + 2\ HX \qquad [5]
$$

Quaternary Ammonium Salt Catalysis

As an alternative to a homogeneous reaction, a *two-phase* reaction can be considered when the organic phase contains the alkene and a haloform CHX_3 and the aqueous phase contains the base OH^-. Unfortunately, under these conditions the reaction will be slow because the two primary reactants, CHX_3 and OH^-, are in different phases. The reaction rate can be substantially increased, however, by adding a quarternary ammonium salt such as benzyltriethylammonium chloride as a **phase-transfer catalyst.**

$$
\text{C}_6\text{H}_5-CH_2-\overset{\overset{\displaystyle CH_2CH_3}{|}}{\underset{\underset{\displaystyle CH_2CH_3}{|}}{{}^+N}}-CH_2CH_3 \ + \ Cl^-
$$

A phase-transfer catalyst: Benzyltriethylammonium chloride

Other common catalysts are tetrabutylammonium bisulfate, triocetyl-methylammonium chloride, and cetyltrimethylammonium chloride. All these catalysts, including benzyltriethylammonium chloride, have at least 13 carbon atoms. The numerous carbon atoms give the catalyst organic character (hydrophobic) and allow it to be soluble in the organic phase. At the same time, the catalyst also has ionic character (hydrophilic) and can therefore be soluble in the aqueous phase.

Because of this *dual* nature, the large cation can cross the phase boundary efficiently and transport a hydroxide ion from the aqueous phase to the organic phase (see figure). Once in the organic phase, the hydroxide ion will react with the haloform to give dihalocarbene by Reactions 1 and 2. Water, a product of the reaction, will move from the organic phase to the aqueous phase, thus keeping the water concentration in the organic phase at a low level. Because the water content in the organic phase is low, it will not interfere with the desirable reaction of the carbene with an alkene by Reaction 3. Thus, the undesirable side Reactions 4 and 5 are minimized. Finally, the halide ion, which is also produced in Reactions 1 and 2, is transported to the aqueous phase by the tetraalkylammonium cation. In this way, electrical neutrality is maintained, and the phase-transfer catalyst, R_4N^+, is returned to the aqueous phase to repeat the whole procedure. The figure shown on the next page summarizes the overall process. This process probably goes on at the interface rather than in the bulk, organic phase.

There are numerous examples of other reactions that might be effectively accelerated by a quaternary ammonium salt or other phase-transfer catalyst (see References). These reactions often involve simple experimental techniques, give shorter reaction times than noncatalyzed reactions, and avoid relatively expensive aprotic solvents that have been widely used to give one phase. Examples of reactions are shown.

A two-phase reaction. The organic phase contains the alkene and the haloform, CHX_3, whereas the aqueous phase contains the base, OH^-.

Ether synthesis	$ROH + R'Cl \xrightarrow[\text{aq. NaOH}]{\text{catalyst}} ROR'$

Nitrile synthesis	$R-Cl + CN^- \xrightarrow[\text{H}_2\text{O}]{\text{catalyst}} RCN$

Oxidation reactions

Alkylation reactions

Wittig reactions

Phosphonium salts act as catalysts.

Increased nucleophilicity   Anions are heavily solvated in an aqueous solvent and are therefore poor nucleophiles in some S_N2 reactions. When they are transported into the organic phase with the catalyst R_4N^+, X^- is no longer solvated with water and may have increased reactivity.

Crown Ether Catalysis

Another important class of phase-transfer catalysts includes the crown ethers (not used in this experiment). Crown ethers are used to dissolve organic and inorganic alkali metal salts in organic solvents. The crown ether complexes the cation and provides it with an organic exterior (hydrophobic) so that it is soluble in organic solvents. The anion is carried along into solution as the counterion. One example of a crown ether is dicyclohexyl-18-crown-6. Potassium permanganate $KMnO_4$ complexed to the crown ether is soluble in benzene and is known as purple benzene. It is useful in various oxidation reactions.

The crown ethers catalyze many of the same types of reactions listed in the preceding section on quaternary ammonium salt catalysis. Crown ethers are expensive relative to ammonium salts and are not used as widely for large-scale reactions. In some cases, however, these ethers may be necessary to obtain an efficient and high-yield reaction.

The Experiment

In this experiment, you will prepare 7,7-dichlorobicyclo[4.1.0]heptane, also known as 7,7-dichloronorcarane, by the reaction

Chloroform $CHCl_3$ and base are used in excess in this reaction. Although most of the chloroform reacts to give the 7,7-dichloronorcarane via the carbene intermediate, a significant portion is hydrolyzed by the base to formate ion and carbon monoxide (Equations 4 and 5, p. 218). Bromoform $CHBr_3$ can be used to prepare the corresponding 7,7-dibromonorcarane via the dibromocarbene.

REQUIRED READING

Review:	Technique 12	Sections 12.4, 12.9, and 12.10
	Technique 25	Sections 25.2, 25.9, and 25.10
New:	Technique 26	Nuclear Magnetic Resonance Spectroscopy
	Technique 27	Carbon-13 Nuclear Magnetic Resonance Spectroscopy

SPECIAL INSTRUCTIONS

> **CAUTION**
>
> **Chloroform is a suspected carcinogen; therefore, do not let it touch your skin and avoid breathing the vapor.**

This entire experiment must be performed in a hood. Avoid contact with the caustic 50% aqueous sodium hydroxide.

SUGGESTED WASTE DISPOSAL

Dispose of all aqueous solutions produced in this experiment in the container for aqueous waste.

PROCEDURE

Reaction Mixture

Preweigh a 5-mL conical vial with cap and transfer 0.40 mL of cyclohexene (*MW* = 82.2) to the vial in a hood. Cap the vial and reweigh it to determine the weight of cyclohexene. Add 1.0 mL of 50% aqueous sodium hydroxide[1] to the vial, being careful to avoid getting any solution on the glass joint. In a hood, add 1.0 mL of chloroform (*MW* = 119.4, *d* = 1.49 g/mL) to the conical vial. Add a magnetic spin vane to the vial. Weigh 0.040 g of the phase-transfer catalyst, benzyltriethylammonium chloride, on a smooth piece of paper and *reclose the bottle* immediately. (It is hygroscopic!)[2] Add the catalyst to the vial and cap it.

> **CAUTION**
>
> **Chloroform and cyclohexene should be kept in a hood. Do your measuring and transferring operations in the hood. Avoid contact with these substances. Do not breathe the vapors.**

Reaction Period

Prepare a hot water bath at 40°C using a 250-mL beaker and hot plate. Attach an air condenser to the vial containing the reaction mixture. Clamp the condenser so that the vial is immersed in the water bath. Stir the mixture as *rapidly* as possible for 1 hour. An emulsion forms during this time.

Extraction of Product

After this reaction time, remove the vial from the water bath and allow the reaction mixture to cool to room temperature. Using a Pasteur pipet, transfer the reaction mixture to a centrifuge tube with a screw cap (you do not need to remove the spin vane). Add 1.5 mL of water and 1.0 mL of methylene chloride to the mixture. Cap the tube and shake the mixture *gently* for about 30 seconds. Allow the layers

---

[1] This reagent should be prepared by the instructor. Dissolve 15 g of sodium hydroxide in 15 mL of water. Cool the solution to room temperature and store it in a plastic bottle.

[2] *Note to the Instructor:* The activity of benzyltriethylammonium chloride varies, depending on the source of the catalyst. Try the reaction in advance of the laboratory session to make sure it works properly. We use Aldrich Chemical Co., #14,655-2.

Infrared spectrum of 7,7-dichloronorcarane (neat).

to separate. Swirl the tube gently to help break up the emulsion. Remove the lower methylene chloride layer with a Pasteur pipet and transfer it to a 5-mL conical vial. The small amount of emulsion that forms at the interface should be left behind with the aqueous layer. Add another 1.0-mL portion of methylene chloride, shake the mixture for 30 seconds, remove the lower organic layer with the Pasteur pipet, and transfer the organic layer to the same storage vial. Discard the remaining aqueous layer in the centrifuge tube (avoid contact with the liquid because it is very basic). Discard it into the container for aqueous waste. Clean the centrifuge tube.

Transfer the methylene chloride extracts from the 5-mL conical vial to the centrifuge tube. Add 1.0 mL of saturated aqueous sodium chloride to the tube and shake the mixture for 30 seconds. Using a dry Pasteur pipet, transfer the lower organic layer to a dry conical vial and dry it over granular anhydrous sodium sulfate (Technique 12, Section 12.9, page 680). Cap the vial and swirl it occasionally for at least 10 minutes to dry the organic layer.

Evaporation of Solvent

Transfer the dried organic layer with a dry Pasteur pipet to a dried preweighed conical vial. Evaporate the methylene chloride, together with any remaining cyclohexene and chloroform, in a hood in a warm water bath.[3] Use a stream of dry air or nitrogen to aid the evaporation process. *Be careful or you may also evaporate the product!* The product, 7,7-dichloronorcarane, is a liquid. Continue the evaporation until the level of the liquid is no longer changing (about 0.2 mL).

Analysis of Product

After removal of methylene chloride, you are left with 7,7-dichloronorcarane of sufficient purity for spectroscopy. Weigh the conical vial, determine the weight of product, and calculate the percentage yield. Obtain the infrared spectrum (Technique 25, Section 25.2, p. 834). At the option of the instructor, obtain the decoupled and coupled carbon-13 spectra of your product. Submit any remaining product in a labeled vial with your laboratory report.

---

[3] Alternatively, you may set the uncapped vial in a hood overnight. There is less risk of evaporating the product with this method.

Decoupled carbon-13 spectrum of 7,7-dichloronorcarane, CDCl₃. Letters indicate appearance of the spectrum when carbons are coupled to protons (s = singlet, d = doublet, t = triplet.)

REFERENCES

Dehmlow, E. V. "Phase-Transfer Catalyzed Two-Phase Reactions in Preparative Organic Chemistry." *Angewandte Chemie, International Edition in English, 13* (1974): 170.

Dehmlow, E. V. "Advances in Phase-Transfer Catalysis." *Angewandte Chemie, International Edition in English, 16* (1977): 493.

Dehmlow, E. V., and Dehmlow, S. S. *Phase-Transfer Catalysis,* 3rd ed. Weinheim: VCH Publishers, 1992.

Gokel, G. W., and Weber, W. P. "Phase Transfer Catalysis." *Journal of Chemical Education, 55* (1978): 350, 429.

Lee, A. W. M., and Yip, W. C. "Fabric Softeners as Phase-Transfer Catalysts in Organic Synthesis." *Journal of Chemical Education, 68* (1991): 69.

Makosza, M., and Wawrzyniewicz, M. "Catalytic Method for Preparation of Dichlorocyclopropane Derivatives in Aqueous Medium." *Tetrahedron Letters* (1969): 4659.

Starks, C. M. "Phase-Transfer Catalysis." *Journal of the American Chemical Society, 93* (1971): 195.

Starks, C. M., Liotta, C. L., and Halpern, M. *Phase-Transfer Catalysis.* New York: Chapman and Hall, 1994.

Weber, W. P., and Gokel, G. W. *Phase Transfer Catalysis in Organic Synthesis.* Berlin: Springer-Verlag, 1977.

QUESTIONS

1. Why did you need to stir the mixture vigorously during reaction?

2. Why did you wash the organic phase with saturated sodium chloride solution?

3. What short chemical test could you make on the product to indicate whether cyclohexene is present or absent?

4. Would you expect 7,7-dichloronorcarane to give a positive sodium iodide in acetone test?

5. Assign the C—H stretch for the cyclopropane ring hydrogens in the infrared spectrum.

6. Suggest why it may be necessary to use a large excess of chloroform in this reaction.

7. A student obtained a proton NMR spectrum of the product isolated in this experiment. The spectrum shows peaks at about 7.3 and 5.6 ppm. What do you think these peaks indicate? Are they part of the 7,7-dichloronorcarane spectrum?

8. Draw the structures of the products that you would expect from the reactions of *cis*- and *trans*-2-butene with dichlorocarbene.

9. Draw the structure of the expected dichlorocarbene adduct of methyl methacrylate (methyl 2-methylpropenoate). With compounds of this type, another product could have been obtained. It is the chloroform adduct to the double bond (Michael-type reaction). What would this structure look like?

10. Provide mechanisms for the following abnormal dichlorocarbene addition reactions. In both cases, the usual adduct is first obtained, and then a subsequent reaction occurs.

EXPERIMENT 27

27   EXPERIMENT 27

Relative Reactivities of Several Aromatic Compounds

Aromatic substitution

Relative activating ability of aromatic substituents

Crystallization

When substituted benzenes undergo electrophilic aromatic substitution reactions, both the reactivity and the orientation of the electrophilic attack are affected by the nature of the original group attached to the benzene ring. Substituent groups that make the ring more reactive than benzene are called **activators.** Such groups are also said to be **ortho, para** directors because the products formed are those in which substitution occurs either ortho or para to the activating group. Various products may be formed, depending on whether substitution occurs at the ortho or para position and the number of times substitution occurs on the same molecule. Some groups may activate

Relative Reactivities of Several Aromatic Compounds

Aromatic substitution
Relative activating ability of aromatic substituents
Crystallization

When substituted benzenes undergo electrophilic aromatic substitution reactions, both the reactivity and the orientation of the electrophilic attack are affected by the nature of the original group attached to the benzene ring. Substituent groups that make the ring more reactive than benzene are called **activators**. Such groups are also said to be **ortho, para** directors because the products formed are those in which substitution occurs either ortho or para to the activating group. Various products may be formed, depending on whether substitution occurs at the ortho or para position and the number of times substitution occurs on the same molecule. Some groups may activate the benzene ring so strongly that multiple substitution consistently occurs, whereas other groups may be moderate activators, and benzene rings containing such groups may undergo only a single substitution. The purpose of this experiment is to determine the relative activating effects of several substituent groups.

In this experiment, you will study the bromination of acetanilide, aniline, and anisole:

Acetanilide   Aniline   Anisole

© Cengage Learning 2013

The acetamido group, —NHCOCH$_3$, the amino group, —NH$_2$, and the methoxy group, —OCH$_3$, are all activators and ortho, para directors. Each student will carry out the bromination of one of these compounds and determine its melting point. By sharing your data, you will have information on the melting points of the brominated products for acetanilide, aniline, and anisole. Using the table, it will then be possible for you to rank the three substituents in order of activating strength.

The classical method of brominating an aromatic compound is to use Br$_2$ and a catalyst such as FeBr$_3$, which acts as a Lewis acid. The first step is the reaction between bromine and the Lewis acid:

$$Br_2 + FeBr_3 \longrightarrow [FeBr_4^- \ Br^+]$$

The positive bromine ion then reacts with the benzene ring in an aromatic electrophilic substitution reaction:

© Cengage Learning 2013

Aromatic compounds that contain activating groups can be brominated without the use of the Lewis acid catalyst because the π electrons in the benzene ring are more available and polarize the bromine molecule sufficiently to produce the required electrophile Br^+. This is illustrated by the first step in the reaction between anisole and bromine:

© Cengage Learning 2013

Melting points of relevant compounds

Compound	Melting Points (°C)
o-Bromoacetanilide	99
p-Bromoacetanilide	168
2,4-Dibromoacetanilide	145
2,6-Dibromoacetanilide	208
2,4,6-Tribromoacetanilide	232
o-Bromoaniline	32
p-Bromoaniline	66
2,4-Dibromoaniline	80
2,6-Dibromoaniline	87
2,4,6-Tribromoaniline	122
o-Bromoanisole	3
p-Bromoanisole	13
2,4-Dibromoanisole	60
2,6-Dibromoanisole	13
2,4,6-Tribromoanisole	87

© Cengage Learning 2013

In this experiment, the brominating mixture consists of bromine, hydrobromic acid HBr, and acetic acid. The presence of bromide ion from the hydrobromic acid helps to solubilize the bromine and increase the concentration of the electrophile.

REQUIRED READING

Review: Technique 11

You should review the chapters in your lecture textbook that deal with electrophilic aromatic substitution. Pay special attention to halogenation reactions and the effect of activating groups.

SPECIAL INSTRUCTIONS

Bromine is a skin irritant, and its vapors cause severe irritation to the respiratory tract. It will also oxidize many pieces of jewelry. Hydrobromic acid may cause skin or eye irritation. Aniline is highly toxic and a suspected teratogen. All bromoanilines are toxic. This experiment should be carried out in a fume hood or in a well-ventilated laboratory.

Each person will carry out the bromination of only one of the aromatic compounds according to your instructor's directions. The procedures are identical except for the initial compound used and the final recrystallization step.

NOTE TO THE INSTRUCTOR: Prepare the brominating mixture in advance.

SUGGESTED WASTE DISPOSAL

Dispose of the filtrate from the Hirsch funnel filtration of the crude product into a container specifically designated for this mixture. Place all other filtrates into the container for halogenated organic solvents.

PROCEDURE

Running the Reaction

To a tared 5-mL conical vial with a cap, add the given amount of one of the following compounds: 0.090 g of acetanilide, 0.060 mL of aniline, or 0.070 mL of anisole. Reweigh the conical vial to determine the actual weight of the aromatic compound. Add 0.5 mL of glacial acetic acid and a spin vane to the conical vial. Attach an air condenser and place the conical vial in a water bath at 23–27°C, as shown in Technique 6, Figure 6.6. Stir the mixture until the aromatic compound is completely dissolved. While the compound is dissolving, pack a drying tube loosely with glass wool. Add about 0.5 mL of 1*M* sodium bisulfite dropwise to the glass wool until it is moistened but not soaked. This apparatus will capture any bromine given off during the following reaction.

Under the hood, obtain 1.0 mL of the bromine/hydrobromic acid mixture[1] in a 3-mL conical vial. Place the cap on the vial before returning to your lab bench. While stirring, add all the bromine/hydrobromic acid mixture through the top of the air condenser, using a Pasteur pipette.

> ### CAUTION
>
> **Be careful not to spill any of this mixture.**

Attach the drying tube prepared above. Continue stirring the reaction mixture for 20 minutes.

---

[1] *Note to the Instructor:* The brominating mixture is prepared by adding 2.6 mL of bromine to 17.4 mL of 48% hydrobromic acid. This will provide enough solution for 20 students, assuming no waste of any type. This solution should be stored in the hood.

Crystallization and Isolation of Product

When the reaction is complete, transfer the mixture to a 10-mL Erlenmeyer flask containing 5 mL of water and 0.5 mL of saturated sodium bisulfite solution. Stir this mixture with a glass stirring rod until the red color of bromine disappears.[2] If an oil has formed, it may be necessary to stir the mixture for several minutes. Place the Erlenmeyer flask in an ice bath for 10 minutes. If the product does not solidify, scratch the bottom of the flask with a glass stirring rod to induce crystallization. It may take 10–15 minutes to induce crystallization of the brominated anisole product.[3] Filter the product on a Hirsch funnel with suction and rinse with several 1-mL portions of cold water. Air-dry the product on the funnel for about 5 minutes with the vacuum on.

Recrystallization and Melting Point of Product

If you started with **aniline,** transfer the solid to a 10-mL Erlenmeyer flask and recrystallize the product from 95% ethanol (see Technique 11, Section 11.3, and Figure 11.4). Filter the crystals on a Hirsch funnel and dry them for several minutes with suction. The brominated products from either **acetanilide** or **anisole** should be crystallized using a Craig tube (Technique 11, Section 11.4 and Figure 11.6). Use 95% ethanol to crystallize the acetanilide product and hexane to crystallize the brominated anisole compound. Allow the crystals to air-dry and determine the weight and melting point.

According to the melting point and the preceding table, you should be able to identify your product. Calculate the percentage yield and submit your product, along with your report, to your instructor.

REPORT

By collecting data from other students, you should be able to determine which product was obtained from the bromination of each of the three aromatic compounds. Using this information, arrange the three substituent groups (acetamido, amino, and methoxy) in order of decreasing ability to activate the benzene ring.

REFERENCE

Zaczek, N. M., and Tyszklewicz, R. B. Relative Activating Ability of Various Ortho, Para-Directors. *Journal of Chemical Education,* **1986,** *63,* 510.

QUESTIONS

1. Using resonance structures, show why the amino group is activating. Consider an attack by the electrophile E^+ at the *para* position.

2. For the substituent in this experiment that was found to be least activating, explain why bromination took place at the position on the ring indicated by the experimental results.

3. What other experimental techniques (including spectroscopy) might be used to identify the products in this experiment?

---

[2] If the color of bromine is still present, add a few more drops of saturated sodium bisulfite and stir the mixture for a few more minutes. The entire mixture, including liquid and solid (or oil), should be colorless.

[3] If crystals fail to form after 15 minutes, it may be necessary to seed the mixture with a small crystal of product.

EXPERIMENT 29

Methyl Stearate from Methyl Oleate

Catalytic hydrogenation

Recrystallization

Unsaturation tests

In this experiment, you will convert the liquid methyl oleate, an "unsaturated" fatty acid ester, to solid methyl stearate, a "saturated" fatty acid ester, by catalytic hydrogenation.

$$CH_3(CH_2)_7-CH=CH-(CH_2)_7-\overset{\overset{\displaystyle O}{\|}}{C}-OCH_3 \quad \xrightarrow[H_2]{Pd/C}$$

Methyl oleate
(methyl *cis*-9-octadecenoate)

$$CH_3(CH_2)_7-\underset{\underset{\displaystyle H}{|}}{CH}-\underset{\underset{\displaystyle H}{|}}{CH}-(CH_2)_7-\overset{\overset{\displaystyle O}{\|}}{C}-OCH_3$$

Methyl stearate
(methyl octadecanoate)

By commercial methods such as those described in this experiment, the unsaturated fatty acids of vegetable oils are converted to margarine (see the essay "Fats and Oils"). However, rather than using the mixture of triglycerides that would be present in a cooking oil such as Mazola (corn oil), we use as a model the pure chemical methyl oleate.

For this procedure, a chemist would usually use a cylinder of hydrogen gas. Because many students will be following the procedure simultaneously, however, we use the simpler expedient of causing zinc metal to react with dilute sulfuric acid:

$$Zn + H_2SO_4 \xrightarrow{H_2O} H_2(g) + ZnSO_4$$

The hydrogen so generated will be passed into a solution containing methyl oleate and the palladium on carbon catalyst (10% Pd/C).

REQUIRED READING

Review: Techniques 1–6

New: Technique 8   Filtration, Sections 8.3–8.5

            Technique 9   Physical Constants of Solids: The Melting Point

            Essay   Fats and Oils

You should also read those sections in your lecture textbook that deal with catalytic hydrogenation. If the instructor indicates that you should perform the optional unsaturation tests on your starting material and product, read the descriptions of the Br_2/CH_2Cl_2 test on page 466 and in Experiment 25 on page 216.

SPECIAL INSTRUCTIONS

Because this experiment calls for generating hydrogen gas, no flames will be allowed in the laboratory.

CAUTION	

No flames allowed.

Because a buildup of hydrogen is possible within the apparatus, it is especially important to remember to wear your safety goggles; you can thus protect yourself against the possibility of minor "explosions" from joints popping open, from fires, or from any glassware accidentally cracking under pressure.

CAUTION	

Wear safety goggles.

When you operate the hydrogen generator, be sure to add sulfuric acid at a rate that does not cause hydrogen gas to evolve too rapidly. The hydrogen pressure in the vial should not rise much above atmospheric pressure. Neither should the hydrogen evolution be allowed to stop. If this happens, your reaction mixture may be "sucked back" into your hydrogen generator.

SUGGESTED WASTE DISPOSAL

Dispose of the sulfuric acid (from the hydrogen generator) by pouring it into the waste container designated for acid waste. Place any leftover zinc in the container designated for this material. After centrifugation, transfer the Pd/C catalyst to a container designated for this material. After collecting the methyl stearate by filtration, place the methanol filtrate in the nonhalogenated organic waste container. Discard the solutions that remain after the bromine test for unsaturation into a waste container designated for the disposal of halogenated organic solvents.

NOTES TO THE INSTRUCTOR

Use methyl oleate that is 100% or nearly 100% pure. We use Aldrich Chemical Co. No. 31,111-1.

PROCEDURE

Apparatus

Assemble the apparatus as illustrated in the figure on page 241. The apparatus can be simplified by using the multipurpose adapter (Fig. 14.9, p. 712) in place of the Claisen head and both thermometer adapters. The apparatus consists of basically three parts:

1. Hydrogen generator
2. Reaction flask
3. Mineral oil bubbler trap

Apparatus for Experiment 29.

The mineral oil bubbler trap has two functions. First, it allows you to keep a pressure of hydrogen within the system that is slightly above atmospheric. Second, it prevents back-diffusion of air into the system. The functions of the other two units are self-explanatory.

So that hydrogen leakage is prevented, the tubing used to connect the various subunits of the apparatus should be either relatively new rubber tubing, without cracks or breaks, or Tygon tubing. The tubing can be checked for cracks or breaks simply by stretching and bending it before use. It should be of such a size that it will fit onto all connections tightly. Similarly, if any rubber stoppers are used, they should be fitted with a size of glass tubing that fits firmly through the holes in their centers. If the seal is tight, it will not be easy to slide the glass tubing up and down in the hole. The inlet tube (Pasteur pipet) in the round-bottom flask should reach almost to the bottom of the flask. Hydrogen must bubble *through* the solution.

Preparing for the Reaction

Fill the bubbler trap (second side-arm test tube) about one-third full with mineral oil. The end of the glass tube should be submerged below the surface of the oil.

To charge the hydrogen generator, weigh out about 2 g of mossy zinc and place it in the side-arm test tube. Seal the large opening at its top using a rubber stopper. Obtain about 10 mL of 6*M* sulfuric acid and place it in a small Erlenmeyer flask or beaker **but do not add it yet.**

Weigh a 10-mL round-bottom flask and then place 1.00 mL of methyl oleate into it. Reweigh the flask in order to obtain the exact amount of methyl oleate used. After this, add 6.0 mL of methanol solvent to the flask. Also place a magnetic stirring bar into the flask. Place the flask into a small beaker. Using smooth weighing paper, weigh about 0.030 g (30 mg) of 10% Pd/C. Carefully place about one-third of the catalyst into the flask and gently swirl the liquid until the solid catalyst has sunk into the liquid. Repeat this with the rest of the catalyst, adding one-third of the original amount each time.

CAUTION

Be careful when adding the catalyst; sometimes it will cause a flame. Do not hold onto the flask; it should be in a small beaker on the lab bench. Have a watch glass handy to cover the opening and smother the flame should this occur.

Running the Reaction

Complete the assembly of the apparatus, making sure that all the seals are gas tight. Place the round-bottom flask in a warm water bath maintained at 40°C. This will help to keep the product dissolved in the solution throughout the course of the reaction. If the temperature rises above 40°C, you will lose a significant amount of the methanol solvent. If this occurs, do not hesitate to add more methanol to the reaction flask through the side arm of the Claisen head, using a Pasteur pipet. Begin stirring the reaction mixture with the magnetic stirring bar. Start the evolution of hydrogen by removing the rubber stopper and adding a portion of the 6*M* sulfuric acid solution (about 6 mL) to the hydrogen generator. Replace the rubber stopper. A good rate of bubbling in the reaction flask is about three to four bubbles a second. Continue the evolution of hydrogen for 45–60 minutes. If necessary, open the generator, empty it, and refresh the zinc and sulfuric acid. (Keep in mind that the acid is used up and becomes more dilute as the zinc reacts.)

Stopping the Reaction

After the reaction is complete, stop the reaction by disconnecting the reaction flask. Decant the acid in the side-arm test tube into a designated waste container, being careful not to transfer any zinc metal. Rinse the zinc in the test tube several times with water and then place any unreacted zinc in a waste container provided for this purpose.

Keep the temperature of the reaction mixture at about 40°C until you perform the centrifugation; otherwise, the methyl stearate may crystallize and interfere with removal of the catalyst. There should not be any white solid (product) in the round-bottom flask. If there is a white solid, add more methanol and stir until the solid dissolves.

Removal of the Catalyst

Pour the reaction mixture into a centrifuge tube. Place the centrifuge tube into the water bath at 40°C until just before you are ready to centrifuge the mixture. Centrifuge the mixture for several minutes. After centrifugation, the black catalyst should be at the bottom of the tube. If some of the catalyst is still suspended in the liquid, heat the mixture to 40°C and centrifuge the mixture again. Carefully pour the supernatant liquid (leaving the black catalyst in the centrifuge tube) into a small beaker and cool to room temperature.

Crystallization and Isolation of Product

Place the beaker in an ice bath to induce crystallization. If crystals do not form or if only a few crystals form, you may need to reduce the volume of solvent. Do this by heating the beaker in a water bath and directing a slow stream of air into the beaker, using a Pasteur pipet for a nozzle (Fig. 7.12A, p. 608). If crystals begin to form while you are evaporating the solvent, remove the beaker from the water bath. If crystals do not form, reduce the volume of the solvent by about one third. Allow the solution to cool and then place it in an ice bath.

Collect the crystals by vacuum filtration, using a small Hirsch funnel (Technique 8, Section 8.3, p. 621). Save both the crystals and the filtrate for the tests later. After the crystals are dry, weigh them and determine their melting point (literature value, 39°C). Calculate the percentage yield. Submit your remaining sample to your instructor in a properly labeled container, along with your report.

Unsaturation Tests (Optional)

Number three test tubes (1, 2, 3) and place one of the following samples into each test tube:

1. About 0.1 mL of methyl oleate dissolved in a small amount of methylene chloride
2. A small spatulaful of your methyl stearate product dissolved in a small amount of methylene chloride
3. About 0.1 mL of the filtrate that you saved as directed earlier

To each test tube, add a solution of bromine in methylene chloride, drop by drop, to the contents of the test tubes until the red color is no longer discharged. Record the results in each case, including the number of drops required. What do these results indicate about the presence of unsaturated compounds in each sample?

QUESTIONS

1. Using the information in the essay on fats and oils, draw the structure of the triacylglycerol (triglyceride) formed from oleic acid, linoleic acid, and stearic acid. Give a balanced equation and show how much hydrogen would be needed to reduce the triacylglycerol completely; show the product.

2. A 0.150-g sample of a pure compound subjected to catalytic hydrogenation takes up 25.0 mL of H_2 at 25°C and 1 atm pressure. Calculate the molecular weight of the compound, assuming that it has only one double bond.

3. A compound with the formula C_5H_6 takes up 2 moles of H_2 on catalytic hydrogenation. Give one possible structure that would fit the information given.

4. A compound of formula C_6H_{10} takes up 1 mole of H_2 on reduction. Give one possible structure that would fit the information.

 ESSAY

Soaps and Detergents

Soaps as we know them today were virtually unknown before the first century A.D. Clothes were cleaned primarily by the abrasive action of rubbing them on rocks in water. Somewhat later, it was discovered that certain types of leaves, roots, nuts, berries, and barks formed soapy lathers that solubilized and removed dirt from clothes. We now refer to these natural materials that lather as **saponins.** Many saponins contain pentacyclic triterpene carboxylic acids, such as oleanolic acid or ursolic acid, chemically combined with a sugar molecule. These acids also appear in the uncombined state. Saponins were probably the first known "soaps." They may have also been an early source of pollution in that they are known to be toxic to fish. The pollution problem associated with the development of soap and detergents has been long and controversial.

| Oleanolic acid | Ursolic acid |

Soap as we know it today has evolved over many centuries from experimentation with crude mixtures of alkaline and fatty materials. Pliny the Elder described the manufacture of soap during the first century A.D. A modest soap factory was even built in Pompeii. During the Middle Ages, cleanliness of the body or clothing was not considered important. Those who could afford perfumes used them to hide their body odor. Perfumes, like fancy clothes, were status symbols for the rich. An interest in cleanliness again emerged during the eighteenth century, when disease-causing microorganisms were discovered.

Soaps

The process of making soap has remained practically unchanged for 2,000 years. The procedure involves the basic hydrolysis or **saponification** of an animal fat or a vegetable oil. Chemically, fats and oils are referred to as **triglycerides** or **triacylglycerols**. They contain ester functional groups. Saponification involves heating a fat or oil with an alkaline solution. This alkaline solution was originally obtained by leaching wood ashes or from the evaporation of natural alkaline waters. Today, lye (sodium hydroxide) is used as the source of the alkali. The alkaline solution hydrolyzes the fat or oil into its component parts, the sodium salt of a long-chain carboxylic acid (soap) and an alcohol (glycerol). When common salt is added, the soap precipitates. The soap is washed free of unreacted sodium hydroxide and molded into bars. The following equation shows how soap is produced from a fat or oil.

| Triglycerides (fat or oil) | Carboxylic acid salts (soap) | Glycerol |

The carboxylic acids represented in soap are rarely of a single type in any given fat or oil. In fact, a single triglyceride (triacylglycerol) molecule in a fat may contain three different acid residues (R_1COOH, R_2COOH, R_3COOH), and not every triglyceride in the substance will be identical. Each fat or oil, however, has a characteristic *statistical distribution* of the various types of acids possible. The carboxylic acid salts of soap usually contain 12–18 carbons arranged in a straight chain. The carboxylic acids containing even numbers of carbon atoms predominate, and the chains may contain unsaturation. The composition of the common fats and oils is given in the essay "Fats and Oils" (p. 233).

The fats and oils that are most common in soap preparations are lard and tallow from animal sources and coconut, palm, and olive oils from vegetable sources. The length of the hydrocarbon chain and the number of double bonds in the carboxylic acid portion of the fat or oil determine the properties of the resulting soap. For example, a salt of a saturated long-chain acid makes a harder, more insoluble soap. Chain length also affects solubility.

Tallow is the principal fatty material used in making soap. The solid fats of cattle are melted with steam, and the tallow layer formed at the top is removed. Soap makers usually blend tallow with coconut oil and saponify this mixture. The resulting soap contains mainly the salts of palmitic, stearic, and oleic acids from the tallow and the salts of lauric and myristic acids from the coconut oil. The coconut oil is added to produce a softer, more soluble soap. Lard (from hogs) differs from tallow (from cattle or sheep) in that lard contains more oleic acid.

Pure coconut oil yields a soap that is soluble in water. The soap contains essentially the salt of lauric acid, with some myristic acid. It is so soft (soluble) that it will lather even in seawater. Palm oil contains mainly two acids, palmitic acid and oleic acid, in about equal amounts. Saponification of this oil yields a soap that is an important constituent of toilet soaps. Olive oil contains mainly oleic acid. It is used to prepare Castile soap, named after the region in Spain in which it was first made.

Tallow	$CH_3(CH_2)_{14}COOH$	$CH_3(CH_2)_{16}COOH$
	Palmitic acid	Stearic acid

$$CH_3(CH_2)_7CH{=}CH(CH_2)_7COOH$$
Oleic acid

Coconut oil	$CH_3(CH_2)_{10}COOH$	$CH_3(CH_2)_{12}COOH$
	Lauric acid	Myristic acid

Toilet soaps generally have been carefully washed free of any alkali remaining from the saponification. As much glycerol as possible is usually left in the soap, and perfumes and medicinal agents are sometimes added. Floating soaps are produced by blowing air into the soap as it solidifies. Soft soaps are made by using potassium hydroxide, yielding potassium salts rather than the sodium salts of the acids. They are used in shaving creams and liquid soaps. Scouring soaps have abrasives added, such as fine sand or pumice.

A disadvantage of soap is that it is an ineffective cleanser in hard water. Hard water contains salts of magnesium, calcium, and iron in solution. When soap is used in hard water, "calcium soap," the insoluble calcium salts of the fatty acids, and other precipitates are deposited as **curds.**

This precipitate, or curd, is referred to as "bathtub ring." Although soap is a poor cleanser in hard water, it is an excellent cleanser in soft water.

$$2 \ R\overset{O}{\underset{\|}{-C}}-O^-Na^+ \ + \ Ca^{2+} \ \longrightarrow \ \left(R\overset{O}{\underset{\|}{-C}}-\bar{O} \right)_2 Ca^{2+}$$

Soap   Curd

Water softeners are added to soaps to help remove the troublesome hard-water ions so that the soap will remain effective in hard water. Sodium carbonate or trisodium phosphate will precipitate the ions as the carbonate or phosphate. Unfortunately, the precipitate may become lodged in the fabric of items being laundered, causing a grayish or streaked appearance.

$$Ca^{2+} + CO_3^{2-} \longrightarrow CaCO_3 \ (s)$$

$$3 \ Ca^{2+} + 2 \ PO_4^{3-} \longrightarrow Ca_3(PO_4)_2 \ (s)$$

An important advantage of soap is that it is **biodegradable.** Microorganisms can consume the linear soap molecules and convert them to carbon dioxide and water. The soap is thus eliminated from the environment.

Action of Soap in Cleaning

Dirty clothes, skin, or other surfaces have particles of dirt suspended in a layer of oil or grease. Polar water molecules cannot remove the dirt embedded in nonpolar oil or grease. One can remove the dirt with soap, however, because of its dual nature. The soap molecule has a polar, *water-soluble* head (carboxylate salt) and a long, *oil-soluble* tail (the hydrocarbon chain). The hydrocarbon tail of soap dissolves in the oily substance, but the ionic end remains outside the oily surface. When enough soap molecules have oriented themselves around an oil droplet with their hydrocarbon ends dissolved in the oil, the oil droplet, together with the suspended dirt particles, is removed from the surface of the cloth or skin. The oil droplet is removed because the heavily negatively charged oil droplet is now strongly attracted to water and solvated by the water. The solvated oil droplet is called a **micelle.**

Detergents

Detergents are synthetic cleaning compounds, often referred to as **syndets.** They were developed as an alternative to soaps because they are effective in *both* soft and hard water. No precipitates form when calcium, magnesium, or iron ions are present in a detergent solution. One of the earliest detergents developed was sodium lauryl sulfate. It is prepared by the action of sulfuric acid or chlorosulfonic acid on lauryl alcohol (1-dodecanol). This detergent is relatively expensive, however. The following reactions show one industrial method of preparation:

$$CH_3(CH_2)_{10}CH_2OH + H_2SO_4 \longrightarrow CH_3(CH_2)_{10}CH_2OSO_3H + H_2O$$

Lauryl alcohol

$$CH_3(CH_2)_{10}CH_2OSO_3H + Na_2CO_3 \longrightarrow CH_3(CH_2)_{10}CH_2OSO_3^-Na^+ + NaHCO_3$$

Sodium lauryl sulfate

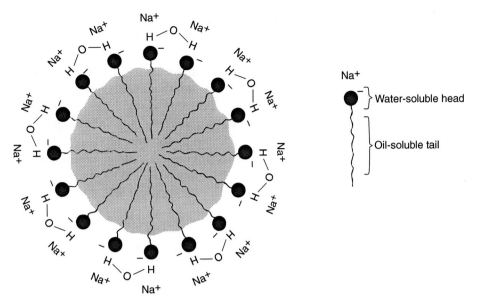

A soap micelle solvating a droplet of oil. (From W. W. Linstromberg, Organic Chemistry: A Brief Course, *D. C. Heath, 1978.)*

The first of the inexpensive detergents appeared about 1950. These detergents, called alkylbenzenesulfonates (ABS), can be prepared from inexpensive petroleum sources by the following set of reactions:

$$4 \ CH_3CH{=}CH_2 \xrightarrow{H^+} CH_3-\underset{\underset{CH_3}{|}}{CH}\left(CH_2-\underset{\underset{CH_3}{|}}{CH}\right)_{\!\!2}CH{=}\underset{\underset{CH_3}{|}}{CH}$$ **Alkene polymerization**

$$CH_3-\underset{\underset{CH_3}{|}}{CH}\left(CH_2-\underset{\underset{CH_3}{|}}{CH}\right)_{\!\!2}CH{=}\underset{\underset{CH_3}{|}}{CH} \ + \ \bigcirc \xrightarrow{AlCl_3}$$

$$CH_3-\underset{\underset{CH_3}{|}}{CH}\left(CH_2-\underset{\underset{CH_3}{|}}{CH}\right)_{\!\!3}\bigcirc$$ **Friedel–Crafts alkylation**

$$CH_3-\underset{\underset{CH_3}{|}}{CH}\left(CH_2-\underset{\underset{CH_3}{|}}{CH}\right)_{\!\!3}\bigcirc \xrightarrow[\text{(2) Na}_2\text{CO}_3]{\text{(1) H}_2\text{SO}_4;}$$

$$CH_3-\underset{\underset{CH_3}{|}}{CH}\left(CH_2-\underset{\underset{CH_3}{|}}{CH}\right)_{\!\!3}\bigcirc-SO_3^-Na^+$$ **Sulfonation**

An alkylbenzenesulfonate (ABS)

Detergents became popular because they could be used effectively in all types of water and were cheap. They rapidly displaced soap as the most popular cleaning agent. A problem with the detergents was that they passed through sewage-treatment plants without being degraded by the microorganisms present, a process necessary for the full sewage treatment. Rivers and streams in many sections of the country became polluted with detergent foam. The detergents even found their way into the drinking water supplies of numerous cities. The reason for the persistence of the detergents was that bacterial enzymes, which could degrade straight-chain soaps and sodium lauryl sulfate, could not destroy the highly branched detergents such as ABS.

It was soon found that the bacterial enzymes could degrade only a chain of carbons that contained, at the most, one branch. Numerous cities and states banned the sale of the nonbiodegradable detergents, and by 1966, they were replaced by the new biodegradable detergents called linear alkyl-sulfonates (LAS). One example of an LAS detergent is shown here. Notice that there is one branch next to the aromatic ring.

$$CH_3(CH_2)_9 - \overset{\overset{\displaystyle CH_3}{|}}{CH} - \langle\!\!\!\bigcirc\!\!\!\rangle - SO_3^- Na^+$$

A linear alkylsulfonate detergent (LAS)

New Problems with Detergents

Detergents (also soaps) are not sold as pure compounds. A typical heavy-duty, controlled **sudser** may contain only 8–20% of the linear alkylsulfonate. A large quantity (30–50%) of a **builder** such as sodium tripolyphosphate, $Na_5P_3O_{10}$ may be present. Other additives include corrosion inhibitors, antideposition agents, and perfumes. Optical brighteners are also added. Brighteners absorb invisible ultraviolet light and reemit it as visible light, so laundry appears white and thus "clean." The phosphate builder is added to complex the hard-water ions, calcium and magnesium, and keep them in solution. Builders seem to enhance the washing ability of the LAS and also act as a cheap filler.

Unfortunately, phosphates speed the **eutrophication** of lakes and other bodies of water. The phosphates, along with other substances, are nutrients for algae. When algae begin to die and decompose, they consume so much dissolved oxygen from the water that no other life can exist in that water. The lake rapidly "dies." This is eutrophication.

Because phosphates have this undesirable effect, a search was initiated for a replacement for the phosphate builders. Some replacements have been made, but most also have problems associated with them. Two replacement builders, sodium metasilicate and sodium perborate, are highly basic sub-stances, and they have caused injuries to children. In addition, they appear to destroy bacteria in sewage-treatment plants and may have other un-known environmental effects.

Many people have suggested a return to soap. The main problem is that we probably cannot produce enough soap to meet the demand because of the limited amount of animal fat available. Where do we go from here?

REFERENCES

Davidson, A., and Milwidsky, B. M. *Synthetic Detergents,* 6th ed. New York: Wiley, 1978.

Greek, B. F. "Detergent Components Become Increasingly Diverse, Complex." *Chemical and Engineering News, 66* (January 25, 1988): 21.

Greek, B. F., and Layman, P. L. "Higher Costs Spur New Detergent Formulations." *Chemical and Engineering News, 67* (January 23, 1989): 29.

Kirschner, E. M. "Soaps and Detergents." *Chemical and Engineering News, 76* (January 26, 1998): 39.

"LAS Detergents End Stream Foam." *Chemical and Engineering News, 45* (1967): 29.

Levey, M. "The Early History of Detergent Substances." *Journal of Chemical Education, 31* (1954): 521.

Meloan, C. E. "Detergents—Soaps and Syndets." *Chemistry, 49* (September 1976): 6.

Newell, J. "Why Plants Make Soap." *Chemistry in Britain, 34* (April 1998): 19.

Rosen, M. J. "Geminis: A New Generation of Surfactants." *Chemtech, 23* (March 1993): 30.

Rosen, M. J. *Surfactants and Interfacial Phenomena*, 2nd ed. New York: Wiley, 1989.

Rosen, M. J. "Surfactants: Designing Structure for Performance." *Chemtech, 15* (May 1985): 292.

Snell, F. D. "Soap and Glycerol." *Journal of Chemical Education, 19* (1942): 172.

Snell, F. D., and Snell, C. T. "Syndets and Surfactants." *Journal of Chemical Education, 35* (1958): 271.

Stinson, S. C. "Consumer Preferences Spur Innovation in Detergents." *Chemical and Engineering News, 65* (January 26, 1987): 21.

30   **E X P E R I M E N T   3 0**

Preparation of a Soap

Hydrolysis of a fat (ester)

Filtration

In this experiment, we prepare soap from animal fat (lard). Animal fats and vegetable oils are esters of carboxylic acids; they have a high molecular weight and contain the alcohol glycerol. Chemically, these fats and oils are called **triglycerides.** The principal acids in animal fats and vegetable oils can be prepared from the natural triglycerides by alkaline hydrolysis (saponification). See the preceding essay for a complete discussion of soaps and detergents.

Triglycerides (fat or oil) → (NaOH, saponification or hydrolysis) → Carboxylic acid salts (soap) + Glycerol

Multistep Reaction Sequences: The Conversion of Benzaldehyde to Benzilic Acid

Green chemistry

Multistep reactions

Thiamine-catalyzed reaction

Oxidation with nitric acid

Rearrangement

Crystallization

Computational chemistry (optional)

The experiment demonstrates multistep synthesis of benzilic acid starting from benzaldehyde. In Experiment 32A, benzaldehyde is converted to benzoin using a thiamine-catalyzed reaction. This part of the experiment demonstrates how a "green" reagent can be utilized in organic chemistry. In Experiment 32B, nitric acid oxidizes benzoin to benzil. Finally, in Experiment 32C, benzil is rearranged to benzilic acid. The scheme on the next page shows the reactions.

REQUIRED READING

Review:	Technique 6	Heating and Cooling Methods, Sections 6.1–6.3
	Technique 7	Reaction Methods, Sections 7.1–7.4
	Technique 8	Filtration, Section 8.3
	Technique 9	Physical Constants of Solids: The Melting Point, Sections 9.7 and 9.8
	Technique 11	Crystallization: Purification of Solids, Section 11.3
	Technique 12	Extractions, Separations, and Drying Agents, Section 12.4
	Technique 25	Infrared Spectroscopy, Section 25.4
New:	Essay and Experiment 19 Computational Chemistry (Optional)	

NOTES TO THE INSTRUCTOR

Although this experiment is intended to illustrate a multistep synthesis to the students, each part may be done separately, or two out of the three reactions can be linked together. The sections on "Special Instructions" and "Suggested Waste Disposal" are included in each part of this experiment.

EXPERIMENT 32A

Preparation of Benzoin by Thiamine Catalysis

In this experiment, two molecules of benzaldehyde will be converted to benzoin using the catalyst thiamine hydrochloride. This reaction is known as a benzoin condensation reaction:

Thiamine hydrochloride is structurally similar to thiamine pyrophosphate (TPP). TPP is a coenzyme universally present in all living systems. It catalyzes several biochemical reactions in natural systems. It was originally discovered as a required nutritional factor (vitamin) in humans by its link with the disease beriberi. **Beriberi** is a disease of the peripheral nervous system caused by a deficiency of Vitamin B_1 in the diet. Symptoms include pain and paralysis of the extremities, emaciation, and swelling of the body. The disease is most common in Asia.

Thiamine pyrophosphate   **Thiamine hydrochloride**

Thiamine binds to an enzyme before the enzyme is activated. The enzyme also binds to the substrate (a large protein). Without the coenzyme thiamine, no chemical reaction would occur. The coenzyme is the **chemical reagent.** The protein molecule (the enzyme) helps and mediates the reaction by controlling stereochemical, energetic, and entropic factors, but it is nonessential to the overall course of reactions that it catalyzes. A special name, vitamins, is given to coenzymes that are essential to the nutrition of the organism.

The most important part of the entire thiamine molecule is the central ring, the thiazole ring, which contains nitrogen and sulfur. This ring constitutes the **reagent** portion of the coenzyme. Experiments with the model compound 3,4-dimethylthiazolium bromide have explained how thiamine-catalyzed reactions work. It was found that this model thiazolium compound rapidly exchanged the C-2 proton for deuterium in D_2O solution. At a pD of 7 (no pH here), this proton was completely exchanged in seconds!

This indicates that the C-2 proton is more acidic than one would have expected. It is apparently easily removed because the conjugate base is a highly stabilized ylide. An **ylide** is a compound or intermediate with positive and negative formal charges on adjacent atoms.

3,4-Dimethylthiazolium   **Ylide**
bromide

The sulfur atom plays an important role in stabilizing this ylide. This was shown by comparing the rate of exchange of 1,3-dimethyl-imidazolium ion with the rate for the thiazolium compound shown in the previous equation. The dinitrogen compound exchanged its C-2 proton more slowly than the sulfur-containing ion. Sulfur, being in the third row of the periodic chart, has *d* orbitals available for bonding to adjacent atoms. Thus, it has fewer geometrical restrictions than carbon and nitrogen atoms do and can form carbon–sulfur multiple bonds in situations in which carbon and nitrogen normally would not.

1,3-Dimethylimidazolium
bromide

In Experiment 32A, we will utilize thiamine hydrochloride rather than TPP to catalyze the benzoin condensation. The mechanism is shown on the next page. For simplicity, only the thiazole ring is shown.

Thiamine hydrochloride

Thiazole ring in thiamine hydrochloride

The mechanism involves the removal of the proton at C-2 from the thiazole ring with a weak base to give the ylide (Step 1). The ylide acts as a nucleophile that adds to the carbonyl group of benzaldehyde forming an intermediate (Step 2). A proton is removed to yield a new intermediate with a double bond (Step 3). Notice that the nitrogen atom helps to increase the acidity of that proton. This intermediate can now react with a second benzaldehyde molecule to yield a new intermediate (Step 4). A base removes a proton to produce benzoin and also regenerates the ylide (Step 5). The ylide reenters the mechanism to form more benzoin by the condensation of two more molecules of benzaldehyde.

SPECIAL INSTRUCTIONS

This experiment may be conducted concurrently with another experiment. It involves a few minutes at the beginning of a laboratory period for mixing reagents. The remaining portion of the period may be used for another experiment.

SUGGESTED WASTE DISPOSAL

Pour all of the aqueous solutions produced in this experiment into a waste container designated for aqueous waste. The ethanolic mixtures obtained from the crystallization of crude benzoin should be poured into a waste container designated for nonhalogenated waste.

NOTES TO THE INSTRUCTOR

It is essential that the benzaldehyde used in this experiment be *pure*. Benzaldehyde is easily oxidized in air to benzoic acid. Even when benzaldehyde *appears* free of benzoic acid by infrared spectroscopy, you should check the purity of your benzaldehyde and thiamine by following the instructions given in the first paragraph of the Procedure ("Reaction Mixture"). When the benzaldehyde is pure, the solution will be nearly filled with solid benzoin after 2 days (you may need to scratch the inside of the flask to induce crystallization). If no solid appears or very little appears, then there is a problem with the purity of the benzaldehyde. If possible, use a newly opened bottle that has been purchased recently. However, it is essential that you check both the old and new benzaldehyde before doing the laboratory experiment.

We have found that the following procedure does an adequate job of purifying benzaldehyde. The procedure does not require distillation of benzaldehyde. Shake the benzaldehyde in a separatory funnel with an equal volume of 5% aqueous sodium carbonate solution. Shake gently and occasionally open the stopcock of the funnel to vent carbon dioxide gas. An emulsion forms that may take 2–3 hours to separate. It is helpful to stir the mixture occasionally during this period to help break the emulsion. Remove the lower sodium carbonate layer, including any remaining emulsion. Add about ¼ volume of water to the benzaldehyde and shake the mixture gently to avoid an emulsion. Remove the cloudy lower organic layer and dry the benzaldehyde with calcium chloride until the next day. Any remaining cloudiness is removed by gravity filtration through fluted filter paper. The resulting clear, purified benzaldehyde should be suitable for this experiment without vacuum distillation. You *must* check the purified benzaldehyde to see if it is suitable for the experiment by following the instructions in the first paragraph of the Procedure.

It is advisable to use a fresh bottle of thiamine hydrochloride, which should be stored in the refrigerator. Fresh thiamine does not seem to be as important as pure benzaldehyde for success in this experiment.

PROCEDURE

Reaction Mixture

Add 0.30 g thiamine hydrochloride to a 25-mL Erlenmeyer flask. Dissolve the solid in 0.45 mL of water by swirling the flask. Add 3.0 mL of 95% ethanol and swirl the solution until it is homogeneous. To this solution, add 0.90 mL of an aqueous sodium hydroxide[1] solution and swirl the flask until the bright yellow color fades to a pale yellow. Weigh the flask and solution, add 0.90 mL of benzaldehyde, and reweigh the flask to determine an accurate weight of benzaldehyde introduced to the flask. Swirl the contents of the flask until it is homogeneous. Stopper the flask and let it stand in a dark place for at least 2 days.

Isolation of Crude Benzoin

If crystals have not formed after 2 days, initiate crystallization by scratching the inside of the flask with a glass stirring rod. Allow about 5 minutes for the crystals of benzoin to form fully. Place the flask, with crystals, into an ice bath for 5–10 minutes.

If for some reason the product separates as an oil, it may be helpful to scratch the flask with a glass rod or seed the mixture by allowing a small amount of solution to dry on the end of a glass rod and then placing this into the mixture. Cool the mixture in an ice bath before filtering.

Break up the crystalline mass with a spatula, swirl the flask rapidly, and quickly transfer the benzoin to a Hirsch funnel under vacuum (Technique 8, Section 8.3, and Figure 8.5). Wash the crystals with three 1-mL portions of ice-cold water. Allow the benzoin to dry in the Hirsch funnel by drawing air through the crystals for about 5 minutes. Transfer the benzoin to a watch glass and allow it to dry in air until the next laboratory period. The product may also be dried in a few minutes in an oven set at about 100°C.

Yield Calculation and Melting-Point Determination

Weigh the benzoin and calculate the percentage yield based on the amount of benzaldehyde used initially. Determine the melting point (pure benzoin melts between 134°C and 135°C). Because your crude benzoin will normally melt between 129°C and 132°C, the benzoin should be crystallized before the conversion to benzil (Experiment 32B).

Crystallization of Benzoin

Purify the crude benzoin by crystallization from hot 95% ethanol (use 0.8 mL of alcohol/0.1 g of crude benzoin) using a 10-mL Erlenmeyer flask for the crystallization (Technique 11, Section 11.3, omit step 2 shown in Figure 11.4). After the crystals have cooled in an ice bath, collect the crystals on a Hirsch funnel. The product may be dried in a few minutes in an oven set at about 100°C. Determine the melting point of the purified benzoin. If you are not scheduled to perform Experiment 32B, submit the sample of benzoin, along with your report, to the instructor.

Spectroscopy

Determine the infrared spectrum of the benzoin by the dry film method (Technique 25, Section 25.4). A spectrum is shown here for comparison.

---

[1] Dissolve 8.0 g of NaOH in 100 mL water.

QUESTIONS

1. The infrared spectra of benzoin and benzaldehyde are given in this experiment. Interpret the principal peaks in the spectra.

Infrared spectrum of benzoin, KBr.

Infrared spectrum of benzaldehyde (neat).

2. How do you think the appropriate enzyme would have affected the reaction (degree of completion, yield, stereochemistry)?

3. What modifications of conditions would be appropriate if the enzyme were to be used?

4. Draw a mechanism for the cyanide-catalyzed conversion of benzaldehyde to benzoin. The intermediate, shown in brackets, is thought to be involved in the mechanism.

Benzaldehyde   **Benzoin**

32B EXPERIMENT 32B

Preparation of Benzil

In this experiment, benzil is prepared by the oxidation of an α-hydroxyketone, benzoin. This experiment uses the benzoin prepared in Experiment 32A and is the second step in the multistep synthesis. This oxidation can be done easily with mild oxidizing agents such as Fehling's solution (alkaline cupric tartrate complex) or copper sulfate in pyridine. In this experiment, the oxidation is performed with nitric acid.

Benzoin $\xrightarrow[\substack{\text{Experiment} \\ \text{32B}}]{\text{HNO}_3}$ **Benzil**

© Cengage Learning 2013

SPECIAL INSTRUCTIONS

Nitric acid should be dispensed in a good hood to avoid the choking odor of this substance. The vapors will irritate your eyes. Avoid contact with your skin. During the reaction, considerable amounts of noxious nitrogen oxide gases are evolved. Be sure to run the reaction in a good fume hood.

SUGGESTED WASTE DISPOSAL

The aqueous nitric acid wastes should be poured into a container designated for nitric acid wastes. Do not put them into the aqueous waste container. The ethanolic wastes from the crystallization should be poured into the nonhalogenated waste container.

PROCEDURE

Reaction Mixture

Place 0.30 g of benzoin (Experiment 32A) into a 5-mL conical vial and add 1.5 mL of concentrated nitric acid. Add a magnetic spin vane and attach an air condenser. In a hood, set up the apparatus for heating in a hot water bath, as shown in Technique 6, Figure 6.6. Heat the mixture in a hot water bath at about 70°C for 1 hour, with stirring. Avoid heating the mixture above this temperature to reduce the possibility of forming a by-product.[1] During the 1-hour heating period, nitrogen oxide gases (red) will be evolved. If it appears that gases are still being evolved after 1 hour, continue heating for another 15 minutes but then discontinue heating at that time.

Isolation of Crude Benzil

Cool the mixture for a few minutes and detach the air condenser. With a Pasteur pipette, transfer the reaction mixture to a beaker containing 4 mL of ice-cold water. Rinse the conical vial and spin vane with a small amount of water. Cool the mixture in an ice bath until the crystals have formed. If the material oils out rather than crystallizes, scratch the oil vigorously with a spatula until it does crystallize completely. Collect the crude product on a Hirsch funnel under vacuum. Wash it well with cold water (about 5 mL) to remove the nitric acid. Continue drawing air through the solid mass on the Hirsch funnel to help dry the solid. Weigh the solid.

Crystallization of Product

Purify the solid by dissolving it in hot 95% ethanol in a small Erlenmeyer flask (about 5 mL per 0.5 g of product) using a hot plate as the heating source. Be careful not to melt the solid on the hot plate. You can avoid melting the benzil by occasionally lifting the flask from the hot plate and swirling the contents of the flask. You want the solid to dissolve in the hot solvent rather than melt. You will obtain better

Infrared spectrum of benzil, KBr.

---

[1] At higher temperatures, some 4-nitrobenzil will be formed along with benzil.

crystals if you add a little extra solvent after it dissolves completely. Remove the flask from the hot plate and allow the solution to cool slowly. As the solution cools, seed it with a solid product that forms on a spatula after the spatula is dipped into the solution. The solution may become supersaturated unless this is done, and crystallization will occur too rapidly. Yellow crystals are formed. Cool the mixture in an ice bath to complete the crystallization. Collect the product on a Hirsch funnel under vacuum. Rinse the flask with small amounts (about 1 mL total) of ice-cold 95% ethanol to complete the transfer of product to the Hirsch funnel. Continue drawing air through the crystals on the Hirsch funnel by suction for about 5 minutes. Then remove the crystals and air-dry them.

Yield Calculation and Melting-Point Determination

Weigh the dry benzil and calculate the percentage yield. Determine the melting point. The melting point of pure benzil is 95°C. Submit the benzil to the instructor unless it is to be used to prepare benzilic acid (Experiment 32C). Obtain the infrared spectrum of benzil using the dry film method. Compare the spectrum to the one shown. Also compare the spectrum with that of benzoin. What differences do you notice?

  EXPERIMENT 32C

Preparation of Benzilic Acid

In this experiment, benzilic acid will be prepared by causing the rearrangement of the α-diketone benzil. Preparation of benzil is described in Experiment 32B. The rearrangement of benzil proceeds in the following way:

$$Ph{-}\overset{\overset{O}{\|}}{C}{-}\overset{\overset{O}{\|}}{C}{-}Ph \xrightarrow{\text{(1) KOH}} Ph{-}\overset{\overset{O}{\rightharpoonup}}{\underset{\underset{Ph}{|}}{C}}{-}\overset{\overset{O^{-}\ K^{+}}{|}}{C}{-}OH \longrightarrow Ph{-}\overset{\overset{O^{-}}{|}}{\underset{\underset{Ph}{|}}{C}}{-}\overset{\overset{O}{\|}}{C}{-}OH \longrightarrow$$

Benzil
(an α-diketone)

$$Ph{-}\overset{\overset{OH}{|}}{\underset{\underset{Ph}{|}}{C}}{-}\overset{\overset{O}{\|}}{C}{-}O^{-}K^{+} \xrightarrow{\text{(2) } H_3O^+} Ph{-}\overset{\overset{OH}{|}}{\underset{\underset{Ph}{|}}{C}}{-}\overset{\overset{O}{\|}}{C}{-}OH$$

Potassium
benzilate

Benzilic acid
(an α-hydroxyacid)

The driving force for the reaction is provided by the formation of a stable carboxylate salt (potassium benzilate). Once this salt is produced, acidification yields benzilic acid. The reaction can generally be used to convert aromatic α-diketones to aromatic α-hydroxyacids. Other compounds, however, also will undergo benzilic acid–type of rearrangement (see questions).

SPECIAL INSTRUCTIONS

This experiment works best with pure benzil. The benzil prepared in Experiment 32B is usually of sufficient purity after it has been crystallized.

SUGGESTED WASTE DISPOSAL

Pour all of the aqueous filtrates into the waste bottle designated for aqueous waste. Ethanolic filtrates should be put in the nonhalogenated organic waste bottle.

PROCEDURE

Running the Reaction

Add 0.100 g benzil and 0.30 mL 95% ethanol to a 3-mL conical vial. Place a spin vane in the vial and attach an air condenser. Heat the mixture with an aluminum block (90–100°C) while stirring until the benzil has dissolved (see inset in Technique 6, Figure 6.1A). Using a 9-inch Pasteur pipette, add dropwise 0.25 mL of an aqueous potassium hydroxide solution[1] downward through the condenser into the vial. Gently boil the mixture (aluminum block about 110°C) while stirring for 15 minutes. The mixture will be blue-black. As the reaction proceeds, the color will turn to brown, and the solid should dissolve completely. Solid potassium benzilate may form during the reaction period. At the end of the heating period, remove the assembly from the aluminum block and allow it to cool for a few minutes.

Crystallization of Potassium Benzilate

Detach the air condenser when the apparatus is cool enough to handle. Transfer the reaction mixture, which may contain some solid, with a Pasteur pipette into a 10-mL beaker. Allow the mixture to cool to room temperature and then cool in an ice-water bath for about 15 minutes until crystallization is complete. It may be necessary to scratch the inside of the beaker with a glass stirring rod to induce crystallization. Crystallization is complete when virtually the entire mixture has solidified. Collect the crystals on a Hirsch funnel by vacuum filtration and wash the crystals thoroughly with three 1-mL portions of ice-cold 95% ethanol. The solvent should remove most of the color from the crystals.

Transfer the solid, which is mainly potassium benzilate, to a 10-mL Erlenmeyer flask containing 3 mL of hot (70°C) water. Stir the mixture until all solid has dissolved or until it appears that the remaining solid will not dissolve. Any remaining solid will likely form a fine suspension. If solid does remain in the flask, filter the mixture in the following manner. Place about 0.5 g of Celite (Filter Aid) in a beaker with about 5 mL of water. Stir the mixture vigorously and then pour the contents into a Hirsch funnel (with filter paper) or a small Büchner funnel while applying a *gentle* vacuum, as in a vacuum filtration (Technique 8, Section 8.3, and Figure 8.5). Be careful not to let the Celite dry completely. This procedure will cause a thin layer of Celite to be deposited on the filter paper. Discard the water that passes through this filter. Pass the mixture containing potassium benzilate through this filter, using *gentle* suction. The filtrate should be clear. Transfer the filtrate to a 10-mL Erlenmeyer flask. If no solid remains in the flask, the filtration step may be omitted. In either case, proceed to the next step.

---

[1] The aqueous potassium hydroxide solution should be prepared for the class by dissolving 2.75 g of potassium hydroxide in 6.0 mL of water. This will provide enough solution for 20 students, assuming little solution is wasted.

Formation of Benzilic Acid

With swirling of the flask, add dropwise 0.50 mL of 1*M* hydrochloric acid to the solution of potassium benzilate. As the solution becomes acidic, solid benzilic acid will begin to precipitate. The pH should be about 2; if it is higher than this, add a few more drops of acid and check the pH again. Allow the mixture to cool to room temperature and then complete the cooling in an ice bath. Collect the benzilic acid by vacuum filtration using a Hirsch funnel. Wash the crystals with 3–4 mL of ice-cold water to remove potassium chloride salt that sometimes coprecipitates with benzilic acid during the neutralization with hydrochloric acid. Remove the wash water by drawing air through the filter. Dry the product thoroughly by allowing it to stand until the next laboratory period.

Melting Point and Crystallization of Benzilic Acid

Weigh the dry benzilic acid and determine the percentage yield. Determine the melting point of the dry product. Pure benzilic acid melts at 150°C. If necessary, crystallize the product from hot water using a Craig tube (Technique 11, Section 11.4, and Figure 11.6). If some impurities remain undissolved, filter the mixture using the following procedure. It will be necessary to keep the mixture hot during this filtration step. Transfer the hot mixture to a test tube with a Pasteur pipette. Clean the Craig tube and filter the mixture by transferring it back to the Craig tube with a filter-tip pipette. Cool the solution and induce crystallization, if necessary. Allow the mixture to stand at room temperature until crystallization is complete (about 15 minutes). Cool the mixture in an ice bath and collect the crystals by centrifugation. Determine the melting point of the crystallized product after it is thoroughly dry.

Infrared spectrum of benzilic acid, KBr.

At the instructor's option, determine the infrared spectrum of the benzilic acid in potassium bromide (Technique 25, Section 25.5). Calculate the percentage yield. Submit the sample to your laboratory instructor in a labeled vial.

QUESTIONS

1. Show how to prepare the following compounds, starting from the appropriate aldehyde.

(a)   (b)

2. Give the mechanisms for the following transformations:

(a)

(b)

(c)

3. Interpret the infrared spectrum of benzilic acid.

Preparation of an α,β-Unsaturated Ketone via Michael and Aldol Condensation Reactions

Crystallization

Michael reaction (conjugate addition)

Aldol condensation reaction

This experiment illustrates how two important synthetic reactions can be combined to prepare an α,β-unsaturated ketone, 6-ethoxycarbonyl-3,5-diphenyl-2-cyclohexenone. The first step in this synthesis is a sodium hydroxide–catalyzed conjugate addition of ethyl acetoacetate to *trans*chalcone (a Michael addition reaction). Sodium hydroxide serves as a source of hydroxide ion to catalyze the reaction.[1] In the reactions that follow, Ph and Et are abbreviations for the phenyl and ethyl groups, respectively.

The second step of the synthesis is a base-catalyzed aldol condensation reaction. The methyl group loses a proton in the presence of base, and the resulting methylene carbanion nucleophilically attacks the carbonyl group. A stable six-membered ring is formed. Ethanol supplies a proton to yield the aldol intermediate.

---

[1] Barium hydroxide has also been used as a catalyst (see References).

Finally, the aldol intermediate is dehydrated to form the final product, 6-ethoxy-carbonyl-3,5-diphenyl-2-cyclohexenone. The α,β-unsaturated ketone that is formed is stable because of the conjugation of the double bond with both the carbonyl group and a phenyl group.

6-Ethoxycarbonyl-3,5-diphenyl-
2-cyclohexenone

© Cengage Learning 2013

REQUIRED READING

Review: Techniques 7, 8, 11, 12

SUGGESTED WASTE DISPOSAL

Dispose of all aqueous wastes containing ethanol in the bottle designated for aqueous wastes. Ethanolic filtrates from the crystallization of the product should be poured into the nonhalogenated organic waste container.

NOTES TO THE INSTRUCTOR

The *trans*-chalcone (Aldrich Chemical Co., #13,612-3) should be finely ground for use by the class.

PROCEDURE

Assembling the Apparatus

To a 10-mL round-bottom flask, add 0.24 g of finely ground *trans*-chalcone, 0.15 g of ethyl acetoacetate, and 5 mL of absolute ethanol. Swirl the flask until all or most of the solid dissolves and place a boiling stone in the flask. Add 0.25 mL of 2.2*M* NaOH to the mixture. Attach a water-jacketed condenser to the round-bottom flask and heat the mixture to reflux using an aluminum block and hot plate. Once the mixture has been brought to a gentle boil, continue to reflux the mixture for at least 1 hour. During this reflux, the mixture will become very cloudy.

Isolation of the Crude Product

After the end of the reflux period, let the mixture cool to room temperature. Add 2 mL of water and scratch the inside of the flask with a glass stirring rod to induce crystallization (an oil may form; scratch vigorously). Place the flask in an ice bath for a minimum of 30 minutes. It is essential to cool the mixture thoroughly in order to completely crystallize the product. Because the product may precipitate slowly, you should also scratch the inside of the flask occasionally over the 30-minute period, as well as cool it in an ice bath.

Vacuum-filter the crystals on a Hirsch funnel, using 1 mL of ice-cold water to aid in the transfer. Then rinse the round-bottom flask with 1 mL of ice-cold 95% ethanol to complete the transfer of the remaining solid from the flask to the Hirsch funnel. Allow the crystals to air-dry overnight. Alternatively, the crystals may be dried for 30 minutes in an oven set at 75–80°C. Weigh the dry product. The solid contains some sodium hydroxide and sodium carbonate, which are removed in the next step.

Removal of Catalyst

Place the solid product in a test tube. Add 1.5 mL of reagent-grade acetone and stir the mixture with a spatula.[2] Most of the solid dissolves in acetone, but do not expect all of it to dissolve. Using a Pasteur pipette, remove the liquid and transfer it to a glass centrifuge tube, leaving as much solid as possible behind in the test tube. It is impossible to avoid drawing some solid up into the pipette, so the transferred liquid will contain suspended solids and the solution will be very cloudy. You should not be concerned about the suspended solids in the cloudy acetone extract, because the centrifugation step will clear the liquid completely. Centrifuge the acetone extract for approximately 2–3 minutes or until the liquid clears. Using a clean, dry Pasteur pipette, transfer the *clear* acetone extract from the centrifuge tube to a *dry, preweighed* test tube. If the transfer operation is done carefully, you should be able to leave the solid behind in the centrifuge tube. The solids left behind in the test tube and centrifuge tube are inorganic materials related to the sodium hydroxide originally used as the catalyst.

Evaporate the acetone solvent by carefully heating the test tube in a hot water bath while directing a light stream of dry air or nitrogen in the tube. Use a *slow* stream of gas to avoid blowing your product out of the tube. When the acetone has evaporated, you may be left with an oily solid in the bottom of the tube. Scratch the oily product with a spatula to induce crystallization. You may need to redirect air or nitrogen in the test tube to remove all traces of acetone. Reweigh the test tube to determine the yield of this partially purified product.

Crystallization of Product

Crystallize the product in a 10-mL Erlenmeyer flask using a minimum amount (approximately 2 mL) of hot 95% ethanol.[3] After the solid has dissolved, allow the flask to cool slightly. Scratch the inside of the flask with a glass stirring rod until crystals appear. Allow the flask to sit undisturbed at room temperature for a few minutes. Then place the flask in an ice-water bath for at least 15 minutes.

Collect the crystals by vacuum filtration on a Hirsch funnel. Use two 0.5-mL portions of ice-cold 95% ethanol to aid in the transfer. Allow the crystals to dry overnight or dry them for 30 minutes in a 75–80°C oven. Weigh the dry 6-ethoxy-carbonyl-3,5-diphenyl-2-cyclohexenone and calculate the percentage yield. Determine the melting point of the product (literature value, 111–112°C). Submit the sample to the instructor in a labeled vial.

---

[2] You may need to add more acetone than indicated in the procedure because a larger yield of product may have been obtained. You can add upto 3 mL of acetone. Excess acetone will not affect the results.

[3] The 2 mL of ethanol indicated in the procedure is an approximation. You may need to add *more hot or less hot* 95% ethanol to dissolve the solid. Add boiling ethanol until the solid just dissolves.

Spectroscopy

At the option of the instructor, obtain the infrared spectrum using the dry-film method (see Technique 25, Section 25.4) or in KBr (see Technique 25, Section 25.5A). You should observe absorbances at 1734 and 1660 cm^{-1} for the ester carbonyl and enone groups, respectively. Compare your spectrum to that shown in Figure 1. Your instructor may also want you to determine the ^{1}H and ^{13}C spectra. The spectra may be run in CDCl$_3$ or DMSO-d_6. The ^{1}H spectrum (500 MHz CDCl$_3$) is shown in Figure 2. Assignments have been made on the spectrum using data from a paper by Delaude, Grandjean, and Noels (see references below.) No attempt has been made to analyze the phenyl resonances, other than to show the integral value (10 H) for the two monosubstituted benzene rings. For reference, the ^{13}C spectrum (75 MHz, CDCl$_3$) shows 17 peaks: 14.1, 36.3, 44.3, 59.8, 61.1, 124.3, 126.4, 127.5, 127.7, 129.0, 129.1, 130.7, 137.9, 141.2, 158.8, 169.5, and 194.3.

REFERENCES

García-Raso, A.; García-Raso, J.; Campaner, B.; Mestres, R.; Sinisterra, J. V. An Improved Procedure for the Michael Reaction of Chalcones. *Synthesis* **1982,** 1037.

García-Raso, A.; García-Raso, J.; Sinisterra, J. V.; Mestres, R. Michael Addition and Aldol Condensation: A Simple Teaching Model for Organic Laboratory. *J. Chem. Educ.* **1986,** *63,* 443.

Delaude, L.; Grandjean, J.; Noels, A. F. The Step-by-Step Robinson Annulation of Chalcone and Ethyl Acetoacetate. *J. Chem. Educ.* **2006,** *83,* 1225–1228 and supplementary materials submitted with this article.

© Cengage Learning 2013

Figure 1
Infrared spectrum of 6-ethoxycarbonyl-3,5-diphenyl-2-cyclohexenone, KBr.

Figure 2

500 MHz ^{1}H NMR spectrum of 6-ethoxycarbonyl-3,5-diphenyl-2-cyclohexenone, CDCl$_3$. Integral values for each of the patterns are inserted under the peaks to assign the number of protons in each pattern. Protons H$_d$ and H$_e$ overlap at 3.8 ppm in CDCl$_3$ integrating for 2H. In DMSO-d_6, the protons H$_d$ and H$_e$ are totally resolved and appear individually at 3.6 and 4.1 ppm, respectively. The other protons appear at nearly the same values in both solvents. Small impurity peaks appearing in the spectrum can be ignored.

QUESTIONS

1. Why was it possible to separate the product from sodium hydroxide using acetone?

2. The white solid that remains in the centrifuge tube after acetone extraction fizzes when hydrochloric acid is added, suggesting that sodium carbonate is present. How did this substance form? Give a balanced equation for its formation. Also give an equation for the reaction of sodium carbonate with hydrochloric acid.

3. Draw a mechanism for each of the three steps in the preparation of the 6-ethoxycarbonyl-3,5-diphenyl-2-cyclohexenone. You may assume that sodium hydroxide functions as a base and ethanol serves as a proton source.

4. Indicate how you could synthesize *trans*-chalcone. (*Hint:* Experiment 37)

1,4-Diphenyl-1,3-butadiene

Wittig reaction
Working with sodium ethoxide
Thin-layer chromatography
UV/NMR spectroscopy
Solventless Wittig reactions

The Wittig reaction is often used to form alkenes from carbonyl compounds. In this experiment, the isomeric dienes *cis, trans-*, and *trans, trans*-1,4-diphenyl-1,3-butadiene will be formed from cinnamaldehyde and benzyltriphenyl-phosphonium chloride.

Two procedures are provided for preparing *trans, trans*-1,4-diphenyl-1,3-butadiene. In Experiment 39B, the reaction uses sodium ethoxide in ethanol solvent as the base, whereas in Experiment 39C, a green chemistry alternative is provided whereby potassium phosphate is employed as the base that is conducted without any solvent. The mechanism of the Wittig reaction in the presence of either sodium ethoxide or potassium phosphate is essentially identical. Sodium ethoxide is shown as the base in the mechanism that follows. In Experiment 39A, an optional procedure is provided for preparing one of the starting materials for the Wittig reaction.

trans,trans   *cis,trans*

The reaction is carried out in two steps. First, the phosphonium salt is formed by the reaction of triphenylphosphine with benzyl chloride in Experiment 39A. The reaction is a simple nucleophilic displacement of chloride ion by triphenylphosphine. The salt that is formed is called the "Wittig reagent" or "Wittig salt."

Benzyltriphenylphosphonium chloride
"Wittig salt"

© Cengage Learning 2013

117

When treated with base, the Wittig salt forms an **ylide.** An ylide is a species having adjacent atoms oppositely charged. The ylide is stabilized due to the ability of phosphorus to accept more than eight electrons in its valence shell. Phosphorus uses its 3d orbitals to form the overlap with the 2p orbital of carbon that is necessary for resonance stabilization. Resonance stabilizes the carbanion.

An ylide

The ylide is a carbanion that acts as a nucleophile, and it adds to the carbonyl group in the first step of the mechanism. Following the initial nucleophilic addition, a remarkable sequence of events occurs, as outlined in the following mechanism:

Triphenylphosphine oxide   An alkene

© Cengage Learning 2013

The addition intermediate, formed from the ylide and the carbonyl compound, cyclizes to form a four-membered-ring intermediate. This new intermediate is unstable and fragments into an alkene and triphenylphosphine oxide. Notice that the ring breaks open differently from the way it was formed. The driving force for this ring-opening process is the formation of a very stable substance, triphenylphosphine oxide. A large decrease in potential energy is achieved on the formation of this thermodynamically stable compound.

In this experiment, cinnamaldehyde is used as the carbonyl compound and yields mainly the *trans,trans*-1,4-diphenyl-1,3-butadiene, which is obtained as a solid. The *cis,trans* isomer is formed in smaller amounts, but it is a liquid that is not isolated in this experiment. The *trans,trans* isomer is the more stable isomer and is formed preferentially.

Cinnamaldehyde

trans,trans-1,4-Diphenyl-1,3-butadiene + *cis,trans* + Triphenylphosphine oxide

© Cengage Learning 2013

REQUIRED READING

Review: Technique 8   Section 8.3

Technique 20

SPECIAL INSTRUCTIONS

Your instructor may ask you to prepare 1,4-diphenyl-1,3-butadiene starting with commercially available benzyltriphenylphosphonium chloride. If so, start with Experiment 39B or 39C. The sodium ethoxide solution used in Experiment 39B must be kept tightly stoppered when not in use because it reacts readily with atmospheric water. Fresh cinnamaldehyde must be used in this experiment. Old cinnamaldehyde should be checked by infrared spectroscopy to be certain that it does not contain any cinnamic acid.

If your instructor asks you to prepare benzyltriphenylphosphonium chloride in Experiment 39A, you can conduct another experiment concurrently during the 1.5-hour reflux period. Triphenylphosphine is rather toxic.

Be careful not to inhale the dust. Benzyl chloride is a skin irritant and a lachrymator. It should be handled in the hood with care.

SUGGESTED WASTE DISPOSAL

If you conducted Experiment 39A, place the wastes in the nonhalogenated waste container. For Experiment 39B and 39C, dispose of organic wastes in the nonhalogenated waste container. Place the aqueous waste into the bottle designated for aqueous wastes.

39A   EXPERIMENT 39A (OPTIONAL)

Benzyltriphenylphosphonium Chloride (Wittig Salt)

Place 0.550 g of triphenylphosphine (MW = 262.3) into a 5-mL conical vial. In a hood, transfer 0.36 mL of benzyl chloride (MW = 126.6, d = 1.10 g/mL) to the vial and add 2.0 mL of xylenes (mixture of *o*-, *m*-, and *p*-isomers).

CAUTION

Benzyl chloride is a lachrymator, a tear-producing substance.

Add a magnetic spin vane to the conical vial and attach a water-cooled condenser. Boil the mixture using an aluminum block at about 165°C for at least 1.5 hours. An increased yield may be expected when the mixture is heated longer. In fact, you may begin heating the mixture before the temperature has reached the values given, but do not include this time in the 1.5-hour reaction period. The solution will be homogeneous at first, and then the Wittig salt will begin to precipitate. Maintain the stirring during the entire heating period or bumping may occur. Remove the apparatus from the aluminum block and allow it to cool for a few minutes. Remove the vial and cool it thoroughly in an ice bath for about 5 minutes.

Collect the Wittig salt by vacuum filtration using a Hirsch funnel. Use three 1-mL portions of cold petroleum ether (bp 60–90°C) to aid the transfer and to wash the crystals free of the xylene solvent. Dry the crystals, weigh them, and calculate the percentage yield of the Wittig salt. At the option of the instructor, obtain the proton NMR spectrum of the salt in $CDCl_3$. The methylene group appears as a doublet (J = 14 Hz) at 5.5 ppm because of ^1H-^{31}P coupling.

39B   EXPERIMENT 39B

Preparation of 1,4-Diphenyl-1,3-Butadiene Using Sodium Ethoxide to Generate the Ylide

In the following operations, cap the 5-mL conical vial whenever possible to avoid contact with moisture from the atmosphere. If you prepared your own benzyltriphenylphosphonium chloride in Experiment 39A, you may need to supplement your yield in this part of the experiment.

Preparation of the Ylide

Place 0.480 g of benzyltriphenylphosphonium chloride (*MW* = 388.9) in a *dry* 5-mL conical vial. Add a magnetic spin vane. Transfer 2.0 mL of absolute (anhydrous) ethanol to the vial and stir the mixture to dissolve the phosphonium salt (Wittig salt). Add 0.75 mL of sodium ethoxide solution[1] to the vial using a *dry* pipette while stirring continuously. Cap the vial and stir this mixture for 15 minutes. During this period, the cloudy solution acquires the characteristic yellow color of the ylide.

Reaction of the Ylide with Cinnamaldehyde

Measure 0.15 mL of *pure* cinnamaldehyde (*MW* = 132.2, *d* = 1.11 g/mL) and place it in another small conical vial. Add 0.50 mL of absolute ethanol to the cinnamaldehyde Cap the vial until it is needed. After the 15-minute period, use a Pasteur pipette to mix the cinnamaldehyde with the ethanol and add this solution to the ylide in the reaction vial. A color change should be observed as the ylide reacts with the aldehyde and the product precipitates. Stir the mixture for 10 minutes.

Separation of the Isomers of 1,4-Diphenyl-1,3-Butadiene

Cool the vial thoroughly in an ice-water bath (10 min), stir the mixture with a spatula, and transfer the material from the vial to a Hirsch funnel under vacuum. Use two 1-mL portions of ice-cold absolute ethanol to aid the transfer and to rinse the product. Dry the crystalline *trans,trans*-1,4-diphenyl-1,3-butadiene by drawing air through the solid. The product has a small amount of sodium chloride that is removed as described in the next paragraph. The cloudy material in the filter flask contains triphenylphosphine oxide, the *cis,trans*-isomer, and some *trans,trans* product. Pour the filtrate into a beaker and save it for the thin-layer chromatography experiment described in the next section.

Remove the *trans,trans*-1,4-diphenyl-1,3-butadiene from the filter paper, place the solid in a 10-mL beaker, and add 3 mL of water. Stir the mixture and filter it on a Hirsch funnel, under vacuum, to collect the nearly colorless crystalline *trans,trans* product. Use about 1 mL of water to aid the transfer. Allow the solid to dry thoroughly.

Thin-Layer Chromatography

Use thin-layer chromatography to analyze the filtrate that you saved in the previous section. This mixture must be analyzed as soon as possible so that the *cis,trans* isomer will not be photochemically converted to the *trans,trans* compound. Use a 2 × 8-cm silica gel TLC plate that has a fluorescent indicator (Eastman Chromatogram Sheet, No. EK 1224294). At one position on the TLC plate, spot the filtrate, as is, without dilution. Dissolve a few crystals of the *trans,trans*-1,4-diphenyl-1,

---

[1] This reagent is prepared in advance by the instructor. Carefully dry a 250-mL Erlenmeyer flask and insert a drying tube filled with calcium chloride into a one-hole rubber stopper. Obtain a large piece of sodium, clean it by cutting off the oxidized surface, weigh out a 2.30-g piece, cut it into 20 smaller pieces, and store it under xylene. Using tweezers, remove each piece, wipe off the xylene, and add the sodium slowly over a period of about 30 minutes to 40 mL of absolute (anhydrous) ethanol in the 250-mL Erlenmeyer flask. After the addition of each piece, replace the stopper. The ethanol will warm as the sodium reacts, but do not cool the flask. After the sodium has been added, warm the solution and shake it *gently* until all the sodium reacts. Cool the sodium ethoxide solution to room temperature. This reagent may be prepared in advance of the laboratory period, but it must be stored in a refrigerator between laboratory periods. When it is stored in a refrigerator, it may be kept for about 3 days. Before using this reagent, bring it to room temperature and swirl it gently in order to redissolve any precipitated sodium ethoxide. Keep the flask stoppered between each use.

3-butadiene in a few drops of acetone and spot it at another position on the plate. Use hexane as a solvent to develop (run) the plate.

Visualize the spots with a UV lamp using both the long and short wavelength settings. The order of increasing R_f values is as follows: triphenylphosphine oxide, *trans,trans*-diene, and *cis,trans*-diene. It is easy to identify the spot for the *trans,trans* isomer because it fluoresces brilliantly. What conclusion can you make about the contents of the filtrate and the purity of the *trans,trans* product? Report the results that you obtain, including R_f values and the appearance of the spots under illumination. Discard the filtrate in the container designated for nonhalogenated waste.

Yield Calculation and Melting-Point Determination

When the *trans,trans*-1,4-diphenyl-1,3-butadiene is dry, determine the melting point (literature, 151°C). Weigh the solid and determine the percentage yield. If the melting point is below 145°C, recrystallize a portion of the compound from hot 95% ethanol (20 mg/1.3 mL ethanol) in a Craig tube. Redetermine the melting point.

 EXPERIMENT 39C

Preparation of 1,4-Diphenyl-1,3-Butadiene Using Potassium Phosphate to Generate the Ylide

Experiment 39C provides an alternative green chemistry method for preparing 1,4-diphenyl-1,3-butadiene by the Wittig reaction. No solvent is used in this experiment. Instead, the starting materials are ground together with potassium phosphate in a mortar and pestle. This experiment will demonstrate to students a more environmentally friendly method for carrying out a reaction that might be performed on a larger scale in industry.

The reaction will be accomplished by grinding cinnamaldehyde with benzyltriphenylphosphonium chloride and potassium phosphate (tribasic, K_3PO_4). This is done using a mortar and pestle. TLC will be used to analyze the crystallized *trans,trans*-1,4-diphenyl-1,3-butadiene product, as well as the filtrate from the crystallization procedure that contains both the *cis,trans* and *trans,trans*-1,4-diphenyl-1,3,-butadiene isomers.

Reaction

Using an analytical balance, weigh out 309 mg of benzyltriphenylphosphonium chloride and 656 mg of potassium phosphate (tribasic, K_3PO_4) and place the solids into a clean and dry 6-cm (inside diameter) porcelain mortar with a pour lip. Using an automatic pipette, measure and add 100 μL of cinnamaldehyde to the mixture in the mortar. Grind the mixture together for a total of 20 minutes. It is much easier to use a pestle that is long enough to grip securely in one's hand, thus saving one's fingers from getting sore or tired. At the beginning of the grinding operation, the mixture will act like putty and will have a definite yellow color. After a few minutes of grinding, the mixture starts to turn into a thick paste that adheres to the inside of the mortar and the edges of the pestle. Bend the end of a spatula as shown in the figure. This bent spatula is useful for scraping the material off of the inside of the mortar and pestle and directing the mass into the center of the mortar. Repeat the scraping operation after every 1 to 2 minutes of grinding. Include that time in the total of 20 minutes of grinding time.

Isolation of Crude 1,4-Diphenyl-1,3-Butadiene

After 20 minutes, add a few milliliters of de-ionized water to the material in the mortar. Scrape the mortar and pestle a final time to loosen all of the product from the mortar. Pour the mixture into a Hirsch funnel inserted into a filter flask under vacuum. Use a squirt bottle with de-ionized water to transfer any remaining off-white product into the Hirsch funnel. Discard the filtrate that contains potassium phosphate and some triphenylphosphine oxide. The off-white solid consists mainly of the *trans,trans* isomer, but some of the *cis,trans* isomer will be present, as well.

Crystallization

Purify the off-white solid by crystallization from absolute ethanol in a small test tube using the standard technique of adding hot solvent until the solid dissolves. A small amount of impurity might not dissolve. If this is the case, use a Pasteur pipette to *rapidly* remove the hot solution away from the impurity and transfer the hot solution to another test tube. Cork the test tube and place it in a warm 25-mL Erlenmeyer flask. Allow the solution to cool slowly. Once the test tube has cooled and crystals have formed, place the test tube in an ice bath for at least 10 minutes to complete the crystallization process. Place 2 mL of absolute ethanol in another test tube and cool the solvent in the ice bath (this solvent will be used to aid the transfer of the product). Loosen the crystals in the test tube with a microspatula and pour the contents of the test tube into a Hirsch funnel under vacuum. Remove the remaining crystals from the test tube using the chilled ethanol and a spatula. Dry the colorless crystalline (plates) of *trans,trans*-1,4-diphenyl-1,3-butadiene on the Hirsch funnel for about 5 minutes to completely dry them. Save the filtrate from the crystallization for analysis by thin-layer chromatography. The *cis,trans*-1,4-diphenyl-1,3-butadiene, which is also formed in the Wittig reaction, is a liquid, and crystallization effectively removes the isomer from the solid *trans,trans* product.

Yield Calculation and Melting Point Determination

Weigh the purified *trans,trans* product and calculate the percentage yield. Determine the melting point of the product (literature, 151°C).

Thin-Layer Chromatography

Following the procedure in Experiment 39B, analyze the filtrate from the crystallization and the purified solid product by thin-layer chromatography. Develop the plate with hexane. This solvent will separate the *cis,trans*-diene from the *trans,trans* isomer. The order of increasing R_f values is as follows: triphenylphosphine oxide, *trans,trans*-diene, and *cis-trans*-diene. Triphenylphosphine oxide is so polar that the R_f value will be nearly zero. After developing the plate in hexane, as indicated in Experiment 39B, use the short and long wavelength settings with a UV lamp to visualize the spots. Calculate the R_f values and record them in your notebook.

Spectroscopy (Optional)

Prepare an NMR sample by dissolving at least 20 mg of crystallized product in about 1 ml of CDCl$_3$ in a small test tube. Transfer the solution to an NMR tube and add more solvent until the level of the solution is about 50 mm in the tube. Run the proton and carbon NMR spectra on the sample. At 300 MHz, the proton spectrum shows multiplets at 6.68 ppm and 6.95 ppm for the vinyl protons and 7.24 ppm (triplet, 2 H), 7.34 ppm (triplet, 4 H), and 7.44 ppm (doublet, 4 H) for the aromatic protons. The carbon spectrum shows peaks at 125.4, 126.6, 127.7, 128.3, 131.8, and 136.4 ppm. To determine the UV spectrum of the product, dissolve a 10-mg sample in 100 mL of hexane in a volumetric flask. Remove 10 mL of this solution and dilute it to 100 mL in another volumetric flask. This concentration should be adequate for analysis. The *trans,trans* isomer absorbs at 328 nm and possesses fine structure, whereas the *cis,trans* isomer absorbs at 313 nm and has a smooth curve.[2] See if your spectrum is consistent with these observations. Submit the spectral data with your laboratory report.

QUESTIONS

1. There is an additional isomer of 1,4-diphenyl-1,3-butadiene (mp 70°C), which has not been shown in this experiment. Draw the structure and name it. Why is it not produced in this experiment? (*Hint:* The cinnamaldehyde has *trans* stereochemistry.)

2. Why should the *trans,trans* isomer be the thermodynamically most stable one?

3. A lower yield of phosphonium salt is obtained in refluxing benzene than in xylene (Experiment 39A). Look up the boiling points for these solvents, and explain why the difference in boiling points might influence the yield.

4. Outline a synthesis for *cis* and *trans* stilbene (the 1,2-diphenylethenes) using the Wittig reaction.

5. The sex attractant of the female housefly (*Musca domestica*) is called **muscalure,** and its structure follows. Outline a synthesis of muscalure, using the Wittig reaction. Will your synthesis lead to the required *cis* isomer?

$$CH_3(CH_2)_7 \qquad (CH_2)_{12}CH_3$$
$$C=C$$
$$H \qquad\qquad H$$

Muscalure

---

[2] The comparative study of the stereoisometric 1,4-diphenyl-1,3-butadienes has been published: Pinkard, J. H., Wille, B., and Zechmeister, L. *Journal of the American Chemical Society, 70* (1948): 1938.

Preparation and Properties of Polymers: Polyester, Nylon, and Polystyrene

Condensation polymers
Addition polymers
Cross-linked polymers
Infrared spectroscopy

In this experiment, the syntheses of two polyesters (Experiment 46A), nylon (Experiment 46B), and polystyrene (Experiment 46C) will be described. These polymers represent important commercial plastics. They also represent the main classes of polymers: condensation (linear polyester, nylon), addition (polystyrene), and cross-linked (Glyptal polyester). Infrared spectroscopy is used in Experiment 46D to determine the structure of polymers.

REQUIRED READING

Review: Technique 25   Infrared Spectroscopy, Section 25B
New: Essay   Polymers and Plastics

SPECIAL INSTRUCTIONS

Experiments 46A, 46B, and 46C all involve toxic vapors. Each experiment should be conducted in a well-ventilated hood. The styrene used in Experiment 46C irritates the skin and eyes. Avoid breathing its vapors. Styrene must be dispensed and stored in a hood. Benzoyl peroxide is flammable and may detonate on impact or on heating.

SUGGESTED WASTE DISPOSAL

The test tubes containing the polyester polymers from Experiment 46A should be placed in a box designated for disposal of these samples. The nylon from Experiment 46B should be washed thoroughly with water and placed in a waste container. The liquid wastes from Experiment 46B (nylon) should be poured into a container designated for disposal of these wastes. The polystyrene prepared in Experiment 46C should be placed in the container designated for solid wastes.

46A EXPERIMENT 46A

Polyesters

Linear and cross-linked polyesters will be prepared in this experiment. Both are examples of condensation polymers. The linear polyester is prepared as follows:

This linear polyester is isomeric with Dacron, which is prepared from terephthalic acid and ethylene glycol (see the preceding essay). Dacron and the linear polyester made in this experiment are both thermoplastics.

If more than two functional groups are present in one of the monomers, the polymer chains can be linked to one another (cross-linked) to form a three-dimensional network. Such structures are usually more rigid than linear structures and are useful in making paints and coatings. They may be classified as thermosetting plastics. The polyester Glyptal is prepared as follows:

$$\text{HOCH}_2\overset{\overset{\text{OH}}{|}}{\text{C}}\text{HCH}_2\text{OH} \; + \;$$

Cross-linked polyester
(Glyptal resin)

$$+ \; H_2O$$

The reaction of phthalic anhydride with a diol (ethylene glycol) is described in the procedure. This linear polyester is compared with the cross-linked polyester (Glyptal) prepared from phthalic anhydride and a triol (glycerol).

PROCEDURE

Place 1 g of phthalic anhydride and 0.05 g of sodium acetate in each of two test tubes. To one tube, add 0.4 mL of ethylene glycol and to the other, add 0.4 mL of glycerol. Clamp both tubes so that they can be heated simultaneously with a flame. Heat the tubes gently until the solutions appear to boil (water is eliminated during the esterification); then continue heating for 5 minutes.

If you are performing the optional infrared analysis of the polymer, immediately save a sample of the polymer formed from ethylene glycol only. After removing a sample for infrared spectroscopy, allow the two test tubes to cool and compare the viscosity and brittleness of the two polymers. The test tubes cannot be cleaned.

Optional Exercise: Infrared Spectroscopy

Lightly coat a watch glass with stopcock grease. Pour some of the *hot* polymer from the tube containing ethylene glycol; use a wooden applicator stick to spread the polymer on the surface to create a thin film of the polymer. Remove the polymer from the watch glass and save it for Experiment 46D.

46B EXPERIMENT 46B

Polyamide (Nylon)

Reaction of a dicarboxylic acid, or one of its derivatives, with a diamine leads to a linear polyamide through a condensation reaction. Commercially, nylon 6–6 (so called because each monomer has six carbons) is made from adipic acid and hexamethylenediamine. In this experiment, you will use the acid chloride instead of adipic acid. The acid chloride is dissolved in cyclohexane, and this is added *carefully* to hexamethylenediamine dissolved in water. These liquids do not mix, so two layers will form. The polymer can then be drawn out continuously to form a long strand of nylon. Imagine how many molecules have been linked in this long strand! It is a fantastic number.

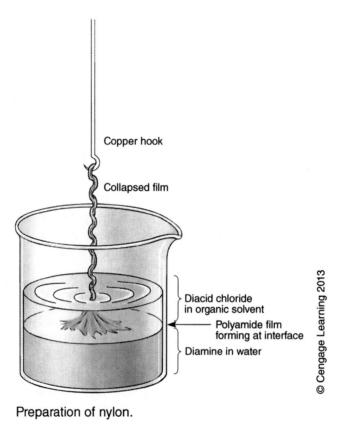

$$
\begin{array}{c}
\underset{\textbf{Adipoyl chloride}}{\text{Cl}-\overset{\overset{\text{O}}{\|}}{\text{C}}\text{CH}_2\text{CH}_2\text{CH}_2\text{CH}_2\overset{\overset{\text{O}}{\|}}{\text{C}}-\text{Cl}} + \underset{\textbf{Hexamethylenediamine}}{\text{H}-\overset{\overset{\text{H}}{|}}{\text{N}}\text{CH}_2\text{CH}_2\text{CH}_2\text{CH}_2\text{CH}_2\text{CH}_2\overset{\overset{\text{H}}{|}}{\text{N}}-\text{H}} \longrightarrow
\end{array}
$$

$$
\underset{\textbf{Nylon 6-6}}{-\overset{\overset{\text{O}}{\|}}{\text{C}}\text{CH}_2\text{CH}_2\text{CH}_2\text{CH}_2\overset{\overset{\text{O}}{\|}}{\text{C}}-\overset{\overset{\text{H}}{|}}{\text{N}}\text{CH}_2\text{CH}_2\text{CH}_2\text{CH}_2\text{CH}_2\text{CH}_2\overset{\overset{\text{H}}{|}}{\text{N}}-}
$$

Copper hook

Collapsed film

Diacid chloride
in organic solvent

Polyamide film
forming at interface

Diamine in water

© Cengage Learning 2013

Preparation of nylon.

PROCEDURE

Pour 10 mL of a 5% aqueous solution of hexamethylenediamine (1,6-hexanediamine) into a 50-mL beaker. Add 10 drops of 20% sodium hydroxide solution. Carefully add 10 mL of a 5% solution of adipoyl chloride in cyclohexane to the solution by pouring it down the wall of the slightly tilted beaker. Two layers will form (see figure), and there will be an immediate formation of a polymer film at the liquid–liquid interface. Using a copper-wire hook (a 6-inch piece of wire bent at one end), gently free the walls of the beaker from polymer strings. Then hook the mass at the center and slowly raise the wire so that polyamide forms continuously, producing a rope that can be drawn out for many feet. The strand can be broken by pulling it faster. Rinse the rope several times with water and lay it on a paper towel to dry. With the piece of wire, vigorously stir the remainder of the two-phase system to form additional polymer. Decant the liquid and wash the polymer thoroughly with water. Allow the polymer to dry. Do not discard the nylon in the sink; use a waste container.

46C EXPERIMENT 46C

Polystyrene

An addition polymer, polystyrene, will be prepared in this experiment. Reaction can be brought about by free-radical, cationic, or anionic catalysts (initiators), the first of these being the most common. In this experiment, polystyrene is prepared by free-radical–initiated polymerization.

The reaction is initiated by a free-radical source. The initiator will be benzoyl peroxide, a relatively unstable molecule, which at 80–90°C decomposes with homolytic cleavage of the oxygen–oxygen bond:

Benzoyl peroxide $\xrightarrow{\text{heat}}$ 2   **Benzoyl radical**

© Cengage Learning 2013

If an unsaturated monomer is present, the radical adds to it, initiating a chain reaction by producing a new free radical. If we let R stand for the initiator radical, the reaction with styrene can be represented as

$$R \cdot + CH_2{=}CH \longrightarrow R{-}CH_2{-}CH \cdot$$

The chain continues to grow:

$$R{-}CH_2{-}CH \cdot + CH_2{=}CH \longrightarrow R{-}CH_2{-}CH{-}CH_2{-}CH \cdot \text{, etc.}$$

© Cengage Learning 2013

The chain can be terminated by causing two radicals to combine (either both polymer radicals or one polymer radical and one initiator radical) or by causing a hydrogen atom to become abstracted from another molecule.

PROCEDURE

Because it is difficult to clean the glassware, this experiment is best performed by the laboratory instructor. One large batch of polystyrene should be made for the entire class (at least 10 times the amounts given). After the polystyrene is prepared, a small amount will be dispensed to each student. The students will provide their own watch glass for this purpose. Perform the experiment in a hood. Place several thicknesses of newspaper in the hood.

CAUTION

Styrene vapor is very irritating to eyes, mucous membranes, and upper respiratory tract. Do not breathe the vapor and do not get it on your skin. Exposure can cause nausea and headaches. All operations with styrene must be conducted in a hood.

Benzoyl peroxide is flammable and may detonate on impact or on heating (or grinding). It should be weighed on glassine (glazed, not ordinary) paper. Clean all spills with water. Wash the glassine paper with water before discarding it.

Place 12–15 mL of styrene monomer in a 100-mL beaker and add 0.35 g of benzoyl peroxide. Heat the mixture on a hot plate until the mixture turns yellow. When the color disappears and bubbles begin to appear, immediately take the beaker of styrene off the hot plate because the reaction is exothermic (use tongs or an insulated glove). After the reaction subsides, put the beaker of styrene back on the hot plate and continue heating it until the liquid becomes very syrupy. With a stirring rod, draw out a long filament of material from the beaker. If this filament can be cleanly snapped after a few seconds of cooling, the polystyrene is ready to be poured. If the filament does not break, continue heating the mixture and repeat this process until the filament breaks easily.

If you are performing the optional infrared analysis of the polymer, immediately save a sample of the polymer. After removing a sample for infrared spectroscopy, pour the remainder of the syrupy liquid on a watch glass that has been lightly coated with stopcock grease. After being cooled, the polystyrene can be lifted from the glass surface by gently prying with a spatula.

Optional Exercise: Infrared Spectroscopy

Pour a small amount of the *hot* polymer from the beaker onto a warm watch glass (no grease) and spread the polymer with a wooden applicator stick to create a thin film of the polymer. Peel the polymer from the watch glass and save it for 46D.

 EXPERIMENT 46D

Infrared Spectra of Polymer Samples

Infrared spectroscopy is an excellent technique for determining the structure of a polymer. For example, polyethylene and polypropylene have relatively simple spectra because they are saturated hydrocarbons. Polyesters have stretching frequencies associated with the C=O and C—O groups in the polymer chain. Polyamides (nylon) show absorptions that are characteristic for the C=O stretch and N—H stretch. Polystyrene has characteristic features of a monosubstituted aromatic compound (see Technique 25, Figure 25.12). You may determine the infrared spectra of the linear polyester from Experiment 46A and polystyrene from Experiment 46C in this part of the experiment. Your instructor may ask you to analyze a sample that you bring to the laboratory or one supplied to you.

PROCEDURE

Mounting the Samples

Prepare cardboard mounts for your polymer samples. Cut 3 × 5-inch index cards so that they fit into the sample cell holder of your infrared spectrometer. Then cut a 0.5-inch-wide × 1-inch-high rectangular hole in the center of the cardstock. Attach a polymer sample on the cardboard mount with tape.

Choices of Polymer Samples

If you have completed Experiments 46A and 46C, you can obtain the spectra of your polyester or polystyrene. Alternatively, your instructor may provide you with known or unknown polymer samples for you to analyze.

Your instructor may ask you to bring a polymer sample of your own choice. If possible, these samples should be clear and as thin as possible (similar to the thickness of plastic sandwich wrap). Good choices of plastic materials include windows from envelopes, plastic sandwich wrap, sandwich bags, soft-drink bottles, milk containers, shampoo bottles, candy wrappers, and shrink-wrap. If necessary, the samples can be heated in an oven and stretched to obtain thinner samples. If you are bringing a sample cut from a plastic container, obtain the recycling code from the bottom of the container, if one is given.

Running the Infrared Spectrum

Insert the cardboard mount into the cell holder in the spectrometer so that your polymer sample is centered in the infrared beam of the instrument. Find the thinnest place in your polymer sample. Determine the infrared spectrum of your sample. Because of the thickness of your polymer sample, many absorptions are so strong that you will not be able to see individual bands. To obtain a better spectrum, try moving the sample to a new position in the beam and rerun the spectrum.

Analyzing the Infrared Spectrum

You can use the essay "Polymers and Plastics" and Technique 25 with your spectrum to help determine the structure of the polymer. Most likely, the polymers will consist of plastic materials listed in Table Three of the essay. This table lists the recycling codes for a number of household plastics used in packaging. Submit the infrared spectrum along with the structure of the polymer to your instructor. Do your spectrum and structure agree with the recycling code? Label the spectrum with the important absorption bands consistent with the structure of the polymer.

Using a Polymer Library

If your particular instrument has a polymer library, you can search the library for a match. Do this after you have made a preliminary "educated guess" as to the structure of the polymer. The library search should help confirm the structure you determined.

QUESTIONS

1. Ethylene dichloride ($ClCH_2CH_2Cl$) and sodium polysulfide (Na_2S_4) react to form a chemically resistant rubber, Thiokol A. Draw the structure of the rubber.

2. Draw the structure for the polymer produced from the monomer vinylidene chloride ($CH_2{=}CCl_2$).

3. Draw the structure of the copolymer produced from vinyl acetate and vinyl chloride. This copolymer is employed in some paints, adhesives, and paper coatings.

$$
\begin{matrix}
& & & \overset{\displaystyle O}{\underset{\displaystyle \|}{}} & & & \\
\underset{\displaystyle H}{H}\!\!\diagdown & & \diagup O{-}\!\!\overset{\| }{C}{-}CH_3 & & \underset{\displaystyle H}{H}\!\!\diagdown & & \diagup Cl \\
& C{=}C & & & & C{=}C & \\
\underset{\displaystyle H}{H}\!\!\diagup & & \diagdown\underset{\displaystyle H}{H} & & \underset{\displaystyle H}{H}\!\!\diagup & & \diagdown\underset{\displaystyle H}{H}
\end{matrix}
$$

          Vinyl acetate   **Vinyl chloride**

4. Isobutylene, $CH_2=C(CH_3)_2$, is used to prepare cold-flow rubber. Draw a structure for the addition polymer formed from this alkene.

5. Kel-F is an addition polymer with the following partial structure. What is the monomer used to prepare it?

$$-\overset{\displaystyle F}{\underset{\displaystyle F}{C}}-\overset{\displaystyle F}{\underset{\displaystyle Cl}{C}}-\overset{\displaystyle F}{\underset{\displaystyle F}{C}}-\overset{\displaystyle F}{\underset{\displaystyle Cl}{C}}-\overset{\displaystyle F}{\underset{\displaystyle F}{C}}-\overset{\displaystyle F}{\underset{\displaystyle Cl}{C}}-$$

6. Maleic anhydride reacts with ethylene glycol to produce an alkyd resin. Draw the structure of the condensation polymer produced.

Maleic anhydride

7. Kodel is a condensation polymer made from terephthalic acid and 1,4-cyclohexanedimethanol. Write the structure of the resulting polymer.

Terephthalic acid   **1,4-Cyclohexanedimethanol**

Diels–Alder Reaction and Insecticides

Since the 1930s, it has been known that the addition of an unsaturated molecule across a diene system forms a substituted cyclohexene. The original research dealing with this type of reaction was performed by Otto Diels and Kurt Alder in Germany, and the reaction is known today as the **Diels–Alder reaction.** The Diels–Alder reaction is the reaction of a **diene** with a species capable of reacting with the diene, the **dienophile.**

© Cengage Learning 2013

The product of the Diels–Alder reaction is usually a structure that contains a cyclohexene ring system. If the substituents as shown are simply alkyl groups or hydrogen atoms, the reaction proceeds only under extreme conditions of temperature and pressure. With more complex substituents, however, the Diels–Alder reaction may proceed at low temperatures and under mild conditions. The reaction of cyclopentadiene with maleic anhydride (Experiment 47) is an example of a Diels–Alder reaction carried out under reasonably mild conditions.

In the past, a commercially important use of the Diels–Alder reaction involved the use of hexachlorocyclopentadiene as the diene. Depending on the dienophile, a variety of chlorine-containing addition products may be synthesized. Nearly all these products were powerful insecticides. Three insecticides synthesized by the Diels–Alder reaction are shown below.

Dieldrin and Aldrin are named after Diels and Alder. These insecticides were once used against the insect pests of fruits, vegetables, and cotton; against soil insects, termites, and moths; and in the treatment of seeds. Chlordane was used in veterinary medicine against insect pests of animals, including fleas, ticks, and lice. These insecticides are seldom used today.

Aldrin

Dieldrin

Chlordane

(isomers)

The best known insecticide, DDT, is not prepared by the Diels–Alder reaction, but is nevertheless the best illustration of the difficulties that were experienced when chlorinated insecticides were used indiscriminately. DDT was first synthesized in 1874, and its insecticidal properties were first demonstrated in 1939. It is easily synthesized commercially, with inexpensive reagents.

Chloral

Chlorobenzene

DDT

At the time DDT was introduced, it was an important boon to humanity. It was effective in controlling lice, fleas, and malaria-carrying mosquitoes and thus helped control human and animal disease. The use of DDT rapidly spread to the control of hundreds of insects that damage fruit, vegetable, and grain crops.

Pesticides that persist in the environment for a long time after application are called **hard pesticides.** Beginning in the 1960s, some of the harmful effects of such hard pesticides as DDT and the other chlorocarbon materials became known. DDT is a fat-soluble material and is therefore likely to collect in the fat, nerve, and brain tissues of animals. The concentration of DDT in tissues increases in animals high in the food chain. Thus, birds that eat poisoned insects accumulate large quantities of

© Cengage Learning 2013

DDT. Animals that feed on the birds accumulate even more DDT. In birds, at least two undesirable effects of DDT have been recognized. First, birds whose tissues contain large amounts of DDT have been observed to lay eggs having shells too thin to survive until young birds are ready to hatch. Second, large quantities of DDT in the tissues seem to interfere with normal reproductive cycles. The massive destruction of bird populations that sometimes occurred after heavy spraying with DDT became an issue of great concern. The brown pelican and the bald eagle were placed in danger of extinction. The use of chlorocarbon insecticides was identified as the principal reason for the decline in the numbers of these birds.

Because DDT is chemically inert, it persists in the environment without decomposing to harmless materials. It can decompose very slowly, but the decomposition products are every bit as harmful as DDT itself. Consequently, each application of DDT means that still more DDT will pass from species to species—from food source to predator—until it concentrates in the higher animals, possibly endangering their existence. Even humans may be threatened. As a result of evidence of the harmful effects of DDT, the Environmental Protection Agency (EPA) banned general use of DDT in the early 1970s; it may still be used for certain purposes, although permission of the EPA is required. In 1974, the EPA granted permission to use DDT against the tussock moth in the forests of Washington and Oregon.

Because the life cycles of insects are short, they can evolve an immunity to insecticides within a short period. As early as 1948, several strains of DDT-resistant insects were identified. Today, the malaria-bearing mosquitoes are almost completely resistant to DDT, an ironic development. Other chlorocarbon insecticides were developed to use as alternatives to DDT against resistant insects. Examples of these chlorocarbon materials include Dieldrin, Aldrin, Chlordane, and the substances whose structures are shown here. Heptachlor and Mirex are prepared using Diels-Alder reactions.

Lindane   Heptachlor   Mirex

© Cengage Learning 2013

In spite of structural similarity, Chlordane and Heptachlor behave differently than DDT, Dieldrin, and Aldrin. Chlordane, for instance, is short-lived and less toxic to mammals. Nevertheless, all the chlorocarbon insecticides have been the objects of much suspicion. A ban on the use of Dieldrin and Aldrin has also been ordered by the EPA. In addition, strains of insects resistant to Dieldrin, Aldrin, and other materials have been observed. Some insects become addicted to a chlorocarbon insecticide and thrive on it!

The problems associated with chlorocarbon materials have led to the development of "soft" insecticides. These usually are organophosphorus or carbamate derivatives, and they are characterized by a short lifetime before they are decomposed to harmless materials in the environment.

The organic structures of some organophosphorus insecticides are shown here.

$$CH_3CH_2-O-\overset{\overset{S}{\|}}{\underset{\underset{CH_3CH_2-O}{|}}{P}}-O-\!\!\!\!\!\bigcirc\!\!\!\!\!-NO_2$$

Parathion

$$CH_3O-\overset{\overset{S}{\|}}{\underset{\underset{CH_3O}{|}}{P}}-O-\overset{\overset{}{\underset{\underset{CH_2-\overset{\overset{O}{\|}}{C}-OCH_2CH_3}{|}}{O}}}{CH}-\overset{\overset{O}{\|}}{C}-OCH_2CH_3$$

Malathion

$$CH_3O-\overset{\overset{O}{\|}}{\underset{\underset{CH_3O}{|}}{P}}-O-CH=\!C\overset{\diagup Cl}{\diagdown Cl}$$

DDVP or Dichlorvos

© Cengage Learning 2013

Parathion and Malathion are used widely for agriculture. DDVP is contained in "pest strips," which are used to combat household insect pests. The organophosphorus materials do not persist in the environment, so they are not passed between species up the food chain, as the chlorocarbon compounds are. However, the organophosphorus compounds are highly toxic to humans. Some migrant and other agricultural workers have lost their lives because of accidents involving these materials. Stringent safety precautions must be applied when organophosphorus insecticides are being used.

The carbamate derivatives, including Carbaryl, tend to be less toxic than the organophosphorus compounds. They are also readily degraded to harmless materials. Nevertheless, insects resistant to soft insecticides have also been observed. Furthermore, the organophosphorus and carbamate derivatives destroy many more nontarget pests than the chlorocarbon compounds do. The danger to earthworms, mammals, and birds is very high.

$$CH_3-NH-\overset{\overset{O}{\|}}{C}-O$$

Carbaryl

© Cengage Learning 2013

ALTERNATIVES TO INSECTICIDES

Several alternatives to the massive application of insecticides have recently been explored. Insect attractants, including the pheromones (see the essay preceding Experiment 45), have been used in localized traps. Such methods have been effective against the gypsy moth. A "confusion technique," whereby a pheromone is sprayed into the air in such high concentrations that male insects are no longer able to locate females, has been studied. These methods are specific to the target pest and do not cause repercussions in the general environment.

Recent research has focused on using an insect's own biochemical processes to control pests. Experiments with **juvenile hormone** have shown promise. Juvenile hormone is one of three internal secretions used by insects to regulate growth and metamorphosis from larva to pupa and thence to the adult. At certain stages in the metamorphosis from larva to pupa, juvenile hormone must be secreted; at other stages it must be absent, or the insect will either develop abnormally or fail to mature. Juvenile hormone is important in maintaining the juvenile, or larval, stage of the growing insect. The male cecropia moth, which is the mature form of the silkworm, has been used as a source of juvenile hormone. The structure of the cecropia juvenile hormone is shown below. This material has been found to prevent the maturation of yellow-fever mosquitoes and human body lice. Because insects are not expected to develop a resistance to their own hormones, it is hoped that insects will be unlikely to develop a resistance to juvenile hormone.

Cecropea juvenile hormone   **Paper factor**

© Cengage Learning 2013

Although it is very difficult to get enough of the natural substance for use in agriculture, synthetic analogues have been prepared, that have been shown to be similar in properties and effectiveness to the natural substance. A substance has been found in the American balsam fir *(Abies balsamea)* known as **paper factor**. Paper factor is active against the linden bug, *Pyrrhocoris apterus,* a European cotton pest. This substance is merely one of thousands of terpenoid materials synthesized by the fir tree. Other terpenoid substances are being investigated as potential juvenile hormone analogues.

Pyrethrin

R = CH$_3$ or COOCH$_3$
R' = CH$_2$CH═CHCH═CH$_2$ or CH$_2$CH═CHCH$_3$
or CH$_2$CH═CHCH$_2$CH$_3$

© Cengage Learning 2013

Certain plants are capable of synthesizing substances that protect them against insects. Included among these natural insecticides are the **pyrethrins** and derivatives of **nicotine**.

The search for environmentally suitable means of controlling agricultural pests continues with a great sense of urgency. Insects cause billions of dollars of damage to food crops each year. With food becoming increasingly scarce and with the world's population growing at an exponential rate, preventing such losses to food crops is absolutely essential.

REFERENCES

Berkoff, C. E. Insect Hormones and Insect Control. *J. Chem. Educ.* **1971,** *48,* 577.

Bowers, W. S; Nishida, R. Juvocimenes: Potent Juvenile Hormone Mimics from Sweet Basil. *Science* **1980,** *209,* 1030.

Carson, R. *Silent Spring;* Houghton Mifflin: Boston. 1962.

Keller, E. The DDT Story. *Chemistry* **1970**, *43* (Feb), 8.

O'Brien, R. D. *Insecticides: Action and Metabolism;* Academic Press: New York, 1967.

Peakall, D. B. Pesticides and the Reproduction of Birds. *Sci Am.* **1970**, *222* (Apr), 72.

Saunders, H. J. New Weapons against Insects. *Chem. Eng. News* **1975**, *53* (Jul 28), 18.

Williams, C. M. Third-Generation Pesticides. *Sci. Am.* **1967**, *217* (Jul), 13.

Williams, W. G.; Kennedy, G. G.; Yamamoto, R. T.; Thacker, J. D.; Bordner, J. 2-Tridecanone: A Naturally Occurring Insecticide from the Wild Tomato. *Science* **1980**, *207*, 888.

Luminol

Chemiluminescence
Energy transfer
Reduction of a nitro group
Amide formation

In this experiment, the chemiluminescent compound **luminol,** or **5-amino-phthalhydrazide,** will be synthesized from 3-nitrophthalic acid.

3-Nitrophthalic acid   Hydrazine   5-Nitrophthalhydrazide   Luminol

The first step of the synthesis is the simple formation of a cyclic diamide, 5-nitrophthalhydrazide, by reaction of 3-nitrophthalic acid with hydrazine. Reduction of the nitro group with sodium dithionite affords luminol.

In neutral solution, luminol exists largely as a dipolar anion (zwitterion). This dipolar ion exhibits a weak blue fluorescence after being exposed to light. However, in alkaline solution, luminol is converted to its dianion, which may be oxidized by molecular oxygen to give an intermediate that is chemiluminescent. The reaction is thought to have the following sequence:

Luminol   Dianion

3-Aminophthalate
triplet dianion (T_1)

3-Aminophthalate
single dianion (S_1)

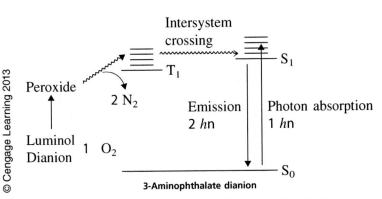

$$\left[\begin{array}{c} \text{S}_1 \end{array} \right]^1 \xrightarrow{\text{fluorescence}} \text{3-Aminophthalate} + h\nu$$

3-Aminophthalate
ground-state dianion, S_0

The dianion of luminol undergoes a reaction with molecular oxygen to form a peroxide of unknown structure. This peroxide is unstable and decomposes with the evolution of nitrogen gas, producing the 3-aminophthalate dianion in an electronically excited state. The excited dianion emits a photon that is visible as light. One very attractive hypothesis for the structure of the peroxide postulates a cyclic endoperoxide that decomposes by the following mechanism:

A postulate

© Cengage Learning 2013

Certain experimental facts argue against this intermediate, however. For instance, certain acyclic hydrazides that cannot form a similar intermediate have also been found to be chemiluminescent.

1-Hydroxy-2-anthroic acid
hydrazide (chemiluminescent)

© Cengage Learning 2013

Although the nature of the peroxide is still debatable, the remainder of the reaction is well understood. The chemical products of the reaction have been shown to be the 3-aminophthalate dianion and molecular nitrogen. The intermediate that emits light has been identified definitely as the *excited state singlet* of the 3-aminophthalate dianion.[1] Thus, the fluorescence emission spectrum of the 3-aminophthalate dianion (produced by photon absorption) is identical to the spectrum of the light emitted from the chemiluminescent reaction. However, for numerous complicated reasons, it is believed that the

Intersystem crossing

T_1

Emission
2 *h*n

Photon absorption
1 *h*n

S_1

S_0

Peroxide

2 N_2

Luminol
Dianion   1 O_2

3-Aminophthalate dianion

© Cengage Learning 2013

Fluorescence emission spectrum of the 3-aminophthalate dianion.

---

[1] The terms *singlet, triplet, intersystem crossing, energy transfer,* and *quenching* are explained in Experiment 49.

3-aminophthalate dianion is formed first as a vibrationally excited triplet state molecule, which makes the intersystem crossing to the singlet state before emission of a photon.

The excited state of the 3-aminophthalate dianion may be quenched by suitable acceptor molecules, or the energy (about 50–80 Kcal/mol) may be transferred to give emission from the acceptor molecules. Several such experiments are described in the following procedure.

The system chosen for the chemiluminescence studies of luminol in this experiment uses dimethylsulfoxide $(CH_3)_2SO$ as the solvent, potassium hydroxide as the base required for the formation of the dianion of luminol, and molecular oxygen. Several alternative systems have been used, substituting hydrogen peroxide and an oxidizing agent for molecular oxygen. An aqueous system using potassium ferricyanide and hydrogen peroxide is an alternative system used frequently.

REFERENCES

Rahaut, M. M. Chemiluminescence from Concerted Peroxide Decomposition Reactions. *Accounts of Chemical Research,* **1969**, 2, 80.

White, E. H., and Roswell, D. F. The Chemiluminescence of Organic Hydrazides. *Accounts of Chemical Research,* **1970**, 3, 54.

REQUIRED READING

Review: Technique 3   Reaction Methods, Section 7.10
New: Essay   Fireflies and Photochemistry

SPECIAL INSTRUCTIONS

This entire experiment can be completed in about 1 hour. When you are working with hydrazine, you should remember that it is toxic and should not be spilled on the skin. It is also a suspected carcinogen. Dimethylsulfoxide may also be toxic; avoid breathing the vapors or spilling it on your skin.

A darkened room is required to observe adequately the chemiluminescence of luminol. A darkened hood that has had its window covered with butcher paper or aluminum foil also works well. Other fluorescent dyes besides those mentioned (for instance, 9,10-diphenylanthracene) can also be used for the energy-transfer experiments. The dyes selected may depend on what is immediately available. The instructor may have each student use one dye for the energy-transfer experiments, with one student making a comparison experiment without a dye.

SUGGESTED WASTE DISPOSAL

Dispose of the filtrate from the vacuum filtration of 5-nitrophthalhydrazide in the container designated for nonhalogenated organic solvents. The filtrate from the vacuum filtration of 5-aminophthalhydrazide may be diluted with water and poured into the waste container designated for aqueous waste. The mixture containing potassium hydroxide, dimethylsulfoxide, and luminol should be placed in the special container designated for this material.

PROCEDURE

Part A. 5-Nitrop-hthalhydrazide

Place 0.300 g of 3-nitrophthalic acid and 0.4 mL of a 10% aqueous solution of hydrazine (use gloves) in a small side-arm test tube.[2] At the same time, heat 4 mL of water in a beaker on a hot plate to about 80°C. Heat the test tube over a microburner until the solid dissolves. Add 0.8 mL of triethylene glycol and clamp the test tube in an upright position on a ring stand. Place a thermometer (do not seal the system) and a boiling stone in the test tube and attach a piece of pressure tubing to the side arm. Connect this tubing to an aspirator (use a trap). The thermometer bulb should be in the liquid as much as possible. Heat the solution with a microburner until the liquid boils vigorously and the refluxing water vapor is drawn away by the aspirator vacuum (the temperature will rise to about 120°C). Continue heating and allow the temperature to increase rapidly until it rises just above 200°C. This heating requires 1–2 minutes, and you must watch the temperature closely to avoid heating the mixture well above 200°C. Remove the burner briefly when this temperature has been achieved and then resume gentle heating to maintain a fairly constant temperature of 210–220°C for about 2 minutes. Allow the test tube to cool to about 100°C, add the 4.0 mL of hot water that was prepared previously, and cool the test tube to room temperature by allowing tap water to flow over the outside of the test tube. Collect the brown crystals of 5-nitrophthalhydrazide by vacuum filtration, using a small Hirsch funnel. It is not necessary to dry the product before you go on with the next reaction step.

Part B. Luminol (5-Aminophth-alhydrazide)

Transfer the moist 5-nitrophthalhydrazide to a 13 x 100-mm test tube. Add 1.30 mL of a 10% sodium hydroxide solution and agitate the mixture until the hydrazide dissolves. Add 0.80 g of sodium dithionite dihydrate (sodium hydrosulfite dihydrate, $Na_2S_2O_4 \cdot 2H_2O$). Using a Pasteur pipette, add 1–2 mL of water to wash the solid from the walls of the test tube. Add a boiling stone to the test tube. Heat the test tube until the solution boils, agitate the solution, and maintain the boiling, continuing agitation, for 5 minutes. Add 0.50 mL of glacial acetic acid and cool the test tube to room temperature by allowing tap water to flow over the outside of it. Agitate the mixture during the cooling step. Collect the light yellow or gold crystals of luminol by vacuum filtration, using a small Hirsch funnel. Save a small sample of this product, allow it to dry overnight, and determine its melting point (mp 319–320°C). The remainder of the luminol may be used without drying for the chemiluminescence experiments.

CAUTION

Be careful not to let any of the mixture touch your skin while shaking the flask. Hold the stopper securely.

Part C. Chemilum-inescence Experiments

Cover the bottom of a 10-mL Erlenmeyer flask with a layer of potassium hydroxide pellets. Add enough dimethylsulfoxide to cover the pellets. Add about 0.025 g of the moist luminol to the flask, stopper it, and shake it vigorously to mix

---

[2] A 10% aqueous solution of hydrazine can be prepared by diluting 15.6 g of a commercial 64% hydrazine solution to a volume of 100 mL using water.

air into the solution.[3] In a dark room, a faint glow of bluish white light will be visible. The intensity of the glow will increase with continued shaking of the flask and occasional removal of the stopper to admit more air.

To observe energy transfer to a fluorescent dye, dissolve one or two crystals of the indicator dye in about 0.25 mL of water. Add the dye solution to the dimethylsulfoxide solution of luminol, stopper the flask, and shake the mixture vigorously. Observe the intensity and the color of the light produced.

The following table shows some dyes and the colors produced when they are mixed with luminol. Other dyes not included on this list may also be tested in this experiment.

Fluorescent Dye	Color
No dye	Faint blush white
2,6-Dichloroindophenol	Blue
9-Aminoacridine	Blue-green
Eosin	Salmon pink
Fluorescein	Yellow-green
Dichlorofluorescein	Yellow-orange
Rhodamine B	Green
Phenolphthalein	Purple

---

[3]An alternative method for demonstrating chemiluminescence, using potassium ferricyanide and hydrogen peroxide as oxidizing agents, is described in E. H. Huntress, L. N. Stanley, and A. S. Parker, *Journal of Chemical Education*, 11 (1934): 142.

The Chemistry of Sweeteners

Americans, as no other nationalities in the world do, possess a particularly demanding sweet tooth. Our craving for sugar, either added to food or included in candies and desserts, is astounding. Even when we are choosing a food that is not considered to be sweet, we ingest large quantities of sugar. A casual examination of the *Nutrition Facts* label and the list of ingredients of virtually any processed food will reveal that sugar is generally one of the principal ingredients.

Americans, paradoxically, are also obsessed by the need to diet. As a result, the search for noncaloric substitutes for natural sugar represents a multimillion-dollar business in this country. There is a ready market for foods that taste sweet but don't contain sugar.

For a molecule to taste sweet, it must fit into a taste bud site where a nerve impulse can carry the message of sweetness from the tongue to the brain. Not all natural sugars, however, trigger an equivalent neural response. Some sugars, such as glucose, have a relatively bland taste, and others, such as fructose, taste very sweet. Fructose, in fact, has a sweeter taste than common table sugar or sucrose. Furthermore, individuals vary in their ability to perceive sweet substances. The relationship between perceived sweetness and molecular structure is very complicated, and, to date, it is rather poorly understood.

The most common sweetener is, of course, common table sugar or sucrose. Sucrose is a disaccharide, consisting of a unit of glucose and a unit of fructose connected by a 1,2-glycosidic linkage. Sucrose is purified and crystallized from the syrups that are extracted from such plants as sugar cane and sugar beets.

When sucrose is hydrolyzed, it yields one molecule of D-fructose and one molecule of D-glucose. This hydrolysis is catalyzed by an enzyme, **invertase,** and produces a mixture known as **invert sugar**. Invert sugar derives its name from the fact that the mixture is levorotatory, whereas sucrose is dextrorotatory. Thus, the sign of rotation has been "inverted" in the course of hydrolysis. Invert sugar is somewhat sweeter than sucrose, owing to the presence of free fructose. Honey is composed mostly of invert sugar, which is the reason it has such a sweet taste.

High-fructose corn syrup (HFCS), which is often used to replace sucrose, has become a widely used sweetener since it was first introduced in the mid-1970s. Although more sucrose is used worldwide, the amounts of sucrose and HFCS that are consumed in the United States are about equal. HFCS is produced from corn starch by the enzymatic breakdown of starch into glucose along with the enzymatic isomerization of some of the glucose into fructose. HFCS may have different percentages of fructose and glucose, depending on the use. A common form called HFCS 55, which is widely used in soft drinks, consists of 55% fructose and 42% glucose. HFCS is cheaper than sucrose in the U.S. because of government subsidies to corn farmers and tariffs on imported sucrose.

Because the increase in obesity in the U.S. has roughly paralleled the increase in the use of HFCS, there has been much speculation that HFCS has played a role

145

$$\overbrace{\hspace{3cm}}^{\text{Glucose}}\overbrace{\hspace{3cm}}^{\text{Fructose}}$$
moiety   moiety

Sucrose

Sorbitol

Xylitol

Saccharine (sodium salt)

Sodium cyclamate

Aspartame

Sucralose

© Cengage Learning 2013

in this obesity trend. Recently, two studies at Princeton University on rats seem to support this theory. In both short-term and long-term studies, half of the rats were given HFCS-sweetened water along with a standard diet, while half were given sucrose-sweetened water along with the standard diet. In both studies, the rats given water sweetened with HFCS gained significantly more weight and exhibited many of the symptoms normally associated with obesity, including increases in abdominal fat and triglyceride concentration. More studies are required to determine whether this apparent correlation between obesity and HFCS in rats can be applied to humans, too.

Persons who suffer from diabetes are urged to avoid sugar in their diets. Nevertheless, those individuals may also have a craving for sweet foods. A substitute sweetener that is used for food items recommended for diabetics is **sorbitol,** which is an alcohol formed by the catalytic hydrogenation of glucose. Sorbitol has about 60% of the sweetness of sucrose. It is a common ingredient in products such as sugarless chewing gum since it is not a fermentable sugar and is much less likely than sugars to promote tooth decay. Even though sorbitol is a different substance from sucrose, it still possesses about the same number of calories per gram. Therefore, sorbitol is not a suitable sweetener for diet foods or beverages.

Another sweetener with some similarities to sorbitol is **xylitol**. Xylitol is a natural poly alcohol that can be isolated from sources such as birch trees and fibers of corn husks. Xylitol is used for some of the same reasons as sorbitol: xylitol can be consumed safely by diabetics and is even more effective than sorbitol in preventing cavities in teeth. However, it is more expensive than sorbitol and there is anecdotal evidence that xylitol is toxic in dogs.

As sucrose and honey are implicated in problems of tooth decay, as well as being culprits in the continuing battle against obesity, an active field of study is the search for new, noncaloric, noncarbohydrate sweeteners. Even if such a nonnutritive sweetener possessed some calories, if it were very sweet, it would not be necessary to use as much of the sweetener; therefore, the impact on dental hygiene and on diet would be less.

The first artificial sweetener to be used extensively was **saccharine,** which is used commonly as its more soluble sodium salt. Saccharine is about 300 times sweeter than sucrose. The discovery of saccharine was hailed as a great benefit for diabetics because it could be used as an alternative to sugar. As a pure substance, the sodium salt of saccharine has a very intense sweet taste, with a somewhat bitter aftertaste. Because it has such an intense taste, it can be used in very small amounts to achieve the desired effect. In some preparations, sorbitol is added to ameliorate the bitter aftertaste. Prolonged studies on laboratory animals have shown that saccharine is a possible carcinogen. In spite of this health risk, the government has permitted saccharine to be used in foods that are primarily intended to be used by diabetics.

Another artificial sweetener, which gained wide use in the 1960s and 1970s, is **sodium cyclamate**. Sodium cyclamate, which is 33 times as sweet as sucrose, belongs to the class of compounds known as the **sulfamates**. The sweet taste of many of the sulfamates has been known since 1937, when Sveda accidentally discovered that sodium cyclamate had a powerfully sweet taste. The availability of sodium cyclamate spurred the popularity of diet soft drinks. Unfortunately, in the 1970s, research showed that a metabolite of sodium cyclamate, cyclohexylamine, posed some potentially serious health risks, including a risk of cancer. This sweetener has thus been withdrawn from the market.

One of the most widely used artificial sweeteners available today is a dipeptide, consisting of a unit of aspartic acid linked to a unit of phenylalanine. The carboxyl group of the phenylalanine moiety has been converted to the methyl ester. This substance is known commercially as **aspartame,** but it is also sold under the trade names **NutraSweet** and **Equal**. Aspartame is about 200 times sweeter than sucrose. It is found in diet soft drinks, puddings, juices, and many other foods. Unfortunately, aspartame is not stable when heated, so it is not suitable as an ingredient in cooking. Other dipeptides that have structures similar to that of aspartame are many thousands of times sweeter than sucrose.

When aspartame was being developed as a commercial product, concern was raised over potential health hazards associated with its use. The potential cancer-causing effects of aspartame, along with other potential adverse side effects, were considered. Extensive testing of this product demonstrated that it met health-risk criteria established by the Food and Drug Administration, which granted approval for the sale of aspartame as a food additive in 1974. Nonetheless, the controversy around aspartame continues and it has been associated with some adverse psychological effects such as depression.

Sucralose, which is found in **Splenda** along with some glucose, was discovered in 1976 and it has become very competitive with aspartame in the battle for the best-selling artificial sweetener in this country. Sucralose is 600 times sweeter than sucrose. It is synthesized in the laboratory by a series of reactions in which three hydroxyl groups in sucrose are replaced by chlorine atoms. Since the starting material is sucrose, it has sometimes been marketed as being like sugar (in fact, the ose ending implies this); however, that is deceptive advertising since the body does not recognize sucralose as a carbohydrate. Most of the ingested sucralose is not absorbed or metabolized by the body. Although it has been approved for use as a sweetener, studies on the long-term effects in humans have not yet been done.

There are obviously many benefits associated with the use of artificial sweeteners. However, a recent study at Purdue University indicates that the veracity of some of these benefits may not be so certain as most people think. In these studies, rats were fed on two different diets. One group of rats was fed yogurt that had been sweetened with saccharine; the other group was fed yogurt sweetened with glucose. Otherwise, both groups had access to as much of their regular food as they wanted. The group of rats eating yogurt sweetened with saccharine gained considerably more weight than the other group! It is not understood why this happened, but the researchers suggested than when the rats on the saccharine-sweetened yogurt diet tasted something sweet, their body anticipated a meal with carbohydrate. Since no carbohydrate was available, these rats were not satisfied with what they had eaten and they tended to eat more of the other available food. On the other hand, the group of rats eating glucose-sweetened yogurt did ingest the carbohydrate that their body was expecting and they did not eat as much of the other food. It is premature to conclude that these studies can be applied to humans, but it is certainly food for thought!

The search for new substances that can serve as sweeteners continues. There is a great deal of interest in substances that are naturally occurring and that can be isolated from various plants. In addition, research, including molecular modeling studies and spectroscopic investigations, is attempting to clarify exactly what structural features are required for a sweet taste. Armed with that information, chemists will then be able to synthesize molecules that will be designed specifically for their sweet taste.

REFERENCES

Barker, S. A., Garegg, P. J.; Bucke, C.; Rastall, R. A.; Sharon, N.; Lis, H.; and Hounsell, E. F. Contemporary Carbohydrate Chemistry. *Chem. Br.* **1990,** *26,* 663. (This is a series of five articles, each written by one or two of the cited authors, compiled as part of a series of articles on carbohydrate chemistry.)

Bocarsly, M.E.; Powell, E. S.; Avena, N. M.; Hoebel, B. G. High-fructose Com Syrup Causes Characteristics of Obesity in Rats: Increased Body Weight, Body Fat and Triglyceride Levels. *Pharmacology Biochemistry and Behavior.* **2010,** *94,* 363.

Bragg, R. W.; Chow, Y.; Dennis, L.; Ferguson, L. N.; Howell, S.; Morga, G.; Ogino, C.; Pugh, H.; Winters, M. Sweet Organic Chemistry. *J. Chem. Educ.* **1978,** *55,* 281.

Burt, B. A. The Use of Sorbitol- and Xylitol-sweetened Chewing Gum in Caries Control. *Journal of American Dental Association.* **2006,** *137, 190.*

Crammer, B.; and Ikan, R. Sweet Glycosides from the Stevia Plant. *Chem. Br.* **1986,** *22,* 915.

Ellis, J. W. Overview of Sweeteners. *J. Chem. Educ.* **1995,** *72,* 669.

Sharon, N. Carbohydrates. *Sci. Am.* **1980,** *243,* 90.

Swithers, S.E.; Davison, T. L. A Role for Sweet Taste: Caloric Predictive Relations in Energy Regulation by Rats. *Behavioral Neuroscience.* **2008,** *122,* 161.

The Techniques

Laboratory Safety

In any laboratory course, familiarity with the fundamentals of laboratory safety is critical. Any chemistry laboratory, particularly an organic chemistry laboratory, can be a dangerous place in which to work. Understanding potential hazards will serve you well in minimizing that danger. It is ultimately your responsibility, along with your laboratory instructor's, to make sure that all laboratory work is carried out in a safe manner.

1.1 Safety Guidelines

It is vital that you take necessary precautions in the organic chemistry laboratory. Your laboratory instructor will advise you of specific rules for the laboratory in which you work. The following list of safety guidelines should be observed in all organic chemistry laboratories.

A. Eye Safety

Always Wear Approved Safety Glasses or Goggles. It is essential to wear eye protection whenever you are in the laboratory. Even if you are not actually carrying out an experiment, a person near you might have an accident that could endanger your eyes. Even dishwashing can be hazardous. We know of cases in which a person has been cleaning glassware only to have an undetected piece of reactive material explode, throwing fragments into the person's eyes. To avoid such accidents, wear your safety glasses or goggles at all times.

Learn the Location of Eyewash Facilities. If there are eyewash fountains in your laboratory, determine which one is nearest to you before you start to work. If any chemical enters your eyes, go immediately to the eyewash fountain and flush your eyes and face with large amounts of water. If an eyewash fountain is not available, the laboratory will usually have at least one sink fitted with a piece of flexible hose. When the water is turned on, this hose can be aimed upward, and the water can be directed into the face, working much as an eyewash fountain does. To avoid damaging the eyes, the water flow rate should not be set too high, and the water temperature should be slightly warm.

B. Fires

Use Care with Open Flames in the Laboratory. Because an organic chemistry laboratory course deals with flammable organic solvents, the danger of fire is frequently present. Because of this danger, DO NOT SMOKE IN THE LABORATORY. Furthermore, use extreme caution when you light matches or use any open flame. Always check to see whether your neighbors on either side, across the bench, and behind you are using flammable solvents. If so, either wait or move to a safe location, such as a fume hood, to use your open flame. Many flammable organic substances are the source of dense vapors that can travel for some distance down a bench. These vapors present a fire danger, and you should be careful because the source of those vapors may be far away from you. Do not use the bench sinks to

152

dispose of flammable solvents. If your bench has a trough running along it, pour only *water* (no flammable solvents!) into it. The troughs and sinks are designed to carry water—not flammable materials—from the condenser hoses and aspirators.

Learn the Location of Fire Extinguishers, Fire Showers, and Fire Blankets. For your own protection in case of a fire, you should immediately determine the location of the nearest fire extinguisher, fire shower, and fire blanket. You should learn how to operate these safety devices, particularly the fire extinguisher. Your instructor can demonstrate this.

If there is a fire, the best advice is to get away from it and let the instructor or laboratory assistant take care of it. DON'T PANIC! Time spent in thought before action is never wasted. If it is a small fire in a container, it can usually be extinguished quickly by placing a wire-gauze screen with a ceramic fiber center or, possibly, a watch glass over the mouth of the container. It is good practice to have a wire screen or watch glass handy whenever you are using a flame. If this method does not extinguish the fire and if help from an experienced person is not readily available, then extinguish the fire yourself with a fire extinguisher.

Should your clothing catch on fire, DO NOT RUN. Walk *purposefully* toward the fire shower station or the nearest fire blanket. Running will fan the flames and intensify them.

C. Organic Solvents: Their Hazards

Avoid Contact with Organic Solvents. It is essential to remember that most organic solvents are flammable and will burn if they are exposed to an open flame or a match. Remember also that on repeated or excessive exposure, some organic solvents may be toxic, carcinogenic (cancer-causing), or both. For example, many chlorocarbon solvents, when accumulated in the body, result in liver deterioration similar to cirrhosis caused by excessive use of ethanol. The body does not easily rid itself of chlorocarbons, nor does it detoxify them; they build up over time and may cause future illness. Some chlorocarbons are also suspected of being carcinogens. MINIMIZE YOUR EXPOSURE. Long-term exposure to benzene may cause a form of leukemia. Do not sniff benzene, and avoid spilling it on yourself. Many other solvents, such as chloroform and ether, are good anesthetics and will put you to sleep if you breathe too much of them. They subsequently cause nausea. Many of these solvents have a synergistic effect with ethanol, meaning that they enhance its effect. Pyridine causes temporary impotence. In other words, organic solvents are just as dangerous as corrosive chemicals, such as sulfuric acid, but manifest their hazardous nature in other, more subtle ways.

If you are pregnant, you may want to consider taking this course at a later time. Some exposure to organic fumes is inevitable and any possible risk to an unborn baby should be avoided.

Minimize any direct exposure to solvents and treat them with respect. The laboratory room should be well ventilated. Normal cautious handling of solvents should not result in any health problem. If you are trying to evaporate a solution in an open container, you must do the evaporation in the hood. Excess solvents should be discarded in a container specifically intended for waste solvents, rather than down the drain at the laboratory bench.

A sensible precaution is to wear gloves when working with solvents. Gloves made from polyethylene are inexpensive and provide good protection. The disadvantage of polyethylene gloves is that they are slippery. Disposable surgical gloves provide a better grip on glassware and other equipment, but they do not offer as much protection as polyethylene gloves. Nitrile gloves offer better protection.

Do Not Breathe Solvent Vapors. In checking the odor of a substance, be careful not to inhale very much of the material. The technique for smelling flowers is not advisable here; you could inhale dangerous amounts of the compound. Rather, a technique for smelling minute amounts of a substance is used. Pass a stopper or spatula moistened with the substance (if it is a liquid) under your nose. Or hold the substance away from you and waft the vapors toward you with your hand. But *never* hold your nose over the container and inhale deeply!

The hazards associated with organic solvents you are likely to encounter in the organic laboratory are discussed in detail in section 1.3. If you use proper safety precautions, your exposure to harmful organic vapors will be minimized and should present no health risk.

Safe Transportation of Chemicals. When transporting chemicals from one location to another, particularly from one room to another, it is always best to use some form of **secondary containment.** This means that the bottle or flask is carried inside another, larger container. This outer container serves to contain the contents of the inner vessel in case a leak or breakage should occur. Scientific suppliers offer a variety of chemical-resistant carriers for this purpose.

D. Waste Disposal

Do Not Place Any Liquid or Solid Waste in Sinks; Use Appropriate Waste Containers. Many substances are toxic, flammable, and difficult to degrade; it is neither legal nor advisable to dispose of organic solvents or other liquid or solid reagents by pouring them down the sink.

The correct disposal method for wastes is to put them in appropriately labeled waste containers. These containers should be placed in the hoods in the laboratory. The waste containers will be disposed of safely by qualified persons using approved protocols.

Specific guidelines for disposing of waste will be determined by the people in charge of your laboratory and by local regulations.

Two alternative systems for handling waste disposal are presented here. For each experiment that you are assigned, you will be instructed to dispose of all wastes according to the system that is in operation in your laboratory.

In one model of waste collection, a separate waste container for each experiment is placed in the laboratory. In some cases, more than one container, each labeled according to the type of waste that is anticipated, is set out. The containers will be labeled with a list that details each substance that is present in the container. In this model, it is common practice to use separate waste containers for aqueous solutions, organic halogenated solvents, and other organic nonhalogenated materials. At the end of the laboratory class period, the waste containers are transported to a central hazardous materials storage location. These wastes may be later consolidated and poured into large drums for shipping. Complete labeling, detailing each chemical contained in the waste, is required at each stage of this waste handling process, even when the waste is consolidated into drums.

In a second model of waste collection, you will be instructed to dispose of all wastes in one of the following ways:

Nonhazardous solids. Nonhazardous solids such as paper and cork can be placed in an ordinary wastebasket.

Broken glassware. Broken glassware should be put into a container specifically designated for broken glassware.

Organic solids. Solid products that are not turned in or any other organic solids should be disposed of in the container designated for organic solids.

Inorganic solids. Solids such as alumina and silica gel should be put in a container specifically designated for them.

Nonhalogenated organic solvents. Organic solvents such as diethyl ether, hexane, and toluene, or any solvent that does not contain a halogen atom, should be disposed of in the container designated for nonhalogenated organic solvents.

Halogenated solvents. Methylene chloride (dichloromethane), chloroform, and carbon tetrachloride are examples of common halogenated organic solvents. Dispose of all halogenated solvents in the container designated for them.

Strong inorganic acids and bases. Strong acids such as hydrochloric, sulfuric, and nitric acid will be collected in specially marked containers. Strong bases such as sodium hydroxide and potassium hydroxide will also be collected in specially designated containers.

Aqueous solutions. Aqueous solutions will be collected in a specially marked waste container. It is not necessary to separate each type of aqueous solution (unless the solution contains heavy metals); rather, unless otherwise instructed, you may combine all aqueous solutions into the same waste container. Although many types of solutions (aqueous sodium bicarbonate, aqueous sodium chloride, and so on) may seem innocuous and it may seem that their disposal down the sink drain is not likely to cause harm, many communities are becoming increasingly restrictive about what substances they will permit to enter municipal sewage-treatment systems. In light of this trend toward greater caution, it is important to develop good laboratory habits regarding the disposal of *all* chemicals.

Heavy metals. Many heavy-metal ions such as mercury and chromium are highly toxic and should be disposed of in specifically designated waste containers.

Whichever method is used, the waste containers must eventually be labeled with a complete list of each substance that is present in the waste. Individual waste containers are collected, and their contents are consolidated and placed into drums for transport to the waste-disposal site. Even these drums must bear labels that detail each of the substances contained in the waste.

In either waste-handling method, certain principles will always apply:

- Aqueous solutions should not be mixed with organic liquids.
- Concentrated acids should be stored in separate containers; certainly they must *never* be allowed to come into contact with organic waste.
- Organic materials that contain halogen atoms (fluorine, chlorine, bromine, or iodine) should be stored in separate containers from those used to store materials that do not contain halogen atoms.

In each experiment in this textbook, we have suggested a method of collecting and storing wastes. Your instructor may opt to use another method for collecting wastes.

E. Use of Flames

Even though organic solvents are frequently flammable (for example, hexane, diethyl ether, methanol, acetone, and petroleum ether), there are certain laboratory procedures for which a flame must be used. Most often, these procedures involve an aqueous solution. In fact, as a general rule, use a flame to heat only aqueous solutions. Heating methods that do not use a flame are discussed in detail in Technique 6. Most organic solvents boil below 100°C, and an aluminum block, heating mantle, sand bath, or water bath may be used to heat these solvents safely. Common organic solvents are listed in Technique 10, Table 10.3. Solvents marked in the table with boldface type will burn. Diethyl ether, pentane, and hexane are especially dangerous because, in combination with the correct amount of air, they may explode.

Some common sense rules apply to using a flame in the presence of flammable solvents. Again, we stress that you should check to see whether anyone in your vicinity is using flammable solvents before you ignite any open flame. If someone is using a flammable solvent, move to a safer location before you light your flame. Your laboratory should have an area set aside for using a burner to prepare micropipettes or other pieces of glassware.

The drainage troughs or sinks should never be used to dispose of flammable organic solvents. They will vaporize if they are low-boiling and may encounter a flame farther down the bench on their way to the sink.

F. Inadvertently Mixed Chemicals

To avoid unnecessary hazards of fire and explosion, never pour any reagent back into a stock bottle. There is always the chance that you may accidentally pour back some foreign substance that will react explosively with the chemical in the stock bottle. Of course, by pouring reagents back into the stock bottles, you may introduce impurities that could spoil the experiment for the person using the stock reagent after you. Pouring things back into bottles is not only a dangerous practice but also an inconsiderate one. Thus, you should not take more chemicals than you need.

G. Unauthorized Experiments

Never undertake any unauthorized experiments. The risk of an accident is high, particularly if the experiment has not been completely checked to reduce hazards. Never work alone in the laboratory. The laboratory instructor or supervisor must always be present.

H. Food in the Laboratory

Because all chemicals are potentially toxic, avoid accidentally ingesting any toxic substance; therefore, never eat or drink any food while in the laboratory. There is always the possibility that whatever you are eating or drinking may become contaminated with a potentially hazardous material.

I. Clothing

Always wear closed shoes in the laboratory; open-toed shoes or sandals offer inadequate protection against spilled chemicals or broken glass. Do not wear your best clothing in the laboratory because some chemicals can make holes in or permanent stains on your clothing. To protect yourself and your clothing, it is advisable to wear a full-length laboratory apron or coat.

When working with chemicals that are very toxic, wear some type of gloves. Disposable gloves are inexpensive, offer good protection, provide acceptable "feel," and can be bought in many departmental stockrooms and college bookstores. Disposable latex surgical or polyethylene gloves are the least expensive type of glove; they are satisfactory when working with inorganic reagents and solutions. Better protection is afforded by disposable nitrile gloves. This type of glove provides good protection against organic chemicals and solvents. Heavier nitrile gloves are also available.

Finally, hair that is shoulder length or longer should be tied back. This precaution is especially important if you are working with a burner.

J. First Aid: Cuts, Minor Burns, and Acid or Base Burns

If any chemical enters your eyes, immediately irrigate the eyes with copious quantities of water. Tempered (slightly warm) water, if available, is preferable. Be sure that the eyelids are kept open. Continue flushing the eyes in this way for 15 minutes.

In case of a cut, wash the wound well with water unless you are specifically instructed to do otherwise. If necessary, apply pressure to the wound to stop the flow of blood. If you are assisting someone else, prudence dictates that you wear gloves in order to avoid contact with the blood of another person. Minor burns caused by flames or contact with hot objects may be soothed by immediately immersing the burned area in cold water or cracked ice until you no longer feel a burning sensation. Applying salves to burns is discouraged. Severe burns must be examined and treated by a physician. For chemical acid or base burns, rinse the burned area with copious quantities of water for at least 15 minutes.

If you accidentally ingest a chemical, call the local poison control center for instructions. Do not drink anything until you have been told to do so. It is important that the examining physician be informed of the exact nature of the substance ingested.

1.2 Right-to-Know Laws

The federal government and most state governments now require that employers provide their employees with complete information about hazards in the workplace. These regulations are often referred to as **Right-to-Know Laws.** At the federal level, the Occupational Safety and Health Administration (OSHA) is charged with enforcing these regulations.

In 1990, the federal government extended the Hazard Communication Act, which established the Right-to-Know Laws, to include a provision that requires the establishment of a Chemical Hygiene Plan at all academic laboratories. Every college and university chemistry department should have a Chemical Hygiene Plan. Having this plan means that all the safety regulations and laboratory safety procedures should be written in a manual. The plan also provides for the training of all employees in laboratory safety. Your laboratory instructor and assistants should have this training.

One of the components of Right-to-Know Laws is that employees and students have access to information about the hazards of any chemicals with which they are working. Your instructor will alert you to dangers to which you need to pay particular attention. However, you may want to seek additional information. Two excellent sources of information are labels on the bottles that come from a chemical manufacturer and **Material Safety Data Sheets** (MSDSs). The MSDSs are also provided by the manufacturer and must be kept available for all chemicals used at educational institutions.

A. Material Safety Data Sheets

Reading an MSDS for a chemical can be a daunting experience, even for an experienced chemist. MSDSs contain a wealth of information, some of which must be decoded to understand. The MSDS for methanol is shown on the following pages.

MSDS Number: M2015	Effective Date: 12/8/96

 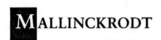 **Material Safety Data Sheet**

24 Hour Emergency Telephone: 908-859-2151
CHEMTREC: 1-800-424-9300

National Response in Canada
CANUTEC: 613-996-6666

From: Mallinckrodt Baker, Inc.
222 Red School Lane
Phillipsburg, NJ 08865

Outside U.S. and Canada
Chemtrec: 202-483-7616

MALLINCKRODT   **J.T.Baker**

NOTE: CHEMTREC, CANUTEC and National Response Center emergency numbers to be used only in the event of chemical emergencies involving a spill, leak, fire, exposure or accident involving chemicals.

All non-emergency questions should be directed to Customer Service (1-800-582-2537) for assistance.

METHYL ALCOHOL

1. Product Identification

Synonyms: Wood alcohol; methanol; carbinol
CAS No: 67-56-1
Molecular Weight: 32.04
Chemical Formula: CH_3OH
Product Codes: **J.T. Baker:**
5217, 5370, 5794, 5807, 5811, 5842, 5869, 9049, 9063, 9066, 9067, 9069, 9070, 9071, 9073, 9075, 9076, 9077, 9091, 9093, 9096, 9097, 9098, 9263, 9893
Mallinckrodt:
3004, 3006, 3016, 3017, 3018, 3024, 3041, 3701, 4295, 5160, 8814, H080, H488, H603, V079, V571

2. Composition/Information on Ingredients

Ingredient	CAS No.	Percent	Hazardous
Methyl Alcohol	67-56-1	100%	Yes

3. Hazards Identification

Emergency Overview

POISON! DANGER! VAPOR HARMFUL. MAY BE FATAL OR CAUSE BLINDNESS IF SWALLOWED. HARMFUL IF INHALED OR ABSORBED THROUGH SKIN. CANNOT BE MADE NONPOISONOUS. FLAMMABLE LIQUID AND VAPOR. CAUSES IRRITATION TO SKIN, EYES AND RESPIRATORY TRACT. AFFECTS THE LIVER.

J.T. Baker SAF-T-DATA(tm) Ratings
(Provided here for your convenience)

Health:	Flammability:	Reactivity:	Contact:
3 - Severe (Poison)	4 - Extreme (Flammable)	1 - Slight	1 - Slight
Lab Protection Equip:	GOGGLES & SHIELD; LAB COAT & APRON; VENT HOOD; PROPER GLOVES; CLASS B EXTINGUISHER		
Storage Color Code:	Red (Flammable)		

Potential Health Effects

Inhalation:
A slight irritant to the mucous membranes. Toxic effects exerted upon nervous system, particularly the optic nerve. Once absorbed into the body, it is very slowly eliminated. Symptoms of overexposure may include headache, drowsiness, nausea, vomiting, blurred vision, blindness, coma, and death. A person may get better but then worse again up to 30 hours later.

Ingestion:
Toxic. Symptoms parallel inhalation. Can intoxicate and cause blindness. Usual fatal dose: 100-125 milliliters.

Skin Contact:
Methyl alcohol is a defatting agent and may cause skin to become dry and cracked. Skin absorption can occur; symptoms may parallel inhalation exposure.

Eye Contact:
Irritant. Continued exposure may cause eye lesions.

© Cengage Learning 2013

Chronic Exposure:

Marked impairment of vision and enlargement of the liver has been reported. Repeated or prolonged exposure may cause skin irritation.

Aggravation of Pre-existing Conditions:

Persons with pre-existing skin disorders or eye problems or impaired liver or kidney function may be more susceptible to the effects of the substance.

4. First Aid Measures

Inhalation:

Remove to fresh air. If not breathing, give artificial respiration. If breathing is difficult, give oxygen. Call a physician.

Ingestion:

Induce vomiting immediately as directed by medical personnel. Never give anything by mouth to an unconscious person.

Skin Contact:

Remove any contaminated clothing. Wash skin with soap or mild detergent and water for at least 15 minutes. Get medical attention if irritation develops or persists.

Eye Contact:

Immediately flush eyes with plenty of water for at least 15 minutes, lifting lower and upper eyelids occasionally. Get medical attention immediately.

5. Fire Fighting Measures

Fire:

Flash point: 12°C (54°F) CC
Autoignition temperature: 464°C (867°F)
Flammable limits in air % by volume:
lel: 7.3; uel: 36
Flammable.

Explosion:

Above flash point, vapor-air mixtures are explosive within flammable limits noted above. Moderate explosion hazard and dangerous fire hazard when exposed to heat, sparks or flames. Sensitive to static discharge.

Fire Extinguishing Media:

Water spray, dry chemical, alcohol foam, or carbon dioxide.

Special Information:

In the event of a fire, wear full protective clothing and NIOSH-approved self-contained breathing apparatus with full facepiece operated in the pressure demand or other positive pressure mode. Use water spray to blanket fire, cool fire exposed containers, and to flush non-ignited spills or vapors away from fire. Vapors can flow along surfaces to distant ignition source and flash back.

6. Accidental Release Measures

Ventilate area of leak or spill. Remove all sources of ignition. Wear appropriate personal protective equipment as specified in Section 8. Isolate hazard area. Keep unnecessary and unprotected personnel from entering. Contain and recover liquid when possible. Use non-sparking tools and equipment. Collect liquid in an appropriate container or absorb with an inert material (e. g., vermiculite, dry sand, earth), and place in a chemical waste container. Do not use combustible materials, such as saw dust. Do not flush to sewer! J. T. Baker SOLUSORB® solvent adsorbent is recommended for spills of this product.

7. Handling and Storage

Protect against physical damage. Store in a cool, dry well-ventilated location, away from any area where the fire hazard may be acute. Outside or detached storage is preferred. Separate from incompatibles. Containers should be bonded and grounded for transfers to avoid static sparks. Storage and use areas should be No Smoking areas. Use non-sparking type tools and equipment, including explosion proof ventilation. Containers of this material may be hazardous when empty since they retain product residues (vapors, liquid); observe all warnings and precautions listed for the product.

8. Exposure Controls/Personal Protection

Airborne Exposure Limits:

For Methyl Alcohol:
- OSHA Permissible Exposure Limit (PEL):
    200 ppm (TWA)
- ACGIH Threshold Limit Value (TLV):
    200 ppm (TWA), 250 ppm (STEL) skin

Ventilation System:

A system of local and/or general exhaust is recommended to keep employee exposures below the Airborne Exposure Limits. Local exhaust ventilation is generally preferred because it can control the emissions of the contaminant at its source, preventing dispersion of it into the general work area. Please refer to the ACGIH document, "Industrial Ventilation, A Manual of Recommended Practices", most recent edition, for details.

Personal Respirator (NIOSH Approved)
If the exposure limit is exceeded, wear a supplied air, full-facepiece respirator, airlined hood, or full-facepiece self-contained breathing apparatus.
Skin Protection:
Rubber or neoprene gloves and additional protection including impervious boots, apron, or coveralls, as needed in areas of unusual exposure.
Eye Protection:
Use chemical safety goggles. Maintain eye wash fountain and quick-drench facilities in work area.

9. Physical and Chemical Properties

Appearance:
Clear, colorless liquid.
Odor:
Characteristic odor.
Solubility:
Miscible in water.
Specific Gravity:
0.8
pH:
No information found.
% Volatiles by volume @ 21°C (70°F):
100

Boiling Point:
64.5°C (147°F)
Melting Point:
-98°C (-144°F)
Vapor Density (Air=1):
1.1
Vapor Pressure (mm Hg):
97 @ 20°C (68°F)
Evaporation Rate (BuAc=1):
5.9

10. Stability and Reactivity

Stability:
Stable under ordinary conditions of use and storage.
Hazardous Decomposition Products:
May form carbon dioxide, carbon monoxide, and formaldehyde when heated to decomposition.
Hazardous Polymerization:
Will not occur.
Incompatabilities:
Strong oxidizing agents such as nitrates, perchlorates or sulfuric acid. Will attack some forms of plastics, rubber, and coatings. May react with metallic aluminum and generate hydrogen gas.
Conditions to Avoid:
Heat, flames, ignition sources and incompatibles.

11. Toxicological Information

Methyl Alcohol (Methanol) Oral rat LD50: 5628 mg/kg; inhalation rat LC50: 64000 ppm/4H; skin rabbit LD50: 15800 mg/kg; Irritation data-standard Draize test: skin, rabbit: 20mg/24 hr. Moderate; eye, rabbit: 100 mg/24 hr. Moderate; Investigated as a mutagen, reproductive effector.

Cancer Lists

Ingredient	—NTP Carcinogen—		IARC Category
	Known	Anticipated	
Methyl Alcohol (67-56-1)	No	No	None

12. Ecological Information

Environmental Fate:
When released into the soil, this material is expected to readily biodegrade. When released into the soil, this material is expected to leach into groundwater. When released into the soil, this material is expected to quickly evaporate. When released into the water, this material is expected to have a half-life between 1 and 10 days. When released into water, this material is expected to readily biodegrade. When released into the air, this material is expected to exist in the aerosol phase with a short half-life. When released into the air, this material is expected to be readily degraded by reaction with photochemically produced hydroxyl radicals. When released into air, this material is expected to have a half-life between 10 and 30 days. When released into the air, this material is expected to be readily removed from the atmosphere by wet deposition.
Environmental Toxicity:
This material is expected to be slightly toxic to aquatic life.

13. Disposal Considerations

Whatever cannot be saved for recovery or recycling should be handled as hazardous waste and sent to a RCRA approved incinerator or disposed in a RCRA approved waste facility. Processing, use or contamination of this product may change the waste management options. State and local disposal regulations may differ from federal disposal regulations.

Dispose of container and unused contents in accordance with federal, state and local requirements.

14. Transport Information

Domestic (Land, D.O.T.)
    Proper Shipping Name: METHANOL
    Hazard Class: 3
    UN/NA: UN1230   **Packing Group:** II
    Information reported for product/size: 350LB
International (Water, I.M.O.)
    Proper Shipping Name: METHANOL
    Hazard Class: 3.2, 6.1
    UN/NA: UN1230   **Packing Group:** II
    Information reported for product/size: 350LB

15. Regulatory Information

Chemical Inventory Status

Ingredient	TSCA	EC	Japan	Australia	Korea	Canada DSL	Canada NDSL	Phil.
Methyl Alcohol (67-56-1)	Yes	Yes	Yes	Yes	Yes	Yes	No	Yes

Federal, State & International Regulations

Ingredient	SARA 302 RQ	SARA 302 TPQ	SARA 313 List	SARA 313 Chemical Catg.	CERCLA	-RCRA- 261.33	-TSCA- 8(d)
Methyl Alcohol (67-56-1)	No	No	Yes	No	5000	U154	No

Chemical Weapons Convention: No   **TSCA 12(b):** No   **CDTA:** No

SARA 311/312: Acute: Yes Chronic: Yes Fire: Yes Pressure: No Reactivity: No   (Pure / Liquid)

Australian Hazchem Code: 2PE   **Australian Poison Schedule:** S6

WHMIS: This MSDS has been prepared according to the hazard criteria of the Controlled Products Regulations (CPR) and the MSDS contains all of the information required by the CPR.

16. Other Information

NFPA Ratings:

Health: 1 Flammability: 3 Reactivity: 0

Label Hazard Warning:

POISON! DANGER! VAPOR HARMFUL. MAY BE FATAL OR CAUSE BLINDNESS IF SWALLOWED. HARMFUL IF INHALED OR ABSORBED THROUGH SKIN. CANNOT BE MADE NONPOISONOUS. FLAMMABLE LIQUID AND VAPOR. CAUSES IRRITATION TO SKIN, EYES AND RESPIRATORY TRACT. AFFECTS THE LIVER.

Label Precautions:

Keep away from heat, sparks and flame.
Keep container closed.
Use only with adequate ventilation.
Wash thoroughly after handling.
Avoid breathing vapor.
Avoid contact with eyes, skin and clothing.

Label First Aid:

If swallowed, induce vomiting immediately as directed by medical personnel. Never give anything by mouth to an unconscious person. In case of contact, immediately flush eyes or skin with plenty of water for at least 15 minutes while removing contaminated clothing and shoes. Wash clothing before reuse. If inhaled, remove to fresh air. If not breathing give artificial respiration. If breathing is difficult, give oxygen. In all cases get medical attention immediately.

Product Use:

Laboratory Reagent.

Revision Information:

New 16 section MSDS format, all sections have been revised.

Disclaimer:

Mallinckrodt Baker, Inc. provides the information contained herein in good faith but makes no representation as to its comprehensiveness or accuracy. This document is intended only as a guide to the appropriate precautionary handling of the material by a properly trained person using this product. Individuals receiving the information must exercise their independent judgment in determining its appropriateness for a particular purpose. MALLINCKRODT BAKER, INC. MAKES NO REPRESENTATIONS OR WARRANTIES, EITHER EXPRESS OR IMPLIED, INCLUDING WITHOUT LIMITATION ANY WARRANTIES OR MERCHANTABILITY, FITNESS FOR A PARTICULAR PURPOSE WITH RESPECT TO THE INFORMATION SET FORTH HEREIN OR THE PRODUCT TO WHICH THE INFORMATION REFERS. ACCORDINGLY, MALLINCKRODT BAKER, INC. WILL NOT BE RESPONSIBLE FOR DAMAGES RESULTING FROM USE OF OR RELIANCE UPON THIS INFORMATION.

Prepared By: Strategic Services Division
    Phone Number: (314) 539-1600 (U.S.A.)

Only the information that might be of interest to you is described in the paragraphs that follow.

Section 1. The first part of Section 1 identifies the substance by name, formula, and various numbers and codes. Most organic compounds have more than one name. In this case, the systematic (or International Union of Pure and Applied Chemistry [IUPAC]) name is methanol, and the other names are common names or are from an older system of nomenclature. The Chemical Abstract Service Number (CAS No.) is often used to identify a substance, and it may be used to access extensive information about a substance found in many computer databases or in the library.

Section 3. The Baker SAF-T-DATA System is found on all MSDSs and bottle labels for chemicals supplied by J. T. Baker, Inc. For each category listed, the number indicates the degree of hazard. The lowest number is 0 (very low hazard), and the highest number is 4 (extreme hazard). The Health category refers to damage involved when the substance is inhaled, ingested, or absorbed. Flammability indicates the tendency of a substance to burn. Reactivity refers to how reactive a substance is with air, water, or other substances. The last category, Contact, refers to how hazardous a substance is when it comes in contact with external parts of the body. Note that this rating scale is applicable only to Baker MSDSs and labels; other rating scales with different meanings are also in common use.

Section 4. This section provides helpful information for emergency and first aid procedures.

Section 6. This part of the MSDS deals with procedures for handling spills and disposal. The information could be very helpful, particularly if a large amount of the chemical was spilled. More information about disposal is also given in Section 13.

Section 8. Much valuable information is found in Section 8. To help you understand this material, some of the more important terms used in this section are defined:

> *Threshold Limit Value (TLV).* The American Conference of Governmental Industrial Hygienists (ACGIH) developed the TLV: This is the maximum concentration of a substance in air that a person should be exposed to on a regular basis. It is usually expressed in ppm or mg/m³. Note that this value assumes that a person is exposed to the substance 40 hours per week, on a long-term basis. This value may not be particularly applicable in the case of a student performing an experiment in a single laboratory period.

> *Permissible Exposure Limit (PEL).* This has the same meaning as TLV; however, PELs were developed by OSHA. Note that for methanol, the TLV and PEL are both 200 ppm.

Section 10. The information contained in Section 10 refers to the stability of the compound and the hazards associated with mixing of chemicals. It is important to consider this information before carrying out an experiment not previously done.

Section 11. More information about the toxicity is given in this section. Another important term must first be defined:

> *Lethal Dose, 50% Mortality (LD$_{50}$).* This is the dose of a substance that will kill 50% of the animals administered a single dose. Different means of administration are used, such as oral, intraperitoneal (injected into the lining of the abdominal cavity), subcutaneous (injected under the skin), and application to the surface of the skin. The LD$_{50}$ is usually expressed in milligrams (mg) of substance per kilogram (kg) of animal weight. The lower the value of LD$_{50}$, the more toxic the substance. It is assumed that the toxicity in humans will be similar.

Unless you have considerably more knowledge about chemical toxicity, the information in Sections 8 and 11 is most useful for comparing the toxicity of one substance with another. For example, the TLV for methanol is 200 ppm, whereas the TLV for benzene is 10 ppm. Clearly, performing an experiment involving benzene would require much more stringent precautions than an experiment involving methanol. One of the LD_{50} values for methanol is 5628 mg/kg. The comparable LD_{50} value of aniline is 250 mg/kg. Clearly, aniline is much more toxic, and because it is easily absorbed through the skin, it presents a significant hazard. It should also be mentioned that both TLV and PEL ratings assume that the worker comes in contact with a substance on a repeated and long-term basis. Thus, even if a chemical has a relatively low TLV or PEL, it does not mean that using it for one experiment will present a danger to you. Furthermore, by performing experiments using small amounts of chemicals and with proper safety precautions, your exposure to organic chemicals in this course will be minimal.

Section 16. Section 16 contains the National Fire Protection Association (NFPA) rating. This is similar to the Baker SAF-T-DATA (discussed in Section 3), except that the number represents the hazards when a fire is present. The order here is Health, Flammability, and Reactivity. Often, this is presented in graphic form on a label (see figure). The small diamonds are often color coded: blue for Health, red for Flammability, and yellow for Reactivity. The bottom diamond (white) is sometimes used to display graphic symbols denoting unusual reactivity, hazards, or special precautions to be taken.

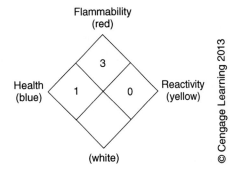

B. Bottle Labels

Reading the label on a bottle can be a helpful way of learning about the hazards of a chemical. The amount of information varies greatly, depending on which company supplied the chemical.

Apply some common sense when you read MSDSs and bottle labels. Using these chemicals does not mean you will experience the consequences that can potentially result from exposure to each chemical. For example, an MSDS for sodium chloride states, "Exposure to this product may have serious adverse health effects." Despite the apparent severity of this cautionary statement, it would not be reasonable to expect people to stop using sodium chloride in a chemistry experiment or to stop sprinkling a small amount of it (as table salt) on eggs to enhance their flavor. In many cases, the consequences described in MSDSs from exposure to chemicals are somewhat overstated, particularly for students using these chemicals to perform a laboratory experiment.

1.3 Common Solvents Most organic chemistry experiments involve an organic solvent at some step in the procedure. A list of common organic solvents follows, with a discussion of toxicity, possible carcinogenic properties, and precautions that you should use when handling these solvents. A tabulation of the compounds currently suspected of being carcinogens appears at the end of Technique 1.

Acetic Acid. Glacial acetic acid is corrosive enough to cause serious acid burns on the skin. Its vapors can irritate the eyes and nasal passages. Care should be exercised not to breathe the vapors and not to allow them to escape into the laboratory.

Acetone. Relative to other organic solvents, acetone is not very toxic. It is flammable, however. Do not use acetone near open flames.

Benzene. Benzene can damage bone marrow; it causes various blood disorders, and its effects may lead to leukemia. Benzene is considered a serious carcinogenic hazard. It is absorbed rapidly through the skin and also poisons the liver and kidneys. In addition, benzene is flammable. Because of its toxicity and its carcinogenic properties, benzene should not be used in the laboratory; you should use some less dangerous solvent instead. Toluene is considered a safer alternative solvent in procedures that specify benzene.

Carbon Tetrachloride. Carbon tetrachloride can cause serious liver and kidney damage, as well as skin irritation and other problems. It is absorbed rapidly through the skin. In high concentrations, it can cause death as a result of respiratory failure. Moreover, carbon tetrachloride is suspected of being a carcinogenic material. Although this solvent has the advantage of being nonflammable (in the past, it was used on occasion as a fire extinguisher), it causes health problems, so it should not be used routinely in the laboratory. If no reasonable substitute exists, however, it must be used in small quantities, as in preparing samples for infrared (IR) and nuclear magnetic resonance (NMR) spectroscopy. In such cases, you must use it in a hood.

Chloroform. Chloroform is similar to carbon tetrachloride in its toxicity. It has been used as an anesthetic. However, chloroform is currently on the list of suspected carcinogens. Because of this, do not use chloroform routinely as a solvent in the laboratory. If it is occasionally necessary to use chloroform as a solvent for special samples, then you must use it in a hood. Methylene chloride is usually found to be a safer substitute in procedures that specify chloroform as a solvent. Deuterochloroform, $CDCl_3$, is a common solvent for NMR spectroscopy. Caution dictates that you should treat it with the same respect as chloroform.

1,2-Dimethoxyethane (Ethylene Glycol Dimethyl Ether or Monoglyme). Because it is miscible with water, 1,2-dimethoxyethane is a useful alternative to solvents such as dioxane and tetrahydrofuran, which may be more hazardous. 1,2-Dimethoxyethane is flammable and should not be handled near an open flame. On long exposure of 1,2-dimethoxyethane to light and oxygen, explosive peroxides may form. 1,2-Dimethoxyethane is a possible reproductive toxin.

Dioxane. Dioxane has been used widely because it is a convenient, water miscible solvent. It is now suspected, however, of being carcinogenic. It is also toxic, affecting the central nervous system, liver, kidneys, skin, lungs, and mucous membranes. Dioxane is also flammable and tends to form explosive peroxides when it is exposed to light and air. Because of its carcinogenic properties, it is no longer used in the laboratory unless absolutely necessary. Either 1,2-dimethoxyethane or tetrahydrofuran is a suitable, water-miscible alternative solvent.

Ethanol. Ethanol has well-known properties as an intoxicant. In the laboratory, the principal danger arises from fires because ethanol is a flammable solvent. When using ethanol, take care to work where there are no open flames.

Ether (Diethyl Ether). The principal hazard associated with diethyl ether is fire or explosion. Ether is probably the most flammable solvent found in the laboratory. Because ether vapors are much denser than air, they may travel along a laboratory bench for a considerable distance from their source before being ignited. Before using ether, it is important to be sure that no one is working with matches or any open flame. Ether is not a particularly toxic solvent, although in high enough concentrations it can cause drowsiness and perhaps nausea. It has been used as a general anesthetic. Ether can form highly explosive peroxides when exposed to air. Consequently, you should never distill it to dryness.

Hexane. Hexane may be irritating to the respiratory tract. It can also act as an intoxicant and a depressant of the central nervous system. It can cause skin irritation because it is an excellent solvent for skin oils. The most serious hazard, however, comes from its flammability. The precautions recommended for using diethyl ether in the presence of open flames apply equally to hexane.

Ligroin. See Hexane.

Methanol. Much of the material outlining the hazards of ethanol applies to methanol. Methanol is more toxic than ethanol; ingestion can cause blindness and even death. Because methanol is more volatile, the danger of fires is more acute.

Methylene Chloride (Dichloromethane). Methylene chloride is not flammable. Unlike other members of the class of chlorocarbons, it is not currently considered a serious carcinogenic hazard. Recently, however, it has been the subject of much serious investigation, and there have been proposals to regulate it in industrial situations in which workers have high levels of exposure on a day-to-day basis. Methylene chloride is less toxic than chloroform and carbon tetrachloride. It can cause liver damage when ingested, however, and its vapors may cause drowsiness or nausea.

Pentane. See Hexane.

Petroleum Ether. See Hexane.

Pyridine. Some fire hazard is associated with pyridine. However, the most serious hazard arises from its toxicity. Pyridine may depress the central nervous system; irritate the skin and respiratory tract; damage the liver, kidneys, and gastrointestinal system; and even cause temporary sterility. You should treat pyridine as a highly toxic solvent and handle it only in the fume hood.

Tetrahydrofuran. Tetrahydrofuran may cause irritation of the skin, eyes, and respiratory tract. It should never be distilled to dryness because it tends to form potentially explosive peroxides on exposure to air. Tetrahydrofuran does present a fire hazard.

Toluene. Unlike benzene, toluene is not considered a carcinogen. However, it is at least as toxic as benzene. It can act as an anesthetic and damage the central nervous system. If benzene is present as an impurity in toluene, expect the usual hazards associated with benzene. Toluene is also a flammable solvent, and the usual precautions about working near open flames should be applied.

You should not use certain solvents in the laboratory because of their carcinogenic properties. Benzene, carbon tetrachloride, chloroform, and dioxane are among these solvents. For certain applications, however, notably as solvents for infrared or NMR spectroscopy, there may be no suitable alternative. When it is necessary to use one of these solvents, use safety precautions and refer to the discussions in Techniques 25–28.

Because relatively large amounts of solvents may be used in a large organic laboratory class, your laboratory supervisor must take care to store these substances safely. Only the amount of solvent needed for a particular experiment should be kept in the laboratory. The preferred location for bottles of solvents being used during a class period is in a hood. When the solvents are not being used, they should be stored in a fireproof storage cabinet for solvents. If possible, this cabinet should be ventilated into the fume hood system.

1.4 Carcinogenic Substances

A **carcinogen** is a substance that causes cancer in living tissue. The usual procedure for determining whether a substance is carcinogenic is to expose laboratory animals to high dosages over a long period. It is not clear whether short-term exposure to these chemicals carries a comparable risk, but it is prudent to use these substances with special precautions.

Many regulatory agencies have compiled lists of carcinogenic substances or substances suspected of being carcinogenic. Because these lists are inconsistent, compiling a definitive list of carcinogenic substances is difficult. The following common substances are included in many of these lists.

Acetamide	4-Methyl-2-oxetanone (β-butyrolactone)
Acrylonitrile	1-Naphthylamine
Asbestos	2-Naphthylamine
Benzene	*N*-Nitroso compounds
Benzidine	2-Oxetanone (β-propiolactone)
Carbon tetrachloride	Phenacetin
Chloroform	Phenylhydrazine and its salts
Chromic oxide	Polychlorinated biphenyl (PCB)
Coumarin	Progesterone
Diazomethane	Styrene oxide
1,2-Dibromoethane	Tannins
Dimethyl sulfate	Testosterone
p-Dioxane	Thioacetamide
Ethylene oxide	Thiourea
Formaldehyde	*o*-Toluidine
Hydrazine and its salts	Trichloroethylene
Lead (II) acetate	Vinyl chloride

REFERENCES

Aldrich Catalog and Handbook of Fine Chemicals. Aldrich Chemical Co.: Milwaukee, WI, current edition.

Armour, M. A. *Pollution Prevention and Waste Minimization in Laboratories.* Reinhardt, P. A., Leonard, K. L., Ashbrook, P. C., eds.; Lewis Publishers: Boca Raton, FL, 1996.

Fire Protection Guide on Hazardous Materials. 10th ed. National Fire Protection Association: Quincy, MA, 1991.

Flinn Chemical Catalog Reference Manual. Current ed. Flinn Scientific: Batavia, IL.

Gosselin, R. E., Smith, R. P., and Hodge, H. C. *Clinical Toxicology of Commercial Products.* 5th ed. Williams & Wilkins: Baltimore, MD, 1984.

Lenga, R. E., ed. *The Sigma-Aldrich Library of Chemical Safety Data.* Sigma-Aldrich: Milwaukee, WI, 1985.

Lewis, R. J. *Carcinogenically Active Chemicals: A Reference Guide.* Van Nostrand Reinhold: New York, 1990.

Lewis, R. J. *Sax's Dangerous Properties of Industrial Materials.* 11th edition. Van Nostrand Reinhold: New York, 2007.

The Merck Index. 14th ed. Merck and Co.: Rahway, NJ, 2006.

Prudent Practices in the Laboratory: Handling and Disposal of Chemicals. Committee on Prudent Practices for Handling, Storage, and Disposal of Chemicals in Laboratories; Board on Chemical Sciences and Technology; Commission on Physical Sciences, Mathematics, and Applications; National Research Council, National Academy Press: Washington, DC, 1995.

Renfrew, M. M., ed. *Safety in the Chemical Laboratory.* Division of Chemical Education, American Chemical Society: Easton, PA, 1967–1991.

Safety in Academic Chemistry Laboratories, 4th ed. Committee on Chemical Safety, American Chemical Society: Washington, DC, 1985.

Sax, N. I., and Lewis, R. J., eds. *Rapid Guide to Hazardous Chemicals in the Work Place,* 4th ed. New York: Van Nostrand Reinhold, 2000.

Useful Safety-Related Internet Addresses

Interactive Learning Paradigms, Inc.:
http://www.ilpi.com/msds/(accessed April 19, 2011). This is an excellent general site for MSDS sheets. The site lists chemical manufacturers and suppliers. Selecting a company will take you directly to the appropriate place to obtain an MSDS sheet. Many of the sites listed require you to register in order to obtain an MSDS sheet for a particular chemical. Ask your departmental or college safety supervisor to obtain the information for you.

Acros chemicals and Fisher Scientific:
http://www.fishersci.com/ecomm/servlet/home (accessed April 19, 2001).

Alfa Aesar:
http://www.alfa.com/alf/index.htm (accessed April 19, 2011).

Cornell University, Department of Environmental Health and Safety:
http://www.chs.cornell.edu/msds/msds.cfm (accessed April 19, 2011). This is an excellent searchable database of more than 325,000 MSDS files. No registration is required.

Eastman Kodak:
http://msds.kodak.com/ehswww/external/index.jsp (accessed April 19, 2011).
EMD Chemicals (formerly EM Science) and Merck: http://www.emdchemicals.com/corporate/emd_corporate.asp (accessed April 19, 2011).

J. T. Baker and Mallinckrodt Laboratory Chemicals:
http://www.avantormaterials.com/search.aspx?searchtype=msds (accessed April 21, 2011).

National Institute for Occupational Safety and Health (NIOSH) has an excellent Web site that includes databases and information resources, including links:
http://www.cdc.gov/niosh/topics/chemical-safety/default.html (accessed April 19, 2011).

Sigma, Aldrich and Fluka:
http://www.sigmaaldrich.com/Area_of_Interest/The_Americas/United_States.html (accessed April 19, 2011).

VWR Scientific Products:
http://www.vwrsp.com/search/index.cgi?tmpl=msds (accessed April 19, 2011).

The Laboratory Notebook, Calculations, and Laboratory Records

It is important that you do some advance preparation for all laboratory work. Presented here are some suggestions about what specific information you should try to obtain in your advance studying. Because much of this information must be obtained while preparing your laboratory notebook, the two subjects, advance study and notebook preparation, are developed simultaneously.

An important part of any laboratory experience is learning to maintain complete records of every experiment undertaken and every item of data obtained. Far too often, careless recording of data and observations has resulted in mistakes, frustration, and lost time due to needless repetition of experiments. If reports are required, you will find that proper collection and recording of data can make your report writing much easier.

Because organic reactions are seldom quantitative, special problems result. Frequently, reagents must be used in large excess to increase the amount of product. Some reagents are expensive, and, therefore, care must be used in measuring the amounts of these substances. Often, many more reactions take place than you desire. These extra reactions, or **side reactions,** may form products other than the desired product. These are called **side products.** For all these reasons, you must plan your experimental procedure carefully before undertaking the actual experiment.

2.1 The Notebook

For recording data and observations during experiments, use a *bound notebook.* The notebook should have consecutively numbered pages. If it does not, number the pages immediately. A spiral-bound notebook or any other notebook from which the pages can be removed easily is not acceptable, because the possibility of losing the pages is great.

All data and observations must be recorded in the notebook. Paper towels, napkins, toilet tissue, or scratch paper tend to become lost or destroyed. It is bad laboratory practice to record information on such random and perishable pieces of paper. All entries must be recorded in *permanent ink.* It can be frustrating to have important information disappear from the notebook because it was recorded in washable ink or pencil and could not survive a flood caused by the student at the next position on the bench. Because you will be using your notebook in the laboratory, the book will probably become soiled or stained by chemicals, filled with scratched-out entries, or even slightly burned. That is expected and is a normal part of laboratory work.

Your instructor may check your notebook at any time, so you should always have it up to date. If your instructor requires reports, you can prepare them quickly from the material recorded in the laboratory notebook.

2.2 Notebook Format   A. Advance Preparation

Individual instructors vary greatly in the type of notebook format they prefer; such variation stems from differences in philosophies and experience. You must obtain specific directions from your own instructor for preparing a notebook. Certain features, however, are common to most notebook formats. The following discussion indicates what might be included in a typical notebook.

It will be helpful and you can save much time in the laboratory if for each experiment you know the main reactions, the potential side reactions, the mechanism, and the stoichiometry and you understand fully the procedure and the theory underlying it before you come to the laboratory. Understanding the procedure by which the desired product is to be separated from undesired materials is also important. If you examine each of these topics before coming to class, you will be prepared to do the experiment efficiently. You will have your equipment and reagents already prepared when they are to be used. Your reference material will be at hand when you need it. Finally, with your time efficiently organized, you will be able to take advantage of long reaction or reflux periods to perform other tasks, such as doing shorter experiments or finishing previous ones.

For experiments in which a compound is synthesized from other reagents, that is, **preparative experiments,** it is essential to know the main reaction. To perform stoichiometric calculations, you should balance the equation for the main reaction. Therefore, before you begin the experiment, your notebook should contain the balanced equation for the pertinent reaction. Using the preparation of isopentyl acetate, or banana oil, as an example, you should write the following:

Also enter in the notebook the possible side reactions that divert reagents into contaminants (side products), before beginning the experiment. You will have to separate these side products from the major product during purification.

You should list physical constants such as melting points, boiling points, densities, and molecular weights in the notebook when this information is needed to perform an experiment or to do calculations. These data are located in sources such as the *CRC Handbook of Chemistry and Physics, The Merck Index, Lange's Handbook of Chemistry,* or *Aldrich Handbook of Fine Chemicals.* Write physical constants required for an experiment in your notebook before you come to class.

Advance preparation may also include examining some subjects, including information not necessarily recorded in the notebook, that should prove useful in understanding the experiment. Included among these subjects are an understanding of the mechanism of the reaction, an examination of other methods by which the same compound might be prepared, and a detailed study of the experimental procedure. Many students find that an outline of the procedure, prepared *before* they come to class, helps them use their time more efficiently once they begin the experiment. Such an outline could well be prepared on some loose sheet of paper rather than in the notebook itself.

Once the reaction has been completed, the desired product does not magically appear as purified material; it must be isolated from a frequently complex mixture of side products, unreacted starting materials, solvents, and catalysts. You should try to outline a **separation scheme** in your notebook for isolating the product from its contaminants. At each stage, you should try to understand the reason for the particular instruction given in the experimental procedure. This not only will familiarize you with the basic separation and purification techniques used in organic chemistry but also will help you understand when to use these techniques. Such an outline might take the form of a flowchart. For example, see the separation scheme for isopentyl acetate (Figure 2.1). Careful attention to understanding the separation, besides familiarizing you with the procedure by which the desired product is separated from impurities in your particular experiments, may prepare you for original research in which no experimental procedure exists.

In designing a separation scheme, note that the scheme outlines those steps undertaken once the reaction period has been concluded. For this reason, the represented scheme does not include steps such as the addition of the reactants (isopentyl alcohol and acetic acid) and the catalyst (sulfuric acid) or the heating of the reaction mixture. See Technique 12, Section 12.12, for a more thorough discussion about how to outline a separation scheme using a flowchart.

Figure 2.1
Separation scheme for isopentyl acetate.

© Cengage Learning 2013

For experiments in which a compound is isolated from a particular source and is not prepared from other reagents, some information described in this section will not be applicable. Such experiments are called **isolation experiments.** A typical isolation experiment involves isolating a pure compound from a natural source. Examples include isolating caffeine from tea or isolating cinnamaldehyde from cinnamon. Although isolation experiments require somewhat different advance preparation, this advance study may include looking up physical constants for the compound isolated and outlining the isolation procedure. A detailed examination of the separation scheme is important here because it is the heart of such an experiment.

B. Laboratory Records

When you begin the actual experiment, keep your notebook nearby so you will be able to record those operations you perform. When you are working in the laboratory, the notebook serves as a place in which to record a rough transcript of your experimental method. Data from actual weighings, volume measurements, and determinations of physical constants are also noted. This section of your notebook should *not* be prepared in advance. The purpose is not to write a recipe but rather to record what you *did* and what you *observed.* These observations will help you write reports without resorting to memory. They will also help you or other workers repeat the experiment in as nearly as possible the same way. The sample notebook pages found in Figures 2.2 and 2.3 illustrate the type of data and observations that should be written in your notebook.

When your product has been prepared and purified, or isolated if it is an isolation experiment, record pertinent data such as the melting point or boiling point of the substance, its density, its index of refraction, and the conditions under which spectra were determined.

C. Calculations

A chemical equation for the overall conversion of the starting materials to products is written on the assumption of simple ideal stoichiometry. Actually, this assumption is seldom realized. Side reactions or competing reactions will also occur, giving other products. For some synthetic reactions, an equilibrium state will be reached in which an appreciable amount of starting material is still present and can be recovered. Some of the reactant may also remain if it is present in excess or if the reaction was incomplete. A reaction involving an expensive reagent illustrates another reason for needing to know how far a particular type of reaction converts reactants to products. In such a case, it is preferable to use the most efficient method for this conversion. Thus, information about the efficiency of conversion for various reactions is of interest to the person contemplating the use of these reactions.

The quantitative expression for the efficiency of a reaction is found by calculating the **yield** for the reaction. The **theoretical yield** is the number of grams of the product expected from the reaction on the basis of ideal stoichiometry, with side reactions, reversibility, and losses ignored. To calculate the theoretical yield, it is first necessary to determine the **limiting reagent.** The limiting reagent is the reagent that is not present in excess and on which the overall yield of product depends. The method for determining the limiting reagent in the isopentyl acetate experiment is illustrated in the sample notebook pages shown in Figures 2.2 and 2.3. You should consult your general chemistry textbook for more complicated examples. The theoretical yield is then calculated from the expression

Theoretical yield = (moles of limiting reagent)(ratio)(molecular weight of product)

The ratio here is the stoichiometric ratio of product to limiting reagent. In preparing isopentyl acetate, that ratio is 1:1. One mole of isopentyl alcohol, under ideal circumstances, should yield 1 mole of isopentyl acetate.

Figure 2.2

A sample notebook, page 1.

THE BOILING STONE WAS REMOVED AND THE REACTION MIXTURE WAS EXTRACTED THREE TIMES WITH 1.0mL OF 5% $NaHCO_3$. THE BOTTOM AQUEOUS LAYER WAS REMOVED AND DISCARDED AFTER EACH EXTRACTION. DURING THE FIRST TWO EXTRACTIONS, MUCH CO_2 GAS WAS GIVEN OFF. THE ORGANIC LAYER WAS A LIGHT YELLOW COLOR. IT WAS TRANSFERRED TO A DRY CONICAL VIAL, AND 2 FULL MICROSPATULAS OF ANHYDROUS Na_2SO_4 WERE ADDED TO DRY THE CRUDE PRODUCT. IT WAS ALLOWED TO SET WITH OCCASIONAL STIRRING FOR 10 MINS.

THE DRY PRODUCT WAS TRANSFERRED TO A 3-mL CONICAL VIAL, AND A BOILING STONE WAS ADDED. A DISTILLATION APPARATUS USING A HICKMAN STILL, A WATER-COOLED CONDENSER, AND A DRYING TUBE PACKED WITH $CaCl_2$ WAS ASSEMBLED. THE SAMPLE WAS HEATED IN AN ALUMINUM BLOCK AT ABOUT 180°C. THE LIQUID BEGAN BOILING AFTER ABOUT FIVE MINS, BUT NO DISTILLATE APPEARED IN THE HICKMAN STILL UNTIL ABOUT 20 MINS. LATER. ONCE THE PRODUCT BEGAN COLLECTING IN THE HICKMAN STILL, THE DISTILLATION REQUIRED ONLY ABOUT TWO MINS. TO COMPLETE. ABOUT 1-2 DROPS REMAINED IN THE DISTILLING VIAL. THE ISOPENTYL ACETATE WAS TRANSFERRED TO A PREWEIGHED 3-mL CONICAL VIAL.

$$
\begin{array}{rl}
\text{VIAL + PRODUCT} & 20.428g \\
\text{VIAL} & \underline{20.074g} \\
& 0.354g \quad \text{ISOPENTYL ACETATE}
\end{array}
$$

THE PRODUCT WAS COLORLESS AND CLEAR. BP (MICRO TECHNIQUE): 140°C. THE IR SPECTRUM WAS OBTAINED.

CALCULATIONS

DETERMINE LIMITING REAGENT:

ISOPENTYL ALCOHOL $0.569g \left(\dfrac{1 \text{ MOL ISOPENTYL ALCOHOL}}{88.2g} \right) = 6.45 \times 10^{-3}$ MOL

ACETIC ACID $1.40 \, mL \left(\dfrac{1.06g}{mL} \right) \left(\dfrac{1 \text{ MOL ACETIC ACID}}{60.1g} \right) = 2.47 \times 10^{-2}$ MOL

SINCE THEY REACT IN A 1:1 RATIO, ISOPENTYL ALCOHOL IS THE LIMITING REAGENT.

THEORETICAL YIELD =

6.45×10^{-3} MOL ISOPENTYL ALCOHOL $\left(\dfrac{1 \text{ MOL ISOPENTYL ACETATE}}{1 \text{ MOL ISOPENTYL ALCOHOL}} \right) \left(\dfrac{1.30.2g \text{ ISOPENTYL ACETATE}}{1 \text{ MOL ISOPENTYL ACETATE}} \right)$

$= 0.840g$ ISOPENTYL ACETATE

PERCENTAGE YIELD $= \dfrac{0.354g}{0.840g} \times 100 = 42.1\%$

Figure 2.3
A sample notebook, page 2.

The **actual yield** is simply the number of grams of desired product obtained. The **percentage yield** describes the efficiency of the reaction and is determined by

$$\text{Percentage yield} = \frac{\text{Actual yield}}{\text{Theoretical yield}} \times 100$$

Calculation of the theoretical yield and percentage yield can be illustrated using hypothetical data for the isopentyl acetate preparation:

$$\text{Theoretical yield} = (6.45 \times 10^{-3} \text{ mol isopentyl alcohol}) \left(\frac{1 \text{ mol isopentyl acetate}}{1 \text{ mol isopentyl alcohol}} \right)$$

$$\times \left(\frac{130.2 \text{ g isopentyl acetate}}{1 \text{ mol isopentyl acetate}} \right) = 0.840 \text{ g isopentyl acetate}$$

Actual yield = 0.354 g isopentyl acetate

$$\text{Percentage yield} = \frac{0.354 \text{ g}}{0.840 \text{ g}} \times 100 = 42.1\%$$

For experiments that have the principal objective of isolating a substance such as a natural product rather than preparing and purifying some reaction product, the **weight percentage recovery** and not the percentage yield is calculated. This value is determined by

$$\text{Weight percentage recovery} = \frac{\text{Weight of substance isolated}}{\text{Weight of original material}} \times 100$$

Thus, for instance, if 0.014 g of caffeine was obtained from 2.3 g of tea, the weight percentage recovery of caffeine would be

$$\text{Weight percentage recovery} = \frac{0.014 \text{ g Caffeine}}{2.3 \text{ g Tea}} \times 100 = 0.61\%$$

2.3 Laboratory Reports

Various formats for reporting the results of the laboratory experiments may be used. You may write the report directly in your notebook in a format similar to the sample notebook pages included in this section. Alternatively, your instructor may require a more formal report that is not written in your notebook. When you do original research, these reports should include a detailed description of all the experimental steps undertaken. Frequently, the style used in scientific periodicals such as *Journal of the American Chemical Society* is applied to writing laboratory reports. Your instructor is likely to have his or her own requirements for laboratory reports and should describe the requirements to you.

2.4 Submission of Samples

In all preparative experiments and in some isolation experiments, you will be required to submit to your instructor the sample of the substance you prepared or isolated. How this sample is labeled is important. Again, learning a correct method of labeling bottles and vials can save time in the laboratory because fewer mistakes will be made. More important, learning to label properly can decrease the danger inherent in having samples of material that cannot be identified correctly at a later date.

Solid materials should be stored and submitted in containers that permit the substance to be removed easily. For this reason, narrow-mouthed bottles or vials are not used for solid substances. Liquids should be stored in containers that will not let them escape through leakage. Be careful not to store volatile liquids in containers that have plastic caps, unless the cap is lined with an inert material such as Teflon. Otherwise, the vapors from the liquid are likely to contact the plastic and dissolve some of it, thus contaminating the substance being stored.

On the label, print the name of the substance, its melting or boiling point, the actual and percentage yields, and your name. An illustration of a properly prepared label follows:

Isopentyl Acetate
BP 140°C
Yield 3.81 g (42.1%)
Joe Schmedlock

Laboratory Glassware:
Care and Cleaning

Because your glassware is expensive and you are responsible for it, you will want to give it proper care and respect. If you read this chapter carefully and follow the procedures presented here, you may be able to avoid some unnecessary expense. You may also save time because cleaning problems and replacing broken glassware are time-consuming.

If you are unfamiliar with the equipment found in an organic laboratory or are uncertain about how such equipment should be treated, this chapter provides some useful information. It includes topics such as cleaning glassware, caring for glassware when using corrosive or caustic reagents, and assembling components from your organic laboratory kit. At the end of this section are illustrations and names of most of the equipment you are likely to find in your drawer or locker.

3.1 Cleaning Glassware

Glassware can be cleaned easily if you clean it immediately. It is good practice to do your "dishwashing" right away. With time, organic tarry materials left in a container begin to attack the surface of the glass. The longer you wait to clean glassware, the more extensively this interaction will have progressed. Cleaning is then more difficult because water will no longer wet the surface of the glass as effectively. If you can't wash your glassware immediately after use, soak the dirty pieces in soapy water. A half-gallon plastic container is convenient for soaking and washing glassware. Using a plastic container also helps prevent the loss of small pieces of equipment used in microscale techniques.

Various soaps and detergents are available for washing glassware. They should be tried first when washing dirty glassware. Organic solvents can also be used because the residue remaining in dirty glassware is likely to be soluble in some organic solvent. After the solvent has been used, the conical vial or flask probably will have to be washed with soap and water to remove the residual solvent. When you use solvents in cleaning glassware, use caution, because the solvents are hazardous (see Technique 1). Use fairly small amounts of a solvent for cleaning purposes. Usually 1–2 mL will be sufficient. Acetone is commonly used, but it is expensive. Your **wash acetone** can be used effectively several times before it is "spent." Once your acetone is spent, dispose of it as your instructor directs. If acetone does not work, other organic solvents such as methylene chloride or toluene can be used.

CAUTION

Acetone is very flammable. Do not use it around flames.

For troublesome stains and residues that adhere to the glass despite your best efforts, use a mixture of sulfuric acid and nitric acid. Cautiously add about 20 drops of concentrated sulfuric acid and 5 drops of concentrated nitric acid to the flask or vial.

C A U T I O N

You must wear safety glasses when you are using a cleaning solution made from sulfuric acid and nitric acid. Do not allow the solution to come into contact with your skin or clothing. It will cause severe burns on your skin and create holes in your clothing. The acids may also react with the residue in the container.

Swirl the acid mixture in the container for a few minutes. If necessary, place the glassware in a warm-water bath and heat cautiously to accelerate the cleaning process. Continue heating until any sign of a reaction ceases. When the cleaning procedure is completed, decant the mixture into an appropriate waste container.

C A U T I O N

Do not pour the acid solution into a waste container that is intended for organic wastes.

Rinse the piece of glassware thoroughly with water and then wash with soap and water. For most common organic chemistry applications, any stains that survive this treatment are not likely to cause difficulty in subsequent laboratory procedures.

If the glassware is contaminated with stopcock grease (unlikely with the glassware recommended in this book), rinse the glassware with a small amount (1–2 mL) of methylene chloride. Discard the rinse solution into an appropriate waste container. Once the grease is removed, wash the glassware with soap or detergent and water.

3.2 Drying Glassware

The easiest way to dry glassware is to let it stand overnight. Store conical vials, flasks, and beakers upside down on a piece of paper towel to permit the water to drain from them. Drying ovens can be used to dry glassware if they are available, and if they are not being used for other purposes. Rapid drying can be achieved by rinsing the glassware with acetone and air-drying it or placing it in an oven. First, thoroughly drain the glassware of water. Then rinse it with one or two *small* portions (1–2 mL) of acetone. Do not use any more acetone than is suggested here. Return the used acetone to a waste acetone container for recycling. After you rinse the glassware with acetone, dry it by placing it in a drying oven for a few minutes or allow it to air-dry at room temperature. The acetone can also be removed by aspirator suction. In some laboratories, it may be possible to dry the glassware by blowing a *gentle* stream of dry air into the container. (Your laboratory instructor will indicate if you should do this.) Before drying the glassware with air, make sure that the air line is not filled with oil. Otherwise, the oil will be blown into the container, and you will have to clean it again. It is not necessary to blast the acetone out of the glassware with a wide-open stream of air; a gentle stream of air is just as effective and will not startle other people in the room.

Do not dry your glassware with a paper towel unless the towel is lint-free. Most paper will leave lint on the glass that can interfere with subsequent procedures performed in the equipment. Sometimes it is not necessary to dry a piece of equipment thoroughly. For example, if you are going to place water or an aqueous solution in a container, it does not need to be completely dry.

3.3 Ground-Glass Joints

It is likely that the glassware in your organic kit has **standard-taper ground-glass joints.** For example, the air condenser in the figure consists of an inner (male) ground-glass joint at the bottom and an outer (female) joint at the top. Each end

Figure 3.1
Illustration of ⟙ 14/10 inner and outer joints showing dimensions.

Figure 3.2
A microscale standard-taper joint assembly.

is ground to a precise size, which is designated by the symbol ⟙ followed by two numbers. A common joint size in microscale glassware is ⟙ 14/10. The first number indicates the diameter (in millimeters) of the joint at its widest point, and the second number refers to its length (see Figure 3.1). One advantage of standard-taper joints is that the pieces fit together snugly and form a good seal. In addition, standard-taper joints allow all glassware components with the same joint size to be connected, thus permitting the assembly of a wide variety of apparatus. One disadvantage of glassware with ground-glass joints, however, is that it is expensive.

Some pieces of glassware with ground-glass joints also have threads cast into the outside surface of the outer joints (see top of air condenser in Figure 3.1). The threaded joint allows the use of a plastic screw cap with a hole in the top to fasten two pieces of glassware together securely. The plastic cap is slipped over the inner joint of the upper piece of glassware, followed by a rubber O-ring (see Figure 3.2). The O-ring should be pushed down so that it fits snugly on top of the ground-glass joint. The inner ground-glass joint is then fitted into the outer joint of the bottom piece of glassware. The screw cap is tightened without excessive force to attach the entire apparatus firmly together. The O-ring provides an additional seal that makes this joint airtight. With this connecting system, it is unnecessary to use any type of grease to seal the joint. The O-ring *must be used* to obtain a good seal and to lessen the chances of breaking the glassware when you tighten the plastic cap.

It is important to make sure no solid or liquid is on the joint surfaces. Such material will lessen the efficiency of the seal, and the joints may leak. The presence of solid particles could cause the ground-glass joints to break when the plastic cap is tightened. Also, if the apparatus is to be heated, material caught between the joint surfaces will increase the tendency for the joints to stick. If the joint surfaces are coated with liquid or adhering solid, you should wipe them with a cloth or lint-free paper towel before assembling.

3.4 Separating Ground-Glass Joints

The most important thing you can do to prevent ground-glass joints from becoming "frozen," or stuck together, is to disassemble the glassware as soon as possible after a procedure is completed. Even when this precaution is followed, ground-glass joints may become stuck tightly together. The same is true of glass stoppers in bottles or conical vials. Because microscale glassware is small and fragile, it is relatively easy to break a piece of glassware when trying to pull two pieces apart. If the pieces do not separate easily, you must be careful when you try to pull them apart. The best way is to hold the two pieces, with your hands touching, as close as possible to the joint. With a firm grasp, try to loosen the joint with a slight twisting motion (do not twist very hard). If this does not work, try to pull your hands apart without pushing sideways on the glassware.

If it is not possible to pull the pieces apart, the following methods may help. A frozen joint can sometimes be loosened if you tap it *gently* with the wooden handle of a spatula. Then, try to pull it apart as already described. If this procedure fails, you may try heating the joint in hot water or a steam bath. If this heating fails, the instructor may be able to advise you. As a last resort, you may try heating the joint in a flame. You should not try this unless the apparatus is hopelessly stuck, because heating by flame often causes the joint to expand rapidly and crack or break. If you use a flame, make sure the joint is clean and dry. Heat the outer part of the joint slowly, in the yellow portion of a low flame, until it expands and breaks away from the inner section. Heat the joint very slowly and carefully or it may break.

3.5 Etching Glassware

Glassware that has been used for reactions involving strong bases such as sodium hydroxide or sodium alkoxides must be cleaned thoroughly *immediately* after use. If these caustic materials are allowed to remain in contact with the glass, they will etch the glass permanently. The etching makes later cleaning more difficult because dirt particles may become trapped within the microscopic surface irregularities of the etched glass. Furthermore, the glass is weakened, so the lifetime of the glassware is shortened. If caustic materials are allowed to come into contact with ground-glass joints without being removed promptly, the joints will become fused, or "frozen." It is extremely difficult to separate fused joints without breaking them.

3.6 Assembling the Apparatus

Care must be taken when assembling the glass components into the desired apparatus. Always remember that Newtonian physics applies to chemical apparatus, and unsecured pieces of glassware are certain to respond to gravity. You should always clamp the glassware securely to a ring stand. Throughout this textbook, the illustrations of the various glassware arrangements include the clamps that attach the apparatus to a ring stand. You should assemble your apparatus using the clamps as shown in the illustrations.

3.7 Capping Conical Vials or Openings

The plastic screw caps used to join two pieces of glassware together can also be used to cap conical vials (see Figure 3.3) or other openings. A Teflon insert, or liner, fits inside the cap to cover the hole when the cap is used to seal a vial. Only one side of the liner is coated with Teflon. This side should always face toward the inside of the vial. (Note that the O-ring is not used when the cap is used to seal a vial.) To seal a vial, it is necessary to tighten the cap firmly but not too tightly. It is possible to crack the vial if you apply too much force. Some Teflon liners have a soft backing material (silicone rubber) that allows the liner to compress slightly when the cap is screwed down. It is easier to cap a vial securely with these liners without breaking the vial than with liners that have a harder backing material.

Plastic cap

Insert on liner
(Teflon on one side,
silicone rubber on
the other)

Figure 3.3
Plastic cap and Teflon insert.

3.8 Attaching Rubber Tubing to Equipment

When you attach rubber tubing to the glass apparatus or when you insert glass tubing into rubber stoppers, first lubricate the rubber tubing or the rubber stopper with either water or glycerin. Without such lubrication, it can be difficult to attach rubber tubing to the side arms of items of glassware such as condensers and filter flasks. Furthermore, glass tubing may break when it is inserted into rubber stoppers. Water is a good lubricant for most purposes. Do not use water as a lubricant when it might contaminate the reaction. Glycerin is a better lubricant than water and should be used when there is considerable friction between the glass and rubber. If glycerin is the lubricant, be careful not to use too much.

3.9 Description of Equipment

The components of the organic kit recommended for use in this textbook are given in Figures 3.4–3.7. Notice that most of the joints in these pieces of glassware are

*Alternative types of distillation equipment are shown.

Figure 3.4
Components of a microscale organic kit.

Conical reaction vial
(0.1 mL – ꟷ 5/5 joints)

Equipment for
preparative gas
chromatography
(optional)

G.C. collection tube
(ꟷ 5/5 joints)

Microchromatographic
column (optional)

© Cengage Learning 2013

Figure 3.5
Optional pieces of microscale glassware.
Note: The optional pieces of equipment
shown in this figure are not part of the
standard microscale kit. They must be
purchased separately.

ꟷ 14/10, and all the outer joints are threaded. The organic kits used in your laboratory may have different joint sizes, or some of the outer joints may not be threaded.
In particular, some older organic kits contain a number of pieces of glassware with
ꟷ 7/10 joints. These kits will work as well with the experiments in this book as
the glassware recommended in the figures. In addition, there are microscale kits
containing glassware that is connected without the use of ground-glass joints. The
experiments in this book can also be performed with these glassware kits. Modifications with organic kits not containing the recommended glassware are discussed
in the Technique chapters and in some of the experiments.

Figures 3.4–3.7 include glassware and equipment that are commonly used in
the organic laboratory. Your glassware and equipment may vary slightly from the
pieces shown on this spread and on the following pages.

Erlenmeyer flask

Beaker

Test tube

Side arm test tube

Filter flask

Hirsch funnel

Neoprene adapter

Rubber septum

Conical funnel

Watch glass

pipette bulb

Pasteur pipette

Centrifuge tube

Separatory funnel

Büchner funnel

Graduated cylinder

Graduated pipette

Figure 3.6
Equipment commonly used in the organic laboratory.

Test tube holder

Brushes

Micro three-finger clamp

Forceps

Clamp holder

Microspatulas

Microburner

Aluminum block
(large holes)

Aluminum
collars (2)

Stir   Heat

Hot plate/stirrer with
aluminum block
(small holes)

© Cengage Learning 2013

Figure 3.7
Equipment commonly used in the organic laboratory.

How to Find Data for Compounds: Handbooks and Catalogs

The best way to find information quickly on organic compounds is to consult a handbook. We will discuss the use of the *CRC Handbook of Chemistry and Physics, Lange's Handbook of Chemistry, The Merck Index,* and the *Aldrich Handbook of Fine Chemicals.* Complete citations to these handbooks are provided in Technique 29. Depending on the type of handbook consulted, the following information may be found:

Name and common synonyms

Formula

Molecular weight

Boiling point for a liquid or melting point for a solid

Beilstein reference

Solubility data

Density

Refractive index

Flash point

Chemical Abstracts Service (CAS) Registry Number

Toxicity data

Uses and synthesis

We often make use of the Internet to obtain information rapidly. To search the Internet, you can perform an online search using a browser (for example, Mozilla Firefox or Internet Explorer) and a search engine (such as Google or Bing) to find the structures of compounds. Although this works well for obtaining the structures of organic compounds, some of the data, such as melting points and boiling points, may not be as reliable as data obtained from the handbooks listed above. If you are using the Internet to obtain data, make sure that you check several sources and confirm these values with those found in a handbook.

4.1 CRC Handbook of Chemistry and Physics

This is the handbook that is most often consulted for data on organic compounds. Although a new edition of the handbook is published each year, the changes that are made are often minor. An older copy of the handbook will often suffice for most purposes. In addition to the extensive tables of properties of organic compounds, the *CRC Handbook* includes sections on nomenclature and ring structures, an index of synonyms, and an index of molecular formulas.

The nomenclature used in this book most closely follows the Chemical Abstracts system of naming organic compounds. This system differs, but only slightly,

Table 4.1 Examples of Names of Compounds in the *CRC Handbook*

Name of Organic Compound	Location in *CRC Handbook*
1-Chloropentane	Pentane, 1-chloro-
1,4-Dichlorobenzene	Benzene, 1,4-dichloro-
4-Chlorotoluene	Benzene, 1-chloro-4-methyl-
Ethanoic acid	Acetic acid
tert-Butyl acetate (ethanoate)	Acetic acid, 1,1-dimethylethyl ester
Ethyl propanoate	Propanoic acid, ethyl ester
Isopentyl alcohol	1-Butanol, 3-methyl-
Isopentyl acetate (banana oil)	1-Butanol, 3-methyl-, acetate
Salicylic acid	Benzoic acid, 2-hydroxy-
Acetylsalicylic acid (aspirin)	Benzoic acid, 2-acetyloxy-

from standard IUPAC nomenclature. Table 4.1 lists some examples of how some commonly encountered compounds are named in this handbook. The first thing you will notice is that this handbook is not like a dictionary. Instead, you must first identify the *parent* name of the compound of interest. The parent names are found in alphabetical order. Once the parent name is identified and found, then you look for the particular substituent or substituents that may be attached to this parent.

For most compounds, it is easy to find what you are looking for as long as you know the parent name. Alcohols are, as expected, named by IUPAC nomenclature. Notice in Table 4.1 that the branched-chain alcohol, isopentyl alcohol, is listed as 1-butanol, 3-methyl.

Esters, amides, and acid halides are usually named as derivatives of the parent carboxylic acid. Thus, in Table 4.1, you find ethyl propanoate listed under the parent carboxylic acid, propanoic acid. If you have trouble finding a particular ester under the parent carboxylic acid, try looking under the alcohol part of the name. For example, isopentyl acetate is not listed under acetic acid, as expected, but instead is found under the alcohol part of the name (see Table 4.1). Fortunately, this handbook has a Synonym Index that nicely locates isopentyl acetate for you in the main part of the handbook.

Once you locate the compound by its name, you will find the following useful information:

CRC number	This is an identification number for the compound. You can use this number to find the molecular structure located elsewhere in the handbook. This is especially useful when the compound has a complicated structure.
Name and synonym	The Chemical Abstracts name and possible synonyms.
Mol. form.	Molecular formula for the compound.
Mol. wt.	Molecular weight.
CAS RN	Chemical Abstracts Service Registry Number. This number is useful for locating additional information on the compound in the primary chemical literature (see Technique 29, Section 29.11).
mp/°C	Melting point of the compound in degrees Celsius.

bp/°C		Boiling point of the compound in degrees Celsius. A number without a superscript indicates that the recorded boiling point was obtained at 760 mm Hg pressure (atmospheric pressure). A number with a superscript indicates that the boiling point was obtained at reduced pressure. For example, for an entry of 234, 122[16] would indicate that the compound boils at 234°C at 760 mm Hg and 122°C at 16 mm Hg pressure.
Den/g cm^{-3}		Density of a liquid. A superscript indicates the temperature in degrees Celsius at which the density was obtained.
n_D		Refractive index determined at a wavelength of 589 nm, the yellow line in a sodium lamp (D line). A superscript indicates the temperature at which the refractive index was obtained (see Technique 24).

	Solubility classification	Solvent abbreviations
Solubility	1 = insoluble	ace = acetone
	2 = slightly soluble	bz = benzene
	3 = soluble	chl = chloroform
	4 = very soluble	EtOH = ethanol
	5 = miscible	eth = ether
	6 = decomposes	hx = hexane

Beil. ref.	Beilstein reference. An entry of 4-02-00-00157 would indicate that the compound is found in the 4th supplement in Volume 2, with no subvolume, on page 157 (see Technique 29, Section 29.10 for details on the use of Beilstein).
Merck No.	*Merck Index* number in the 11th edition of the handbook. These numbers change each time a new edition of *The Merck Index* is issued.

Examples of sample handbook entries for isopentyl alcohol (1-butanol, 3-methyl) and isopentyl acetate (1-butanol, 3-methyl, acetate) are shown in Table 4.2.

4.2 Lange's Handbook of Chemistry

This handbook tends not to be as available as the *CRC Handbook,* but it has some interesting differences and advantages. *Lange's Handbook* has synonyms listed at the bottom of each page, along with structures of more complicated molecules. The most noticeable difference is in how compounds are named. For many compounds, the system lists names as they would appear in a dictionary. Table 4.3 lists examples of

Table 4.2 Properties of Isopentyl Alcohol and Isopentyl Acetate as Listed in the *CRC Handbook*

No.	Name Synonym	Mol. Form. Mol. Wt.	CAS RN mp/°C	Merck No. bp/°C	Beil. Ref. den/g cm^{-3}	Solubility n_D
3627	1-Butanol, 3-methyl	$C_5H_{12}O$	123-51-3	5081	4-01-00-01677	ace 4; eth 4; EtOH 4
	Isopentyl alcohol	88.15	−117.2	131.1	0.8104[20]	1.4053[20]
3631	1-Butanol, 3-methyl, acetate	$C_7H_{14}O_2$	123-92-2	4993	4-02-00-00157	H_2O 2; EtOH5; eth 5; ace 3
	Isopentyl acetate	130.19	−78.5	142.5	0.876[15]	1.4000[20]

Table 4.3 Examples of Names of Compounds in *Lange's Handbook*

Name of Organic Compound	Location in *Lange's Handbook*
1-Chloropentane	1-Chloropentane
1,4-Dichlorobenzene	1,4-Dichlorobenzene
4-Chlorotoluene	4-Chlorotoluene
Ethanoic acid	Acetic acid
tert-Butyl acetate (ethanoate)	*tert*-Butyl acetate
Ethyl propanoate	Ethyl propionate
Isopentyl alcohol	3-Methyl-1-butanol
Isopentyl acetate (banana oil)	Isopentyl acetate
Salicylic acid	2-Hydroxybenzoic acid
Acetylsalicylic acid (aspirin)	Acetylsalicylic acid

how some commonly encountered compounds are named in this handbook. Most often, you do not need to identify the *parent* name. Unfortunately, *Lange's Handbook* frequently uses common names that are becoming obsolete. For example, propionate is used rather than propanoate. Nevertheless, this handbook often names compounds as a practicing organic chemist would tend to name them. Notice how easy it is to find the entries for isopentyl acetate and acetylsalicylic acid (aspirin) in this handbook.

Once you locate the compound by its name, you will find the following useful information:

Lange's number	This is an identification number for the compound.
Name	See examples in Table 4.3.
Formula	Structures are drawn out. If they are complicated, then the structures are shown at the bottom of the page.
Formula weight	Molecular weight of the compound.
Beilstein reference	An entry of 2, 132 would indicate that the compound is found in Volume 2 of the main work on page 132. An entry of 3^2, 188 would indicate that the compound is found in Volume 3 of the second supplement on page 188 (see Technique 29, Section 29.10 for details on the use of *Beilstein*).
Density	Density is usually expressed in units of g/mL or g/cm^3. A superscript indicates the temperature at which the density was measured. If the density is also subscripted, usually 4°, it indicates that the density was measured at a certain temperature relative to water at its maximum density, 4°C. Most of the time you can simply ignore the subscripts and superscripts.
Refractive index	A superscript indicates the temperature at which the refractive index was determined (see Technique 24).
Melting point	Melting point of the compound in degrees Celsius. When a "d" or "dec" appears with the melting point, it indicates that the compound decomposes at the melting point. When decomposition occurs, you will often observe a change in color of the solid.
Boiling point	Boiling point of the compound in degrees Celsius. A number without a superscript indicates that the recorded

boiling point was obtained at 760 mm Hg pressure (atmospheric pressure). A number with a superscript indicates that the boiling point was obtained at reduced pressure. For example, an entry of 102^{11} mm would indicate that the compound boils at 102°C at 11 mm Hg pressure.

Flash point

This number is the temperature in degrees Celsius at which the compound will ignite when heated in air and a spark is introduced into the vapor. There are a number of different methods that are used to measure this value, so this number varies considerably. It gives a crude indication of flammability. You may need this information when heating a substance with a hot plate. Hot plates can be a serious source of trouble because of the sparking action that can occur with switches and thermostats used in hot plates.

Solubility in 100 parts solvent

Parts by weight of a compound that can be dissolved in 100 parts by weight of solvent at room temperature. In some cases, the values given are expressed as the weight in grams that can be dissolved in 100 mL of solvent. This handbook is not consistent in describing solubility. Sometimes gram amounts are provided, but in other cases the description will be more vague, using terms such as *soluble, insoluble,* or *slightly soluble.*

Solvent abbreviations

acet = acetone

bz = benzene

chl = chloroform

aq = water

alc = ethanol

eth = ether

HOAc = acetic acid

Solubility characteristics

i = insoluble

s = soluble

sls = slightly soluble

vs = very soluble

misc = miscible

Examples of sample handbook entries for isopentyl alcohol (3-methyl-1-butanol) and isopentyl acetate are shown in Table 4.4.

4.3 The Merck Index

The Merck Index is a very useful book because it has additional information not found in the other two handbooks. This handbook, however, tends to emphasize medicinally related compounds, such as drugs and biological compounds, although it also lists many other common organic compounds. It is not revised each year; new editions are published in five- or six-year cycles. It does not contain all of

Table 4.4 Properties of 3-Methyl-1-Butanol and Isopentyl Acetate as Listed in *Lange's Handbook*

No.	Name	Formula	Formula Weight	Beilstein Reference	Density	Refractive Index	Melting Point	Boiling Point	Flash Point	Solubility in 100 Parts Solvent
m155	3-methyl-1-butanol	$(CH_3)_2CHCH_2CH_2OH$	88.15	1,392	0.8129^{15}_4	1.4085^{15}	−117.2	132.0	45	2 aq; misc alc, bz, chl, eth, HOAc
i80	Isopentyl acetate	$CH_3COOCH_2CH_2CH(CH_3)_2$	130.19	2,132	0.876^{15}_4	1.4007^{20}	−78.5	142.0	80	0.25 aq; misc alc, eth

the compounds listed in *Lange's Handbook* or the *CRC Handbook*. However, for the compounds listed, it provides a wealth of useful information. The handbook will provide you with some or all of the following data for each entry.

Merck number, which changes each time a new edition is issued

Name, including synonyms and stereochemical designation

Molecular formula and structure

Molecular weight

Percentages of each of the elements in the compound

Uses

Source and synthesis, including references to the primary literature

Optical rotation for chiral molecules

Density, boiling point, and melting point

Solubility characteristics, including crystalline form

Pharmacology information

Toxicity data

One of the problems with looking up a compound in this handbook is trying to decide the name under which the compound will be listed. For example, isopentyl alcohol can also be named as 3-methyl-1-butanol or isoamyl alcohol. In the 12th edition of the handbook, it is listed under the name isopentyl alcohol (#5212) on page 886. Finding isopentyl acetate is an even more challenging task. It is located in the handbook under the name isoamyl acetate (#5125) on page 876. Often, it is easier to look up the name in the name index or to find it in the formula index.

The handbook has some useful appendices that include the CAS registry numbers, a biological activity index, a formula index, and a name index that also includes synonyms. When looking up a compound in one of the indexes, you need to remember that the numbers provided are compound numbers, rather than page numbers. There is also a very useful section on organic name reactions that includes references to the primary literature.

4.4 Aldrich Handbook of Fine Chemicals

The *Aldrich Handbook* is actually a catalog of chemicals sold by the Aldrich Chemical Company. The company includes in its catalog a large body of useful data on each compound that it sells. Because the catalog is reissued each year at no cost to the user, you should be able to find an old copy when the new one is issued. As you are mainly interested in the data on a particular compound and not the price, an old volume is perfectly fine. Isopentyl alcohol is listed as 3-methyl-1-butanol, and isopentyl acetate is listed as isoamyl acetate in the *Aldrich Handbook*. The following includes some of the properties and information listed for individual compounds.

Aldrich catalog number

Name: Aldrich uses a mixture of common and IUPAC names. It takes a bit of time to master the names. Fortunately, the catalog does a good job of cross-referencing compounds and has a very good molecular formula index.

CAS Registry Number

Structure

Synonym

Formula weight

Boiling point/melting point

Index of refraction

Density

Beilstein reference

Merck reference

Infrared spectrum reference to the Aldrich Library of FT-IR spectra

NMR spectrum reference to the Aldrich Library of ^{13}C and ^{1}H FT-NMR spectra

Literature references to the primary literature on the uses of the compound

Toxicity

Safety data and precautions

Flash point

Prices of chemicals

4.5 Strategy for Finding Information: Summary

Most students and professors find *The Merck Index* and *Lange's Handbook* easier and more "intuitive" to use than the *CRC Handbook.* You can go directly to a compound without rearranging the name according to the parent or base name followed by its substituents. Another great source of information is the *Aldrich Handbook,* which contains those compounds that are easily available from a commercial source. Many compounds are found in the *Aldrich Handbook* that you may never find in any of the other handbooks. The Sigma–Aldrich Web site (*http://www.sigmaaldrich.com/*) allows you to search by name, synonym, and catalog number.

PROBLEMS

1. Using *The Merck Index,* find and draw structures for the following compounds:

a. atropine

b. quinine

c. saccharin

d. benzo[*a*]pyrene (benzpyrene)

e. itaconic acid

f. adrenosterone

g. chrysanthemic acid (chrysanthemumic acid)

h. cholesterol

i. vitamin C (ascorbic acid)

2. Find the melting points for the following compounds in the *CRC Handbook, Lange's Handbook,* or the *Aldrich Handbook:*

a. biphenyl

b. 4-bromobenzoic acid

c. 3-nitrophenol

3. Find the boiling point for each compound in the references listed in problem 2:

a. octanoic acid at reduced pressure

b. 4-chloroacetophenone at atmosphere and reduced pressure

c. 2-methyl-2-heptanol

4. Find the index of refraction n_D and density for the liquids listed in problem 3.

5. Using the *Aldrich Handbook,* report the specific rotations for the enantiomers of camphor.

6. Read the section on carbon tetrachloride in *The Merck Index* and list some of the health hazards for this compound.

Measurement of Volume and Weight

Special care must be taken when working with small amounts of liquid or solids. In the typical microscale experiment, a student will use from 10 to 1000 mg of a liquid or solid. Specially designed microscale equipment will be used for these small-scale reactions. You may not be used to working with such small quantities, but after a while you will adjust to "thinking small."

Liquids to be used for an experiment will usually be found in small containers in a hood. For experiments in this book, an automatic pipette, dispensing pump, or calibrated pipette will be used for measuring the volume of a liquid. It is critical that **limiting reactants** be weighed for accuracy purposes. *Do not calculate the weight using densities!* Measurement of a small volume of a liquid is subject to a large experimental error when converted to a weight using the density of a liquid. To determine the weight of a liquid when dealing with limiting reactants, preweigh the container before adding the liquid to the container and then reweigh the container after adding the liquid. This gives an **exact weight** and avoids the experimental error involved in using densities to calculate weights when working with smaller amounts of a liquid. For **nonlimiting** liquid reactants, you may calculate the weight of the liquid from the volume you have delivered using the density of the liquid and the following equation:

$$\text{Weight (g)} = \text{density (g/mL)} \times \text{volume (mL)}$$

Solids may be found near the balance. When an accurate measurement is required, solids must be weighed on a balance that reads to the nearest milligram (0.001 g) or tenth of a milligram (0.0001 g). To weigh a solid, place your conical vial or round-bottom flask in a small beaker and take these with you to the balance. Place a piece of paper that has been folded once on the balance pan. The folded paper will enable you to pour the solid into the conical vial or flask without spilling. Use the larger of your two spatulas to aid the transfer of the solid to the paper. Never weigh directly into a conical vial or flask and never pour, dump, or shake a material from a bottle. While still at the balance, carefully transfer the solid from the paper to your vial or flask. The vial or flask should be in a beaker while you are transferring the solid. The beaker traps any material that fails to make it into the container. It also supports the vial or flask so that it does not fall over. It is not necessary to obtain the exact amount specified in the experimental procedure, and trying to be exact requires too much time at the balance. For example, if you obtained 0.140 g of a solid, rather than the 0.136 g specified in a procedure, you could use it, but the actual amount weighed should be recorded in your notebook. Use the amount you weighed to calculate the theoretical yield, if this solid is the limiting agent.

Careless dispensing of liquids and solids is a hazard in any laboratory. When reagents are spilled, you may be subjected to an unnecessary health or fire hazard. In addition, you may waste expensive chemicals, destroy balance pans and clothing, and damage the environment. Always clean up any spills immediately.

5.1 Automatic Pipettes   When available, an automatic pipette increases the speed of transfer of liquids from reagent bottles. These pipettes are expensive and must be shared by the entire laboratory. A number of types of units are available commercially. We describe the use of the continuously adjustable automatic pipette. This type of pipette can be adjusted for any volume within its defined range using a three- or four-digit readout. Several types of adjustable automatic pipettes are shown in Figure 5.1. The typical laboratory may have several units available: one 10–100 μL (0.01–0.10 mL) pipette for smaller volumes, and two 100–1000 μL (0.10–1.00 mL) pipettes for larger volumes. Disposable tips are available for each of these units and are color coded: yellow and blue for the small and large units, respectively. The automatic pipette is accurate with aqueous solutions, but it is not as accurate with organic liquids.

In most cases, the instructor will adjust the pipette so that it will deliver the desired volume. It will be placed in a convenient location near the reagent bottle, usually in a hood, and students will reuse the tip. Your instructor will give directions for the correct use of the automatic pipette. Students must practice using the automatic pipette. Remember that the automatic pipette is expensive and must be handled carefully. To protect the unit, you must always use a tip on the end of the pipette. Liquid must be drawn only into this plastic tip and never up into the unit itself. If this happens, you should notify your laboratory instructor immediately. Keep the pipette upright and immerse the tip just below the surface of the liquid. Automatic pipettes should never be used with corrosive liquids, such as sulfuric acid or hydrochloric acid.

5.2 Dispensing Pumps   Dispensing pumps may be used in place of automatic pipettes when larger amounts (more than 0.1 mL) of liquids are being dispensed in the laboratory. The pumps

© Cengage Learning 2013

Figure 5.1
The adjustable automatic pipette.

Figure 5.2
Dispensing pump.

are simple to operate, chemically inert, and accurate. Because the plunger assembly is made of Teflon, the dispensing pump may be used with most corrosive liquids and organic solvents. Dispensing pumps come in a variety of sizes, but the 1-, 2-, and 5-mL sizes are most useful in the microscale organic laboratory. The pump is attached to a bottle containing the liquid being dispensed. The liquid is drawn up from this reservoir into the pump assembly through a piece of inert plastic tubing.

Dispensing pumps are somewhat more difficult to adjust to the proper volume than automatic pipettes. Normally, the instructor or assistant will carefully adjust the unit to deliver the proper amount of liquid. As shown in Figure 5.2, the plunger is pulled up as far as it will travel to draw in the liquid from the glass reservoir. To expel the liquid from the spout into a container, slowly guide the plunger down. With low-viscosity liquids, the weight of the plunger will expel the liquid. With more viscous liquids, however, you may need to push the plunger gently to deliver the liquid into a container. Remove the last drop of liquid on the end of the spout by touching the tip on the interior wall of the container. When the liquid being transferred is a limiting reagent or when you need to know the weight precisely, you should weigh the liquid to determine the amount accurately.

As you pull up the plunger, look to see if the liquid is being drawn up into the pump unit. Some volatile liquids may not be drawn up in the expected manner, and you will observe an air bubble. Air bubbles are commonly observed when the pump has not been used for a while. The air bubble can be removed from the pump by dispensing and discarding several volumes of liquid to "reprime" the dispensing pump. Also check to see if the spout is filled completely with liquid. An accurate volume will not be dispensed unless the spout is filled with liquid before you lift up the plunger.

5.3 Graduated Pipettes

A suitable alternative to an automatic pipette or a dispensing pump is the graduated serological pipette. These *glass* pipettes are available commercially in a number of sizes. "Disposable" pipettes may be used many times and discarded only when the graduations become too faint to be seen. A good assortment of these pipettes consists of the following:

0.50-mL pipettes calibrated in 0.01-mL divisions (5/10 in 1/100 mL)

1.00-mL pipettes calibrated in 0.01-mL divisions (1 in 1/100 mL)

2.00-mL pipettes calibrated in 0.01-mL divisions (2 in 1/100 mL)

Liquids may be measured and transferred using a graduated pipette and a pipette pump. The style of pipette pump shown in Figure 5.3A is available in four sizes. The 2-mL size (blue) works well with the range of pipettes previously indicated. To fill the pipette, one simply rotates the knurled wheel forward so that the piston moves upward. The liquid is discharged by slowly turning the wheel backward until the proper amount of liquid has been expelled. The top of the pipette must be inserted securely into the pump and held there with one hand to obtain an adequate seal. The other hand is used to load and release the liquid.

The pipette pump shown in Figure 5.3B may also be used with graduated pipettes. The knob is turned counterclockwise to draw in the liquid, and then the liquid is released by turning the knob clockwise. With this style of pipette, the top of the pipette is held securely by a rubber O-ring, and it is easily handled with one hand. You should be certain that the pipette is held securely by the O-ring before using it. Disposable pipettes may not fit tightly in the O-ring, because they often have smaller diameters than nondisposable pipettes.

A   B   C

© Cengage Learning 2013

Figure 5.3
Pipette pumps.

A syringe may be used as a pipette pump, as shown in Figure 5.3C. In the design shown here, a 1- or 2-mL syringe is attached to the graduated pipette using a short piece of plastic tubing. The liquid is drawn up into the pipette when the plunger is pulled up, and it is expelled when the plunger is pushed down.

Excellent results may be obtained with graduated pipettes if you transfer by difference between marked calibrations and avoid transferring the entire contents of the pipette. When expelling the liquid, be sure to touch the tip of the pipette to the inside of the container before withdrawing the pipette. Graduated pipettes are commonly used when dispensing corrosive liquids, such as sulfuric acid or hydrochloric acid. The pipette will be supplied with a bulb or pipette pump.

Pipettes may be obtained in a number of styles, but only three types will be described here (Figure 5.4). One type of graduated pipette is calibrated "to deliver" (TD) its total capacity when the last drop is blown out. This style of pipette, shown in Figure 5.4A, is probably the most common type of graduated pipette in use in the laboratory; it is designated by two rings at the top. Of course, one does not need to transfer the entire volume to a container. To deliver a more accurate volume, you should transfer an amount less than the total capacity of the pipette using the graduations on the pipette as a guide.

Another type of graduated pipette is shown in Figure 5.4B. This pipette is calibrated to deliver its total capacity when the meniscus is located on the last

A
Graduated
Blow-out

B
Graduated
No blow-out

C
Volumetric
Touch-off

© Cengage Learning 2013

Figure 5.4
Pipettes.

graduation mark near the bottom of the pipette. For example, the pipette shown in Figure 5.4B delivers 10.0 mL of liquid when it has been drained to the point where the meniscus is located on the 10.0-mL mark. With this type of pipette, you must not drain the entire pipette or blow it out. In contrast, notice that the pipette shown in Figure 5.4A has its last graduation at 0.90 mL. The last 0.10-mL volume is blown out to give the 1.00-mL volume.

A nongraduated volumetric pipette is shown in Figure 5.4C. It is easily identified by the large bulb in the center of the pipette. This pipette is calibrated so that it will retain its last drop after the tip is touched on the side of the container. It must not be blown out. These pipettes often have a single colored band at the top that identifies it as a "touch-off" pipette. The color of the band is keyed to its total volume. This type of pipette is commonly used in analytical chemistry.

5.4 Pipettes The Pasteur pipette is shown in Figure 5.5A with a 2-mL rubber bulb attached. There are two sizes of pipettes: a long one (9 inch) and a short one (5¾ inch). It is important that the pipette bulb fit securely. You should not use a medicine dropper bulb, because of its small capacity. A Pasteur pipette is an indispensable piece of equipment for the routine transfer of liquids. It is also used for separations (Technique 12). Pasteur pipettes may be packed with cotton for use in gravity filtration (Technique 8) or packed with an adsorbent for small-scale column chromatography (Technique 19). Although they are considered disposable, you should be able to clean them for reuse as long as the tip remains unchipped.

A Pasteur pipette may be supplied by your instructor for dropwise addition of a particular reagent to a reaction mixture. For example, concentrated sulfuric acid is often dispensed in this way. When sulfuric acid is transferred, take care to avoid getting the acid into the rubber or latex dropper bulb. It is best to avoid the rubber dropper bulb entirely by using one-piece transfer pipettes made entirely of polyethylene. These plastic pipettes are available in 1- or 2-mL sizes. They come from the manufacturers with approximate calibration marks stamped on them (Figure 5.5B).

Pipettes may be calibrated for use in operations where the volume does not need to be known precisely. Examples include measurement of solvents needed for extraction and for washing a solid obtained following crystallization. It is suggested that you calibrate several 5¾-inch pipettes following the procedure given in Experiment 1. A calibrated Pasteur pipette is shown in Figure 5.5C. Your instructor may provide you with a calibrated Pasteur pipette and bulb for transferring liquids where an accurate volume is not required. The pipette may be used to transfer a volume of 1.5 mL or less. You may find that the instructor has taped a test tube to the side of the storage bottle. The pipette is stored in the test tube with that particular reagent.

In general, Pasteur pipettes should not be used to measure volumes of reagents needed for organic reactions, because they are not accurate enough for this purpose.

A
Pasteur pipette
for general
purpose transfers

B
One-piece
polyethylene
transfer pipette

C
Calibrated
Pasteur
pipette

D
Filter-tip
pipette for
transfer of
volatile liquids

© Cengage Learning 2013

Figure 5.5
Pasteur and transfer pipettes.

In some cases, however, your instructor may have available a calibrated pipette for transferring nonlimiting reagents that may damage an automatic pipette. For example, a calibrated Pasteur pipette may be used with concentrated acids.

NOTE: You should not assume that a certain number of drops equals a 1-mL volume. The common rule that 20 drops equal 1 mL does not hold true for a Pasteur pipette!

A Pasteur pipette may be packed with cotton to create a filter-tip pipette as shown in Figure 5.5D. This pipette is prepared by the instructions given in Technique 8, Section 8.6. Pipettes of this type are useful in transferring volatile solvents during extractions and in filtering small amounts of solid impurities from solutions.

5.5 Syringes

Syringes may be used to add a pure liquid or a solution to a reaction mixture. They are especially useful when anhydrous conditions must be maintained. The needle is inserted through a septum, and the liquid is added to the reaction mixture. Although syringes come in a number of sizes, we will use a 1-mL unit in this textbook. Caution should be used with disposable syringes because they often use solvent-soluble rubber gaskets on the plungers. A syringe should be cleaned carefully after each use by drawing acetone or another volatile solvent into it and expelling the solvent with the plunger. Repeat this procedure several times to clean the syringe thoroughly. Draw air through the barrel with an aspirator to dry the syringe.

Syringes are usually supplied with volume graduations inscribed on the barrel. Large-volume syringes are not accurate enough to be used for measuring liquids in microscale experiments. A small microliter syringe, however, such as that used in gas chromatography, delivers a precise volume.

5.6 Graduated Cylinders

Graduated cylinders are used to measure relatively large volumes of liquids where accuracy is not required. For example, you could use a 10-mL graduated cylinder to obtain about 2 mL of a solvent for a crystallization procedure. You should use an automatic pipette, dispensing pump, or graduated pipette for accurate transfer of liquids in microscale work. Use a *clean and dry* Pasteur pipette to transfer the liquid from the storage container into the graduated cylinder. Do not attempt to pour the liquid directly into the cylinder from the storage bottle or you may spill the fluid. Some instructors may want you to pour some of the liquid into a beaker first and then use a Pasteur pipette to transfer the liquid to a graduated cylinder. Remember that you should not take more than you need. Excess material should never be returned to the storage bottle. Unless you can convince someone else to take it, it must be poured into the appropriate waste container. You should be frugal in estimating amounts needed.

5.7 Measuring Volumes with Conical Vials, Beakers, and Erlenmeyer Flasks

Conical vials, beakers, and Erlenmeyer flasks all have graduations inscribed on them. Beakers and flasks can be used to give only a crude approximation of the volume. They are much less precise than graduated cylinders for measuring volume. In some cases, a conical vial may be used to estimate volumes. For example, the graduations are sufficiently accurate for measuring a solvent needed to wash a solid obtained on a Hirsch funnel after a crystallization. You should use an automatic pipette, dispensing pump, or graduated transfer pipette for accurate measurement of liquids.

5.8 Balances

Solids and some liquids will need to be weighed on a balance that reads to at least the nearest milligram (0.001 g). A top-loading balance (see Figure 5.6) works well if the balance pan is covered with a plastic draft shield. The shield has a flap that opens to allow access to the balance pan. An analytical balance (see Figure 5.7) may

© Cengage Learning 2013

© Cengage Learning 2013

Figure 5.6
A top-loading balance with plastic draft shield.

Figure 5.7
An analytical balance with glass draft shield.

also be used. This type of balance will weigh to the nearest tenth of a milligram (0.0001 g) when provided with a glass draft shield.

Modern electronic balances have a tare device that automatically subtracts the weight of a container or a piece of paper from the combined weight to give the weight of the sample. With solids, it is easy to place a piece of paper on the balance pan, press the tare device so that the paper appears to have zero weight, and then add your solid until the balance gives the weight you desire. You can then transfer the weighed solid to a container. You should always use a spatula to transfer a solid and never pour material from a bottle. In addition, solids must be weighed on paper and not directly on the balance pan. Remember to clean any spills.

With liquids, you should weigh the conical vial to determine the tare weight, transfer the liquid with an automatic pipette, dispensing pump, or graduated pipette into the vial, and then reweigh it. With liquids, it is usually necessary to weigh only the limiting reagent. The other liquids may be transferred using an automatic pipette, dispensing pump, or graduated pipette. Their weights can be calculated by knowing the volumes and densities of the liquids.

PROBLEMS

1. What measuring device would you use to measure the volume under each of the conditions described below? In some cases, there may be more than one answer to the question.

   a. 5 mL of a solvent needed for a crystallization

   b. 0.76 mL of a liquid needed for a reaction

   c. 1 mL of a solvent needed for an extraction

2. Assume that the liquid used in part (b) is a limiting reagent for a reaction. What should you do after measuring the volume?

3. Calculate the weight of a 0.25-mL sample of each of the following liquids:

   a. Diethyl ether (ether)

   b. Methylene chloride (dichloromethane)

   c. Acetone

4. A laboratory procedure calls for 0.146 g of acetic anhydride. Calculate the volume of this reagent needed in the reaction.

5. Criticize the following techniques:

   a. A 100-mL graduated cylinder is used to measure accurately a volume of 2.8 mL.

   b. A one-piece polyethylene transfer pipette (Figure 5.6B) is used to transfer precisely 0.75 mL of a liquid that is being used as the limiting reactant.

   c. A calibrated Pasteur pipette (Figure 5.6C) is used to transfer 25 mL of a solvent.

   d. The volume markings on a 100-mL beaker are used to transfer accurately 5 mL of a liquid.

   e. An automatic pipette is used to transfer 10 mL of a liquid.

   f. A graduated cylinder is used to transfer 0.126 mL of a liquid.

   g. For a small-scale reaction, the weight of a liquid limiting reactant is calculated from its density and volume.

Heating and Cooling Methods

Most organic reaction mixtures need to be heated in order to complete the reaction. In general chemistry, you may have used a Bunsen burner for heating because nonflammable aqueous solutions were used. In an organic laboratory, however, the student must heat nonaqueous solutions that may contain *highly flammable* solvents. You *should not heat organic mixtures with a Bunsen burner* unless you are directed by your laboratory instructor. Open flames present a fire hazard. Whenever possible you should use one of the alternative heating methods, as described in the following sections.

6.1 Aluminum Block with Hot Plate/Stirrer

Most microscale organic laboratories now use an aluminum block and a hot plate, rather than a sand bath, for heating conical vials or flasks. There are several advantages to heating with an aluminum block. First, the metal will heat faster than a sand bath. Second, you can obtain a higher temperature with an aluminum block. Higher temperatures are often needed when distilling liquids with high boiling points at atmospheric pressure or under vacuum. Third, you can cool the aluminum rapidly by removing it with crucible tongs and immersing it in cold water.

Aluminum heating blocks can be fabricated readily in a machine shop or purchased from commercial suppliers.[1] The two aluminum blocks shown in Figure 6.1 will handle most heating applications in the laboratory. The block with the smaller holes will hold conical vials (Figure 6.1A). Holes have been drilled in the block so that different-sized conical vials will fit into the holes. This aluminum block may also be used in crystallizations using a Craig tube (Techniques 8 and 11). A hole is often provided for a mercury thermometer, but we do not recommend using it (see the caution box that follows). The aluminum block with the larger holes, as shown in Figure 6.1B, is designed to hold 10-, 20-, or 25-mL round-bottom flasks, as well as a thermometer.

Figure 6.2 shows a reaction mixture being heated with an aluminum block on a hot plate/stirrer unit. Also shown in Figure 6.2 is a split aluminum collar that may be used when very high temperatures are required. The collar is split to facilitate easy placement around a 5-mL conical vial. The collar helps distribute heat farther up the wall of the vial.

Because some hot plates vary widely in the temperature achieved for a given dial setting, some instructors may ask you to calibrate the hot plate so you have an approximate idea where to set the control on the hot plate to achieve a desired temperature. Place an aluminum block on the hot plate and

A

Aluminum block with small holes to fit Craig tube and 3-mL and 5-mL conical vials.

B

Aluminum block with large holes to fit 10-mL and 25-mL flasks

© Cengage Learning 2013

Figure 6.1
Aluminum heating blocks.

---

[1] The use of solid aluminum heating devices was developed by Siegfried Lodwig at Centralia College, Centralia, WA: Lodwig, S. N. "The Use of Solid Aluminum Heat Transfer Devices in Organic Chemistry Laboratory Instruction and Research." *Journal of Chemical Education, 66* (1989): 77.

Water condenser

Clamp

Aluminum block

Conical vial

Air condenser

Collar

Aluminum block

Figure 6.2
Heating with an aluminum block.

insert a non-mercury thermometer into the small hole in the block, as shown in Figure 6.2 (without the glassware). *Make sure the thermometer fits loosely in the hole or it may break.* Secure the thermometer with a clamp. Select five equally spaced settings on the heating control of the hot plate. Set the dial to the first of these settings and monitor the temperature recorded on the thermometer. When the thermometer reading arrives at a constant value, record this final temperature, along with the dial setting, in your notebook. Repeat this procedure with the remaining four settings and record the temperatures corresponding to the dial settings. Plot the data and keep it for future reference.

C A U T I O N

You should not use a *mercury* thermometer with an aluminum block. If it breaks, the mercury will vaporize on the hot surface. Instead, use a non-mercury glass thermometer, a metal dial thermometer, or a digital electronic temperature-measuring device.

To avoid the possibility of breaking a glass thermometer, your hot plate may have a hole drilled into the metal plate so that a metal dial thermometer can be inserted into the unit (Figure 6.3A). These metal thermometers, such as the one shown in Figure 6.3B, can be obtained in a number of temperature ranges. For example, a 0–250°C thermometer with 2-degree divisions can be obtained at a

Figure 6.3
Dial thermometers.

reasonable price. Also shown in Figure 6.3 (inset) is an aluminum block with a small hole drilled into it so that a metal thermometer can be inserted.[2] An alternative to the metal thermometer is a digital electronic temperature-measuring device that can be inserted into the aluminum block or hot plate. It is strongly recommended that mercury thermometers be avoided when measuring the surface temperature of the hot plate or aluminum block. If a mercury thermometer is broken on a hot surface, you will introduce toxic mercury vapors into the laboratory. Non-mercury thermometers filled with high-boiling colored liquids are available as alternatives.

It is a good idea to use the same hot plate each time. It is likely that two hot plates of the same type may give different temperatures with an identical setting. Record the identification number printed on the unit that you are using in your notebook to ensure that you always use the same hot plate.

Although we may provide aluminum block temperatures for some experiments in this textbook, they should be taken as *approximate* values. You may need to adjust the temperature of the aluminum block appropriately to achieve the conditions you require. Each student must determine the actual temperature required to carry out a particular procedure. When a temperature is suggested, consider it as nothing more than a guide. Pay more attention to what is going on in your reaction vial or flask. If the temperature of your aluminum block equals the suggested temperature but the solution in the flask is not boiling (and you want it to boil), you clearly will need to increase the temperature of the aluminum block. Likewise, if the solution is boiling too rapidly, then you will need to reduce the temperature of the block.

When an aluminum block temperature is not given in the procedure and the liquid needs to be brought to a boil, you can determine the approximate

---

[2] Garner, C. M. "A Mercury-Free Alternative for Temperature Measurement in Aluminum Blocks." *Journal of Chemical Education, 68* (1991): A244.

Spin vane

A

Stir bar

B

Figure 6.4
Methods of stirring
in a conical vial or
round-bottom flask.

© Cengage Learning 2013

setting from the boiling point of the liquid. Because the temperature inside the vial is lower than the aluminum block temperature, you should add at least 20°C to the boiling point of the liquid and set the aluminum block at this higher temperature. In fact, you may need to raise the temperature even higher than this value.

Many organic mixtures need to be stirred, as well as heated, to achieve satisfactory results. To stir a mixture, place a magnetic spin vane (Technique 7, Figure 7.8B) in a conical vial containing the reaction mixture as shown in Figure 6.4A. If the mixture is to be heated as well as stirred, attach a water condenser or an air condenser, as shown in Figure 6.2. With the combination stirrer/hot plate unit, it is possible to stir and heat a mixture simultaneously. Many reactions in this textbook are stirred continuously during the course of the reaction. With round-bottom flasks, a magnetic stir bar must be used to stir mixtures (Technique 7, Figure 7.8A). This is shown in Figure 6.4B. Many laboratories will have another aluminum block drilled to accommodate 10- and 25-mL round-bottom flasks. More uniform stirring will be obtained if the vial or flask is placed in the aluminum block so that it is centered on the hot plate. Mixing may also be achieved by boiling the mixture. A boiling stone (Technique 7, Section 7.4) should be added when a mixture is boiled without magnetic stirring.

6.2 Sand Bath with Hot Plate/Stirrer

The sand bath is used in some microscale laboratories to heat organic mixtures. Sand provides a clean way of distributing heat to a reaction mixture. To prepare a sand bath, place about a 1-cm depth of sand in a crystallizing dish or a Petri dish and then set the dish on a hot plate/stirrer unit. The apparatus is shown in Figure 6.5. Clamp the thermometer into position in the sand bath. You should calibrate the sand bath in a manner similar to that used with the aluminum block. Because sand heats more slowly than an aluminum block, you will need to begin heating the sand bath well before using it.

Do not heat the sand bath much above 200°C or you may break the dish. If you need to heat at very high temperatures, you should use an aluminum block rather than a sand bath (Section 6.1). With sand baths, it may be necessary to cover the dish with aluminum foil to achieve a temperature near 200°C. Keep in mind that the temperature obtained at a particular setting on the hot plate may vary for several reasons. First, you may place the thermometer at a different depth from time to time. Second, because of the relatively poor heat conduction of sand, you may obtain a different temperature in the conical vial, depending on the depth of the vial in the sand bath. Because of this poor heat conductivity, a temperature gradient is established within the sand bath. It is warmer near the bottom of the sand bath and cooler near the top for a given setting on the hot plate. To make use of this gradient, you may find it convenient to bury the vial or flask in the sand to heat a mixture more rapidly. Once the mixture is boiling, you can then slow the rate of heating by raising the vial or flask. These adjustments may be made easily and do not require a change in the setting on the hot plate.

Thermometer

Clamp

Clamp

Crystallizing dish

Sand

→ H₂O

← H₂O

Magnetic
spin vane

© Cengage Learning 2013

Figure 6.5
Heating with a sand bath.

Figure 6.6
Water bath.

6.3 Water Bath with Hot Plate/Stirrer

The methods described previously may be used over a range of about 50°C to over 200°C. A hot water bath, however, may be a suitable alternative for temperatures below 80°C. A beaker (250 mL or 400 mL) is partially filled with water and heated on a hot plate. A thermometer is clamped into position in the water bath. You may need to cover the water bath with aluminum foil to prevent evaporation, especially at higher temperatures. The water bath is illustrated in Figure 6.6. A mixture can be stirred with a magnetic spin vane (Technique 7, Section 7.3). A hot water bath has some advantage over an aluminum block or a sand bath in that the temperature in the bath is uniform. In addition, it is sometimes easier to establish a lower temperature with a water bath than with other heating devices. Finally, the temperature of the reaction mixture will be closer to the temperature of the water, which allows for more precise control of the reaction conditions.

6.4 Flames

The simplest technique for heating mixtures is to use a Bunsen burner. Because of the high danger of fires, however, the use of the Bunsen burner should be strictly limited to those cases for which the danger of fire is low or for which no reasonable alternative source of heat is available. A flame should generally be used only to heat aqueous solutions or solutions with very high boiling points. You should always check with your instructor about using a burner. If you use a burner at your bench, great care should be taken to ensure that others in the vicinity are not using flammable solvents.

In heating a flask with a Bunsen burner, you will find that using a wire gauze can produce more even heating over a broader area. The wire gauze, when placed under the object being heated, spreads the flame to keep the flask from being heated in one small area only.

Bunsen burners may be used to prepare capillary micropipettes for thin-layer chromatography or to prepare other pieces of glassware requiring an open flame. For these purposes, burners should be used in designated areas in the laboratory and not at your laboratory bench.

6.5 Cold Baths

At times, you may need to cool a conical vial or flask below room temperature. A cold bath is used for this purpose. The most common cold bath is an **ice bath,** which is a highly convenient source of 0°C temperatures. An ice bath requires water along with ice to work well. If an ice bath is made up of only ice, it is not an efficient cooler because the large pieces of ice do not make good contact with the flask or vial. Enough water should be present with ice so that the flask is surrounded by water but not so much that the temperature is no longer maintained at 0°C. In addition, if too much water is present, the buoyancy of a flask resting in the ice bath may cause it to tip over. There should be enough ice in the bath to allow the flask to rest firmly.

For temperatures somewhat below 0°C, you may add some solid sodium chloride to the ice-water bath. The ionic salt lowers the freezing point of the ice so that temperatures from 0 to –10°C can be reached. The lowest temperatures are reached with ice-salt-water mixtures that contain relatively little water.

A temperature of –78.5°C can be obtained with solid carbon dioxide or dry ice. Large chunks of dry ice do not provide uniform contact with a flask being cooled. A liquid such as isopropyl alcohol is mixed with small pieces of dry ice to provide an efficient cooling mixture. Acetone and ethanol can be used in place of isopropyl alcohol. Be careful when handling dry ice because it can inflict severe frostbite. Extremely low temperatures can be obtained with liquid nitrogen (–195.8°C).

6.6 Steam Baths

The steam cone or steam bath is a good source of heat when temperatures less than 100°C are needed. Steam baths are used to heat reaction mixtures and solvents needed for crystallization. A steam cone and a portable steam bath are shown in Figure 6.7. These methods of heating have the disadvantage that water vapor may be introduced, through condensation of steam, into the mixture being heated. A slow flow of steam may minimize this difficulty.

Because water condenses in the steam line when it is not in use, it is necessary to purge the line of water before the steam will begin to flow. This purging should be accomplished before the flask is placed on the steam bath. The steam flow should be started with a high rate to purge the line; then the flow should be reduced to the desired rate. When using a portable steam bath, be certain that condensate (water) is drained into a sink. Once the steam bath or cone is heated, a slow steam flow will maintain the temperature of the mixture being heated. There is no advantage to having a Vesuvius on your desk! An excessive steam flow may cause problems with condensation in the flask. This condensation problem can often be avoided by selecting the correct place at which to locate the flask on top of the steam bath.

The top of the steam bath consists of several flat concentric rings. The amount of heat

© Cengage Learning 2013

Figure 6.7
Steam bath and steam cone.

delivered to the flask being heated can be controlled by selecting the correct sizes of these rings. Heating is most efficient when the largest opening that will still support the flask is used. Heating large flasks on a steam bath while using the smallest opening leads to slow heating and wastes laboratory time.

PROBLEMS

1. What would be the preferred heating device(s) in each of the following situations?
   a. Refluxing a solvent with a 56°C boiling point
   b. Refluxing a solvent with a 120°C boiling point
   c. Distilling a substance that boils at 220°C

2. Obtain the boiling points for the following compounds by using a handbook (Technique 4). In each case, suggest a heating device(s) that should be used for refluxing the substance.
   a. Butyl benzoate
   b. 1-Pentanol
   c. 1-Chloropropane

3. What type of bath would you use to get a temperature of –10°C?

4. Obtain the melting point and boiling point for benzene and ammonia from a handbook (Technique 4) and answer the following questions.
   a. A reaction was conducted in benzene as the solvent. Because the reaction was very exothermic, the mixture was cooled in an ice-salt-water bath. This was a bad choice. Why?
   b. What bath should be used for a reaction that is conducted in *liquid* ammonia as the solvent?

5. Criticize the following techniques:
   a. Refluxing a mixture that contains diethyl ether using a Bunsen burner
   b. Refluxing a mixture that contains a large amount of toluene using a hot water bath
   c. Using a mercury thermometer that is inserted into an aluminum block on a hot plate
   d. Running a reaction with *tert*-butyl alcohol (2-methyl-2-propanol) that is cooled to 0°C in an ice bath

Reaction Methods

The successful completion of an organic reaction requires the chemist to be familiar with a variety of laboratory methods. These methods include operating safely, assembling the apparatus, heating and stirring reaction mixtures, adding liquid reagents, maintaining anhydrous and inert conditions in the reaction, and collecting gaseous products. Several techniques that are used in bringing a reaction to a successful conclusion are discussed here.

7.1 Assembling the Apparatus

Care must be taken when assembling the glass components into the desired apparatus. You should always remember that Newtonian physics applies to chemical apparatus, and unsecured pieces of glassware are certain to respond to gravity.

Assembling an apparatus in the correct manner requires that the individual pieces of glassware be connected to each other securely and the entire apparatus be held in the correct position. This can be accomplished by using **adjustable metal clamps** or a combination of adjustable metal clamps and **plastic joint clips.**

Two types of adjustable metal clamps are shown in Figure 7.1. Although these two types of clamps can usually be interchanged, the extension clamp is more commonly used to hold round-bottom flasks in place, and the three-finger clamp is frequently used to clamp condensers. Both types of clamps must be attached to a ring stand using a clamp holder, shown in Figure 7.1C.

A. Securing Macroscale Apparatus Assemblies

It is possible to assemble an apparatus using only adjustable metal clamps. An apparatus used to perform a distillation is shown in Figure 7.2. It is held together securely with three metal clamps. Because of the size of the apparatus and its geometry, the various clamps would likely be attached to three different ring stands. This apparatus would be somewhat difficult to assemble because it is necessary to ensure that the individual pieces stay together while securing and adjusting the clamps required to hold the entire apparatus in place. In addition, one must be careful not to bump any part of the apparatus or the ring stands after the apparatus is assembled.

A. Extension clamp

B. Three-finger clamp

C. Clamp holder

© Cengage Learning 2013

Figure 7.1
Adjustable metal clamps.

© Cengage Learning 2013

Figure 7.2
Distillation apparatus secured with metal clamps.

© Cengage Learning 2013

A. Plastic joint clip

B. Joint connected by plastic clip

Figure 7.3
Plastic joint clip.

A more convenient alternative is to use a combination of metal clamps and plastic joint clips. A plastic joint clip is shown in Figure 7.3A. These clips are easy to use (they just clip on), will withstand temperatures up to 140°C, and are durable. They hold together two pieces of glassware that are connected by ground-glass joints, as shown in Figure 7.3B. These clips come in different sizes to fit ground-glass joints of different sizes, and they are color coded for each size.

When used in combination with metal clamps, the plastic joint clips make it much easier to assemble most apparatus securely. There is less chance of dropping the glassware while assembling the apparatus, and once the apparatus is set up, it is more secure. Figure 7.4 shows the same distillation apparatus held in place with adjustable metal clamps and plastic joint clips.

To assemble this apparatus, first connect all of the individual pieces using the plastic clips. The entire apparatus is then connected to the ring stands using the adjustable metal clamps. Note that only two ring stands are required and the wooden blocks are not needed.

B. Securing Microscale Apparatus Assemblies

The glassware in most microscale kits is made with standard-taper ground joints. The most common joint size is ⦙ 14/10. Some microscale glassware with ground-glass joints also has threads cast into the outside surface of the outer joints (see top of air condenser in Figure 7.5). The threaded joint allows the use of a plastic screw cap with a hole in the top to fasten two pieces of glassware together securely. The plastic cap is slipped over the inner joint of the upper piece of glassware, followed by a rubber O-ring (see Figure 7.5). The O-ring should be pushed down so that it fits snugly on top of the ground-glass joint. The inner ground-glass joint is then fitted into the outer joint of the bottom piece of glassware. The screw cap is tightened, without excessive force, to attach the entire apparatus firmly together. The O-ring provides an additional seal that makes this joint airtight. With this connecting

Figure 7.4

Distillation apparatus secured with metal clamps and plastic joint clips.

Figure 7.5

A microscale standard-taper joint assembly.

© Cengage Learning 2013

© Cengage Learning 2013

system, it is unnecessary to use any type of grease to seal the joint. The O-ring *must be used* to obtain a good seal and to lessen the chances of breaking the glassware when you tighten the plastic cap.

Microscale glassware connected in this fashion can be assembled easily. The entire apparatus is held together securely, and usually only one metal clamp is required to hold the apparatus onto a ring stand.

7.2 Heating under Reflux

Often we wish to heat a mixture for a long time and to leave it untended. A **reflux apparatus** (see Figure 7.6) allows such heating. It also keeps the solvent from being lost by evaporation. A condenser is attached to the reaction vial or boiling flask.

Choice of Condenser. The condenser used in a reflux apparatus can be either of two types. An **air condenser** is simply a long tube. The surrounding air removes heat from the vapors within the tube and condenses them to liquid. A **water-jacketed condenser** consists of two concentric tubes with the outer cooling tube sealed onto the inner tube. The vapors rise within the inner tube, and water circulates through the outer tube. The circulating water removes heat from the vapors and condenses them. The air condenser is suitable for use with high-boiling liquids or with small quantities of material that are being heated gently. The water-jacketed condenser must be used when the vapors are difficult to condense, usually because the substance is volatile, or when vigorous boiling action is desired. In either case, the condenser prevents the vapors from escaping. Glassware assemblies using both air and water-jacketed condensers are shown in Figure 7.6A. The figure also shows a typical macroscale apparatus for heating large quantities of material under reflux (Figure 7.6B).

A. Reflux apparatus using a water-jacketed condenser (the inset shows an alternative assembly, using an air condenser).

B. Reflux apparatus for large-scale reactions, using a heating mantle and water-jacketed condenser.

→ H_2O

← H_2O

Aluminum block

Reflux ring

A

B

© Cengage Learning 2013

Figure 7.6
Heating under reflux.

When a water-jacketed condenser is used, the direction of the water flow should be such that the condenser will fill with cooling water. The water should enter the bottom of the condenser and leave from the top. The water should flow fast enough to withstand any changes in pressure in the water lines, but it should not flow any faster than absolutely necessary. An excessive flow rate greatly increases the chance of a flood, and high water pressure may force the hose from the condenser. Cooling water should be flowing before heating is begun! If the water is to remain flowing overnight, it is advisable to fasten the rubber tubing securely with wire to the condenser. If a flame is used as a source of heat, it is wise to use a wire gauze beneath the flask to provide an even distribution of heat from the flame. In most cases, an aluminum block, a sand bath, water bath, heating mantle, or steam bath is preferred over a flame.

Stirring. When heating a solution, always use a magnetic stirrer or a boiling stone (see Sections 7.3 and 7.4) to keep the solution from "bumping."

Rate of Heating. If the heating rate has been correctly adjusted, the liquid being heated under reflux will travel only partway up the condenser tube before condensing. Below the condensation point, solvent will be seen running back into the flask; above it, the interior of the condenser will appear dry. The boundary between the two zones will be clearly demarcated, and a **reflux ring** or a ring of liquid will appear there. The reflux ring can be seen in Figure 7.6B. In heating under reflux, the rate of heating should be adjusted so that the reflux ring is no higher than a third to half the distance to the top of the condenser. With microscale experiments, the quantities of vapor rising in the condenser frequently are so small that a clear reflux ring cannot be seen. In those cases, the heating rate must be adjusted so that the liquid boils smoothly but not so rapidly that solvent can escape the condenser. With such small volumes, the loss of even a small amount of solvent can affect the reaction. With large-scale reactions, the reflux ring is much easier to see, and one can adjust the heating rate more easily.

Tended Reflux. It is possible to heat small amounts of a solvent under reflux in an Erlenmeyer flask. With gentle heating, the evaporated solvent will condense in the relatively cold neck of the flask and return to the solution. This technique (see Figure 7.7) requires constant attention. The flask must be swirled frequently and removed from the heating source for a short period if the boiling becomes too vigorous. When heating is in progress, the reflux ring should not be allowed to rise into the neck of the flask.

Figure 7.7
Tended reflux of small quantities on a steam cone (this can also be done with a hot plate).

Reflux ring

© Cengage Learning 2013

How Do I Know How Hot to Heat It? A common problem that inexperienced students encounter when they assemble an apparatus for heating under reflux is that it is difficult to decide what temperature setting to use for heating the contents of a vial or flask to the desired temperature. This problem becomes more acute when the students attempt to reproduce the temperatures that are specified in the laboratory procedures of a textbook.

First, you should understand that the temperatures specified are only approximate suggestions. The actual temperature required to carry out a particular procedure must be determined for each student and each apparatus. When you see a temperature stipulated, consider it as nothing more than a guide. You will have to make adjustments to suit your own situation.

Second, you must always pay attention to what is going on in your reaction flask. If the temperature of your aluminum block or sand bath equals the suggested temperature, but the solution in your flask is not boiling, you clearly will have to increase the temperature of the heating device. Remember that what really matters is what is going on in the flask, not what the textbook says! The *external* temperature, as measured by a thermometer placed into the heating device, is not the important temperature. Far more critical is the temperature *inside* the flask, which may be considerably lower than the external temperature.

7.3 Stirring Methods

When a solution is heated, there is a danger that it may become superheated. When this happens, very large bubbles sometimes erupt violently from the solution; this is called **bumping.** Bumping must be avoided because of the risk that material may be lost from the apparatus, that a fire may start, or that the apparatus may break.

Magnetic stirrers are used to prevent bumping because they produce turbulence in the solution. The turbulence breaks up the large bubbles that form in boiling solutions. An additional purpose for using a magnetic stirrer is to stir the reaction to ensure that all the reagents are thoroughly mixed. A magnetic stirring system consists of a magnet that is rotated by an electric motor. The rate at which this magnet rotates can be adjusted by a potentiometric control. A small magnet, which is coated with a nonreactive material such as Teflon or glass, is placed in the flask. The magnet within the flask rotates in response to the rotating magnetic field caused by the motor-driven magnet. The result is that the inner magnet stirs the solution as it rotates. A common type of magnetic stirrer includes the stirring

A. Standard-sized magnetic stirring bars

B. Microscale magnetic spin vane

C. Small magnetic stirring bar ("disposable" type)

© Cengage Learning 2013

Figure 7.8
Magnetic stirring bars.

system within a hot plate. This type of hot plate/stirrer permits one to heat the reaction and stir it simultaneously. In order for the magnetic stirrer to be effective, the contents of the flask being stirred should be placed as close to the center of the hot plate as possible and not offset.

For macroscale apparatus, magnetic stirring bars of various sizes and shapes are available. For microscale apparatus, a **magnetic spin vane** is often used. It is designed to contain a tiny bar magnet and to have a shape that conforms to the conical bottom of a reaction vial. A small Teflon-coated magnetic stirring bar works well with very small round-bottom boiling flasks. Small stirring bars of this type (often sold as "disposable" stirring bars) can be obtained cheaply. A variety of magnetic stirring bars is illustrated in Figure 7.8.

There is also a variety of simple techniques that may be used to stir a liquid mixture in a centrifuge tube or conical vial. A thorough mixing of the components of a liquid can be achieved by repeatedly drawing the liquid into a Pasteur pipette and then ejecting the liquid back into the container by pressing sharply on the dropper bulb. Liquids can also be stirred effectively by placing the flattened end of a spatula into the container and twirling it rapidly.

7.4 Boiling Stones

A **boiling stone,** also known as a **boiling chip** or **Boileezer,** is a small lump of porous material that produces a steady stream of fine air bubbles when it is heated in a solvent. This stream of bubbles and the turbulence that accompanies it break up the large bubbles of gases in the liquid. In this way, it reduces the tendency of the liquid to become superheated, and it promotes the smooth boiling of the liquid. The boiling stone decreases the chances for bumping.

Two common types of boiling stones are carborundum and marble chips. Carborundum boiling stones are more inert, and the pieces are usually small, suitable for most applications. If available, carborundum boiling stones are preferred for most purposes. Marble chips may dissolve in strong acid solutions, and the pieces are larger. The advantage of marble chips is that they are cheaper.

Because boiling stones act to promote the smooth boiling of liquids, you should always make certain that a boiling stone has been placed in a liquid *before* heating is begun. If you wait until the liquid is hot, it may have become superheated. Adding a boiling stone to a superheated liquid will cause all the liquid to try to boil at once. The liquid, as a result, would erupt entirely out of the flask or froth violently.

As soon as boiling ceases in a liquid containing a boiling stone, the liquid is drawn into the pores of the boiling stone. When this happens, the boiling stone no longer can produce a fine stream of bubbles; it is spent. You may have to add a new boiling stone if you have allowed boiling to stop for a long period.

Wooden applicator sticks are used in some applications. They function in the same manner as boiling stones. Occasionally, glass beads are used. Their presence also causes sufficient turbulence in the liquid to prevent bumping.

7.5 Addition of Liquid Reagents

Liquid reagents and solutions are added to a reaction by several means, some of which are shown in Figure 7.9. For microscale experiments, the simplest approach is simply to add the liquid to the reaction by means of a Pasteur pipette. This method is shown in Figure 7.9A. In this technique, the system is open to the atmosphere. A second microscale method, shown in Figure 7.9B, is suitable for experiments in

A. Addition using a Pasteur pipette inserted into the top of an air condenser

B. Addition with a hypodermic syringe inserted through a rubber septum

C. Macroscale equipment, using a separatory funnel as an addition funnel

D. A pressure-equalizing addition funnel

Figure 7.9
Methods of adding liquid reagents to a reaction.

which the reaction should be kept isolated from the atmosphere. In this approach, the liquid is kept in a hypodermic syringe. The syringe needle is inserted through a rubber septum, and the liquid is added dropwise from the syringe. The septum seals the apparatus from the atmosphere, which makes this technique useful for reactions that are conducted under an atmosphere of inert gas or where anhydrous conditions must be maintained. As an alternative, the rubber septum may be replaced by a cap and Teflon insert or liner. A disadvantage of the Teflon insert, however, is that the insert may no longer form an effective seal after being punctured by the needle.

The most common type of assembly for macroscale experiments is shown in Figure 7.9C. In this apparatus, a separatory funnel is attached to the side arm of a three-necked round-bottom flask. The separatory funnel must be equipped with a standard-taper, ground-glass joint to be used in this manner. The liquid is stored in the separatory funnel (which is called an **addition funnel** in this application) and is added to the reaction. The rate of addition is controlled by adjusting the stopcock. When it is being used as an addition funnel, the upper opening must be kept open to the atmosphere. If the upper hole is stoppered, a vacuum will develop in the funnel and will prevent the liquid from passing into the reaction vessel. Because the funnel is open to the atmosphere, there is a danger that atmospheric moisture can contaminate the liquid reagent as it is being added. To prevent this outcome, a drying tube (see Section 7.6) is attached to the upper opening of the addition funnel. The drying tube allows the funnel to maintain atmospheric pressure without allowing the passage of water vapor into the reaction.

Figure 7.9D shows an alternative type of addition funnel that is useful for reactions that must be maintained under an atmosphere of inert gas. This is the **pressure-equalizing addition funnel.** With this glassware, the upper opening is stoppered. The side arm allows the pressure above the liquid in the funnel to be in equilibrium with the pressure in the rest of the apparatus, and it lets the inert gas flow over the top of the liquid as it is being added.

7.6 Drying Tubes

With certain reactions, atmospheric moisture must be prevented from entering the reaction vessel. A **drying tube** can be used to maintain anhydrous conditions within the apparatus. Two types of drying tubes are shown in Figure 7.10. The typical drying tube is prepared by placing a small, loose plug of glass wool or cotton into the constriction at the end of the tube nearest the ground-glass joint or hose connection. The plug is tamped gently with a glass rod or piece of wire to place it in the correct position. A drying agent, typically calcium sulfate ("Drierite") or calcium chloride (see Technique 12, Section 12.9), is poured on top of the plug to the approximate depth shown in Figure 7.10. Another loose plug of glass wool or cotton is placed on top of the drying agent to prevent the solid material from falling out of the drying tube. The drying tube is then attached to the flask or condenser.

Air that enters the apparatus must pass through the drying tube.

Glass wool (or cotton)

Drying agent

Glass wool (or cotton)

Glass wool (or cotton)

Drying agent

A. Macroscale drying tube

B. Microscale drying tube

© Cengage Learning 2013

Figure 7.10
Drying tubes.

The drying agent absorbs any moisture from air passing through it so that air entering the reaction vessel has had the water vapor removed from it.

7.7 Reactions Conducted under an Inert Atmosphere

Some reactions are sensitive to oxygen and water vapor present in air and require an inert atmosphere in order to obtain satisfactory results. The usual reactions in which it is desirable to exclude air often include organometallic reagents, such as organomagnesium or organolithium reagents, where water vapor and oxygen (air) react with these compounds. The most common inert gases available in a laboratory are nitrogen and argon, which are available in gas cylinders. Nitrogen is probably the gas most often used to carry out reactions under an inert atmosphere, although argon has a distinct advantage because it is denser than air. This allows the argon to push air away from the reaction mixture.

When laboratories are not equipped with individual gas lines to benches or hoods, it is useful to supply nitrogen or argon to the reaction apparatus using a balloon assembly (shown in Figure 7.11A). Your instructor will provide you with the apparatus.

Construct the balloon assembly by cutting off the top of a 3-mL disposable plastic syringe. Attach a small balloon snugly to the top of the syringe, securing it with a small rubber band that has been doubled to hold the balloon securely to the body of the syringe. Attach a needle to the syringe. Fill the balloon with the inert gas through the needle using a piece of rubber tubing attached to the gas source. When the balloon has been inflated to 2–3 inches in diameter, quickly pinch off the neck of the balloon while removing the gas source. Now push the needle into a rubber stopper to keep the balloon inflated. It is possible to keep an assembly like this filled with inert gas for several days without the balloon deflating.

Before you start the reaction, you may need to dry your apparatus thoroughly in an oven. Add all reagents carefully to avoid water. The following instructions are based on the assumption that you are using an apparatus consisting of a round-bottom flask equipped with a condenser. Attach a rubber septum to the top of your condenser. Now flush the air out of the apparatus with the inert gas. It is best not to use the balloon assembly for this purpose, unless you are using argon (see next paragraph). Instead, remove the round-bottom flask from the apparatus and, with the help of your instructor, flush it with the inert gas using a Pasteur pipette to bubble the gas through the solvent and reaction mixture in the flask. In this way, you can remove air from the reaction assembly before attaching the balloon assembly. Quickly reattach the flask to the apparatus. Pinch off the neck of the balloon between your fingers, remove the rubber stopper, and insert the needle into the rubber septum. The reaction apparatus is now ready for use.

When argon is employed as an inert gas, you can use the balloon assembly to remove air from the reaction apparatus in the following way. Insert the balloon assembly into the rubber septum as previously described. Also insert a second needle (no syringe attached) through the septum. The pressure from the balloon will force argon down the reflux condenser (argon is denser than air) and push the less dense air out through the second syringe needle. When the apparatus has been thoroughly flushed with argon, remove the second needle. Nitrogen does not work as well with this method because it is less dense than air, and it will be difficult to remove the air that is in contact with the reaction mixture in the round-bottom flask.

For reactions conducted at room temperature, you can remove the condenser shown in Figure 7.11A. Attach the rubber septum directly to the round-bottom flask and insert the needle of an argon-filled balloon assembly

Figure 7.11A

Conducting a reaction under an inert atmosphere using a balloon assembly.

Labels in figure:
Balloon filled with N_2 or Ar
Rubber band
3-mL Plastic syringe with top cut off and plunger removed
Rubber septum
Syringe needle
H_2O
H_2O
Stir bar or boiling stones
© Cengage Learning 2013

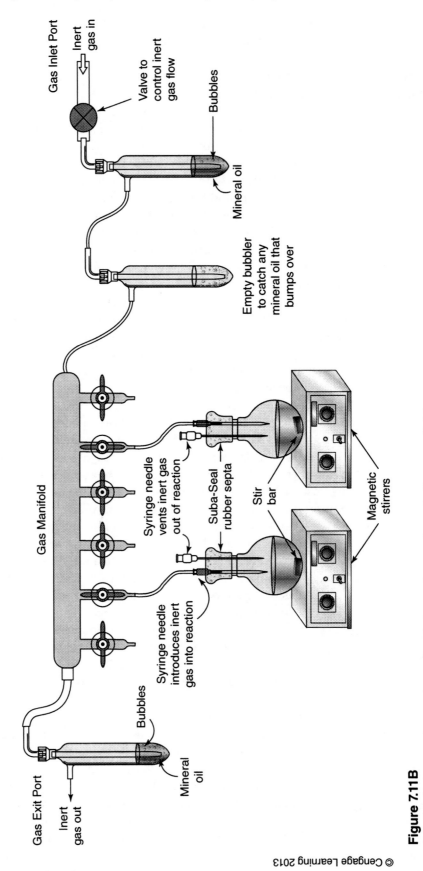

Figure 7.11B
Conducting a reaction under an inert atmosphere using a balloon manifold.

© Cengage Learning 2013

through the rubber septum. To flush the air out of the reaction flask, insert a second syringe needle into the rubber septum. Any air present in the flask will be flushed out through this second syringe needle, and the air will be replaced with argon. Now remove the second needle, and you have a reaction mixture free of air.

A gas manifold, shown in Figure 7.11B, provides another method of conducting reactions under an inert atmosphere. The gas manifold is equipped with multiple stopcocks so that more than one reaction can be conducted with a single tank of an inert gas, either nitrogen or argon. This setup allows a reaction to be maintained under anhydrous conditions in an oxygen-free environment. As shown in Figure 7.11B, the barrel of a cut-off syringe with an attached syringe needle is inserted into the rubber tubing. An inert gas is introduced through the Gas Inlet Port on the right side to expel air from the manifold. The mineral oil bubbler helps to monitor the gas flow into the manifold. The bubbling action in the inlet mineral oil bubbler must equal or exceed the bubbling action in the Gas Exit Port on the left side of Figure 7.11B.

Once the gas flow in the manifold is adjusted, one of the stopcocks on the manifold is opened, and the needle is inserted into a rubber septum on the reaction flask. The gas flow into the reaction flask is controlled with the stopcock on the manifold. Excess gas is vented through another syringe needle inserted into the rubber septum. Often the rate of bubbling observed in the Gas Exit Port will slow when the stopcock to the reaction flask is opened. The gas flow from the Gas Inlet Port will need to be increased in order to maintain bubbling in the Gas Exit Port. A complete description of the use of a gas manifold assembly is given in Experiment 59, *Synthesis of Naproxen by Palladium Catalysis.*

7.8 Capturing Noxious Gases

Many organic reactions involve the production of a noxious gaseous product. The gas may be corrosive, such as hydrogen chloride, hydrogen bromide, or sulfur dioxide, or it may be toxic, such as carbon monoxide. The safest way to avoid exposure to these gases is to conduct the reaction in a ventilated hood where the gases can be safely drawn away by the ventilation system.

In many instances, however, it is safe and efficient to conduct the experiment on the laboratory bench, away from the hood. This is particularly true when the gases are soluble in water. Some techniques for capturing noxious gases are presented in this section.

A. Drying Tube Method

Microscale experiments have the advantage that the amounts of gases produced are small. Hence, it is easy to trap them and prevent them from escaping into the laboratory. You can take advantage of the water solubility of corrosive gases such as hydrogen chloride, hydrogen bromide, and sulfur dioxide. A simple technique is to attach the drying tube (see Figure 7.10B) to the top of the reaction vial or condenser. The drying tube is filled with moistened glass wool. The moisture in the glass wool absorbs the gas, preventing its escape. To prepare this type of gas trap, fill the drying tube with glass wool and then add water dropwise to the glass wool until it has been moistened to the desired degree. Moistened cotton can also be used, although cotton will absorb so much water that it is easy to plug the drying tube.

When using glass wool in a drying tube, moisture from the glass wool must not be allowed to drain from the drying tube into the reaction. It is best to use a drying tube that has a constriction between the part where the glass wool is placed and the neck, where the joint is attached. The constriction acts as a partial barrier preventing the water from leaking into the neck of the drying tube. Make certain not to make the glass wool too moist.

B. External Gas Traps

Another approach to capturing gases is to prepare a trap that is separate from the reaction apparatus. The gases are carried from the reaction to the trap by means of tubing. There are several variations on this type of trap. One method that works well for microscale experiments is to place a thermometer adapter (Technique 14, Figure 14.9A) into the opening in the reaction apparatus. A Pasteur pipette is inserted upside down through the adapter, and a piece of fine flexible tubing is fitted over the narrow tip. It may be helpful to break the Pasteur pipette before using it for this purpose so that only the narrow tip and a short section of the barrel are used. The other end of the flexible tubing is placed through a large plug of moistened glass wool in a test tube. The water in the glass wool absorbs the water-soluble gases. This method is shown in Figure 7.12.

A variation on the Pasteur pipette method uses a hypodermic syringe needle inserted upside down (from the inside) through a rubber septum, which has been fitted over the opening at the top of the reaction apparatus. Flexible tubing, fitted over the syringe needle, leads to a trap such as the one using wet glass wool described previously. This variation is also shown in Figure 7.12.

Another alternative to the apparatus shown in Figure 7.12 is to use a multipurpose adapter in place of the thermometer adapter. The flexible tubing can be attached directly to the side arm of the multipurpose adapter, thus connecting the apparatus to the gas trap. If the multipurpose adapter is used for this purpose, the upper opening of the adapter must be closed; this is accomplished most easily by inserting a piece of glass rod or a short piece of glass tubing sealed at one end into the opening and tightening the fittings around it.

Thermometer adapter

Moistened glass wool

Rubber septum

Syringe needle

© Cengage Learning 2013

Figure 7.12
Microscale external gas trap. (The inset shows an expanded view of an alternative fitting, using a syringe needle and a rubber septum.)

Figure 7.13
An inverted-funnel gas trap.

    With large-scale reactions, a trap using an inverted funnel placed in a beaker of water is used. A piece of glass tubing, inserted through a thermometer adapter attached to the reaction apparatus, is connected to flexible tubing. The tubing is attached to a conical funnel. The funnel is clamped in place inverted over a beaker of water. The funnel is clamped so that its lip *almost touches* the water surface, but is not placed below the surface of the water. With this arrangement, water cannot be sucked back into the reaction if the pressure in the reaction vessel changes suddenly. This type of trap can also be used in microscale applications. An example of the inverted-funnel type of gas trap is shown in Figure 7.13.

C. Removal of Noxious Gases Using an Aspirator

An aspirator can be used to remove noxious gases from the reaction. The simplest approach is to clamp a disposable Pasteur pipette so that its tip is placed well into the condenser atop the reaction vial. An inverted funnel clamped over the apparatus can also be used. The pipette or funnel is attached to an aspirator with flexible tubing. A trap should be placed between the pipette or funnel and the aspirator. As gases are liberated from the reaction, they rise into the condenser. The vacuum draws the gases away from the apparatus. Both types of systems are shown in Figure 7.14. In the special case in which

Figure 7.14
Removal of noxious gases under vacuum. (The inset shows an alternative assembly, using a funnel in place of the Pasteur pipette.)

the noxious gases are soluble in water, connecting a water aspirator to the pipette or funnel removes the gases from the reaction and traps them in the flowing water without the need for a separate gas trap.

7.9 Collecting Gaseous Products

In Section 7.8, means of removing unwanted gaseous products from the reaction system were examined. Some experiments produce gaseous products that you must collect and analyze. Methods to collect gaseous products are all based on the same principle. The gas is carried through tubing from the reaction to the opening of a flask or a test tube, which has been filled with water and is inverted in a container of water. The gas is allowed to bubble into the inverted collection tube (or flask). As the collection tube fills with gas, the water is displaced into the water container. If the collection tube is graduated, as in a graduated cylinder or a centrifuge tube, you can monitor the quantity of gas produced in the reaction.

If the inverted gas-collection tube is constructed from a piece of glass tubing, a rubber septum can be used to close the upper end of the container. This type of collection tube is shown in Figure 7.15. A sample of the gas can be removed using a syringe equipped with a needle. The gas that is removed can be analyzed by gas chromatography (see Technique 22).

Some of the glassware kits for microscale experiments contain a special, all-glass, capillary gas-delivery tube. The tube is attached to the top of the reaction apparatus by means of a ground-glass joint, and the open end of the capillary tubing is placed into an inverted, water-filled flask or test tube, clamped over a water bath. An example of a microscale kit gas-delivery tube is shown in Figure 7.16A. This type of tube is an efficient means of collecting gases. A disadvantage, however, is that it is expensive and relatively easy to break.

Figure 7.15
Gas-collection tube, with rubber septum.

A. Apparatus using a capillary gas-delivery tube

B. The inset shows alternative assemblies, using flexible tubing

Figure 7.16
Gas-delivery tubes.

A simpler, less expensive approach is to use flexible tubing of a fine diameter to lead the gases from the reaction vessel to the collecting container. One method is to place a hypodermic syringe needle, point upward, through a rubber septum. The septum is attached to the top of the reaction apparatus, and a piece of fine flexible tubing is fitted over the end of the needle. The free end of the tubing is placed in the water bath, underneath the opening of the water-filled collection container. The gases bubble into the container, where they are collected. This alternative apparatus is shown in Figure 7.15 and also as an inset in Figure 7.16B.

Another alternative, which may also be used with larger-scale experiments, is to place a piece of glass tubing or the tip of a Pasteur pipette through a thermometer adapter. The thermometer adapter is attached to the top of the reaction apparatus, and flexible tubing is attached to the piece of glass tubing. The free end of the tubing is positioned in the opening of the water-filled collection vessel, as described previously. This variation is also shown as an inset in Figure 7.16. As an option, you may attach a second piece of glass tubing to the free end of the flexible hose. This piece of glass tubing sometimes makes it easier to fix the open end in the proper position in the opening of the collection flask.

7.10 Evaporation of Solvents

In many experiments, it is necessary to remove excess solvent from a solution. An obvious approach is to allow the container to stand unstoppered in the hood for several hours until the solvent has evaporated. This method is generally not practical, however, and a quicker, more efficient means of evaporating solvents must be used. Figures 7.17 and 7.18 show several methods of removing solvents by evaporation. Figure 7.17 depicts microscale methods; Figure 7.18 is devoted to large-scale procedures.

NOTE: It is good laboratory practice to evaporate solvents in the hood.

Microscale Methods. A simple means of evaporating a solvent is to place a conical vial in a warm water bath or a warm sand bath. The heat from the water bath or sand bath will warm the solvent to a temperature where it can evaporate within a short time. The heat from the water bath or sand bath can be adjusted to provide the best rate of evaporation, but the liquid should not be allowed to boil vigorously. The evaporation rate can be increased by allowing a stream of dry air or nitrogen to be directed into the vial (Figure 7.17A). The moving gas stream will sweep the vapors from the vial and accelerate the evaporation. As an alternative, a vacuum can be applied above the vial to draw away solvent vapors (Figure 7.17B and 7.17C).

A convenient water bath suitable for microscale methods can be constructed by placing the aluminum collars, which are generally used with aluminum heating blocks into a 150-mL beaker (Figure 7.17A). In some cases, it may be necessary to round off the sharp edges of the collars with a file in order to allow them to fit properly into the beaker. Held by the aluminum collars, the conical vial will stand securely in the beaker. This assembly can be filled with water and placed on a hot plate for use in the evaporation of small amounts of solvent.

Aluminum heating blocks placed on a hot plate can also be used for the evaporation of solvents (Figure 7.17B). You must be careful, however, not to allow the aluminum block to become too hot, or the sample may decompose thermally.

During a crystallization procedure, you often must remove excess solvent from the solution. If a Craig tube is being used for the crystallization, the excess solvent can be removed directly from the Craig tube (see Technique 11, Section 11.4). The Craig tube is placed in a warm water bath or warm sand bath. Alternatively,

Figure 7.17
Evaporation of solvents (microscale methods).

the Craig tube can be placed into one of the small holes of an aluminum block. A microspatula is placed into the Craig tube, and it is twirled rapidly as the solvent evaporates (Figure 7.17D). The twirling spatula acts in the same manner as a boiling stone; it prevents bumping and accelerates the evaporation.

Commercially available evaporation stations may be useful when a large number of evaporations must be performed at the same time. This type of equipment consists of several holders for vials or flasks. At each position, a piece of tubing equipped with a metal tip is used to direct a stream of air into the vessel. A water bath is used to heat all the containers simultaneously.

Larger-Scale Methods. On a large scale, these evaporation methods can also be applied to standard-sized glassware. Solvents can be evaporated from solutions

Figure 7.18
Evaporation of solvents (large-scale methods).

in Erlenmeyer flasks by adapting the techniques described previously. An Erlenmeyer flask can be placed on a source of heat, and the solvent can be removed by evaporation under a gas stream or a vacuum. Sources of heat that can be used with Erlenmeyer flasks include sand and steam baths and hot plates. A solution can also be placed in a side arm test tube or a filter flask, which is attached to a source of vacuum. A wooden stick or a piece of a melting point capillary is often placed in the solution, and the flask or test tube is swirled over the source of heat to reduce the possibility of bumping. The methods are illustrated in Figure 7.18.

7.11 Rotary Evaporator

In some organic chemistry laboratories, solvents are evaporated under reduced pressure using a **rotary evaporator.** This is a motor-driven device that is designed for rapid evaporation of solvents, with heating, while minimizing the possibility of bumping. A vacuum is applied to the flask, and the motor spins the flask. The rotation of the flask spreads a thin film of the liquid over the surface of the glass, which accelerates evaporation. The rotation also agitates the solution sufficiently to reduce the problem of bumping. A water bath can be placed under the flask to warm the solution and increase the vapor pressure of the solvent. One can select the speed at which the flask is rotated and the temperature of the water bath to attain the desired evaporation rate. As the solvent evaporates from the rotating flask,

Water or other coolant (out)

Valve for releasing vacuum

Water or other coolant (in)

Motor

To vacuum

Condenser with cooling coil

Clamp on ball joint

Solvent collector

Water bath

© Cengage Learning 2013

Figure 7.19
A rotary evaporator.

the vapors are cooled by the condenser, and the resulting liquid collects in the flask. The product remains behind in the rotating flask. A complete rotary evaporator assembly is shown in Figure 7.19. If the coolant is sufficiently cold, virtually all of the solvent can be recovered and recycled. This is a good example of *Green Chemistry* (see Green Chemistry essay, that precedes Experiment 28).

7.12 Microwave-Assisted Organic Chemistry

We are all familiar with the use of a microwave oven in the kitchen and its particular advantages. Cooking food in a microwave oven is much faster than in a conventional oven. Microwave cooking is much simpler, does not require as much crockery, and energy is not wasted in heating the container.

All of these advantages can also be applied to the chemistry laboratory. It is possible to conduct chemical reactions in much less time than with ordinary laboratory methods. Since the mid-1980s, chemists have been working on developing methods to apply microwave heating to chemical synthesis. Microwave-assisted organic chemical methods, or **microwave chemistry**, have gained wide acceptance, especially in industrial and research laboratories. Microwave heating is able to heat the chemical reagents without wasting energy in heating their container. In "green chemistry" applications, it allows the chemist to perform chemical reactions using less energy, in less time, often using water as a solvent, and often without using any solvent at all.

There does not seem to be general agreement as to the mechanism of microwave heating. The arguments are too complex to be included here. A basic understanding is possible, however. Microwave radiation is a form of *electromagnetic radiation*; this means that microwave radiation consists of oscillating electric and magnetic fields. When an oscillating electric field passes through a medium that contains polar or ionic substances, these molecules will attempt to orient themselves or oscillate in response to the electric field. Because these molecules are bound to surrounding

Figure 7.20
A microwave reaction system. (Reprinted courtesy of CEM Corporation.)

molecules in the medium, however, their motions are restricted, and they cannot respond completely to the oscillations of the electric field. This causes a non-equilibrium condition that results in an elevated instantaneous temperature in the immediate microscopic region surrounding the molecules that are being affected. As this localized temperature increases, molecules are activated above the required energy-of-activation threshold. Rates of reactions are dependent upon temperature; as the localized temperature increases, the molecules in that microscopic region will react faster.

Chemists first tried using domestic kitchen microwave ovens to speed up chemical reactions. They found that they were able to accelerate reactions, increase yields, and initiate otherwise impossible reactions. The results were often unsatisfactory, however, owing to uneven heating, lack of reproducibility, and the possibility of explosions. The power output of a typical kitchen microwave oven cannot be adjusted. The oven cycles between periods of full power and periods of zero power. This means that the amount of microwave energy being transmitted into an experiment cannot be controlled precisely.

In recent years, companies have developed state-of-the-art microwave reaction systems to overcome these deficiencies. A modern reaction system, such as the one shown in Figure 7.20, has a specially designed vessel that focuses the microwave energy for efficient heating. Such systems are often equipped with automatic stirring and computer controls. Often a pressure control system may be included; this allows one to conduct a reaction at elevated temperature and pressure in the presence of volatile solvents or reagents. An automated sample changer is a useful accessory; this allows the chemist to conduct a series of repeated experiments without having to spend time watching the system.

Papers describing the advantages of microwave chemistry are appearing with increasing frequency in the chemical literature. Examples of experiments that can be conducted using microwave reaction systems include esterifications, condensation reactions, hydrogenations, cycloadditions, and even peptide syntheses. Besides offering a versatile method of chemical synthesis, microwave reaction systems also include the advantages that many of the reactions can be conducted in water, rather than in harmful organic solvents, or even in the complete absence of solvent. This capability makes microwave chemistry an important tool in "green chemistry."

PROBLEMS

1. What is the best type of stirring device to use for stirring a reaction that takes place in the following type of glassware?

   a. A conical vial

   b. A 10-mL round-bottom flask

   c. A 250-mL round-bottom flask

2. Should you use a drying tube for the following reaction? Explain.

$$CH_3-\overset{\overset{\displaystyle O}{\|}}{C}-OH + CH_3-\underset{\underset{\displaystyle CH_3}{|}}{CH}-CH_2-CH_2-OH \rightleftarrows CH_3-\overset{\overset{\displaystyle O}{\|}}{C}-O-CH_2-CH_2-\underset{\underset{\displaystyle CH_3}{|}}{CH}-CH_3 + H_2O$$

3. For which of the following reactions should you use a trap to collect noxious gases?

a.
$$\text{C}_6\text{H}_5-\overset{\overset{\displaystyle O}{\|}}{C}-OH + SOCl_2 \xrightarrow{\text{heat}} \text{C}_6\text{H}_5-\overset{\overset{\displaystyle O}{\|}}{C}-Cl + SO_2 + HCl$$

b.
$$\text{C}_6\text{H}_5-\overset{\overset{\displaystyle O}{\|}}{C}-Cl + CH_3-CH_2-OH \longrightarrow \text{C}_6\text{H}_5-\overset{\overset{\displaystyle O}{\|}}{C}-O-CH_2-CH_3 + HCl$$

c. $C_{12}H_{22}O_{11} + H_2O \longrightarrow 4\,CH_3-CH_2-OH + 4\,CO_2$
   (Sucrose)

d. $CH_3-\underset{\underset{\displaystyle H}{|}}{C}=NH + H_2O \xrightarrow[\text{heat}]{\text{base}} CH_3-\underset{\underset{\displaystyle H}{|}}{C}=O + NH_3$

4. Criticize the following techniques:

   a. A reflux is conducted with a stopper in the top of the condenser.

   b. Water is passed through the reflux condenser at the rate of 1 gallon per minute.

   c. No water hoses are attached to the condenser during a reflux.

   d. A boiling stone is not added to the round-bottom flask until the mixture is boiling vigorously.

   e. To save money, you decide to save your boiling stones for another experiment.

   f. The reflux ring is located near the top of the condenser in a reflux setup.

   g. A rubber O-ring is omitted when the water condenser is attached to a conical vial.

   h. A gas trap is assembled with the funnel in Figure 7.13, completely submerged in the water in the beaker.

   i. Powdered drying agent is used rather than granular material.

   j. A reaction involving hydrogen chloride is conducted on the laboratory bench and not in a hood.

   k. An air-sensitive reaction apparatus is set up as shown in Figure 7.6.

   l. Air is used to evaporate solvent from an air-sensitive compound.

Filtration

Filtration is a technique used for two main purposes. The first is to remove solid impurities from a liquid. The second is to collect a desired solid from the solution from which it was precipitated or crystallized. Several different kinds of filtration are commonly used: two general methods include gravity filtration and vacuum (or suction) filtration. Two techniques specific to the microscale laboratory are filtration with a filter-tip pipette and filtration with a Craig tube. The various filtration techniques and their applications are summarized in Table 8.1. These techniques are discussed in more detail in the following sections.

Table 8.1 Filtration Methods

Method	*Application*	*Section*
Gravity filtration		
Filter cones	The volume of liquid to be filtered is about 10 mL or greater, and the solid collected in the filter is saved.	8.1A
Fluted filters	The volume of liquid to be filtered is greater than about 10 mL, and solid impurities are removed from a solution; often used in crystallization procedures.	8.1B
Filtering pipettes	Used with volumes less than about 10 mL to remove solid impurities from a liquid.	8.1C
Decantation	Although not a filtration technique, decantation can be used to separate a liquid from large, insoluble particles.	8.1D
Vacuum filtration		
Hirsch funnels	Used in the same way as Büchner funnels, except the volume of liquid is usually smaller (1–10 mL).	8.3
Büchner funnels	Primarily used to collect a desired solid from a liquid when the volume is greater than about 10 mL; used frequently to collect the crystals obtained from crystallization.	8.3
Filtering media	Used to remove finely divided impurities.	8.4
Filter-tip pipettes	May be used to remove a small amount of solid impurities from a small volume (1–2 mL) of liquid; also useful for pipetteting volatile liquids, especially in extraction procedures.	8.6
Craig tubes	Used to collect a small amount of crystals resulting from crystallizations in which the volume of the solution is less than 2 mL.	8.7
Centrifugation	Although not strictly a filtration technique, centrifugation may be used to remove suspended impurities from a liquid (1–25 mL).	8.8

8.1 Gravity Filtration

The most familiar filtration technique is probably filtration of a solution through a paper filter held in a funnel, allowing gravity to draw the liquid through the paper. Because even a small piece of filter paper will absorb a significant volume of liquid in most microscale procedures requiring filtration, this technique is useful only when the volume of mixture to be filtered is greater than 10 mL. For many macroscale and microscale procedures, a more suitable technique, which also makes use of gravity, is to use a Pasteur (or disposable) pipette with a cotton or glass wool plug (called a filtering pipette).

A. Filter Cones

This filtration technique is most useful when the solid material being filtered from a mixture is to be collected and used later. The filter cone, because of its smooth sides, can easily be scraped free of collected solids. Because of the many folds, fluted filter paper, described in the next section, cannot be scraped easily. The filter cone is likely to be used in microscale experiments only when a relatively large volume (greater than 10 mL) is being filtered and when a Hirsch funnel (Section 8.3) is not appropriate.

The filter cone is prepared as indicated in Figure 8.1. It is then placed into a funnel of an appropriate size. With filtrations using a simple filter cone, solvent may form seals between the filter and the funnel and between the funnel and the lip of the receiving flask. When a seal forms, the filtration stops because the displaced air has no possibility of escaping. To avoid the solvent seal, you can insert a small piece of paper, a paper clip, or some other bent wire between the funnel and the lip of the flask to let the displaced air escape. As an alternative, you can support the funnel by a clamp fixed *above* the flask rather than placed on the neck of the flask. A gravity filtration using a filter cone is shown in Figure 8.2.

B. Fluted Filters

This filtration method is also most useful when filtering a relatively large amount of liquid. Because a fluted filter is used when the desired material is expected to remain in solution, this filter is used to remove undesired solid materials, such as dirt particles, decolorizing charcoal, and undissolved impure crystals. A fluted filter is often used to filter a hot solution saturated with a solute during a crystallization procedure.

The technique for folding a fluted filter paper is shown in Figure 8.3. An advantage of a fluted filter is that it increases the speed of filtration in two ways. First, it increases the surface area of the filter paper through which the solvent seeps;

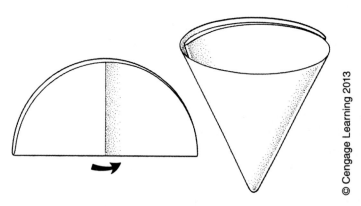

Figure 8.1
Folding a filter cone.

Figure 8.2
Gravity filtration with a filter cone.

Figure 8.3
Folding a fluted filter paper, or origami at work in the organic chemistry laboratory.

second, it allows air to enter the flask along its sides to permit rapid pressure equalization. If pressure builds up in the flask from hot vapors, filtering slows down. This problem is especially pronounced with filter cones. The fluted filter tends to reduce this problem considerably, but it may be a good idea to clamp the funnel above the receiving flask or to use a piece of paper, paper clip, or wire between the funnel and the lip of the flask as an added precaution against solvent seals.

Filtration with a fluted filter is relatively easy to perform when the mixture is at room temperature. However, when it is necessary to filter a hot solution saturated with a dissolved solute, a number of steps must be taken to ensure that the filter does not become clogged by solid material accumulated in the stem of the funnel or in the filter paper. When the hot, saturated solution comes in contact with a relatively cold funnel (or a cold flask, for that matter), the solution is cooled and may become supersaturated. If crystallization then occurs in the filter, either the crystals will fail to pass through the filter paper or they will clog the stem of the funnel.

To keep the filter from clogging, use one of the following four methods. The first is to use a short-stemmed or a stemless funnel. With these funnels, it is less likely that the stem of the funnel will become clogged by solid material. The second method is to keep the liquid to be filtered at or near its boiling point at all times. The third way is to preheat the funnel by pouring hot solvent through it before the actual filtration. This keeps the cold glass from causing instantaneous crystallization. And fourth, it is helpful to keep the **filtrate** (filtered solution) in the receiver hot enough to continue boiling *slightly* (by setting it on a hot plate, for example). The refluxing solvent heats the receiving flask and the funnel stem and washes them clean of solids. This boiling of the filtrate also keeps the liquid in the funnel warm.

C. Filtering Pipettes

A filtering pipette is a microscale technique most often used to remove solid impurities from a liquid with a volume less than 10 mL. It is important that the mixture being filtered be at or near room temperature because it is difficult to prevent premature crystallization in a hot solution saturated with a solute.

To prepare this filtration device, a small piece of cotton is inserted into the top of a Pasteur (disposable) pipette and pushed down to the beginning of the lower constriction in the pipette, as shown in Figure 8.4. It is important to use enough cotton to collect all the solid being filtered; however, the amount of cotton used should not be so large that the flow rate through the pipette is significantly restricted. For the same reason, the cotton should not be packed too tightly.

Pasteur pipette

Cotton

Figure 8.4
A filtering pipette.

The cotton plug can be pushed down gently with a long thin object such as a glass stirring rod or a wooden applicator stick. It is advisable to wash the cotton plug by passing about 1 mL of solvent (usually the same solvent that is to be filtered) through the filter.

In some cases, such as when filtering a strongly acidic mixture or when performing a very rapid filtration to remove dirt or impurities of large particle size from a solution, it may be better to use glass wool in place of the cotton. The disadvantage in using glass wool is that the fibers do not pack together as tightly, and small particles will pass through the filter more easily.

To conduct a filtration (with either a cotton or glass wool plug), the filtering pipette is clamped so that the filtrate will drain into an appropriate container. The mixture to be filtered is usually transferred to the filtering pipette with another Pasteur pipette. If a small volume of liquid is being filtered (less than 1 mL or 2 mL), it is advisable to rinse the filter and plug with a small amount of solvent after the last of the filtrate has passed through the filter. The rinse solvent is then combined with the original filtrate. The rate of filtration can be

© Cengage Learning 2013

increased by gently applying pressure to the top of the pipette using a pipette bulb, if desired.

Depending on the amount of solid being filtered and the size of the particles (small particles are more difficult to remove by filtration), it may be necessary to put the filtrate through a second filtering pipette. This should be done with a new filtering pipette rather than with the one already used.

D. Decantation

It is not always necessary to use filter paper to separate insoluble particles. If you have large, heavy, insoluble particles, with careful pouring you can decant the solution, leaving behind the solid particles that will settle to the bottom of the flask. The term *decant* means "to carefully pour out the liquid, leaving the insoluble particles behind." For example, boiling stones or sand granules in the bottom of an Erlenmeyer flask filled with a liquid can easily be separated in this way. This procedure is often preferred over filtration and usually results in a smaller loss of material. If there are a large number of particles and they retain a significant amount of the liquid, they can be rinsed with solvent and a second decantation performed. The term *decant* was coined in the wine industry, where it is often necessary to let the wine settle and then carefully pour it out of the original bottle into a clean one, leaving the "must" (insoluble particles) behind.

8.2 Filter Paper

Many kinds and grades of filter paper are available. The paper must be correct for a given application. In choosing filter paper, you should be aware of its various properties. **Porosity** is a measure of the size of the particles that can pass through the paper. Highly porous paper does not remove small particles from solution; paper with low porosity removes very small particles. **Retentivity** is a property that is the opposite of porosity. Paper with low retentivity does not remove small particles from the filtrate. The **speed** of filter paper is a measure of the time it takes a liquid to drain through the filter. Fast paper allows the liquid to drain quickly; with slow paper, it takes much longer to complete the filtration. Because all these properties are related, fast filter paper usually has a low retentivity and high porosity, and slow filter paper usually has high retentivity and low porosity.

Table 8.2 compares some commonly available qualitative filter paper types and ranks them according to porosity, retentivity, and speed. Eaton–Dikeman (E&D),

Table 8.2 Some common qualitative filter paper types and approximate relative speeds and retentivities

	Porosity (Fine → Coarse)	Retentivity (High → Low)	Speed (Slow → Fast)	Type (by Number)		
Speed				*E&D*	*S&S*	*Whatman*
Very slow				610	576	5
Slow				613	602	3
Medium				615	597	2
Fast				617	595	1
Very fast				—	604	4

© Cengage Learning 2013

Schleicher and Schuell (S&S), and Whatman are the most common brands of filter paper. The numbers in the table refer to the grades of paper used by each company.

8.3 Vacuum Filtration

Vacuum, or suction, filtration is more rapid than gravity filtration and is most often used to collect solid products resulting from precipitation or crystallization. This technique is used primarily when the volume of liquid being filtered is more than 1–2 mL. With smaller volumes, use of the Craig tube (Section 8.7) is the preferred technique. In a vacuum filtration, a receiver flask with a side arm, a **filter flask,** is used. For microscale work, the most useful size is a 50-mL filter flask. For macroscale laboratory work, the most useful sizes of filter flasks range from 50 mL to 500 mL, depending on the volume of liquid being filtered. The side arm is connected by *heavywalled* rubber tubing (see Technique 16, Figure 16.3) to a source of vacuum. Thin-walled tubing will collapse under vacuum, due to atmospheric pressure on its outside walls, and will seal the vacuum source from the flask. Because this apparatus is unstable and can tip over easily, it must be clamped, as shown in Figure 8.5.

CAUTION

It is essential that the filter flask be clamped.

Two types of funnels are useful for vacuum filtration, the Hirsch funnel and the Büchner funnel. The **Hirsch funnel** is used for filtering smaller amounts of solid from solution. Hirsch funnels are usually made from polypropylene or porcelain. The polypropylene Hirsch funnel (see Figure 8.5A) is sealed to a 50-mL filter flask by a small section of Gooch tubing. This Hirsch funnel has a built-in adapter that forms a tight seal with some 25-mL filter flasks without the Gooch tubing. A fritted polyethylene

Figure 8.5
Vacuum filtration.

© Cengage Learning 2013

disk fits into the bottom of the funnel. To prevent the holes in this disk from becoming clogged with solid material, the funnel should always be used with a circular filter paper that has the same diameter (1.27 cm) as the polyethylene disk. Before beginning the filtration, it is advisable to moisten the paper with a small amount of solvent. The moistened filter paper adheres more strongly to the fritted disk and prevents unfiltered mixture from passing around the edges of the filter paper. A porcelain Hirsch funnel (see Figure 8.5B) is sealed to the filter flask by a rubber stopper or a filter (Neoprene) adapter. The flat bottom of this Hirsch funnel, which should be 1–2 cm in diameter, is covered with an unfolded piece of circular filter paper. To prevent the escape of solid materials from the funnel, you must be certain that the filter paper fits the funnel exactly. It must cover all the holes in the bottom of the funnel but not extend up the sides of the funnel. With a porcelain Hirsch funnel, it is also important to moisten the paper with a small amount of solvent before beginning the filtration.

The **Büchner funnel,** which is shown in Figure 8.5C, operates on the same principle as the Hirsch funnel, but it is usually larger, and its sides are vertical rather than sloped. It is sealed to the filter flask with a rubber stopper or a Neoprene adapter. In the Büchner funnel, the filter paper must also cover all the holes in the bottom but must not extend up the sides.

Because the filter flask is attached to a source of vacuum, a solution poured into a Hirsch funnel or Büchner funnel is literally sucked rapidly through the filter paper. For this reason, vacuum filtration is generally not used to separate fine particles such as decolorizing charcoal, because the small particles would likely be pulled through the filter paper. However, this problem can be alleviated, when desired, by the use of specially prepared filter beds (see Section 8.4).

8.4 Filtering Media

It is occasionally necessary to use specially prepared filter beds to separate fine particles when using vacuum filtration. Often, very fine particles either pass right through a paper filter or clog it so completely that the filtering stops. This is avoided by using a substance called Filter Aid, or Celite. This material is also called **diatomaceous earth** because of its source. It is a finely divided inert material derived from the microscopic shells of dead diatoms (a type of phytoplankton that grows in the sea).

C A U T I O N

Diatomaceous earth is a lung irritant. When using Filter Aid, take care not to breathe the dust.

Filter Aid will not clog the fiber pores of filter paper. It is **slurried,** mixed with a solvent to form a rather thin paste, and filtered through a Hirsch or Büchner funnel (with filter paper in place) until a layer of diatoms about 2–3 mm thick is formed on top of the filter paper. The solvent in which the diatoms were slurried is poured from the filter flask, and, if necessary, the filter flask is cleaned before the actual filtration is begun. Finely divided particles can now be suction-filtered through this layer and will be caught in the Filter Aid. This technique is used for removing impurities, not for collecting a product. The filtrate (filtered solution) is the desired material in this procedure. If the material caught in the filter were the desired material, you would have to try to separate the product from all those diatoms! Filtration with Filter Aid is not appropriate when the desired substance is likely to precipitate or crystallize from solution.

In microscale work, it may sometimes be more convenient to use a column prepared with a Pasteur pipette to separate fine particles from a solution. The Pasteur pipette is packed with alumina or silica gel, as shown in Figure 8.6.

Silica gel or alumina (2-cm depth)

Cotton

© Cengage Learning 2013

Figure 8.6
A Pasteur pipette with filtering media.

8.5 The Aspirator

The most common source of vacuum (approximately 10–20 mm Hg) in the laboratory is the water aspirator, or "water pump," illustrated in Figure 8.7. This device passes water rapidly past a small hole to which a side arm is attached. The water pulls air in through the side arm. This phenomenon, called the Bernoulli effect, causes a reduced pressure along the side of the rapidly moving water stream and creates a partial vacuum in the side arm.

NOTE: The aspirator works most effectively when the water is turned on to the fullest extent.

A water aspirator can never lower the pressure beyond the vapor pressure of the water used to create the vacuum. Hence, there is a lower limit to the pressure (on cold days) of 9–10 mm Hg. A water aspirator does not provide as high a vacuum in the summer as in the winter, because of this water-temperature effect.

A trap must be used with an aspirator. One type of trap is illustrated in Figure 8.5. Another method for securing this type of trap is shown in Figure 8.8. This simple holder can be constructed from readily available material and can be placed anywhere on the laboratory bench. Although not often needed, a trap can prevent water from contaminating your experiment. If the water pressure in the laboratory drops suddenly, the pressure in the filter flask may suddenly become lower than the pressure in the water aspirator. This would cause water to be drawn from the aspirator stream into the filter flask and contaminate the filtrate or even the material in the filter. The trap stops this reverse flow. A similar flow will occur if the water flow at the aspirator is stopped before the tubing connected to the aspirator side arm is disconnected.

NOTE: Always disconnect the tubing before stopping the aspirator.

If a "backup" begins, disconnect the tubing as rapidly as possible before the trap fills with water. Some chemists like to fit a stopcock into the stopper on top of the trap. A three-hole stopper is required for this purpose. With a stopcock in the trap, the system can be vented before the aspirator is shut off. Then water cannot back up into the trap.

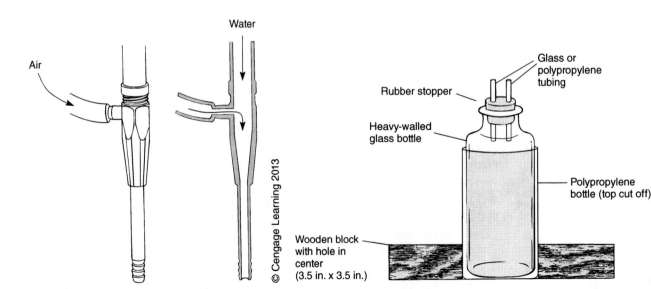

Figure 8.7
An aspirator.

Figure 8.8
A simple aspirator trap and holder.

© Cengage Learning 2013

Aspirators do not work well if too many people use the water line at the same time because the water pressure is lowered. Also, the sinks at the ends of the lab benches or the lines that carry away the water flow may have a limited capacity for draining the resultant water flow from too many aspirators. Care must be taken to avoid floods.

8.6 Filter-Tip Pipette

— Pasteur pipette

— Cotton

Figure 8.9
A filter-tip pipette.

The filter-tip pipette, illustrated in Figure 8.9, has two common uses. The first is to remove a small amount of solid, such as dirt or filter paper fibers, from a small volume of liquid (1–2 mL). It can also be helpful when using a Pasteur pipette to transfer a highly volatile liquid, especially during an extraction procedure (see Technique 12, Section 12.5).

Preparing a filter-tip pipette is similar to preparing a filtering pipette, except that a much smaller amount of cotton is used. A *tiny* piece of cotton is loosely shaped into a ball and placed into the large end of a Pasteur pipette. Using a wire with a diameter slightly smaller than the inside diameter of the narrow end of the pipette, push the ball of cotton to the bottom of the pipette. If it becomes difficult to push the cotton, you have probably started with too much cotton; if the cotton slides through the narrow end with little resistance, you probably have not used enough.

To use a filter-tip pipette as a filter, the mixture is drawn up into the Pasteur pipette using a pipette bulb and then expelled. With this procedure, a small amount of solid will be captured by the cotton. However, very fine particles, such as activated charcoal, cannot be removed efficiently with a filter-tip pipette, and this technique is not effective in removing more than a trace amount of solid from a liquid.

Transferring many organic liquids with a Pasteur pipette can be a somewhat difficult procedure for two reasons. First, the liquid may not adhere well to the glass. Second, as you handle the Pasteur pipette, the temperature of the liquid in the pipette increases slightly, and the increased vapor pressure may tend to "squirt" the liquid out the end of the pipette. This problem can be particularly troublesome when separating two liquids during an extraction procedure. The purpose of the cotton plug in this situation is to slow the rate of flow through the end of the pipette so you can control the movement of liquid in the Pasteur pipette more easily.

8.7 Craig Tubes

— Inner plug (glass or Teflon)

— Outer tube

Figure 8.10
A Craig tube (2 mL).

The **Craig tube,** illustrated in Figure 8.10, is used primarily to separate crystals from a solution after a microscale crystallization procedure has been performed (Technique 11, Section 11.4). Although it may not be a filtration procedure in the traditional sense, the outcome is similar. The outer part of the Craig tube is similar to a test tube, except that the diameter of the tube becomes wider part of the way up the tube, and the glass is ground at this point so that the inside surface is rough. The inner part (plug) of the Craig tube may be made of Teflon or glass. If this part is glass, the end of the plug is also ground. With either a glass or a Teflon inner plug, there is only a partial seal where the plug and the outer tube come together. Liquid may pass through, but solid will not. This is the place where the solution is separated from the crystals.

After crystallization has been completed in the outer Craig tube, replace the inner plug (if necessary) and connect a thin copper wire or strong thread to the narrow part of the inner plug, as indicated in Figure 8.11A. While holding the Craig tube in an upright position, place a plastic centrifuge tube over the Craig tube so that the bottom of the centrifuge tube rests on top of the inner plug, as shown in Figure 8.11B. The copper wire should extend just below the lip of the centrifuge tube and is now bent upward around the lip of the centrifuge tube. This apparatus is then turned over so that the centrifuge tube is upright. The Craig tube is spun in a centrifuge (be sure it is balanced by placing another tube filled with water on the

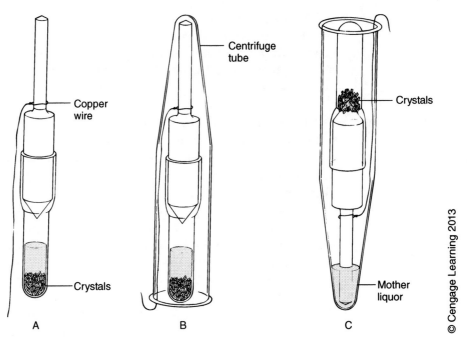

Figure 8.11
Separation with a Craig tube.

opposite side of the centrifuge) for several minutes until the **mother liquor** (solution from which the crystals grew) goes to the bottom of the centrifuge tube and the crystals collect on the end of the inner plug (see Figure 8.11C). Depending on the consistency of the crystals and the speed of the centrifuge, the crystals may spin down to the inner plug, or (if you are unlucky) they may remain at the other end of the Craig tube.[1] If the latter situation occurs, it may be helpful to centrifuge the Craig tube longer or, if this problem is anticipated, to stir the crystal- and solution-mixture with a spatula or stirring rod before centrifugation.

Using the copper wire, then pull the Craig tube out of the centrifuge tube. If the crystals collected on the end of the inner plug, it is now a simple procedure to remove the plug and scrape the crystals with a spatula onto a watch glass, a clay plate, or a piece of smooth paper. Otherwise, it will be necessary to scrape the crystals from the inside surface of the outer part of the Craig tube.

8.8 Centrifugation

Sometimes, centrifugation is more effective in removing solid impurities than conventional filtration techniques. Centrifugation is particularly effective in removing suspended particles, which are so small that the particles would pass through most filtering devices. Centrifugation may also be useful when the mixture must be kept hot to prevent premature crystallization while the solid impurities are removed.

Centrifugation is performed by placing the mixture in one or two centrifuge tubes (be sure to balance the centrifuge) and centrifuging for several minutes. The supernatant liquid is then decanted (poured off) or removed with a Pasteur pipette.

---

[1] *Note to the Instructor:* In some centrifuges, the bottom of the Craig tube may be close to the center of the centrifuge when the Craig tube assembly is placed into the centrifuge. In this situation, very little centrifugal force will be applied to the crystals, and it is likely that the crystals will not spin down. It may then be helpful to use an inner plug with a shorter stem. The stem on a Teflon inner plug can be easily cut off about 0.5 inch with a pair of wire cutters. This will help to spin down the crystals to the inner plug, and also the centrifuge can be run at a lower speed, which can help prevent breakage of the Craig tube.

PROBLEMS

1. In each of the following situations, what type of filtration device would you use? (Do not consider centrifugation when answering this question.)

   a. Remove powdered decolorizing charcoal from 20 mL of solution

   b. Collect crystals obtained from crystallizing a substance from about 1 mL of solution

   c. Remove a very small amount of dirt from 1 mL of liquid

   d. Isolate 0.2 g of crystals from about 5 mL of solution after performing a crystallization

   e. Remove dissolved colored impurities from about 3 mL of solution

   f. Remove solid impurities from 5 mL of liquid at room temperature

Physical Constants of Solids: The Melting Point

9.1 Physical Properties

The physical properties of a compound are those properties that are intrinsic to a given compound when it is pure. A compound may often be identified simply by determining a number of its physical properties. The most commonly recognized physical properties of a compound include its color, melting point, boiling point, density, refractive index, molecular weight, and optical rotation. Modern chemists would include the various types of spectra (infrared, nuclear magnetic resonance, mass, and ultraviolet-visible) among the physical properties of a compound. A compound's spectra do not vary from one pure sample to another. Here, we look at methods of determining the melting point. Boiling point and density of compounds are covered in Technique 13. Refractive index, optical rotation, and spectra are also considered separately.

Many reference books list the physical properties of substances. You should consult Technique 4 for a complete discussion on how to find data for specific compounds. The works most useful for finding lists of values for the nonspectroscopic physical properties include

> *The Merck Index*
>
> *The CRC Handbook of Chemistry and Physics*
>
> *Lange's Handbook of Chemistry*
>
> *Aldrich Handbook of Fine Chemicals*

Complete citations for these references can be found in Technique 29. Although the *CRC Handbook* has good tables, it adheres strictly to IUPAC nomenclature. For this reason, it may be easier to use one of the other references, particularly *The Merck Index* or the *Aldrich Handbook of Fine Chemicals,* in your first attempt to locate information (see Technique 4).

9.2 The Melting Point

The melting point of a compound is used by the organic chemist not only to identify the compound but also to establish its purity. A small amount of material is heated *slowly* in a special apparatus equipped with a thermometer or thermocouple, a heating bath or heating coil, and a magnifying eyepiece for observing the sample. Two temperatures are noted. The first is the point at which the first drop of liquid forms among the crystals; the second is the point at which the whole mass of crystals turns to a *clear* liquid. The melting point is recorded by giving this range of melting. You might say, for example, that the melting point of a substance is 51–54°C. That is, the substance melted over a 3-degree range.

The melting point indicates purity in two ways. First, the purer the material, the higher its melting point. Second, the purer the material, the narrower its melting-point range. Adding successive amounts of an impurity to a pure substance generally causes its melting point to decrease in proportion to the amount of

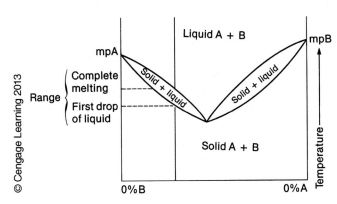

Figure 9.1

A melting-point–composition curve.

impurity. Looking at it another way, adding impurities lowers the freezing point. The freezing point, a colligative property, is simply the melting point (solid → liquid) approached from the opposite direction (liquid → solid).

Figure 9.1 is a graph of the usual melting-point behavior of mixtures of two substances, A and B. The two extremes of the melting range (the low and high temperature) are shown for various mixtures of the two. The upper curves indicate the temperatures at which all the sample has melted. The lower curves indicate the temperature at which melting is observed to begin. With pure compounds, melting is sharp and without any range. This is shown at the left- and right-hand edges of the graph. If you begin with pure A, the melting point decreases as impurity B is added. At some point, a minimum temperature, or **eutectic,** is reached, and the melting point begins to increase to that of substance B. The vertical distance between the lower and upper curves represents the melting range. Notice that for mixtures that contain relatively small amounts of impurity (<15%) and are not close to the eutectic, the melting range increases as the sample becomes less pure. The range indicated by the lines in Figure 9.1 represents the typical behavior.

We can generalize the behavior shown in Figure 9.1. Pure substances melt with a narrow range of melting. With impure substances, the melting range becomes wider, and the entire melting range is lowered. Be careful to note, however, that at the minimum point of the melting-point–composition curves, the mixture often forms a eutectic, which also melts sharply. Not all binary mixtures form eutectics, and some caution must be exercised in assuming that every binary mixture follows the previously described behavior. Some mixtures may form more than one eutectic; others might not form even one. In spite of these variations, both the melting point and its range are useful indications of purity, and they are easily determined by simple experimental methods.

9.3 Melting-Point Theory

Figure 9.2 is a phase diagram describing the usual behavior of a two-component mixture (A + B) on melting. The behavior on melting depends on the relative amounts of A and B in the mixture. If A is a pure substance (no B), then A melts sharply at its melting point t_A. This is represented by point A on the left side of the diagram. When B is a pure substance, it melts at t_B; its melting point is represented by point B on the right side of the diagram. At either point A or point B, the pure solid passes cleanly, with a narrow range, from solid to liquid.

In mixtures of A and B, the behavior is different. Using Figure 9.2, consider a mixture of 80% A and 20% B on a mole-per-mole basis (that is, mole percentage). The melting point of this mixture is given by t_M at point M on the diagram. That is, adding B to A has lowered the melting point of A from t_A to t_M. It has also expanded the melting range. The temperature t_M corresponds to the **upper limit** of the melting range.

Figure 9.2

A phase diagram for melting in a two-component system.

Lowering the melting point of A by adding impurity B comes about in the following way. Substance A has the lower melting point in the phase diagram shown, and if heated, it begins to melt first. As A begins to melt, solid B begins to dissolve in the liquid A that is formed. When solid B dissolves in liquid A, the melting point is depressed. To understand this, consider the melting point from the opposite direction. When a liquid at a high temperature cools, it reaches a point at which it solidifies, or "freezes." The temperature at which a liquid freezes is identical to its melting point. Recall that the freezing point of a liquid can be lowered by adding an impurity. Because the freezing point and the melting point are identical, lowering the freezing point corresponds to lowering the melting point. Therefore, as more impurity is added to a solid, its melting point becomes lower. There is, however, a limit to how far the melting point can be depressed. You cannot dissolve an infinite amount of the impurity substance in the liquid. At some point, the liquid will become saturated with the impurity substance. The solubility of B in A has an upper limit. In Figure 9.2, the solubility limit of B in liquid A is reached at point C, the **eutectic point.** The melting point of the mixture cannot be lowered below t_C, the melting temperature of the eutectic.

Now consider what happens when the melting point of a mixture of 80% A and 20% B is approached. As the temperature is increased, A begins to "melt." This is not really a visible phenomenon in the beginning stages; it happens before liquid is visible. It is a softening of the compound to a point at which it can begin to mix with the impurity. As A begins to soften, it dissolves B. As it dissolves B, the melting point is lowered. The lowering continues until all B is dissolved or until the eutectic composition (saturation) is reached. When the maximum possible amount of B has been dissolved, actual melting begins, and one can observe the first appearance of liquid. The initial temperature of melting will be below t_A. The amount below t_A at which melting begins is determined by the amount of B dissolved in A but will never be below t_C. Once all B has been dissolved, the melting point of the mixture begins to rise as more A begins to melt. As more A melts, the semisolid solution is diluted by more A, and its melting point rises. While all this is happening, you can observe *both* solid and liquid in the melting-point capillary. Once all A has begun to melt, the composition of the mixture M becomes uniform and will reach 80% A and 20% B. At this point, the mixture finally melts sharply, giving a clear solution. The maximum melting-point range will be $t_C - t_M$, because t_A is depressed by the impurity B that is present. The lower end of the melting range will always be t_C; however, melting will not always be observed at this temperature. An observable melting at t_C comes about only when a large amount of B is present. Otherwise, the amount of liquid formed at t_C will be too small to observe. Therefore, the melting behavior that is actually observed will have a smaller range, as shown in Figure 9.1.

9.4 Mixture Melting Points

The melting point can be used as supporting evidence in identifying a compound in two different ways. Not only may the melting points of the two individual compounds be compared but a special procedure called a **mixture melting point** may also be performed. The mixture melting point requires that an authentic sample of the same compound be available from another source. In this procedure, the two compounds (authentic and suspected) are finely pulverized and mixed together in equal quantities. Then the melting point of the mixture is determined. If there is a melting-point depression or if the range of melting is expanded by a large amount compared to that of the individual substances, you may conclude that one compound has acted as an impurity toward the other and that they are not the same compound. If there is no lowering of the melting point for the mixture (the melting point is identical with those of pure A and pure B), then A and B are almost certainly the same compound.

9.5 Packing the Melting-Point Tube

Melting points are usually determined by heating the sample in a piece of thin-walled capillary tubing (1 mm × 100 mm) that has been sealed at one end. To pack the tube, press the open end gently into a *pulverized* sample of the crystalline material. Crystals will stick in the open end of the tube. The amount of solid pressed into the tube should correspond to a column no more than 1–2 mm high. To transfer the crystals to the closed end of the tube, drop the capillary tube, closed end first, down a ⅔-m length of glass tubing, which is held upright on the desktop. When the capillary tube hits the desktop, the crystals will pack down into the bottom of the tube. This procedure is repeated if necessary. Tapping the capillary on the desktop with fingers is not recommended because it is easy to drive the small tubing into a finger if the tubing should break.

Some commercial melting-point instruments have a built-in vibrating device that is designed to pack capillary tubes. With these instruments, the sample is pressed into the open end of the capillary tube, and the tube is placed in the vibrator slot. The action of the vibrator will transfer the sample to the bottom of the tube and pack it tightly.

9.6 Determining the Melting Point—the Thiele Tube

There are two principal types of melting-point apparatus available: the Thiele tube and commercially available, electrically heated instruments. The Thiele tube, shown in Figure 9.3, is the simpler device and was once widely used. It is a glass tube designed to contain a heating oil (mineral oil or silicone oil) and a thermometer to which a capillary tube containing the sample is attached. For best results use a mercury thermometer. The shape of the Thiele tube allows convection currents to form in the oil when it is heated. These currents maintain a uniform temperature distribution through the oil in the tube. The side arm of the tube is designed to generate these convection currents and thus transfer the heat from the flame evenly and rapidly throughout the oil. The sample, which is in a capillary tube attached to the thermometer, is held by a rubber band or a thin slice of rubber tubing. It is important that this rubber band be above the level of the oil (allowing for expansion of the oil on heating) so that the oil does not soften the rubber and allow the capillary tubing to fall into the oil. If a cork or a rubber stopper is used to hold the thermometer, a triangular channel should be cut into the side of it to allow pressure equalization.

The Thiele tube is usually heated by a microburner. During the heating, the rate of temperature increase should be regulated. Hold the burner by its cool base and, using a low flame, move the burner slowly back and forth along the bottom of the arm of the Thiele tube. If the heating is too fast, remove the burner for a few seconds and then resume heating. The rate of heating should be *slow* near the melting point (about 1°C per minute) to ensure that the temperature increase is not faster than the rate at which heat can be transferred to the sample being observed. At the melting point, it is necessary that the mercury in the thermometer and the sample in the capillary tube be at temperature equilibrium.

One-hole rubber stopper with wedge cut

Rubber band

Sample in capillary tube

Bunsen burner

© Cengage Learning 2013

Figure 9.3
A Thiele tube.

Figure 9.4
Melting-point apparatus.

© Cengage Learning 2013

9.7 Determining the Melting Point— Electrical Instruments

Three types of electrically heated melting-point instruments are illustrated in Figure 9.4. In each case, the melting-point tube is filled as described in Section 9.5 and placed in a holder located just behind the magnifying eyepiece. The apparatus is operated by moving the switch to the ON position, adjusting the potentiometric control dial for the desired rate of heating, and observing the sample through the magnifying eyepiece. The temperature is read from a thermometer or, in the most modern instruments, from a digital display attached to a thermocouple. Another option is the Vernier melt station, which can be connected to the Vernier Lab Quest unit or the Vernier LabPro system. (See Technique 13, Section 13.4 for more information about these devices.) Your instructor will demonstrate and explain the type used in your laboratory.

Some electrically heated instruments do not heat or increase the temperature of the sample linearly. Although the rate of increase may be linear in the early stages of heating, it usually decreases and leads to a constant temperature at some upper limit. The upper-limit temperature is determined by the setting of the heating control. Thus, a family of heating curves is usually obtained for various control settings, as shown in Figure 9.5. The four hypothetical curves shown (1–4) might correspond to different control settings. For a compound melting at temperature t_1, the setting corresponding to curve 3 would be ideal. In the beginning of the curve, the temperature is increasing too rapidly to allow determination of an

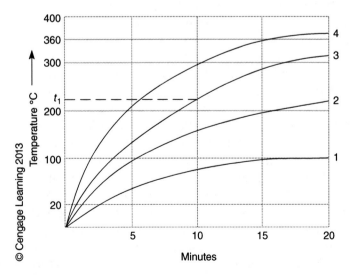

Figure 9.5
Heating-rate curves.

accurate melting point, but after the change in slope, the temperature increase will have slowed to a more usable rate.

If the melting point of the sample is unknown, you can often save time by preparing two samples for melting-point determination. With one sample, you can rapidly determine a crude melting-point value. Then repeat the experiment more carefully using the second sample. For the second determination, you already have an approximate idea of what the melting-point temperature should be, and a proper rate of heating can be chosen.

When temperatures above 150°C are measured, thermometer errors can become significant. For an accurate melting point with a high-melting solid, you may wish to apply a **stem correction** to the thermometer as described in Technique 13, Section 13.4. An even better solution is to calibrate the thermometer as described in Section 9.9.

9.8 Decomposition, Discoloration, Softening, Shrinkage, and Sublimation

Many solid substances undergo some degree of unusual behavior before melting. At times it may be difficult to distinguish these types of behavior from actual melting. You should learn, through experience, how to recognize melting and how to distinguish it from decomposition, discoloration, and particularly, softening and shrinkage.

Some compounds decompose on melting. This decomposition is usually evidenced by discoloration of the sample. Frequently, this decomposition point is a reliable physical property to be used in lieu of an actual melting point. Such decomposition points are indicated in tables of melting points by placing the symbol *d* immediately after the listed temperature. An example of a decomposition point is thiamine hydrochloride, whose melting point would be listed as 248°d, indicating that this substance melts with decomposition at 248°C. When decomposition is a result of reaction with the oxygen in air, it may be avoided by determining the melting point in a sealed, evacuated melting-point tube.

Figure 9.6 shows two simple methods of evacuating a packed tube. Method A uses an ordinary melting-point tube, and method B constructs the melting-point

Figure 9.6
Evacuation and sealing of a melting-point capillary.

tube from a disposable Pasteur pipette. Before using method B, be sure to determine that the tip of the pipette will fit into the sample holder in your melting-point instrument.

Method A

In method A, a hole is punched through a rubber septum using a large pin or a small nail, and the capillary tube is inserted from the inside, sealed end first. The septum is placed over a piece of glass tubing connected to a vacuum line. After the tube is evacuated, the upper end of the tube may be sealed by heating and pulling it closed.

Method B

In method B, the thin section of a 9-inch Pasteur pipette is used to construct the melting-point tube. Carefully seal the tip of the pipette using a flame. Be sure to hold the tip *upward* as you seal it. This will prevent water vapor from condensing inside the pipette. When the sealed pipette has cooled, the sample may be added through the open end using a microspatula. A small wire may be used to compress the sample into the closed tip. (If your melting-point apparatus has a vibrator, it may be used in place of the wire to simplify the packing.) When the sample is in place, the pipette is connected to the vacuum line with tubing and evacuated. The evacuated sample tube is sealed by heating it with a flame and pulling it closed.

Some substances begin to decompose *below* their melting points. Thermally unstable substances may undergo elimination reactions or anhydride formation reactions during heating. The decomposition products formed represent impurities in the original sample, so the melting point of the substance may be lowered due to their presence.

It is normal for many compounds to soften or shrink immediately before melting. Such behavior represents not decomposition but a change in the crystal structure or a mixing with impurities. Some substances "sweat," or release solvent of crystallization, before melting. These changes do not indicate the beginning of melting. Actual melting begins when the first drop of liquid becomes visible, and the melting range continues until the temperature is reached at which all the solid has been converted to the liquid state. With experience, you soon learn to distinguish between softening, or "sweating," and actual melting. If you wish, the temperature of the onset of softening or sweating may be reported as a part of your melting-point range: 211°C (softens), 223–225°C (melts).

Some solid substances have such a high vapor pressure that they sublime at or below their melting points. In many handbooks, the sublimation temperature is listed along with the melting point. The symbols *sub, subl,* and sometimes *s* are used to designate a substance that sublimes. In such cases, the melting-point determination must be performed in a sealed capillary tube to avoid loss of the sample. The simplest way to seal a packed tube is to heat the open end of the tube in a flame and pull it closed with tweezers or forceps. A better way, although more difficult to master, is to heat the center of the tube in a small flame, rotating it about its axis, and keeping the tube straight, until the center collapses. If this is not done quickly, the sample may melt or sublime while you are working. With the smaller chamber, the sample will not be able to migrate to the cool top of the tube that may be above the viewing area. Figure 9.7 illustrates the method.

Figure 9.7
Sealing a tube for a
substance that sublimes.

9.9 Thermometer Calibration

When a melting-point or boiling-point determination has been completed, you expect to obtain a result that duplicates the result recorded in a handbook or in the original literature. It is not unusual, however, to find a discrepancy of several degrees from the literature value. Such a discrepancy does not necessarily indicate that the experiment was incorrectly performed or that the material is impure; rather, it may indicate that the thermometer used for the determination was slightly in error. Most thermometers do not measure the temperature with perfect accuracy.

To determine accurate values, you must calibrate the thermometer that is used. This calibration is done by determining the melting points of a variety of standard substances with the thermometer. A plot is drawn of the observed temperature vs. the published value of each standard substance. A smooth line is drawn through the points to complete the chart. A correction chart prepared in this way is shown in Figure 9.8. This chart is used to correct any melting point determined with that particular thermometer. Each thermometer requires its own calibration curve. A list of suitable standard substances for calibrating thermometers is provided in Table 9.1. The standard substances, of course, must be pure in order for the corrections to be valid.

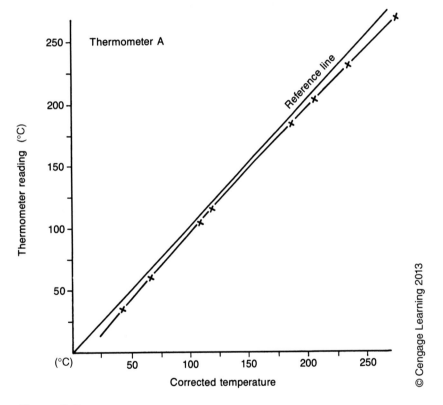

Figure 9.8
A thermometer-calibration curve.

Table 9.1 Melting-point standards

Compound	Melting Point (°C)
Ice (solid–liquid water)	0
Acetanilide	115
Benzamide	128
Urea	132
Succinic acid	189
3,5-Dinitrobenzoic acid	205

PROBLEMS

1. Two substances, A and B, have the same melting point. How can you determine if they are the same without using any form of spectroscopy? Explain in detail.

2. Using Figure 9.5, determine which heating curve would be most appropriate for a substance with a melting point of about 150°C.

3. What steps can you take to determine the melting point of a substance that sublimes before it melts?

4. A compound melting at 134°C was suspected to be either aspirin (mp 135°C) or urea (mp 133°C). Explain how you could determine whether one of these two suspected compounds was identical to the unknown compound without using any form of spectroscopy.

5. An unknown compound gave a melting point of 230°C. When the molten liquid solidified, the melting point was redetermined and found to be 131°C. Give a possible explanation for this discrepancy.

Solubility

The solubility of a solute (a dissolved substance) in a **solvent** (the dissolving medium) is the most important chemical principle underlying three basic techniques you will study in the organic chemistry laboratory: crystallization, extraction, and chromatography. In this discussion of solubility, you will gain an understanding of the structural features of a substance that determine its solubility in various solvents. This understanding will help you to predict solubility behavior and to understand the techniques that are based on this property. Understanding solubility behavior will also help you understand what is going on during a reaction, especially when there is more than one liquid phase present or when a precipitate is formed.

10.1 Definition of Solubility

Although we often describe solubility behavior in terms of a substance being **soluble** (dissolved) or **insoluble** (not dissolved) in a solvent, solubility can be described more precisely in terms of the *extent* to which a substance is soluble. Solubility may be expressed in terms of grams of solute per liter (g/L) or milligrams of solute per milliliter (mg/mL) of solvent. Consider the solubilities at room temperature for the following three substances in water:

Cholesterol   0.002 mg/mL

Caffeine   22 mg/mL

Citric acid   620 mg/mL

In a typical test for solubility, 40 mg of solute is added to 1 mL of solvent. Therefore, if you were testing the solubility of these three substances, cholesterol would be insoluble, caffeine would be partially soluble, and citric acid would be soluble. Note that a small amount (0.002 mg) of cholesterol would dissolve. It is unlikely, however, that you would be able to observe this small amount dissolving, and you would report that cholesterol is insoluble. On the other hand, 22 mg (55%) of the caffeine would dissolve. It is likely that you would be able to observe this, and you would state that caffeine is partially soluble.

When the solubility of a liquid solute in a solvent is described, it is sometimes helpful to use the terms **miscible** and **immiscible.** Two liquids that are miscible will mix homogeneously (one phase) in all proportions. For example, water and ethyl alcohol are miscible. When they are mixed in any proportion, only one layer will be observed. When two liquids are miscible, it is also true that either one of them will be completely soluble in the other one. Two immiscible liquids do not mix homogeneously in all proportions, and under some conditions they will form two layers. Water and diethyl ether are immiscible. When mixed in roughly equal amounts, they will form two layers. However, each liquid is slightly soluble in the other one. Even when two layers are present, a small amount of water will be soluble in the diethyl ether, and a small amount of diethyl ether will be soluble in the water. Furthermore, if only a small amount of either one is added to the other, it

245

may dissolve completely, and only one layer will be observed. For example, if a small amount of water (less than 1.2% at 20°C) is added to diethyl ether, the water will dissolve completely in the diethyl ether, and only one layer will be observed. When more water is added (more than 1.2%), some of the water will not dissolve, and two layers will be present.

Although the terms *solubility* and *miscibility* are related in meaning, it is important to understand that there is one essential difference. There can be different degrees of solubility, such as slightly, partially, very, and so on. Unlike solubility, miscibility does not have any degrees—a pair of liquids is either miscible or it is not.

10.2 Predicting Solubility Behavior

A major goal of this section is to explain how to predict whether a substance will be soluble in a given solvent. This is not always easy, even for an experienced chemist. However, guidelines will help you make a good guess about the solubility of a compound in a specific solvent. In discussing these guidelines, it is helpful to separate the types of solutions we will be looking at into two categories: solutions in which both the solvent and the solute are covalent (molecular), and ionic solutions, in which the solute ionizes and dissociates.

A. Solutions in Which the Solvent and Solute Are Molecular

A useful generalization in predicting solubility is the widely used rule "Like dissolves like." This rule is most commonly applied to polar and nonpolar compounds. According to this rule, a polar solvent will dissolve polar (or ionic) compounds, and a nonpolar solvent will dissolve nonpolar compounds.

The reason for this behavior involves the nature of intermolecular forces of attraction. Although we will not be focusing on the nature of these forces, it is helpful to know what they are called. The force of attraction between polar molecules is called **dipole–dipole interaction;** between nonpolar molecules, forces of attraction are called **van der Waals forces** (also called **London** or **dispersion forces**). In both cases, these attractive forces can occur between molecules of the same compound or different compounds. Consult your lecture textbook for more information on these forces.

To apply the rule "Like dissolves like," you must first determine whether a substance is polar or nonpolar. The polarity of a compound is dependent on both the polarities of the individual bonds and the shape of the molecule. For most organic compounds, evaluating these factors can become quite complicated because of the complexities of the molecules. However, it is possible to make some reasonable predictions just by looking at the types of atoms that a compound possesses. As you read the following guidelines, it is important to understand that although we often describe compounds as being polar or nonpolar, polarity is a matter of degree, ranging from nonpolar to highly polar.

Guidelines for Predicting Polarity and Solubility

1. All hydrocarbons are nonpolar.
    Examples:

$$CH_3CH_2CH_2CH_2CH_2CH_3$$

Hexane   **Benzene**

Hydrocarbons such as benzene are slightly more polar than hexane because of their pi (π) bonds, which allow for greater van der Waals or London attractive forces.

2. Compounds possessing the electronegative elements oxygen or nitrogen are polar.

   Examples:

   The polarity of these compounds depends on the presence of polar C—O, C=O, OH, NH, and CN bonds. The compounds that are most polar are capable of forming hydrogen bonds (see Guideline 6) and have NH or OH bonds. Although all these compounds are polar, the degree of polarity ranges from slightly polar to highly polar. This is due to the effect on polarity of the shape of the molecule and size of the carbon chain and whether the compound can form hydrogen bonds.

3. The presence of halogen atoms, even though their electronegativities are relatively high, does not alter the polarity of an organic compound in a significant way. Therefore, these compounds are only slightly polar. The polarities of these compounds are more similar to those of hydrocarbons, which are nonpolar, than to that of water, which is highly polar.

   Examples:

   CH_2Cl_2

   Methylene chloride (dichloromethane)   **Chlorobenzene**

4. When comparing organic compounds within the same family, note that adding carbon atoms to the chain decreases the polarity. For example, methyl alcohol (CH_3OH) is more polar than propyl alcohol ($CH_3CH_2CH_2OH$). The reason is that hydrocarbons are nonpolar, and increasing the length of a carbon chain makes the compound more hydrocarbon-like.

5. Compounds that contain four or fewer carbons and also contain oxygen or nitrogen are often soluble in water. Almost any functional group containing these elements will lead to water solubility for low-molecular-weight (up to C_4) compounds. Compounds having five or six carbons and containing one of these elements are often insoluble in water or have borderline solubility.

6. As mentioned earlier, the force of attraction between polar molecules is dipole–dipole interaction. A special case of dipole–dipole interaction is hydrogen bonding. Hydrogen bonding is a possibility when a compound possesses a hydrogen atom bonded to a nitrogen, oxygen, or fluorine atom. The bond is formed by the attraction between this hydrogen atom and a nitrogen, oxygen, or fluorine atom in another molecule. Hydrogen bonding may occur between two molecules of the same compound or between molecules of different compounds:

Hydrogen bonding is the strongest type of dipole–dipole interaction. When hydrogen bonding between solute and solvent is possible, solubility is greater than one would expect for compounds of similar polarity that cannot form hydrogen bonds. Hydrogen bonding is very important in organic chemistry, and you should be alert for situations in which hydrogen bonding may occur.

7. Another factor that can affect solubility is the degree of branching of the alkyl chain in a compound. Branching of the alkyl chain in a compound lowers the intermolecular forces between the molecules. This is usually reflected in a greater solubility in water for the branched compound than for the corresponding straight-chain compound. This occurs simply because the molecules of the branched compounds are more easily separated from one another.

8. The solubility rule ("Like dissolves like") may be applied to organic compounds that belong to the same family. For example, 1-octanol (an alcohol) is soluble in the solvent ethyl alcohol. Most compounds within the same family have similar polarity. However, this generalization may not apply if there is a substantial difference in size between the two compounds. For example, cholesterol, an alcohol with a molecular weight (MW) of 386.64, is only slightly soluble in methanol (MW 32.04). The large hydrocarbon component of cholesterol negates the fact that they belong to the same family.

9. Almost all organic compounds that are in the ionic form are water soluble (see next section, B. Solutions in Which the Solute Ionizes and Dissociates).

10. The stability of the crystal lattice also affects solubility. Other things being equal, the higher the melting point (the more stable the crystal) is, the less soluble the compound. For instance, *p*-nitrobenzoic acid (mp 242°C) is, by a factor of 10, less soluble in a fixed amount of ethanol than the *ortho* (mp 147°C) and *meta* (mp 141°C) isomers.

You can check your understanding of some of these guidelines by studying the list given in Table 10.1, which is given in order of increasing polarity. The structures of these compounds are given on the preceding pages.

Table 10.1 Compounds in increasing order of polarity

Increasing Polarity

Aliphatic hydrocarbons
  Hexane (nonpolar)
Aromatic hydrocarbons (π bonds)
  Benzene (nonpolar)
Halocarbons
  Methylene chloride (slightly polar)
Compounds with polar bonds
  Diethyl ether (slightly polar)
  Ethyl acetate (intermediate polarity)
  Acetone (intermediate polarity)
Compounds with polar bonds and hydrogen bonding
  Ethyl alcohol (intermediate polarity)
  Methyl alcohol (intermediate polarity)
  Water (highly polar)

© Cengage Learning 2013

Table 10.2 Solvents in increasing order of polarity

Increasing Polarity (Approximate)

RH	Alkanes (hexane, petroleum ether)
ArH	Aromatics (benzene, toluene)
ROR	Ethers (diethyl ether)
RX	Halides ($CH_2Cl_2 > CHCl_3 > CCl_4$)
RCOOR	Esters (ethyl acetate)
RCOR	Aldehydes, ketones (acetone)
RNH_2	Amines (triethylamine, pyridine)
ROH	Alcohols (methanol, ethanol)
$RCONH_2$	Amides (N, N-dimethylformamide)
RCOOH	Organic acids (acetic acid)
H_2O	Water

© Cengage Learning 2013

This list can be used to make some predictions about solubility, based on the rule "Like dissolves like." Substances that are close to one another on this list will have similar polarities. Thus, you would expect hexane to be soluble in methylene chloride but not in water. Acetone should be soluble in ethyl alcohol. On the other hand, you might predict that ethyl alcohol would be insoluble in hexane. However, ethyl alcohol is soluble in hexane because ethyl alcohol is somewhat less polar than methyl alcohol or water. This last example demonstrates that you must be careful in using the guidelines on polarity for predicting solubilities. Ultimately, solubility tests must be done to confirm predictions until you gain more experience.

The trend in polarities shown in Table 10.1 can be expanded by including more organic families. The list in Table 10.2 gives an approximate order for the increasing polarity of organic functional groups. It may appear that there are some discrepancies between the information provided in these two tables. The reason is that Table 10.1 provides information about specific compounds, whereas the trend shown in Table 10.2 is for major organic families and is approximate.

B. Solutions in Which the Solute Ionizes and Dissociates

Many ionic compounds are highly soluble in water because of the strong attraction between ions and the highly polar water molecules. This also applies to organic compounds that can exist as ions. For example, sodium acetate consists of Na^+ and CH_3COO^- ions, which are highly soluble in water. Although there are some exceptions, **you may assume that all organic compounds that are in the ionic form will be water soluble.**

The most common way by which organic compounds become ions is in acid–base reactions. For example, carboxylic acids can be converted to water-soluble salts when they react with dilute aqueous NaOH:

$$CH_3CH_2CH_2CH_2CH_2CH_2\overset{\overset{\displaystyle O}{\|}}{C}OH \quad + \quad NaOH \text{ (aq)} \longrightarrow$$

Water-insoluble carboxylic acid

$$CH_3CH_2CH_2CH_2CH_2CH_2\overset{\overset{\displaystyle O}{\|}}{C}O^-\,Na^+ \quad + \quad H_2O$$

Water-soluble salt

© Cengage Learning 2013

The water-soluble salt can then be converted back to the original carboxylic acid (which is insoluble in water) by adding another acid (usually aqueous HCl) to the solution of the salt. The carboxylic acid precipitates out of solution.

Amines, which are organic bases, can also be converted to water-soluble salts when they react with dilute aqueous HCl:

Water-insoluble amine   Water-soluble salt

© Cengage Learning 2013

This salt can be converted back to the original amine by adding a base (usually aqueous NaOH) to the solution of the salt.

10.3 Organic Solvents

Organic solvents must be handled safely. Always remember that organic solvents are all at least mildly toxic and that many are flammable. You should become thoroughly familiar with laboratory safety (see Technique 1).

The most common organic solvents are listed in Table 10.3 along with their boiling points. Solvents marked in boldface type will burn. Ether, pentane, and hexane are especially dangerous; if they are combined with the correct amount of air, they will explode.

The terms **petroleum ether** and **ligroin** are often confusing. Petroleum ether is a mixture of hydrocarbons with isomers of formulas C_5H_{12} and C_6H_{14} predominating. Petroleum ether is not an ether at all because there are no oxygen-bearing compounds in the mixture. In organic chemistry, an ether is usually a compound containing an oxygen atom to which two alkyl groups are attached. Figure 10.1 shows some of the hydrocarbons that appear commonly in petroleum ether. It also

Table 10.3 Common organic solvents

Solvent	Bp (°C)	Solvent	Bp (°C)
Hydrocarbons		Ethers	
Pentane	36	**Ether** (diethyl)	35
Hexane	69	**Dioxane**[a]	101
Benzene[a]	80	**1,2-Dimethoxyethane**	83
Toluene	111	Others	
Hydrocarbon mixtures		Acetic acid	118
Petroleum ether	30–60	Acetic anhydride	140
Ligroin	60–90	**Pyridine**	115
Chlorocarbons		**Acetone**	56
Methylene chloride	40	**Ethyl acetate**	77
Chloroform[a]	61	Dimethylformamide	153
Carbon tetrachloride[a]	77	Dimethylsulfoxide	189
Alcohols			
Methanol	65		
Ethanol	78		
Isopropyl alcohol	82		

Note: **Boldface type** indicates flammability.

[a]Suspected carcinogen.

© Cengage Learning 2013

Figure 10.1
A comparison between "ether" (diethyl ether) and "petroleum ether."

shows the structure of ether (diethyl ether). Use special care when instructions call for either **ether** or **petroleum ether;** the two must not become accidentally confused. Confusion is particularly easy when one is selecting a container of solvent from the supply shelf.

Ligroin, or high-boiling petroleum ether, is like petroleum ether in composition except that compared with petroleum ether, ligroin generally includes higher-boiling alkane isomers. Depending on the supplier, ligroin may have different boiling ranges. Whereas some brands of ligroin have boiling points ranging from about 60°C to about 90°C, other brands have boiling points ranging from about 60°C to about 75°C. The boiling-point ranges of petroleum ether and ligroin are often included on the labels of the containers.

PROBLEMS

1. For each of the following pairs of solute and solvent, predict whether the solute would be soluble or insoluble. After making your predictions, you can check your answers by looking up the compounds in *The Merck Index* or the *CRC Handbook of Chemistry and Physics*. Generally, *The Merck Index* is the easier

reference book to use. If the substance has a solubility greater than 40 mg/mL, you may conclude that it is soluble.

a. Malic acid in water

$$HO-\overset{\overset{\displaystyle O}{\|}}{C}-\underset{\underset{\displaystyle OH}{|}}{C}HCH_2-\overset{\overset{\displaystyle O}{\|}}{C}-OH$$

Malic acid

b. Naphthalene in water

Naphthalene

c. Amphetamine in ethyl alcohol

$$-CH_2\underset{\underset{\displaystyle \overset{|}{N}H_2}{}}{C}HCH_3$$

Amphetamine

d. Aspirin in water

Aspirin

e. Succinic acid in hexane (*Note:* the polarity of hexane is similar to that of petroleum ether.)

$$HO-\overset{\overset{\displaystyle O}{\|}}{C}-CH_2CH_2-\overset{\overset{\displaystyle O}{\|}}{C}-OH$$

Succinic acid

f. Ibuprofen in diethyl ether

$$CH_3\underset{\underset{\displaystyle \overset{|}{C}H_3}{}}{C}HCH_2-\!\!\!\!\!\!\!\!\!-CH-COH$$

Ibuprofen

g. 1-Decanol (*n*-decyl alcohol) in water

$$CH_3(CH_2)_8H_2OH$$

1-Decanol

2. Predict whether the following pairs of liquids would be miscible or immiscible:

a. Water and methyl alcohol

b. Hexane and benzene

c. Methylene chloride and benzene

d. Water and toluene

Toluene

e. Ethyl alcohol and isopropyl alcohol

$$\overset{\displaystyle OH}{\underset{\displaystyle \text{Isopropyl alcohol}}{CH_3\overset{|}{C}HCH_3}}$$

3. Would you expect ibuprofen (see problem 1f) to be soluble or insoluble in 1.0 *M* NaOH? Explain.

4. Thymol is very slightly soluble in water and very soluble in 1.0 *M* NaOH. Explain.

Thymol

5. Although cannabinol and methyl alcohol are both alcohols, cannabinol is very slightly soluble in methyl alcohol at room temperature. Explain.

Cannabinol

6. What is the difference between the compounds in each of the following pairs?

a. Ether and petroleum ether

b. Ether and diethyl ether

c. Ligroin and petroleum ether

Crystallization: Purification of Solids

In most organic chemistry experiments, the desired product is first isolated in an impure form. If this product is a solid, the most common method of purification is crystallization. The general technique involves dissolving the material to be crystallized in a *hot* solvent (or solvent mixture) and cooling the solution slowly. The dissolved material has a decreased solubility at lower temperatures and will separate from the solution as it is cooled. This phenomenon is called either **crystallization,** if the crystal growth is relatively slow and selective, or **precipitation,** if the process is rapid and nonselective. Crystallization is an equilibrium process and produces very pure material. A small seed crystal is formed initially, and it then grows layer by layer in a reversible manner. In a sense, the crystal "selects" the correct molecules from the solution. In precipitation, the crystal lattice is formed so rapidly that impurities are trapped within the lattice. Therefore, any attempt at purification with too rapid a process should be avoided. Because the impurities are usually present in much smaller amounts than the compound being crystallized, most of the impurities will remain in the solvent even when it is cooled. The purified substance can then be separated from the solvent and from the impurities by filtration.

In microscale organic work, two methods are commonly used to perform crystallizations. The first method, which is carried out with an Erlenmeyer flask to dissolve the material and a Hirsch funnel to filter the crystals, is normally used when the weight of solid to be crystallized is more than 0.1 g. This technique, called **semimicroscale crystallization,** is discussed in Section 11.3. The second method is performed with a Craig tube and is used with smaller amounts of solid. Referred to as **microscale crystallization,** this technique is discussed in Section 11.4. The weight of solid to be crystallized, however, is not the only factor to consider when choosing a method for crystallization. Because the solubility of a substance in a given solvent must also be taken into account, the weight, 0.1 g, should not be adhered to rigidly in determining which method to use. In this textbook, you will usually be advised which method to use in the experimental procedure.

The method described here for semimicroscale crystallizations is nearly identical to that used for crystallizing larger amounts of materials than those encountered in this textbook. Therefore, this technique can also be used to perform crystallizations at the macroscale level (more than several grams).

PART A. THEORY

11.1 Solubility

The first problem in performing a crystallization is selecting a solvent in which the material to be crystallized shows the desired solubility behavior. In an ideal case, the material should be sparingly soluble at room temperature and yet quite soluble

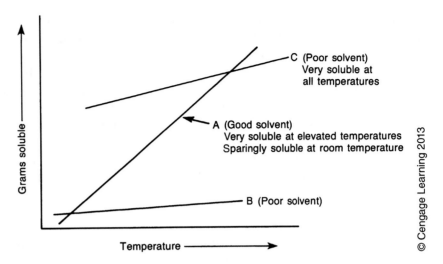

Figure 11.1
Graph of solubility vs. temperature.

Figure 11.2
Solubility of sulfanilamide in 95% ethyl alcohol.

at the boiling point of the solvent selected. The solubility curve should be steep, as can be seen in line A of Figure 11.1. A curve with a low slope (line B) would not cause significant crystallization when the temperature of the solution was lowered. A solvent in which the material is very soluble at all temperatures (line C) also would not be a suitable crystallization solvent. The basic problem in performing a crystallization is to select a solvent (or mixed solvent) that provides a steep solubility-vs.- temperature curve for the material to be crystallized. A solvent that allows the behavior shown in line A is an ideal crystallization solvent. It should also be mentioned that solubility curves are not always linear, as they are depicted in Figure 11.1. This figure represents an idealized form of solubility behavior. The solubility curve for sulfanilamide in 95% ethyl alcohol, shown in Figure 11.2, is typical of many organic compounds and shows what solubility behavior might look like for a real substance. This graph is based on the data in the following table:

Temperature	Solubility (mg/mL)
0°C	14
20°C	24
40°C	46
60°C	88
80°C	210

The solubility of organic compounds is a function of the polarities of both the solvent and the **solute** (dissolved material). A general rule is "Like dissolves like." If the solute is very polar, a very polar solvent is needed to dissolve it; if the solute is nonpolar, a nonpolar solvent is needed. Applications of this rule are discussed extensively in Technique 10, Section 10.2, and in Section 11.5.

11.2 Theory of Crystallization

A successful crystallization depends on a large difference between the solubility of a material in a hot solvent and its solubility in the same solvent when it is cold. When the impurities in a substance are equally soluble in both the hot and the cold solvent, an effective purification is not easily achieved through crystallization. A material can be purified by crystallization when both the desired substance and the impurity have similar solubilities, but only when the impurity represents a small fraction of the total solid. The desired substance will crystallize on cooling, but the impurities will not.

For example, consider a case in which the solubilities of substance A and its impurity B are both 1 g/100 mL of solvent at 20°C and 10 g/100 mL of solvent at 100°C. In the impure sample of A, the composition is 9 g of A and 2 g of B. In the calculations for this example, it is assumed that the solubilities of both A and B are unaffected by the presence of the other substance. To make the calculations easier to understand, 100 mL of solvent are used in each crystallization. Normally, the minimum amount of solvent required to dissolve the solid would be used.

At 20°C, this total amount of material will not dissolve in 100 mL of solvent. However, if the solvent is heated to 100°C, all 11 g dissolve. The solvent has the capacity to dissolve 10 g of A *and* 10 g of B at this temperature. If the solution is cooled to 20°C, only 1 g of each solute can remain dissolved, so 8 g of A and 1 g of B crystallize, leaving 2 g of material in the solution. This crystallization is shown in Figure 11.3. The solution that remains after a crystallization is called the **mother liquor.** If the process is now repeated by treating the crystals with 100 mL of fresh solvent, 7 g of A will crystallize again, leaving 1 g of A and 1 g of B in the mother liquor. As a result of these operations, 7 g of pure A are obtained, but with the loss of 4 g of material (2 g of A plus 2 g of B). Again, this second crystallization step is illustrated in Figure 11.3. The final result illustrates an important aspect of crystallization—it is wasteful. Nothing can be done to prevent this waste; some A must be lost along with the impurity B for the method to be successful. Of course, if the impurity B were *more* soluble than A in the solvent, the losses would be reduced. Losses could also be reduced if the impurity were present in *much smaller* amounts than the desired material.

Note that in the preceding case, the method operated successfully because A was present in substantially larger quantity than its impurity B. If there had been a 50-50 mixture of A and B initially, no separation would have been achieved. In general, a crystallization is successful only if there is a *small* amount of impurity. As the amount of impurity increases, the loss of material must also increase. Two substances with nearly equal solubility behavior, present in equal amounts, cannot be separated. If the solubility behavior of two components present in equal amounts is different, however, a separation or purification is frequently possible.

Figure 11.3
Purification of a mixture by crystallization.

In the preceding example, two crystallization procedures were performed. Normally, this is not necessary; however, when it is, the second crystallization is more appropriately called **recrystallization.** As illustrated in this example, a second crystallization results in purer crystals, but the yield is lower.

In most experiments, you will cool the crystallizing mixture in an ice-water bath before collecting the crystals by filtration. Cooling the mixture increases the yield by decreasing the solubility of the substance; however, even at this reduced temperature, some of the product will be soluble in the solvent. It is not possible to recover all your product in a crystallization procedure even when the mixture is cooled in an ice-water bath. A good example of this is illustrated by the solubility curve for sulfanilamide shown in Figure 11.2. The solubility of sulfanilamide at 0°C is still significant, 14 mg/mL. You should also remember that cooling the crystallizing mixture in an ice-water bath may cause more impurities to come out of solution, too, and the crystals may be less pure.

PART B. SEMIMICROSCALE CRYSTALLIZATION

11.3 Semimicroscale Crystallization— Hirsch Funnel

The crystallization technique described in this section is used when the weight of solid to be crystallized is more than 0.1 g. The four main steps in a semimicroscale crystallization are

1. Dissolving the solid
2. Removing insoluble impurities (when necessary)
3. Crystallization
4. Isolation of crystals

These steps are illustrated in Figure 11.4. It should be pointed out that a microscale crystallization with a Craig tube involves the same four steps, although the apparatus and procedures are somewhat different (see Section 11.4).

A. Dissolving the Solid

To minimize losses of material to the mother liquor, it is desirable to *saturate* the boiling solvent with solute. This solution, when cooled, will return the maximum possible amount of solute as crystals. To achieve this high return, the solvent is brought to its boiling point, and the solute is dissolved in the *minimum amount (!) of boiling solvent.* For this procedure, it is advisable to maintain a container of boiling solvent (on either a hot plate or a sand bath). From this container, add a small portion (about 0.5 mL) of the solvent to the flask[1] (usually a 10- or 25-mL Erlenmeyer flask) containing the solid to be crystallized and heat this mixture while swirling occasionally until it resumes boiling.

CAUTION

Do not heat the flask containing the solid until after you have added the first portion of solvent.

If the solid does not dissolve in the first portion of boiling solvent, then another small portion of boiling solvent is added to the flask. The mixture is heated again until

---

[1] A beaker should not be used, because the large opening allows the solvent to evaporate too rapidly and dust particles to get in too easily.

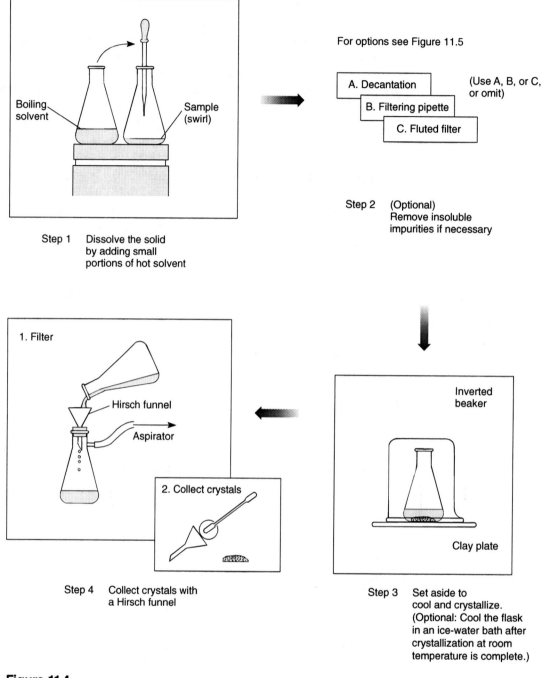

For options see Figure 11.5

A. Decantation   (Use A, B, or C, or omit)

B. Filtering pipette

C. Fluted filter

Step 2   (Optional)
Remove insoluble
impurities if necessary

Step 1   Dissolve the solid
by adding small
portions of hot solvent

Step 3   Set aside to
cool and crystallize.
(Optional: Cool the flask
in an ice-water bath after
crystallization at room
temperature is complete.)

Step 4   Collect crystals with
a Hirsch funnel

Figure 11.4
Steps in a semimicroscale crystallization (no decolorization).

it resumes boiling. If the solid dissolves, no more solvent is added. But if the solid has not dissolved, another portion of boiling solvent is added as before, and the process is repeated until the solid dissolves. (If the solid totally dissolves in less than 2 mL of solvent, a Craig tube should be used for crystallization.) The portions of solvent added each time should be small so that only the *minimum* amount of solvent necessary for dissolving the solid is added. It is also important to emphasize that the procedure requires the addition of solvent to solid. You must never add portions of solid to a fixed quantity of boiling solvent. By this latter method, it is impossible to tell when saturation has been

© Cengage Learning 2013

achieved. You should perform this procedure fairly rapidly. Otherwise, you may lose solvent by evaporation nearly as quickly as you are adding it, and dissolving the solid will take a long time. This is most likely to happen when highly volatile solvents such as methyl alcohol or ethyl alcohol are used. The time from the first addition of solvent until the solid dissolves completely should not be longer than 10–15 minutes.

Comments on This Procedure for Dissolving the Solid

1. One of the most common mistakes is to add too much solvent. This can happen most easily if the solvent is not hot enough or if the mixture is not stirred sufficiently. If too much solvent is added, the percentage recovery will be reduced; it is even possible that no crystals will form when the solution is cooled. If too much solvent is added, you must evaporate the excess by heating the mixture. A nitrogen or air stream directed into the container will accelerate the evaporation process (see Technique 7, Section 7.10).

2. Another common mistake is dissolving the solid in hot solvent that is *below* the boiling point of the solvent. This can significantly reduce the recovery.

3. It is very important not to heat the solid until you have added some solvent. Otherwise, the solid may melt and possibly form an oil or decompose, and it may not crystallize easily (see Section 11.5).

4. It is also important to use an Erlenmeyer flask rather than a beaker for performing the crystallization. A beaker should not be used because the large opening allows the solvent to evaporate too rapidly and allows dust particles to get in too easily.

5. In some experiments, a specified amount of solvent for a given weight of solid will be recommended. In these cases, you should use the amount specified rather than the minimum amount of solvent necessary to dissolve the solid. The amount of solvent recommended has been selected to provide the optimum conditions for good crystal formation.

6. Occasionally, you may encounter an impure solid that contains small particles of insoluble impurities, pieces of dust, or paper fibers that will not dissolve in the hot crystallizing solvent. A common error is to add too much of the hot solvent in an attempt to dissolve these small particles, not realizing that they are insoluble. In such cases, you must be careful not to add too much solvent.

7. It is sometimes necessary to decolorize the solution by adding activated charcoal or by passing the solution through a column containing alumina or silica gel (see Section 11.7 and Technique 19, Section 19.14). A decolorization step should be performed only if the mixture is *highly* colored and it is clear that the color is due to impurities and not to the actual color of the substance being crystallized. If decolorization is necessary, it should be accomplished before the following filtration step.

B. Removing Insoluble Impurities

It is necessary to use one of the following three methods only if insoluble material remains in the hot solution or if decolorizing charcoal has been used.

NOTE: Indiscriminate use of the procedure can lead to needless loss of your product.

Decantation is the easiest method of removing solid impurities and should be considered first. A filtering pipette is used when the volume of liquid to be filtered is less than 10 mL (see Technique 8, Section 8.1, Part C), and you should use gravity filtration through a fluted filter when the volume is 10 mL or greater (see Technique 8, Section 8.1, Part B). These three methods are illustrated in Figure 11.5.

Decantation. If the solid particles are relatively large or they easily settle to the bottom of the flask, it may be possible to separate the hot solution from the impurities by carefully pouring off the liquid, leaving the solid behind. This is accomplished most easily by holding a glass stirring rod along the top of the flask and tilting the flask so that the liquid pours out along one end of the glass rod into another container. A technique similar in principle to decantation, which may be easier to perform with smaller amounts of liquid, is to use a **preheated Pasteur pipette** to remove the hot solution. With this method, it may be helpful to place the tip of the pipette against the bottom of the flask when removing the last portion of solution. The small space between the tip of the pipette and the inside surface of the flask prevents solid material from being drawn into the pipette. An easy way to preheat the pipette is to draw up a small portion of hot *solvent* (not the *solution* being transferred) into the pipette and expel the liquid. Repeat this process several times.

Filtering Pipette. If the volume of solution after dissolving the solid in hot solvent is less than 10 mL, gravity filtration with a filtering pipette may be used to remove solid impurities. However, using a filtering pipette to filter a hot solution saturated with solute can be difficult without premature crystallization. The best way to prevent this from occurring is to add enough solvent to dissolve the desired product at room temperature (be sure not to add too much solvent) and perform the filtration at room temperature, as described in Technique 8, Section 8.1, Part C. After filtration, the excess solvent is evaporated by boiling until the solution is saturated at the boiling point of the mixture (see Technique 7, Section 7.10). If powdered decolorizing charcoal was used, it will probably be necessary to perform two filtrations with a filtering pipette, or else the method described next can be used.

Fluted Filter. This method is the most effective way to remove solid impurities when the volume of liquid is greater than 10 mL or when decolorizing charcoal has been used (see Technique 8, Section 8.1, Part B). You should add a small amount of extra solvent to the hot mixture. This procedure helps to prevent crystal formation in the filter paper or the stem of the funnel during the filtration. The funnel is fitted with a fluted filter and installed at the top of the Erlenmeyer flask to be used for the actual filtration. It is advisable to place a small piece of wire between the funnel and the mouth of the flask to relieve any increase in pressure caused by hot filtrate.

The Erlenmeyer flask containing the funnel and the fluted paper is placed on top of a sand bath or hot plate (low setting). The liquid to be filtered is brought to its boiling point and poured through the filter in portions. (If the volume of the mixture is less than 10 mL, it may be more convenient to transfer the mixture to the filter with a preheated Pasteur pipette.) It is necessary to keep the solutions in both flasks at their boiling temperatures to prevent premature crystallization. The refluxing action of the filtrate keeps the funnel warm and reduces the chance that the filter will clog with crystals that may have formed during the filtration. With low-boiling solvents, be aware that some solvent may be lost through evaporation. Consequently, extra solvent must be added to make up for this loss. If crystals begin to form in the filter during filtration, a minimum amount of boiling solvent is added to redissolve the crystals and to allow the solution to pass through the funnel. If the volume of liquid being filtered is less than 10 mL, a small amount of hot solvent should be used to rinse the filter after all the filtrate has been collected. The rinse solvent is then combined with the original filtrate.

Figure 11.5
Methods for removing insoluble impurities in a semimicroscale crystallization.

After the filtration, it may be necessary to remove extra solvent by evaporation until the solution is saturated at the boiling point of the solvent (see Technique 7, Section 7.10).

C. Crystallizing the Solid

An Erlenmeyer flask, not a beaker, should be used for crystallization. The large open top of a beaker makes it an excellent dust catcher. The narrow opening of the Erlenmeyer flask reduces contamination by dust and allows the flask to be stoppered if it is to be set aside for a long period. Mixtures set aside for long periods must be stoppered after cooling to room temperature to prevent evaporation of solvent. If all the solvent evaporates, no purification is achieved, and the crystals originally formed become coated with the dried contents of the mother liquor. Even if the time required for crystallization to occur is relatively short, it is advisable to cover the top of the Erlenmeyer flask with a small watch glass or inverted beaker to prevent evaporation of solvent while the solution is cooling to room temperature.

The chances of obtaining pure crystals are improved if the solution cools to room temperature slowly. When the volume of solution is 10 mL or less, the solution is likely to cool more rapidly than is desired. This can be prevented by placing the flask on a surface that is a poor heat conductor and covering the flask with a beaker to provide a layer of insulating air. Appropriate surfaces include a clay plate or several pieces of filter paper on top of the laboratory bench. It may also be helpful to use a clay plate that has been warmed slightly on a hot plate or in an oven.

After crystallization at room temperature is complete, it is usually desirable to cool the flask in an ice-water bath. Because the solute is less soluble at lower temperatures, this will increase the yield of crystals.

If a cooled solution does not crystallize, it will be necessary to induce crystallization. Several techniques are described in Section 11.8, Part A.

D. Collecting and Drying the Crystals

After the flask has been cooled, the crystals are collected by vacuum filtration through a Hirsch (or Büchner) funnel (see Technique 8, Section 8.3, and Figure 8.5).

Moisten the filter paper with a few drops of the crystallizing solvent and turn on the vacuum (or aspirator) to the fullest extent. Use a spatula to dislodge the crystals from the bottom of the flask before transferring the material to the funnel. Swirl the mixture in the flask and pour the mixture into the funnel, attempting to transfer both crystals and solvent. You need to pour the mixture quickly, before the crystals have completely resettled on the bottom of the flask. You may need to do this in portions, depending on the size of your funnel. If all of the liquid and crystals will fit into the funnel, the most effective way to make this transfer is to "swirl and dump" all of the mixture as quickly as you can. By doing this, you are more likely to transfer all or most of the crystals without needing to add more solvent to transfer the remaining crystals.

The crystals should be washed with a small amount of *cold* solvent to remove any mother liquor adhering to their surface. Hot or warm solvent will dissolve some of the crystals. The crystals should then be left for a short time in the funnel, where air, as it passes, will dry them free of most of the solvent. It is often wise to cover the Hirsch funnel with an oversize filter paper or towel during this airdrying. This precaution prevents accumulation of dust in the crystals. When the crystals are nearly dry, they should be gently scraped off (so paper fibers are not removed with the crystals) the filter paper onto a watch glass or clay plate for further drying (see Section 11.9).

PART C. MICROSCALE CRYSTALLIZATION

11.4 Microscale Crystallization— Craig Tube

In most microscale experiments, the amount of solid to be crystallized is small enough (generally less than 0.1 g) that a **Craig tube** (see Technique 8, Figure 8.10) is the preferred method for crystallization. The main advantage of the Craig tube is that it minimizes the number of transfers of solid material, thus resulting in a greater yield of crystals. Also, the separation of the crystals from the mother liquor with the Craig tube is very efficient, and little time is required for drying the crystals. The steps involved are, in principle, the same as those performed when a crystallization is accomplished with an Erlenmeyer flask and a Hirsch funnel. The steps in a microscale crystallization using a Craig tube are illustrated in Figure 11.6.

Figure 11.6
Steps in a microscale crystallization (no decolorization).

A. Dissolving the Solid

In crystallizations in which a filtration step is not required to remove insoluble impurities such as dirt or activated charcoal, this first step can be performed directly in the Craig tube. Otherwise, use a small test tube. The solid is transferred to the Craig tube, and the appropriate solvent, contained in a test tube, is heated to boiling on an aluminum block. A small portion (several drops) of hot solvent is added to the Craig tube, which is subsequently heated on the aluminum block until the solution in the Craig tube starts to boil. The hot mixture should be stirred continuously with a microspatula using a twirling motion. Stirring not only helps to dissolve the solute but also prevents the boiling liquid from bumping. Additional portions of hot solvent are added until all the solid has dissolved. In order to obtain the maximum yield, it is important not to add too much solvent, although any excess solvent can be evaporated later. You should perform this procedure fairly rapidly. Otherwise you may lose solvent by evaporation nearly as quickly as you are adding it, and dissolving all the solid will take a long time. The time required to dissolve the solid should not be longer than 15 minutes.

In many of the experiments in this textbook, a specified amount of solvent for a given weight of solid is recommended. In these cases, use the amount specified rather than the minimum amount of solvent necessary for dissolving the solid. The amount of solvent recommended has been selected to provide the optimum conditions for good crystal formation.

If the mixture is *highly* colored, and it is clear that the color is due to impurities and not to the actual color of the substance being crystallized, it will be necessary to decolorize the liquid. If decolorization is necessary, it should be accomplished before the following filtration step. Decolorizing charcoal may be used or the mixture may be passed through an alumina or silica gel column (see Section 11.7, Parts B and C, and Technique 19, Section 19.14).

B. Removing Insoluble Impurities

You should be alert for the presence of impurities that will not dissolve in the hot solvent, no matter how much solvent is added. If it appears that most of the solid has dissolved and the remaining solid has no tendency to dissolve, or if the liquid has been decolorized with charcoal, it will be necessary to remove the solid particles. Two methods are discussed.

If the impurities are relatively large or concentrated in one part of the mixture, it may be possible to use a Pasteur pipette preheated with hot solvent to draw up the liquid without removing any solid. One way to do this is to expel the air from the pipette and then place the end of the pipette on the bottom of the tube, being careful not to trap any solid in the pipette. The small space between the pipette and the bottom of the tube should allow you to draw up the liquid without removing any solid.

When filtration is necessary, a preheated Pasteur pipette is used to transfer the mixture to a test tube. After this transfer is made the Craig tube is rinsed with a few drops of solvent, which are also added to the test tube. The Craig tube is then washed and dried. The test tube containing the mixture is also heated in the sand bath. An additional 5 to 10 drops of solvent are added to the test tube to ensure that premature crystallization does not occur during the filtration step. To filter the mixture, take up the mixture in a filter-tip pipette (see Technique 8, Section 8.6) that has been preheated with hot solvent and quickly transfer the liquid to the clean Craig tube. Passing the liquid through the cotton plug in the filter-tip pipette should remove the solid impurities. If this does not occur, it may be necessary to add more solvent (to prevent crystallization) and filter the mixture through a filtering pipette (Technique 8, Section 8.1, Part C). In either case, once the filtered solution has been returned to the Craig tube, it will be necessary to evaporate some solvent until the solution is saturated near the boiling point of the liquid. This is most conveniently accomplished by placing the Craig tube in the sand bath and, while stirring rapidly using a microspatula (twirling is most effective), bringing the solution to a boil. When you begin to observe a trace of solid material coating the spatula just above the level of the liquid, the solution is near saturation, and evaporation should be stopped.

C. Crystallizing the Solid

The hot solution is cooled slowly in the Craig tube to room temperature. Recall that slow cooling is important in the formation of pure crystals. When the volume of solution is 2 mL or less and the mass of glassware is relatively small, slow cooling is somewhat difficult to achieve. One method of increasing the cooling time is to insert the inner plug into the outer part of the Craig tube and place the Craig tube into a 10-mL Erlenmeyer flask. The layer of air in the flask will help insulate the hot solution as it cools. The Erlenmeyer flask is placed on a surface such as a clay plate (warmed slightly, if desired) or several pieces of paper. Another method is to fill a 10-mL Erlenmeyer flask with 8–10 mL of hot water at a temperature below the boiling point of the solvent. The assembled Craig tube is placed in the Erlenmeyer flask, which is set on an appropriate surface. Be careful not to put so much water in the Erlenmeyer flask that the Craig tube floats. After crystallization at room temperature is complete, the Craig tube can be placed in an ice-water bath to maximize the yield.

If crystals have not formed after the solution has cooled, it will be necessary to induce crystallization. Several techniques are described in Section 11.8.

A common occurrence with crystallizations using a Craig tube is to obtain a seemingly solid mass of small crystals. This may not be a problem, but if there is very little mother liquor present or the crystals are impure, it may be necessary to repeat the crystallization. This situation may have resulted either because the cooling process occurred too rapidly or because the solubility–temperature curve was so steep for a given solvent that very little mother liquor remained after the crystallization. In either case, you may want to repeat the crystallization to obtain a better (purer) yield of crystals. Three measures may be taken to avoid this problem. A small amount of extra solvent may be added before heating the mixture again and allowing it to cool. A second measure is to cool the solution more slowly. Finally, it may be helpful to try to induce crystallization *before* the solution has cooled to room temperature.

D. Collecting and Drying the Crystals

When the crystals have formed and the mixture has cooled in an ice-water bath (if desired), the Craig tube is placed in a centrifuge tube and the crystals are separated from the mother liquor by centrifugation (see Technique 8, Section 8.8). The crystals are then scraped off the end of the inner plug or from inside the Craig tube onto a watch glass or piece of paper. Minimal drying will be necessary (see Section 11.9).

The four steps in a semimicroscale or microscale crystallization are summarized in Table 11.1.

Table 11.1 Steps in a semimicroscale or microscale crystallization

A. Dissolving the Solid

1. Find a solvent with a steep solubility-vs.-temperature characteristic (done by trial and error using small amounts of material or by consulting a handbook).
2. Heat the desired solvent to its boiling point.
3. Dissolve the solid in a **minimum** of boiling solvent (either in a flask or a Craig tube).
4. If necessary, add decolorizing charcoal or decolorize the solution on a silica gel or alumina column.

B. Removing Insoluble Impurities

1. Decant or remove the solution with a Pasteur pipette, or
2. Filter the hot solution through a fluted filter, a filtering pipette, or a filter-tip pipette to remove insoluble impurities or charcoal.

NOTE: If no decolorizing charcoal has been added or if there are no undissolved particles, Part B should be omitted.

C. Crystallizing the Solid

1. Allow the solution to cool.
2. If crystals appear, cool the mixture in an ice-water bath (if desired) and go to Part D. If crystals do not appear, go to the next step.
3. Inducing crystallization
   (a) Scratch the flask with a glass rod; or, if using a Craig tube, dip a glass rod or spatula into the solution, let the liquid evaporate, and place the glass rod or spatula back into the solution to seed it.
   (b) Seed the solution with original solid, if available.
   (c) Cool the solution in an ice-water bath.
   (d) Evaporate excess solvent and allow the solution to cool again.

D. Collecting and Drying the Crystals

1. Collect crystals by vacuum filtration using a Hirsch funnel or by centrifugation using a Craig tube.
2. If using a Hirsch funnel, rinse crystals with a small portion of **cold** solvent.
3. Continue suction until crystals are nearly dry, if using vacuum filtration.
4. Drying
   (a) Air-dry the crystals, or
   (b) Place the crystals in a drying oven, or
   (c) Dry the crystals *in vacuo*.

© Cengage Learning 2013

PART D. ADDITIONAL EXPERIMENTAL CONSIDERATIONS: SEMIMICROSCALE AND MICROSCALE

11.5 Selecting a Solvent

A solvent that dissolves little of the material to be crystallized when it is cold but a great deal of the material when it is hot is a good solvent for crystallization. Quite often, correct crystallization solvents are indicated in the experimental procedures that you will be following. When a solvent is not specified in a procedure, you can determine a good crystallization solvent by consulting a handbook or making an educated guess based on polarities, both discussed in this section. A third approach, involving experimentation, is discussed in Section 11.6.

With compounds that are well known, the correct crystallization solvent has already been determined through the experiments of earlier researchers. In such cases, the chemical literature can be consulted to determine which solvent should be used. Sources such as *The Merck Index* or the *CRC Handbook of Chemistry and Physics* may provide this information.

For example, consider naphthalene, which is found in *The Merck Index,* which states under the entry for naphthalene: "Monoclinic prismatic plates from ether." This statement means that naphthalene can be crystallized from ether. It also gives the type of crystal structure. Unfortunately, the crystal structure may be given without reference to the solvent. Another way to determine the best solvent is by looking at solubility-vs.-temperature data. When this is given, a good solvent is one in which the solubility of the compound increases significantly as the temperature increases. Sometimes, the solubility data will be given for only cold solvent and boiling solvent. This should provide enough information to determine whether this would be a good solvent for crystallization.

In most cases, however, the handbooks will state only whether a compound is soluble or not in a given solvent, usually at room temperature. Determining a good solvent for crystallization from this information can be somewhat difficult. The solvent in which the compound is soluble may or may not be an appropriate solvent for crystallization. Sometimes, the compound may be too soluble in the solvent at all temperatures, and you would recover little of your product if this solvent were used for crystallization. It is possible that an appropriate solvent would be the one in which the compound is nearly insoluble at room temperature because the solubility-vs.- temperature curve is steep. Although the solubility information may give you some ideas about what solvents to try, you will most likely need to determine a good crystallizing solvent by experimentation as described in Section 11.6.

When using *The Merck Index* or *Handbook of Chemistry and Physics,* you should be aware that alcohol is frequently listed as a solvent. This generally refers to 95% or 100% ethyl alcohol. Because 100% (absolute) ethyl alcohol is more expensive than 95% ethyl alcohol, the cheaper grade is usually used in the chemistry laboratory. Another solvent frequently listed is benzene. Benzene is a known carcinogen, so it is rarely used in student laboratories. Toluene is a suitable substitute; the solubility behavior of a substance in benzene and toluene is so similar that you may assume any statement made about benzene also applies to toluene.

Another way to identify a solvent for crystallization is to consider the polarities of the compound and the solvents. Generally, you would look for a solvent that has a polarity somewhat similar to that of the compound to be crystallized. Consider the compound sulfanilamide, shown in the figure. There are several polar bonds in sulfanilamide, the NH and the SO bonds. In addition, the NH_2 groups and the oxygen atoms in sulfanilamide can form hydrogen bonds. Although the benzene ring portion of sulfanilamide is nonpolar, sulfanilamide has an intermediate polarity because of the polar groups. A common organic solvent of intermediate polarity is 95% ethyl alcohol. Therefore, it is likely that sulfanilamide would be soluble in 95% ethyl alcohol because they have similar polarities. (Note that the

Sulfanilamide

© Cengage Learning 2013

other 5% in 95% ethyl alcohol is usually a substance such as water or isopropyl alcohol, which does not alter the overall polarity of the solvent.) Although this kind of analysis is a good first step in determining an appropriate solvent for crystallization, without more information it is not enough to predict the shape of the solubility curve for the temperature-vs.- solubility data (see Figure 11.1). Therefore, knowing that sulfanilamide is soluble in 95% ethyl alcohol does not necessarily mean that this is a good solvent for crystallizing sulfanilamide. You would still need to test the solvent to see if it is appropriate. The solubility curve for sulfanilamide (see Figure 11.2) indicates that 95% ethyl alcohol is a good solvent for crystallizing this substance.

When choosing a crystallization solvent, do not select one whose boiling point is higher than the melting point of the substance (solute) to be crystallized. If the boiling point of the solvent is too high, the substance may come out of solution as a liquid rather than a crystalline solid. In such a case, the solid may **oil out.** Oiling out occurs when, on cooling the solution to induce crystallization, the solute begins to come out of solution at a temperature above its melting point. The solute will then come out of solution as a liquid. Furthermore, as cooling continues, the substance may still not crystallize; rather, it will become a supercooled liquid. Oils may eventually solidify if the temperature is lowered, but often they will not actually crystallize. Instead, the solidified oil will be an amorphous solid or a hardened mass. In this case, purification of the substance will not have occurred as it does when the solid is crystalline. It can be difficult to deal with oils when trying to obtain a pure substance. You must try to redissolve them and hope that the substance will crystallize with slow, careful cooling. During the cooling period, it may be helpful to scratch the glass container where the oil is present with a glass stirring rod that has not been fire-polished. Seeding the oil as it cools with a small sample of the original solid is another technique that is sometimes helpful in working with difficult oils. Other methods of inducing crystallization are discussed in Section 11.8.

One additional criterion for selecting the correct crystallization solvent is the **volatility** of that solvent. Volatile solvents have low boiling points or evaporate easily. A solvent with a low boiling point may be removed from the crystals through evaporation without much difficulty. It will be difficult to remove a solvent with a high boiling point from the crystals without heating them under vacuum. On the other hand, solvents with very low boiling points are not ideal for crystallizations. The recovery will not be as great with low boiling solvents because they cannot be heated past the boiling point and the amount of cooling that occurs during the crystallization step will be relatively small. Diethyl ether (bp = 35°C) and methylene chloride (bp = 41°C) are not often used as crystallization solvents.

Table 11.2 lists common crystallization solvents. The solvents used most commonly are listed in the table first.

11.6 Testing Solvents for Crystallization

When the appropriate solvent is not known, select a solvent for crystallization by experimenting with various solvents and a small amount of the material to be crystallized. Experiments are conducted on a small test tube scale before the entire quantity of material is committed to a particular solvent. Such trial-and-error methods are common when trying to purify a solid material that has not been studied.

Procedure

1. Place about 0.05 g of the sample in a test tube.
2. Add about 0.5 mL of solvent at room temperature and stir the mixture by rapidly twirling a microspatula between your fingers. If all (or almost all) of the

Table 11.2 Common solvents for crystallization

	Boils (°C)	Freezes (°C)	Soluble in H_2O	Flammability
Water	100	0	+	−
Methanol	65	*	+	+
95% Ethanol	78	*	+	+
Ligroin	60–90	*	−	+
Toluene	111	*	−	+
Chloroform**	61	*	−	−
Acetic acid	118	17	+	+
Dioxane**	101	11	+	+
Acetone	56	*	+	+
Diethyl ether	35	*	Slightly	++
Petroleum ether	30–60	*	−	++
Methylene chloride	41	*	−	−
Carbon tetrachloride**	77	*	−	−

© Cengage Learning 2013

*Lower than 0°C (ice temperature).

**Suspected carcinogen.

solid dissolves at room temperature, then your solid is *probably* too soluble in this solvent and little compound would be recovered if this solvent were used. Select another solvent.

3. If none (or very little) of the solid dissolves at room temperature, heat the tube carefully and stir with a spatula. (A hot water bath is perhaps better than an aluminum block because you can more easily control the temperature of the hot water bath. The temperature of the hot water bath should be slightly higher than the boiling point of the solvent.) Add more solvent dropwise while continuing to heat and stir. Continue adding solvent until the solid dissolves, but do not add more than about 1.5 mL (total) of solvent. If all the solid dissolves, go to step 4. If all the solid has not dissolved by the time you have added 1.5 mL of solvent, this is probably not a good solvent. However, if most of the solid has dissolved at this point, you might try adding a little more solvent. Remember to heat and stir at all times during this step.

4. If the solid dissolves in about 1.5 mL or less of boiling solvent, then remove the test tube from the heat source, stopper the tube, and allow it to cool to room temperature. Then place it in an ice-water bath. If a lot of crystals come out, this is most likely a good solvent. If crystals do not come out, scratch the sides of the tube with a glass stirring rod to induce crystallization. If crystals still do not form, this is probably not a good solvent.

Comments about This Procedure

1. Selecting a good solvent is something of an art. There is no perfect procedure that can be used in all cases. You must think about what you are doing and use some common sense in deciding whether to use a particular solvent.

2. Do not heat the mixture above the melting point of your solid. This can occur most easily when the boiling point of the solvent is higher than the melting

point of the solid. Normally, do not select a solvent that has a higher boiling point than the melting point of the substance. If you do, make certain that you do not heat the mixture beyond the melting point of your solid.

11.7 Decolorization

Small amounts of highly colored impurities may make the original crystallization solution appear colored; this color can often be removed by **decolorization,** either by using activated charcoal (often called Norit) or by passing the solution through a column packed with alumina or silica gel. A decolorizing step should be performed only if the color is due to impurities, not to the color of the desired product, and if the color is significant. Small amounts of colored impurities will remain in solution during crystallization, making the decolorizing step unnecessary. The use of activated charcoal is described separately for macroscale and microscale crystallizations, and then the column technique, which can be used with both crystallization techniques, is described.

A. Semimicroscale—Powdered Charcoal

As soon as the solute is dissolved in the minimum amount of boiling solvent, the solution is allowed to cool slightly, and a small amount of Norit (powdered charcoal) is added to the mixture. The Norit adsorbs the impurities. When performing a crystallization in which the filtration is performed with a fluted filter, you should add powdered Norit because it has a larger surface area and can remove impurities more effectively. A reasonable amount of Norit is what could be held on the end of a microspatula, or about 0.01–0.02 g. If too much Norit is used, it will adsorb product as well as impurities. A small amount of Norit should be used, and its use should be repeated if necessary. (It is difficult to determine if the initial amount added is sufficient until after the solution is filtered because the suspended particles of charcoal will obscure the color of the liquid.) Caution should be exercised so that the solution does not froth or erupt when the finely divided charcoal is added. The mixture is boiled with the Norit for several minutes and then filtered by gravity, using a fluted filter (see Section 11.3 and Technique 8, Section 8.1B), and the crystallization is carried forward as described in Section 11.3.

The Norit preferentially adsorbs the colored impurities and removes them from the solution. The technique seems to be most effective with hydroxylic solvents. In using Norit, be careful not to breathe the dust. Normally, small quantities are used so that little risk of lung irritation exists.

B. Microscale—Pelletized Norit

If the crystallization is being performed in a Craig tube, it is advisable to use pelletized Norit. Although this is not as effective in removing impurities as powdered Norit, it is easier to remove, and the amount of pelletized Norit required is more easily determined because you can see the solution as it is being decolorized. Again, the Norit is added to the hot solution (the solution should not be boiling) after the solid has dissolved. This should be performed in a test tube rather than in a Craig tube. About 0.02 g is added, and the mixture is boiled for a minute or so to see if more Norit is required. More Norit is added, if necessary, and the liquid is boiled again. It is important not to add too much pelletized Norit because the Norit will also adsorb some of the desired material, and it is possible that not all the color can be removed no matter how much is added. The decolorized solution is then removed with a preheated filter-tip pipette (see Technique 8, Section 8.6) to filter the mixture and transferred to a Craig tube for crystallization as described in Section 11.4.

C. Decolorization on a Column

The other method for decolorizing a solution is to pass the solution through a column containing alumina or silica gel. The adsorbent removes the colored impurities while allowing the desired material to pass through (see Technique 8, Figure 8.6, and Technique 19, Section 19.14). If this technique is used, it will be necessary to dilute the solution with additional solvent to prevent crystallization from occurring during the process. The excess solvent must be evaporated after the solution is passed through the column (Technique 7, Section 7.10), and the crystallization procedure is continued as described in Sections 11.3 or 11.4.

11.8 Inducing Crystallization

If a cooled solution does not crystallize, several techniques may be used to induce crystallization. Although identical in principle, the actual procedures vary slightly when macroscale and microscale crystallizations are performed.

A. Semimicroscale

In the first technique, you should try scratching the inside surface of the flask vigorously with a glass rod that has not been fire-polished. The motion of the rod should be vertical (in and out of the solution) and should be vigorous enough to produce an audible scratching. Such scratching often induces crystallization, although the effect is not well understood. The high-frequency vibrations may have something to do with initiating crystallization; or perhaps—a more likely possibility—small amounts of solution dry by evaporation on the side of the flask, and the dried solute is pushed into the solution. These small amounts of material would provide "seed crystals," or nuclei, on which crystallization may begin.

A second technique that can be used to induce crystallization is to cool the solution in an ice bath. This method decreases the solubility of the solute.

A third technique is useful when small amounts of the original material to be crystallized are saved. The saved material can be used to "seed" the cooled solution. A small crystal dropped into the cooled flask often will start the crystallization—this is called **seeding.**

If all these measures fail to induce crystallization, it is likely that too much solvent was added. The excess solvent must then be evaporated (Technique 7, Section 7.10) and the solution allowed to cool.

B. Microscale

The strategy is basically the same as described for macroscale crystallizations. Scratching vigorously with a glass rod should be avoided, however, because the Craig tube is fragile and expensive. Scratching *gently* is allowed.

Another measure is to dip a spatula or glass stirring rod into the solution and allow the solvent to evaporate so that a small amount of solid will form on the surface of the spatula or glass rod. When placed back into the solution, the solid will seed the solution. A small amount of the original material, if some was saved, may also be used to seed the solution.

A third technique is to cool the Craig tube in an ice-water bath. This method may also be combined with either of the previous suggestions.

If none of these measures is successful, it is possible that too much solvent is present, and it may be necessary to evaporate some of the solvent (Technique 7, Section 7.10) and allow the solution to cool again.

11.9 Drying Crystals

The most common method of drying crystals involves allowing them to dry in air. Several methods are illustrated in Figure 11.7, below. In all three methods, the crystals must be covered to prevent accumulation of dust particles. Note that in each method, the spout on the beaker provides an opening so that solvent vapor can escape from the system. The advantage of this method is that heat is not required, thus reducing the danger of decomposition or melting; however, exposure to atmospheric moisture may cause the hydration of strongly hygroscopic materials. A **hygroscopic** substance is a substance that absorbs moisture from the air.

Another method of drying crystals is to place the crystals on a watch glass, a clay plate, or a piece of absorbent paper in an oven. Although this method is simple, some possible difficulties deserve mention. Crystals that sublime readily should not be dried in an oven because they might vaporize and disappear. Care should be taken that the temperature of the oven does not exceed the melting point of the crystals. Remember that the melting point of crystals is lowered by the presence of solvent; allow for this melting-point depression when selecting a suitable oven temperature. Some materials decompose on exposure to heat, and they should not be dried in an oven. Finally, when many different samples are being dried in the same oven, crystals might be lost due to confusion or reaction with another person's sample. It is important to label the crystals when they are placed in the oven.

A third method, which requires neither heat nor exposure to atmospheric moisture, is drying *in vacuo*. Two procedures are illustrated in Figure 11.8.

Procedure A

In this method, a desiccator is used. The sample is placed under vacuum in the presence of a drying agent. Two potential problems must be noted. The first deals with samples that sublime readily. Under vacuum, the likelihood of sublimation is increased. The second problem deals with the vacuum desiccator itself. Because the surface area of glass that is under vacuum is large, there is some danger that the desiccator could implode. A vacuum desiccator should never be used unless it has been placed within a protective metal container (cage). If a cage is not available, the desiccator can be wrapped with electrical or duct tape. If you use an aspirator as a source of vacuum, you should use a water trap (see Technique 8, Figure 8.5).

Procedure B

This method can be accomplished with a round-bottom flask and a thermometer adapter equipped with a short piece of glass tubing, as illustrated in Figure 11.8B.

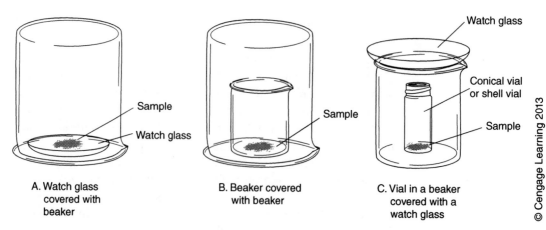

Figure 11.7

Methods for drying crystals in air.

Figure 11.8
Methods for drying crystals in a vacuum.

In microscale work, the apparatus with the round-bottom flask can be modified by replacing the round-bottom flask with a conical vial. The glass tubing is connected by vacuum tubing to either an aspirator or a vacuum pump. A convenient alternative, using a side arm test tube, is also shown in Figure 11.8B. With either apparatus, install a water trap when an aspirator is used.

11.10 Mixed Solvents   Often, the desired solubility characteristics for a particular compound are not found in a single solvent. In these cases, a mixed solvent may be used. You simply select a first solvent in which the solute is soluble and a second solvent, miscible with the first, in which the solute is relatively insoluble. The compound is dissolved in a minimum amount of the boiling solvent in which it is soluble. Following this, the second hot solvent is added to the boiling mixture, dropwise, until the mixture barely becomes cloudy. The cloudiness indicates precipitation. At this point, more of the first solvent should be added. Just enough is added to clear the cloudy mixture. At that point, the solution is saturated, and as it cools, crystals should separate. Common solvent mixtures are listed in Table 11.3.

It is important not to add an excess of the second solvent or to cool the solution too rapidly. Either of these actions may cause the solute to oil out, or separate as a viscous liquid. If this happens, reheat the solution and add more of the first solvent.

Table 11.3 Common solvent pairs for crystallization

Methanol–water	Ether–acetone
Ethanol–water	Ether–petroleum ether
Acetic acid–water	Toluene–ligroin
Acetone–water	Methylene chloride–methanol
Ether–methanol	Dioxane[a]–water

[a]Suspected carcinogen.

PROBLEMS

1. Listed below are solubility-vs.-temperature data for an organic substance A dissolved in water.

Temperature (°C)	Solubility of A in 100 mL of Water (g)
0	1.5
20	3.0
40	6.5
60	11.0
80	17.0

   a. Graph the solubility of A vs. temperature. Use the data given in the table. Connect the data points with a smooth curve.

   b. Suppose 0.1 g of A and 1.0 mL of water were mixed and heated to 80°C. Would all the substance A dissolve?

   c. The solution prepared in (b) is cooled. At what temperature will crystals of A appear?

   d. Suppose the cooling described in (c) were continued to 0°C. How many grams of A would come out of solution? Explain how you obtained your answer.

2. What would likely happen if a hot saturated solution were filtered by vacuum filtration using a Hirsch funnel? (*Hint:* The mixture will cool as it comes in contact with the Hirsch funnel.)

3. A compound you have prepared is reported in the literature to have a pale yellow color. When the substance is dissolved in hot solvent to purify it by crystallization, the resulting solution is yellow. Should you use decolorizing charcoal before allowing the hot solution to cool? Explain your answer.

4. After a crude product is dissolved in 1.5 mL of hot solvent, the resulting solution is dark brown. Because the pure compound is reported in the literature to be colorless, it is necessary to perform a decolorizing procedure. Should you use pelletized Norit or powdered activated charcoal to decolorize the solution? Explain your answer.

5. While performing a crystallization, you obtain a light tan solution after dissolving your crude product in hot solvent. A decolorizing step is determined to be unnecessary, and there are no solid impurities present. Should you perform a filtration to remove impurities before allowing the solution to cool? Why or why not?

6. a. Draw a graph of a cooling curve (temperature vs. time) for a solution of a solid substance that shows no supercooling effects. Assume that the solvent does not freeze.

   b. Repeat the instructions in (a) for a solution of a solid substance that shows some supercooling behavior but eventually yields crystals if the solution is cooled sufficiently.

7. A solid substance A is soluble in water to the extent of 10 mg/mL of water at 25°C and 100 mg/mL of water at 100°C. You have a sample that contains 100 mg of A and an impurity B. See Section 11.2 for guidance in answering these questions.

    a. Assuming that 2 mg of B are present along with 100 mg of A, describe how you can purify A if B is completely insoluble in water. Your description should include the volume of solvent required.

    b. Assuming that 2 mg of the impurity B are present along with 100 mg of A, describe how you can purify A if B has the same solubility behavior as A. Will one crystallization produce pure A? (Assume that the solubilities of both A and B are unaffected by the presence of the other substance.)

    c. Assume that 25 mg of the impurity B are present along with 100 mg of A. Describe how you can purify A if B has the same solubility behavior as A. Each time, use the minimum amount of water to just dissolve the solid. Will one crystallization produce absolutely pure A? How many crystallizations would be needed to produce pure A? How much A will have been recovered when the crystallizations have been completed?

8. Consider the crystallization of sulfanilamide from 95% ethyl alcohol. If impure sulfanilamide is dissolved in the minimum amount of 95% ethyl alcohol at 40°C rather than 78°C (the boiling point of ethyl alcohol), how would this affect the percentage of recovery of pure sulfanilamide? Explain your answer.

Extractions, Separations, and Drying Agents

PART A. THEORY

12.1 Extraction

Transferring a solute from one solvent into another is called **extraction,** or, more precisely, liquid–liquid extraction. The solute is extracted from one solvent into the other because the solute is more soluble in the second solvent than in the first. The two solvents must not be **miscible** (mix freely), and they must form two separate **phases,** or layers, in order for this procedure to work. Extraction is used in many ways in organic chemistry. Many natural products (organic chemicals that exist in nature) are present in animal and plant tissues having high water content. Extracting these tissues with a water-immiscible solvent is useful for isolating natural products. Often, diethyl ether (commonly referred to as "ether") is used for this purpose. Sometimes alternative water-immiscible solvents such as hexane, petroleum ether, ligroin, and methylene chloride are used. For instance, caffeine, a natural product, can be extracted from an aqueous tea solution by shaking it successively with several portions of methylene chloride.

A generalized extraction process that uses a conical vial is illustrated in Figure 12.1. The first solvent contains a mixture of black and white molecules (Figure 12.1A). A second solvent that is not miscible with the first is added.

After the vial is capped and shaken, the layers separate. In this example, the second solvent is less dense, so it becomes the top layer (Figure 12.1B). Because of differences in physical properties, the white molecules are more soluble in the second solvent, whereas the black molecules are more soluble in the first solvent. Most of the white molecules are in the upper layer, but there are some black molecules there, too. Likewise, most of the black molecules are in the lower layer. However, there are a few white molecules in this lower phase. A Pasteur pipette may be used to remove the lower layer (Figure 12.1C). In this way, a partial separation of black and white molecules has been achieved. In this example, notice that it was not possible to effect a complete separation with one extraction. This is a common occurrence in organic chemistry. Many organic substances are soluble in both water and organic solvents.

Water can be used to extract or "wash" water-soluble impurities from an organic reaction mixture. To carry out a "washing" operation, you add water to the reaction mixture contained in a conical vial. After capping the vial and shaking it, you allow the organic layer and the aqueous (water) layer to separate from each other in the vial. A water wash removes highly polar and water-soluble materials, such as sulfuric acid, hydrochloric acid, or sodium hydroxide from the organic layer. A water wash can also be used to remove water-soluble and low-molecular-weight compounds, such as ethanol or acetic acid, from the organic layer.

A. Solvent 1 contains a mixture of molecules (black and white).

B. After shaking with solvent 2 (shaded), most of the white molecules have been extracted into the new solvent. The white molecules are more soluble in the second solvent, whereas the black molecules are more soluble in the original solvent.

C. With removal of the lower phase with a Pasteur pipette, the black and white molecules have been partially separated.

© Cengage Learning 2013

A   B   C

Figure 12.1
The extraction process.

The washing operation helps purify the desired organic compound present in the original reaction mixture.

12.2 Distribution Coefficient

When a solution (solute A in solvent 1) is shaken with a second solvent (solvent 2) with which it is not miscible, the solute distributes itself between the two liquid phases. When the two phases have separated again into two distinct solvent layers, an equilibrium will have been achieved such that the ratio of the concentrations of the solute in each layer defines a constant. The constant, called the **distribution coefficient** (or partition coefficient) K, is defined by

$$K = \frac{C_2}{C_1}$$

where C_1 and C_2 are the concentrations at equilibrium, in grams per liter or milligrams per milliliter of solute A in solvent 1 and in solvent 2, respectively. This relationship is a ratio of two concentrations and is independent of the actual amounts of the two solvents mixed. The distribution coefficient has a constant value for each solute considered and depends on the nature of the solvents used in each case.

Not all the solute will be transferred to solvent 2 in a single extraction unless K is very large. Usually it takes several extractions to remove all the solute from solvent 1. In extracting a solute from a solution, it is always better to use several small portions of the second solvent than to make a single extraction with a large portion. Suppose that, as an illustration, a particular extraction proceeds with a distribution coefficient of 10. The system consists of 50 mg of organic compound dissolved in 1.00 mL of water (solvent 1). In this illustration, the effectiveness of three 0.50-mL extractions with ether (solvent 2) is compared with one 1.50-mL extraction with ether. In the first 0.50-mL extraction, the amount extracted into the ether layer is given by the following calculation. The amount of compound remaining in the aqueous phase is given by x.

$$K = 10 = \frac{C_2}{C_1} = \frac{\left(\dfrac{(50.0 - x)}{0.50} \dfrac{mg}{mL\ ether}\right)}{\left(\dfrac{x}{1.00} \dfrac{mg}{mL\ water}\right)} ; 10 = \frac{(50.0 - x)(1.00)}{0.50x}$$

$$5.0x = 50.0 - x$$
$$6.0x = 50.0$$
$$x = 8.3\ mg\ remaining\ in\ the\ aqueous\ layer$$
$$50.0 - x = 41.7\ mg\ in\ the\ ether\ layer$$

As a check on the calculation, it is possible to substitute the value 8.3 mg for x in the original equation and demonstrate that the concentration in the ether phase divided by the concentration in the water phase equals the distribution coefficient.

$$\frac{\left(\dfrac{(50.0 - x)}{0.50} \dfrac{mg}{mL\ ether}\right)}{\left(\dfrac{x}{1.00} \dfrac{mg}{mL\ water}\right)} \dfrac{\dfrac{41.7}{0.50}}{\dfrac{8.3}{1.00}} = \frac{83\ mg/mL}{8.3\ mg/mL} = 10 = K$$

The second extraction with another 0.50-mL portion of fresh ether is performed on the aqueous phase, which now contains 8.3 mg of the solute. The amount of solute extracted is given by the calculation shown in Figure 12.2. Also shown in the

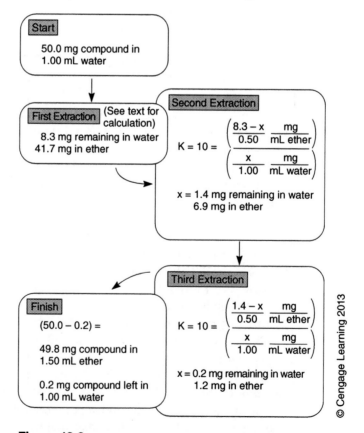

Figure 12.2
The result of extraction of 50.0 mg of compound in 1.00 mL of water by three successive 0.50-mL portions of ether. Compare this result with that of Figure 12.3.

Figure 12.3
The result of extraction of 50.0 mg of compound
in 1.00 mL of water with one 1.5-mL portion of
ether. Compare this result with that of Figure 12.2.

Figure 12.4
Apparatus used for extraction.

figure is a calculation for a third extraction with another 0.50-mL portion of ether. This third extraction will transfer 1.2 mg of solute into the ether layer, leaving 0.2 mg of solute remaining in the water layer. A total of 49.8 mg of solute will be extracted into the combined ether layers, and 0.2 mg will remain in the aqueous phase.

Figure 12.3 shows the result of a *single* extraction with 1.50 mL of ether. As shown there, 46.9 mg of solute was extracted into the ether layer, leaving 3.1 mg of compound in the aqueous phase. One can see that three successive 0.50-mL ether extractions (Figure 12.2) succeeded in removing 2.9 mg more solute from the aqueous phase than using one 1.50-mL portion of ether (Figure 12.3). This differential represents 5.8% of the total material.

12.3 Choosing an Extraction Method and a Solvent

Three types of apparatus are used for extractions: conical vials, centrifuge tubes, and separatory funnels. These are shown in Figure 12.4. Conical vials may be used with volumes of less than 4 mL; volumes of up to 10 mL may be handled in centrifuge tubes. A centrifuge tube equipped with a screw cap is particularly useful for extractions. The separatory funnel is used in large-scale reactions. Each type of equipment is discussed in a separate section.

Before using a conical vial for an extraction, make sure that the capped conical vial does not leak when shaken. To do this, place some water in the conical vial, place the Teflon liner in the cap, and screw the cap securely onto the conical vial. Shake the vial vigorously and check for leaks. Conical vials that are used for extractions must not be chipped on the edge of the vial or they will not seal adequately. If there is a leak, try tightening the cap or replacing the Teflon liner with another one. Sometimes it helps to use the silicone rubber side of the liner to seal the conical vial. Some laboratories are supplied with Teflon stoppers that fit into the 5-mL conical vials. You may find that this stopper eliminates leakage.

Table 12.1 Densities of common extraction solvents

Solvent	Density (g/mL)
Ligroin	0.67–0.69
Diethyl ether	0.71
Toluene	0.87
Water	1.00
Methylene chloride	1.330

© Cengage Learning 2013

When shaking the conical vial, do it gently at first in a rocking motion. When it is clear that an emulsion will not form (see Section 12.10), you can shake it more vigorously.

In some cases, adequate mixing can be achieved by spinning your microspatula for at least 10 minutes in the conical vial. Another technique of mixing involves drawing up the mixture into a Pasteur pipette and squirting it rapidly back into the vial. Repeat this process for at least 5 minutes to obtain an adequate extraction.

If you are using a screw-cap centrifuge tube, put some water in the tube, cap it, and shake it vigorously to check for leaks. If the centrifuge tube leaks, try replacing the cap with another one. If available in the laboratory, a vortex mixer may be used to mix the phases. A vortex mixer works well with a variety of containers, including small flasks, test tubes, conical vials, and centrifuge tubes. You start the mixing action on a vortex mixer by holding the test tube or other container on one of the pads. The unit mixes the sample by high-frequency vibration.

Most extractions consist of an aqueous phase and an organic phase. In order to extract a substance from an aqueous phase, an organic solvent that is not miscible with water must be used. Table 12.1 lists a number of the common organic solvents that are not miscible with water and are used for extraction.

Those solvents that have a density less than that of water (1.00 g/mL) will separate as the top layer when shaken with water. Those solvents that have a greater density than water will separate into the lower layer. For instance, diethyl ether ($d = 0.71$ g/mL) when shaken with water will form the upper layer, whereas methylene chloride ($d = 1.33$ g/mL) will form the lower layer. When an extraction is performed, slightly different methods are used when you wish to separate the lower layer (whether it is the aqueous layer or the organic layer) than when you wish to separate the upper layer.

PART B. MICROSCALE EXTRACTION

12.4 The Conical Vial—Separating the Lower Layer

The 5-mL conical vial is the most useful piece of equipment for carrying out extractions on a microscale level. In this section, we consider the method for removing the lower layer. A concrete example would be the extraction of a desired product from an aqueous layer using methylene chloride ($d = 1.33$ g/mL) as the extraction solvent. Methods for removal of the upper layer are discussed in the next section.

NOTE: Always place a conical vial in a small beaker to prevent the vial from falling over.

Removing the Lower Layer. Suppose that we extract an aqueous solution with methylene chloride. This solvent is denser than water and will settle to the bottom

A. The aqueous solution contains the desired product.

B. Methylene chloride is used to extract the aqueous phase.

C. The Pasteur filter-tip pipette is placed in the vial.

D. The lower organic layer is removed from the aqueous phase.

E. The organic layer is transferred to a dry test tube or conical vial. The aqueous layer remains in the original extraction vial.

CH_2Cl_2

H_2O

Filter tip

A   B   C   D   E

☐ H_2O layer   ▨ CH_2Cl_2 layer

© Cengage Learning 2013

Figure 12.5
Extraction of an aqueous solution using a solvent denser than water: methylene chloride.

of the conical vial. Use the following procedure, which is illustrated in Figure 12.5, to remove the lower layer.

1. Place the aqueous phase containing the dissolved product into a 5-mL conical vial (Figure 12.5A).

2. Add about 1 mL of methylene chloride, cap the vial, and shake the mixture gently at first in a rocking motion and then more vigorously when it is clear that an emulsion will not form. Vent or unscrew the cap slightly to release the pressure in the vial. Allow the phases to separate completely so that you can detect two distinct layers in the vial. The organic phase will be the lower layer in the vial (Figure 12.5B). If necessary, tap the vial with your finger or stir the mixture gently if some of the organic phase is suspended in the aqueous layer.

3. Prepare a Pasteur filter-tip pipette (Technique 8, Section 8.6) using a 5¾-inch pipette. Attach a 2-mL rubber bulb to the pipette, depress the bulb, and insert the pipette into the vial so that the tip touches the bottom (Figure 12.5C). The filter-tip pipette gives you better control in removing the lower layer. In some cases, however, you may be able to use a Pasteur pipette (no filter tip), but considerably more care must be taken to avoid losing liquid from the pipette during the transfer operation. With experience, you should be able to judge how much to squeeze the bulb to draw in the desired volume of liquid.

4. Slowly draw the lower layer (methylene chloride) into the pipette in such a way that you exclude the aqueous layer and any emulsion (Section 12.10) that

Figure 12.6
Method of holding vials
while transferring liquids.

might be at the interface between the layers (Figure 12.5D). Be sure to keep the tip of the pipette squarely in the V at the bottom of the vial.

5. Transfer the withdrawn organic phase into a *dry* test tube or another *dry* conical vial if one is available. It is best to have the test tube or vial located next to the extraction vial. Hold the vials in the same hand between your index finger and thumb, as shown in Figure 12.6. This avoids messy and disastrous transfers. The aqueous layer (upper layer) is left in the original conical vial (Figure 12.5E).

In performing an actual extraction in the laboratory, you would extract the aqueous phase with a second 1-mL portion of fresh methylene chloride to achieve a more complete extraction. Steps 2–5 would be repeated, and the organic layers from both extractions would be combined. In some cases, you may need to extract a third time with yet another 1-mL portion of methylene chloride. Again, the methylene chloride would be combined with the other extracts. The overall process would use three 1-mL portions of methylene chloride to transfer the product from the water layer into methylene chloride. Sometimes you will see the statement "extract the aqueous phase with three 1-mL portions of methylene chloride" in an experimental procedure. This statement describes in a shorter fashion the process described previously. Finally, the methylene chloride extracts will contain some water and must be dried with a drying agent as indicated in Section 12.9.

In this example, we extracted water with the heavy solvent methylene chloride and removed it as the lower layer. If you were extracting a light solvent (for instance, diethyl ether) with water, and you wished to keep the water layer, the water would be the lower layer and would be removed using the same procedure. You would not dry the water layer, however.

12.5 The Conical Vial— Separating the Upper Layer

In this section, we consider the method used when you wish to remove the upper layer. A concrete example would be the extraction of a desired product from an aqueous layer using diethyl ether ($d = 0.71$ g/mL) as the extraction solvent. Methods for removing the lower layer were discussed previously.

NOTE: Always place a conical vial in a small beaker to prevent the vial from falling over.

Removing the Upper Layer. Suppose we extract an aqueous solution with diethyl ether (ether). This solvent is less dense than water and will rise to the top of the conical vial. Use the following procedure, which is illustrated in Figure 12.7, to remove the upper layer.

1. Place the aqueous phase containing the dissolved product in a 5-mL conical vial (Figure 12.7A).

2. Add about 1 mL of ether, cap the vial, and shake the mixture vigorously. Vent or unscrew the cap slightly to release the pressure in the vial. Allow the phases to separate completely so that you can detect two distinct layers in the vial. The ether phase will be the upper layer in the vial (Figure 12.7B).

3. Prepare a Pasteur filter-tip pipette (Technique 8, Section 8.6) using a 5¾-inch pipette. Attach a 2-mL rubber bulb to the pipette, depress the bulb, and insert the pipette into the vial so that the tip touches the bottom. The filter-tip pipette gives you better control in removing the lower layer. In some cases, however, you may be able to use a Pasteur pipette (no filter tip), but considerably more care must be taken to avoid losing liquid from the pipette during the transfer

© Cengage Learning 2013

A. The aqueous solution contains the desired product.

B. Diethyl ether (ether) is used to extract the aqueous phase.

C. The lower aqueous layer is removed from the organic phase.

D. The aqueous layer is transferred to a test tube or conical vial. The ether layer remains in the original extraction vial.

E. The ether layer is transferred to a test tube for storage. The aqueous layer is transferred back into the original vial.

H_2O layer   Ether layer

© Cengage Learning 2013

Figure 12.7
Extraction of an aqueous solution using a solvent less dense than water: diethyl ether.

operation. With experience, you should be able to judge how much to squeeze the bulb to draw in the desired volume of liquid. Slowly draw the lower *aqueous* layer into the pipette. Be sure to keep the tip of the pipette squarely in the V at the bottom of the vial (Figure 12.7C).

4. Transfer the withdrawn aqueous phase into a test tube or another conical vial for temporary storage. It is best to have the test tube or vial located next to the extraction vial. This avoids messy and disastrous transfers. Hold the vials in the same hand between your index finger and thumb as shown in Figure 12.6. The ether layer is left behind in the conical vial (Figure 12.7D).

5. The ether phase remaining in the original conical vial should be transferred with a Pasteur pipette into a test tube for storage and the aqueous phase returned to the original conical vial (Figure 12.7E).

In performing an actual extraction, you would extract the aqueous phase with another 1-mL portion of fresh ether to achieve a more complete extraction. Steps 2–5 would be repeated, and the organic layers from both extractions would be combined in the test tube. In some cases, you may need to extract the aqueous layer a third time with yet another 1-mL portion of ether. Again, the ether would be combined with the other two layers. This overall process uses three 1-mL portions of ether to transfer the product from the water layer into ether. The ether extracts contain some water and must be dried with a drying agent as indicated in Section 12.9.

12.6 The Centrifuge Tube

A screw-cap centrifuge tube may be employed instead of a conical vial for separations (Figure 12.4). Before using the centrifuge tube, be sure to check it for leaks as indicated in Section 12.3. You should use the same extraction and separation procedures described in Sections 12.4 and 12.5. You may also use a "regular" (nonscrew-cap) centrifuge tube for extractions, although it will be necessary to cork the tube before shaking it. Because a regular centrifuge tube will probably leak around the cork, it is best to mix the contents with a vortex mixer (Section 12.3) to avoid shaking the tube. If an emulsion has formed after mixing or shaking, you can use a centrifuge to aid in the separation of the layers (Section 12.10). Once the layers have separated, it is easy to use a Pasteur pipette to withdraw the lower layer from the tapered bottom of the centrifuge tube.

PART C. MACROSCALE EXTRACTION

12.7 The Separatory Funnel

The separatory funnel is often used in large-scale reactions. This apparatus is illustrated in Figure 12.8. To fill the separatory funnel, support it in an iron ring attached to a ring stand. Cut pieces of rubber tubing and attach them to the iron ring to cushion the separatory funnel as shown in Figure 12.8. This protects the funnel against possible breakage.

When beginning an extraction, the first step is to close the stopcock. (Don't forget!) Using a powder funnel (wide bore) placed in the top of the separatory funnel, fill it with both the solution to be extracted and the extraction solvent. Swirl the funnel gently by holding it by its upper neck, and then stopper it. Pick up the separatory funnel with two hands and hold it as shown in Figure 12.9. Hold the stopper in place firmly because the two immiscible liquids will build pressure when they mix, and this pressure may force the stopper out of the separatory funnel. To release this pressure, vent the funnel by holding it upside down (hold the stopper securely) and slowly open the stopcock. Usually the rush of vapors out of the opening can be heard. Continue shaking and venting until the "whoosh" is no longer audible. Now continue shaking the mixture gently for about one minute. This can be done by inverting the funnel in a rocking motion repeatedly or, if the formation of an emulsion is not a problem (see Section 12.10), by shaking the funnel more vigorously for less time.

Top should be open when draining

Ring with pieces of rubber tubing to cushion funnel

layer A

layer B

© Cengage Learning 2013

Figure 12.8
The separatory funnel.

NOTE: There is an art to shaking and venting a separatory funnel correctly, and it usually seems awkward to the beginner. The technique is best learned by observing a person, such as your instructor, who is thoroughly familiar with the separatory funnel's use.

When you have finished mixing the liquids, place the separatory funnel in the iron ring and remove the top stopper immediately. The two immiscible solvents separate into two layers after a short time, and they can be separated from each other by draining most of the lower layer through the stopcock.[1] Allow a few minutes to pass so that any of the lower phase adhering to the inner glass surfaces of the separatory funnel can drain

---

[1] A common error is to try to drain the separatory funnel without removing the top stopper. Under this circumstance, the funnel will not drain, because a partial vacuum is created in the space above the liquid.

Figure 12.9
Correct way of shaking and venting the separatory funnel.

down. Open the stopcock again and allow the remainder of the lower layer to drain until the interface between the upper and lower phases just begins to enter the bore of the stopcock. At this moment, close the stopcock and remove the remaining upper layer by pouring it from the top opening of the separatory funnel.

NOTE: To minimize contamination of the two layers, the lower layer should always be drained from the bottom of the separatory funnel and the upper layer poured out from the top of the funnel.

When methylene chloride is used as the extracting solvent with an aqueous phase, it will settle to the bottom and be removed through the stopcock. The aqueous layer remains in the funnel. A second extraction of the remaining aqueous layer with fresh methylene chloride may be needed.

With a diethyl ether (ether) extraction of an aqueous phase, the organic layer will form on top. Remove the lower aqueous layer through the stopcock and pour the upper ether layer from the top of the separatory funnel. Pour the aqueous phase back into the separatory funnel and extract it a second time with fresh ether. The combined organic phases must be dried using a suitable drying agent (Section 12.9) before the solvent is removed.

For microscale procedures, a 60- or 125-mL separatory funnel is recommended. Because of surface tension, water has a difficult time draining from the bore of smaller funnels. Funnels larger than 125 mL are simply too large for microscale experiments, and a good deal of material is lost in "wetting" their surfaces.

PART D. ADDITIONAL EXPERIMENTAL CONSIDERATIONS: MICROSCALE AND MACROSCALE

12.8 How Do You Determine Which One Is the Organic Layer?

A common problem encountered during an extraction is trying to determine which of the two layers is the organic layer and which is the aqueous (water) layer. The most common situation occurs when the aqueous layer is on the bottom in the presence of an upper organic layer consisting of ether, ligroin, petroleum ether, or hexane (see densities in Table 12.1). However, the aqueous layer will be on the top when you use methylene chloride as a solvent (again, see Table 12.1). Although a laboratory procedure may frequently identify the expected relative positions of the organic and aqueous layers, sometimes their actual positions are reversed. Surprises usually occur in situations in which the aqueous layer contains a high concentration of sulfuric acid or a dissolved ionic compound, such as sodium chloride. Dissolved substances greatly increase the density of the aqueous layer, which may lead to the aqueous layer being found on the bottom even when coexisting with a relatively dense organic layer such as methylene chloride.

NOTE: Always keep both layers until you have actually isolated the desired compound or until you are certain where your desired substance is located.

To determine if a particular layer is the aqueous one, add a few drops of water to the layer. Observe closely as you add the water to see where it goes. If the layer is water, then the drops of added water will dissolve in the aqueous layer and increase its volume. If the added water forms droplets or a new layer, however, you can assume that the suspected aqueous layer is actually organic. You can use a similar procedure to identify a suspected organic layer. This time, try adding more of the solvent, such as methylene chloride. The organic layer should increase in size, without separation of a new layer, if the tested layer is actually organic.

When performing an extraction procedure on the microscale level, you can use the following approach to identify the layers. When both layers are present, it is always a good idea to think carefully about the volumes of materials that you have added to the conical vial. You can use the graduations on the vial to help determine the volumes of the layers in the vial. If, for example, you have 1 mL of methylene chloride in a vial and you add 2 mL of water, you should expect the water to be on top because it is less dense than methylene chloride. As you add the water, watch to see where it goes. By noting the relative volumes of the two layers, you should be able to tell which is the aqueous layer and which is the organic layer. This approach can also be used when performing an extraction procedure using a centrifuge tube. Of course, you can always test to see which layer is the aqueous layer by adding one or two drops of water, as described previously.

12.9 Drying Agents

After an organic solvent has been shaken with an aqueous solution, it will be "wet"; that is, it will have dissolved some water even though its solubility with water is not great. The amount of water dissolved varies from solvent to solvent; diethyl ether represents a solvent in which a fairly large amount of water dissolves. To remove water from the organic layer, use a **drying agent.** A drying agent is an *anhydrous* inorganic salt that acquires waters of hydration when exposed to moist air or a wet solution:

$$\text{Na}_2\text{SO}_4(\text{s}) + \text{Wet Solution } (n\text{H}_2\text{O}) \longrightarrow \text{Na}_2\text{SO}_4 \cdot n\text{H}_2\text{O (s)} + \text{Dry Solution}$$

Insoluble — Anhydrous drying agent

Insoluble — Hydrated drying agent

The insoluble drying agent is placed directly into the solution, where it acquires water molecules and becomes hydrated. If enough drying agent is used, all of the water can be removed from a wet solution, making it "dry," or free of water.

The following anhydrous salts are commonly used: sodium sulfate, magnesium sulfate, calcium chloride, calcium sulfate (Drierite), and potassium carbonate. These salts vary in their properties and applications. For instance, not all will absorb the same amount of water for a given weight, nor will they dry the solution to the same extent. **Capacity** refers to the amount of water a drying agent absorbs per unit weight. Sodium and magnesium sulfates absorb a large amount of water (high capacity), but magnesium sulfate dries a solution more completely. **Completeness** refers to a compound's effectiveness in removing all the water from a solution by the time equilibrium has been reached. Magnesium ion, a strong Lewis acid, sometimes causes rearrangements of compounds such as epoxides. Calcium chloride is a good drying agent but cannot be used with many compounds containing oxygen or nitrogen because it forms complexes. Calcium chloride absorbs methanol and ethanol in addition to water, so it is useful for removing these materials when they are present as impurities. Potassium carbonate is a base and is used for drying solutions of basic substances, such as amines. Calcium sulfate dries a solution completely but has a low capacity.

Table 12.2 Common drying agents

	Acidity	Hydrated	Capacity[a]	Completeness[b]	Rate[c]	Use
Magnesium sulfate	Neutral	$MgSO_4 \cdot 7H_2O$	High	Medium	Rapid	General
Sodium sulfate	Neutral	$Na_2SO_4 \cdot 7H_2O$ $Na_2SO_4 \cdot 10H_2O$	High	Low	Medium	General
Calcium chloride	Neutral	$CaCl_2 \cdot 2H_2O$ $CaCl_2 \cdot 6H_2O$	Low	High	Rapid	Hydrocarbons Halides
Calcium sulfate (Drierite)	Neutral	$CaSO_4 \cdot \frac{1}{2}H_2O$ $CaSO_4 \cdot 2H_2O$	Low	High	Rapid	General
Potassium carbonate	Basic	$K_2CO_3 \cdot 1\frac{1}{2}H_2O$ $K_2CO_3 \cdot 2H_2O$	Medium	Medium	Medium	Amines, esters, bases, ketones
Potassium hydroxide	Basic	—	—	—	Rapid	Amines only
Molecular sieves (3 or 4 Å)	Neutral	—	High	Extremely high	—	General

[a]Amount of water removed per given weight of drying agent.
[b]Refers to amount of H_2O still in solution at equilibrium with drying agent.
[c]Refers to rate of action (drying).

Anhydrous sodium sulfate is the most widely used drying agent. The granular variety is recommended because it is easier to remove the dried solution from it than from the powdered variety. Sodium sulfate is mild and effective. It will remove water from most common solvents, with the possible exception of diethyl ether, in which case a prior drying with saturated salt solution may be advised. Sodium sulfate must be used at room temperature to be effective; it cannot be used with boiling solutions. Table 12.2 compares the various common drying agents.

Drying Procedure with Anhydrous Sodium Sulfate. In experiments that require a drying step, the instructions are usually given in the following way: dry the organic layer (or phase) over granular anhydrous sodium sulfate (or some other drying agent). More specific instructions, such as the amount of drying agent to add, usually will not be given, and you will need to determine this each time that you perform a drying step. The drying procedure consists of four steps:

1. Remove the organic layer from any visible water.
2. Add the appropriate amount of granular anhydrous sodium sulfate (or other drying agent).
3. Allow a drying period during which dissolved water is removed from the organic layer by the drying agent.
4. Separate the dried organic layer from the drying agent.

More specific instructions are given below for both microscale and macroscale procedures. The only differences between these two procedures is that they are intended for different volumes of liquid and they require different glassware. The microscale procedure is generally for volumes up to about 5 mL, and the macroscale procedure is usually appropriate for volumes of 5 mL or greater.

A. Microscale Drying Procedure

Step 1. (Removal of Visible Water). Before attempting to dry an organic layer, check closely to see that there are no visible signs of water. If there is a separate layer of water (top or bottom), droplets or a globule of water floating in the organic layer, or water droplets clinging to the sides of the container, then transfer the organic layer with a *dry* Pasteur pipette to a *dry* container, usually a conical vial or test tube, before adding any drying agent. If there is any doubt about whether water is present, it is advisable to make a transfer to a dry container. Performing this step when necessary may save time later in the drying procedure and result in a greater recovery of the desired substance.

Step 2. (Addition of Drying Agent). Each time a drying procedure is performed, it is necessary to determine how much granular anhydrous sodium sulfate (or other drying agent) should be added. This will depend on the total volume of the organic phase and how much water is dissolved in the solvent. Nonpolar organic solvents such as methylene chloride or hydrocarbons (hexane, pentane, etc.) can dissolve relatively small amounts of water and generally require less drying agent, whereas more polar organic solvents such as ether and ethyl acetate can dissolve more water, and more drying agent will be required. Begin by adding one spatulaful of granular anhydrous sodium sulfate (or other drying agent) from the V-grooved end of a microspatula (smaller microspatula in Experiment 1, Figure 10) into the solution. If all the drying agent "clumps," add another spatulaful of sodium sulfate. To determine if the drying agent has clumped, it is helpful to stir the mixture with a clean, dry spatula or to rapidly swirl the container. If any portion of the drying agent flows freely (does not clump) on the bottom of the container when stirred or swirled, then you can assume that enough of the drying agent has been added. Otherwise, you must continue adding one spatulaful of drying agent at a time until it is clear that the drying agent has stopped clumping. Stir or swirl the mixture after adding each spatulaful of the drying agent. For small amounts of liquid (less than 5 mL), about 1–6 microspatulafuls of drying agent will *usually* be required. However, the actual amount must be determined by experimentation, as just described. It is best to use a slight excess of drying agent; but if too great an excess is used, the recovery may be poor because some of the solution always adheres to the solid drying agent after the liquid is separated from the drying agent (Step 4). Take care not to add so much drying agent that all of the liquid is absorbed (disappears). If you do this you will have to add additional solvent to recover your product from the drying agent!

Step 3. (Drying Period). Stopper or cap the container and let the solution dry for at least 15 minutes.

NOTE: It is important that you stopper or cap the container to prevent evaporation and exposure to atmospheric moisture.

Stir the mixture occasionally with a spatula during the drying period. The mixture is dry if it appears clear (not cloudy) and shows the common signs of a dry solution given in Table 12.3. Note that a "clear" solution may be colorless or colored. If the solution remains cloudy after treatment with the first batch of drying agent, add more drying agent and repeat the drying procedure. However, if a water layer forms or if drops of water are visible, transfer the organic layer to a dry container before adding fresh drying agent, as described in Step 2. It will also be necessary to repeat the 15-minute drying step described in Step 3.

Table 12.3 Common signs that indicate a solution is dry

1. There are no visible water droplets on the side of flask or suspended in solution.
2. There is not a separate layer of liquid or a "puddle."
3. The solution is clear, not cloudy. Cloudiness indicates water is present.
4. The drying agent (or a portion of it) flows freely on the bottom of the container when stirred or swirled and does not "clump" together as a solid mass.

Step 4. (Removal of Liquid from Drying Agent). When the organic phase is dry, use a *dry* Pasteur pipette or a *dry* filter-tip pipette (Technique 8, Section 8.6) to remove the dried organic layer from the drying agent and transfer the solution to a *dry* conical vial or test tube. Be careful not to transfer any of the drying agent when performing this step. Rinse the drying agent with a small amount of fresh solvent and transfer this additional solvent to the vial containing the dried organic layer. To isolate the desired material, remove the solvent by evaporation using heat and a stream of air or nitrogen (Technique 7, Section 7.10).

An alternative method of drying a small volume of organic phase is to pass it through a filtering pipette (Technique 8, Section 8.1C) that has been packed with a small amount (about 2 cm) of drying agent. Again, the solvent is removed by evaporation.

B. Macroscale Drying Procedure

To dry a large amount of organic liquid (greater than about 5 mL), follow the same four steps just described for the "Microscale Drying Procedure." The main differences are that an Erlenmeyer flask is used rather than a test tube or conical vial and more drying agent will be required. The size of the Erlenmeyer flask is not critical, but it's best that the flask not be filled more than half full with the solution being dried.

Step 1. (Removal of Visible Water). Refer to Step 1 above for instructions. If the amount of water is large, it may be best to separate the layers using a separatory funnel or a centrifuge tube. If visible water must be removed in this step, place the separated organic layer in a clean, *dry* Erlenmeyer flask.

Step 2. (Addition of Drying Agent). Refer to Step 2 in the "Microscale Drying Procedure" for the basic instructions. Read these instructions carefully. The only difference is that in this macroscale procedure, more drying agent will be required. A common guideline is to add enough granular anhydrous sodium sulfate (or other drying agent) to give a 1- to 3-mm layer on the bottom of the flask, depending on the volume of the solution. However, it is best to add the drying agent in small portions, as described above. In this procedure, use the larger microspatula shown in Experiment 1, Figure 10 to add the drying agent. Generally, an appropriate portion to add each time is about 0.5–1.0 g.

Step 3. (Drying Period). The instructions are the same as for Step 3 in the "Microscale Drying Procedure."

Step 4. (Removal of Liquid from Drying Agent). When the solution is dry, the drying agent should be removed by using decantation (pouring carefully to leave the drying agent behind). Transfer the liquid to a dry Erlenmeyer flask. If the volume of liquid is relatively small (less than 10 mL), it may be easier to complete this step by using a *dry* Pasteur pipette or a *dry* filter-tip pipette (Technique 8, Section 8.6) to remove the dried organic layer. With granular sodium sulfate, decantation is easy to perform because of the size of the drying-agent particles. If a powdered drying agent, such as magnesium sulfate, is used, it may be necessary to use gravity filtration (Technique 8, Section 8.1B) to remove the drying agent. Finally, to isolate the desired material, remove the solvent by distillation (Technique 14, Section 14.3) or evaporation (Technique 7, Section 7.10).

Saturated Salt Solution. At room temperature, diethyl ether (ether) dissolves 1.5% by weight of water, and water dissolves 7.5% of ether. Ether, however, dissolves a much smaller amount of water from a saturated aqueous sodium chloride solution. Hence, the bulk of water in ether, or ether in water, can be removed by shaking it with a saturated aqueous sodium chloride solution. A solution of high ionic strength is usually not compatible with an organic solvent and forces separation of it from the aqueous layer. The water migrates into the concentrated salt solution. The ether phase (organic layer) will be on top, and the saturated sodium chloride solution will be on the bottom ($d = 1.2$ g/mL). After removing the organic phase from the aqueous sodium chloride, dry the organic layer completely with sodium sulfate or with one of the other drying agents listed in Table 12.2.

12.10 Emulsions

An **emulsion** is a colloidal suspension of one liquid in another. Minute droplets of an organic solvent are often held in suspension in an aqueous solution when the two are mixed or shaken vigorously; these droplets form an emulsion. This is especially true if any gummy or viscous material was present in the solution. Emulsions are often encountered in performing extractions. Emulsions may require a long time to separate into two layers and are a nuisance to the organic chemist.

Fortunately, several techniques may be used to break a difficult emulsion once it has formed.

1. Often an emulsion will break up if it is allowed to stand for some time. Patience is important here. Gently stirring with a stirring rod or spatula may also be useful.

2. If one of the solvents is water, adding a saturated aqueous sodium chloride solution will help destroy the emulsion. The water in the organic layer migrates into the concentrated salt solution.

3. With microscale experiments, the mixture may be transferred to a centrifuge tube. The emulsion will often break during centrifugation. Remember to place another tube filled with water on the opposite side of the centrifuge to balance it. The two tubes should weigh the same.

4. Adding a small amount of a water-soluble detergent may also help. This method has been used in the past for combating oil spills. The detergent helps to solubilize the tightly bound oil droplets.

5. Gravity filtration (see Technique 8, Section 8.1) may help to destroy an emulsion by removing gummy polymeric substances. With large volumes, you might try filtering the mixture through a fluted filter (Technique 8, Section 8.1B) or a piece of cotton. With small-scale reactions, a filtering pipette may work (Technique 8, Section 8.1C). In many cases, once the gum is removed, the emulsion breaks up rapidly.

6. If you are using a separatory funnel, you might try to use a gentle swirling action in the funnel to help break an emulsion. Gently stirring with a stirring rod may also be useful.

When you know through experience that a mixture may form a difficult emulsion, you should avoid shaking the mixture vigorously. When using conical vials for extractions, it may be better to use a magnetic spin vane for mixing and not shake the mixture at all. When using separatory funnels, extractions should be performed with gentle swirling instead of shaking or with several gentle inversions of the separatory funnel. Do not shake the separatory funnel vigorously in these cases. It is important to use a longer extraction period if the more gentle techniques described in this paragraph are being employed. Otherwise, you will not transfer all the material from the first phase to the second one.

12.11 Purification and Separation Methods

In nearly all synthetic experiments undertaken in the organic laboratory, a series of operations involving extractions is used after the actual reaction has been concluded. These extractions form an important part of the purification. Using them, you separate the desired product from unreacted starting materials or from undesired side products in the reaction mixture. These extractions may be grouped into three categories, depending on the nature of the impurities they are designed to remove.

The first category involves extracting or "washing" an organic mixture with water. Water washes are designed to remove highly polar materials, such as inorganic salts, strong acids or bases, and low-molecular-weight, polar substances including alcohols, carboxylic acids, and amines. Many organic compounds containing fewer than five carbons are water soluble. Water extractions are also used immediately following extractions of a mixture with either acid or base to ensure that all traces of acid or base have been removed.

The second category concerns extraction of an organic mixture with a dilute acid, usually 1–2 M hydrochloric acid. Acid extractions are intended to remove basic impurities, especially such basic impurities as organic amines. The bases are converted to their corresponding cationic salts by the acid used in the extraction. If an amine is one of the reactants or if pyridine or another amine is a solvent, such an extraction might be used to remove any excess amine present at the end of a reaction.

$$RNH_2 + HCl \longrightarrow RNH_3^+Cl^-$$
(water-soluble ammonium salt)

Cationic ammonium salts are usually soluble in the aqueous solution, and they are thus extracted from the organic material. A water extraction may be used immediately following the acid extraction to ensure that all traces of the acid have been removed from the organic material.

The third category is extraction of an organic mixture with a dilute base, usually 1 M sodium bicarbonate, although extractions with dilute sodium hydroxide can also be used. Such basic extractions are intended to convert acidic impurities, such as organic acids, to their corresponding anionic salts. For example, in the preparation of an ester, a sodium bicarbonate extraction might be used to remove any excess carboxylic acid that is present.

$$RCOOH + NaHCO_3 \longrightarrow RCOO^-Na^+ + H_2O + CO_2$$
(p$K_a \sim 5$) (water-soluble carboxylate salt)

Anionic carboxylate salts, being highly polar, are soluble in the aqueous phase. As a result, these acid impurities are extracted from the organic material into the basic solution. A water extraction may be used after the basic extraction to ensure that all the base has been removed from the organic material.

Occasionally, phenols may be present in a reaction mixture as impurities, and removing them by extraction may be desired. Because phenols, although they are acidic, are about 10^5 times less acidic than carboxylic acids, basic extractions may be used to separate phenols from carboxylic acids by a careful selection of the base. If sodium bicarbonate is used as a base, carboxylic acids are extracted into the aqueous base, but phenols are not. Phenols are not sufficiently acidic to be deprotonated by the weak base bicarbonate. Extraction with sodium hydroxide, on the other hand, extracts both carboxylic acids and phenols into the aqueous basic solution because hydroxide ion is a sufficiently strong base to deprotonate phenols.

$$R\text{—}\bigcirc\text{—OH} + NaOH \longrightarrow R\text{—}\bigcirc\text{—O}^- Na^+ + H_2O$$
$$(pK_a \sim 10) \qquad\qquad\qquad (\text{water-soluble salt})$$

Mixtures of acidic, basic, and neutral compounds are easily separated by extraction techniques. One such example is shown in Figure 12.10. The original compounds are dissolved in ether.

Organic acids or bases that have been extracted can be regenerated by neutralizing the extraction reagent. This would be done if the organic acid or base were a product of a reaction rather than an impurity. For example, if a carboxylic acid has been extracted with the aqueous base, the compound can be regenerated by acidifying the extract with 6 *M* HCl until the solution becomes *just* acidic, as indicated by litmus or pH paper. When the solution becomes acidic, the carboxylic acid will separate from the aqueous solution. If the acid is a solid at room temperature, it will precipitate and can be purified by filtration and crystallization. If the acid is a liquid, it will form a separate layer. In this case, it would usually be necessary to

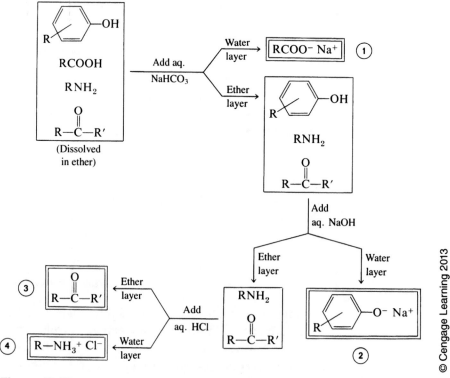

Figure 12.10
Separating a four-component mixture by extraction.

extract the mixture with ether or methylene chloride. After removing the organic layer and drying it, the solvent can be evaporated to yield the carboxylic acid.

In the example shown in Figure 12.10, you also need to perform a drying step at (3) before isolating the neutral compound. When the solvent is ether, you should first extract the ether solution with saturated aqueous sodium chloride to remove much of the water. The ether layer is then dried over a drying agent such as anhydrous sodium sulfate. If the solvent were methylene chloride, it would not be necessary to do the step with saturated sodium chloride.

When acid–base extractions are performed, it is common practice to extract a mixture several times with the appropriate reagent. For example, if you were extracting a carboxylic acid from a mixture, you might extract the mixture three times with 2-mL portions of 1 *M* NaOH. In most published experiments, the procedure will specify the volume and concentration of extracting reagent and the number of times to do the extractions. If this information is not given, you must devise your own procedure. Using a carboxylic acid as an example, if you know the identity of the acid and the approximate amount present, you can actually calculate how much sodium hydroxide is needed. Because the carboxylic acid (assuming it is monoprotic) will react with sodium hydroxide in a 1:1 ratio, you would need the same number of moles of sodium hydroxide as there are moles of acid. To ensure that all the carboxylic acid is extracted, you should use about a *twofold* excess of the base. From this, you could calculate the number of milliliters of base needed. This should be divided into two or three equal portions, one portion for each extraction. In a similar fashion, you could calculate the amount of 5% sodium bicarbonate required to extract an acid or the amount of 1 *M* HCl required to extract a base. If the amount of organic acid or base is not known, then the situation is more difficult. A guideline that sometimes works is to do two or three extractions so that the total volume of the extracting reagent is approximately equal to the volume of the organic layer. To test this procedure, neutralize the aqueous layer from the last extraction. If a precipitate or cloudiness results, perform another extraction and test again. When no precipitate forms, you know that all the organic acid or base has been removed.

For some applications of acid–base extraction, an additional step, called **backwashing** or **back extraction,** is added to the scheme shown in Figure 12.10. Consider the first step, in which the carboxylic acid is extracted by sodium bicarbonate. This aqueous layer may contain some unwanted neutral organic material from the original mixture. To remove this contamination, backwash the aqueous layer with an organic solvent such as ether or methylene chloride. After shaking the mixture and allowing the layers to separate, remove and discard the organic layer. This technique may also be used when an amine is extracted with hydrochloric acid. The resulting aqueous layer is backwashed with an organic solvent to remove unwanted neutral material.

12.12 How to Outline a Separation Scheme Using a Flowchart

In experiments involving the synthesis of an organic compound, it is necessary to separate the desired product from the reaction mixture, which usually contains many other substances. The steps required to accomplish this are sometimes referred to as a separation scheme. An outline of a separation scheme can be conveniently shown in the form of a flowchart. A flowchart for the separation scheme for isopentyl acetate is shown in Technique 2, Figure 2.1. Experimental techniques that may be included in a separation scheme include acid-base extraction, a drying step, sublimation, distillation, and crystallization. It is particularly helpful to outline a separation scheme before coming to the laboratory. Preparing the flowchart will help you to understand all of the steps in the experiment, which may lead to greater success when actually performing an experiment.

The starting point of most separation schemes is at the end of the reaction period. Do not include any of the reaction steps such as adding reagents or the reflux period. The reaction mixture will often contain the desired product, leftover reactants, catalysts, solvents, by-products that are also formed in the main reaction, and side products that are produced by undesired reactions that take place along with the main reaction. The purpose of a separation scheme is to separate the desired product from all other substances, resulting in a pure product. At the beginning of your flowchart, you should list everything that is present at the end of the reaction period, either by name or formula. It may sometimes be convenient to use a condensed or partial formula. For example, octanoic acid might be written as $C_8H_{17}COOH$ or just R-COOH, if this is defined in the beginning list. Every step involved in separating the desired product from the other substances should be shown in your flowchart. When a new reagent such as hydrochloric acid, sodium hydroxide, or anhydrous sodium sulfate is added, you should indicate this in your flowchart and then you must also show how this reagent is removed in the separation scheme. You should indicate by name any experimental procedure that is used, such as distillation, sublimation, and crystallization. If you don't know the physical properties of the product, you should look this up in a handbook before writing the flowchart. This is important because a solid product would require different techniques to separate than a liquid product.

It would be helpful now to study the separation scheme for isopentyl acetate shown in Technique 2, Figure 2.1. Note carefully how the following procedures are shown in a flowchart: the extraction step with $NaHCO_3$, the drying step with anhydrous Na_2SO_4, and the distillation step. Also note that in this experiment it is not possible to identify with certainty the actual impurities present with isopentyl acetate just before the product is distilled. In some experiments it will be possible to make a good guess about the identity of most substances at each step in the separation scheme.

There are several other experimental techniques that may come up in separation schemes that are not shown in Figure 2.1, We will now discuss some of these additional techniques and show how to use a flowchart to illustrate these techniques.

First, consider the extraction of a solid carboxylic acid (the desired product) with sodium bicarbonate, followed by precipitation of the acid and isolation of the solid acid by filtration. It is also necessary to air-dry the filtered solid. See the flowchart for all of these steps in Figure 12.11. Although this procedure sometimes gives the acid in a pure form, it may also be necessary to perform a crystallization procedure. In this example, the carboxylic acid is assumed to be a solid at room temperature. If the carboxylic acid were a liquid at room temperature, the separation scheme would involve different techniques including a distillation. The neutral impurities are not identified here since this example represents a general case rather than a specific experiment. In many experiments it will be possible to determine the identity of most of the impurities. For example, in most synthesis experiments, some of the impurities will be leftover reactants.

Note that the use of $NaHCO_3$ in this separation scheme is different from the $NaHCO_3$ extraction step in Figure 2.1. In the separation scheme shown in Figure 2.1, the $NaHCO_3$ step is used to remove acetic acid from the mixture containing the product and it is not necessary to regenerate the acetic acid in a subsequent step. However, in the procedure shown in Figure 12.11, the carboxylic acid is the desired product and it must be regenerated as a precipitate by the addition of HCl so that it can be isolated.

In the second example, an amine, which is a solid base and the desired product, is separated from the reaction mixture in a similar set of steps, except that HCl is used to extract the base and NaOH is used to regenerate the base. See Figure 12.12 for a flowchart of this separation scheme. The amine is represented by $R-NH_2$.

Figure 12.11
Separation of a solid carboxylic acid from a reaction mixture.

Figure 12.12
Separation of a solid amine from a reaction mixture.

The last example involves a crystallization step in which a solid neutral compound is purified from an impure sample consisting mainly of the neutral compound and a second neutral compound which is an impurity found in a much smaller amount than the compound of interest. For example, in Experiment 6C, fluorenol is synthesized from fluorenone. The crude product contains mainly fluorenol contaminated with a little fluorenone. See Figure 12.13 for a flowchart showing this crystallization step.

Figure 12.13
Purification of a neutral compound by crystallization.

PART E. OTHER EXTRACTION METHODS

12.13 Continuous Solid–Liquid Extraction

The technique of liquid–liquid extraction was described in Sections 12.1–12.8. In this section, solid–liquid extraction is described. Solid–liquid extraction is often used to extract a solid natural product from a natural source, such as a plant. A solvent is chosen that selectively dissolves the desired compound but that leaves behind the undesired insoluble solid. A continuous solid–liquid extraction apparatus, called a Soxhlet extractor, is commonly used in a research laboratory.

As shown in Figure 12.14, the solid to be extracted is placed in a thimble made from filter paper, and the thimble is inserted into the central chamber. A low-boiling solvent, such as diethyl ether, is placed in the round-bottom distilling flask and is heated to reflux. The vapor rises through the left side arm into the condenser where it liquefies. The condensate (liquid) drips into the thimble containing the solid. The hot solvent begins to fill the thimble and extracts the desired compound from the solid. Once the thimble is filled with solvent, the side arm on the right acts as a siphon, and the solvent, which now contains the dissolved compound, drains back into the distillation flask. The vaporization–condensation–extraction–siphoning process is repeated hundreds of times, and the desired product is concentrated in the distillation flask. The product is concentrated in the flask because the product has a boiling point higher than that of the solvent or because it is a solid.

12.14 Continuous Liquid–Liquid Extraction

When a product is very soluble in water, it is often difficult to extract using the techniques described in Sections 12.4–12.7 because of an unfavorable distribution coefficient. In this case, you need to extract the aqueous solution numerous times with fresh batches of an immiscible organic solvent to remove the desired product from water. A less labor-intensive technique involves the use of a continuous liquid–liquid extraction apparatus. One type of extractor, used with solvents that are less dense than water, is shown in Figure 12.15. Diethyl ether is usually the solvent of choice.

The aqueous phase is placed in the extractor, which is then filled with diethyl ether up to the side arm. The round-bottom distillation flask is partially filled with ether. The ether is heated to reflux in the round-bottom flask, and the vapor is liquefied in the water-cooled condenser. The ether drips into the central tube, passes

Figure 12.14
Continuous solid–liquid
extraction using a Soxhlet
extractor.

Figure 12.15
Continuous liquid–liquid extraction using a
solvent less dense than water.

through the porous sintered glass tip, and flows through the aqueous layer. The
solvent extracts the desired compound from the aqueous phase, and the ether is
recycled back into the round-bottom flask. The product is concentrated in the flask.
The extraction is rather inefficient and must be placed in operation for at least 24
hours to remove the compound from the aqueous phase.

**12.15 Solid Phase
Extraction**

Solid phase extraction (SPE) is a relatively new technique, which is similar in
appearance and function to column chromatography and high-performance liquid chromatography (Techniques 19 and 21). In some applications, SPE is also
similar to liquid–liquid extraction, discussed in this technique chapter. In addition
to performing separation processes, SPE can also be used to carry out reactions in
which new compounds are prepared.

A typical SPE column is constructed from the body of a plastic syringe, which is
packed with a **sorbent.** The term *sorbent* is used by many manufacturers as a general
term for materials that can both adsorb (attract to the surface of the sorbent by a
physical attraction) or absorb (penetrate into the material like a sponge). A frit is inserted at the bottom of the column to support the sorbent. After the sorbent is added,
another frit is inserted on top of the sorbent to hold it in place. The remainder of the
tube serves as a reservoir for the solvent. Generally, the column comes packed with

the sorbent from the manufacturer, but unpacked columns can also be purchased and packed by the user for specific applications. The Luer-lock tip at the bottom is connected to a vacuum source that pulls the solvents through the column.

SPE columns can be packed with many kinds of sorbent, depending on how the column will be used. Some common types are identified in the same way that column chromatography adsorbents are classified (see Technique 21, Section 21.1): normal-phase, reversed-phase, and ion exchange. Examples of normal-phase sorbents, which are polar, include silica and alumina. These columns are used to isolate polar compounds from a nonpolar solvent. Reversed-phase sorbents are made by alkylating silica. As a result, nonpolar alkyl groups are bonded to the silica surface, making the sorbent nonpolar. A common column of this type, known as a C_{18} column, is prepared by attaching an octadecyl ($—C_8H_{18}$) group to the silica surface (see Figure 12.16). C_{18} columns most likely function by an adsorption process.

Figure 12.16

Preparation of C-18 silica for reversed-phase extractions using SPE tubes. The process changes polar silica (hydrophilic material) to nonpolar silica (hydrophobic material).

Figure 12.17
Experimental setup for SPE column.

Reversed-phase sorbents are used to isolate relatively nonpolar compounds from polar solvents. Ion-exchange sorbents consist of charged or highly polar materials and are used to isolate charged compounds, either as anions or cations.

A major advantage of SPE columns is that they are fast and convenient to use compared to traditional column chromatography or liquid–liquid extraction. However, there are many other advantages that are of benefit to the environment, and their use is a good example of green chemistry (see essay "Green Chemistry" that precedes Experiment 28). These advantages include the use of more environmentally friendly solvents, higher recovery, elimination of emulsions, enormous decrease in the use of solvents, and reduced toxic waste generation.

A good example of the use of SPE columns for performing a task that is normally done by liquid–liquid extraction is the isolation of caffeine from tea or coffee. In this application, a C_{18} column is used. As the tea or coffee flows through the column, caffeine is attracted to the sorbent, and the polar impurities come off with water. Ethyl acetate is then used to remove the caffeine from the column. The experimental setup for this is shown in Figure 12.17. The SPE column[2] is attached to the filter flask by using two neoprene adapters (sizes #1 and #2). The filter flask is connected to either a vacuum line or a water aspirator to provide the vacuum. After each step, the solvents with impurities or desired product are drawn through the column into the filter flask using the vacuum.

The following steps are used with an SPE tube to remove caffeine from tea or coffee (see Figure 12.18):

A. Condition the C_{18} reversed-phase silica column by passing methanol and water through the tube.

B. Apply the sample of caffeinated drink to the column.

C. Wash the polar impurities from the column with water.

D. Elute the caffeine from the tube with ethyl acetate.

Even though Figure 12.18 is applied to the isolation of caffeine, the general scheme may be used in any application in which it is desired to separate polar substances, such as water, from a relatively nonpolar substance. Numerous applications are found in the medical field, in which analyzing body fluids is important.

There are many other diverse applications that SPE columns can be used for. By modifying the silica with specific chemical reagents, new compounds can be prepared in SPE columns. For example, oxidation reactions can be performed by mixing the silica with the appropriate oxidizing agents. Aldol condensation reactions can also be conducted in SPE columns. In another type of application, SPE has been adopted as an alternative to liquid–liquid extraction.

---

[2] This is a Strata SPE column available from Phenomenex, 411 Madrid Ave., Torrance, CA 90501-1430; phone (310) 212-0555. Part number: 8B-S001-JCH-S, Strata C-18-E, 1000 mg sorbent/6-mL tube.

A. Condition   B. Apply sample

C. Wash   D. Elute

| ○ Caffeine | ▼ Polar compounds |

© Cengage Learning 2013

Figure 12.18
Steps to remove caffeine from tea or coffee.

PROBLEMS

1. Suppose solute A has a distribution coefficient of 1.0 between water and diethyl ether. Demonstrate that if 4.0 mL of a solution of 0.20 g of A in water were extracted with two 1.0-mL portions of ether, a smaller amount of A would remain in the water than if the solution were extracted with one 2.0-mL portion of ether.

2. Write an equation to show how you could recover the parent compounds from their respective salts (1, 2, and 4) shown in Figure 12.10.

3. Aqueous hydrochloric acid was used *after* the sodium bicarbonate and sodium hydroxide extractions in the separation scheme shown in Figure 12.10. Is it possible to use this reagent earlier in the separation scheme to achieve the same overall result? If so, explain where you would perform this extraction.

4. Using aqueous hydrochloric acid, sodium bicarbonate, or sodium hydroxide solutions, devise a separation scheme using the style shown in Figure 12.10 to separate the following two-component mixtures. All the substances are soluble in ether. Also indicate how you would recover each of the compounds

from its respective salts. Outline your procedure using a flowchart (see Section 12.12).

a. Give two different methods for separating this mixture.

$(CH_3CH_2CH_2CH_2)_3N$

b. Give two different methods for separating this mixture.

$CH_3CH_2CH_2CH_2CH_2CH_2OH$

c. Give one method for separating this mixture.

5. Solvents other than those in Table 12.1 may be used for extractions. Determine the relative positions of the organic layer and the aqueous layer in a conical vial or separatory funnel after shaking each of the following solvents with an aqueous phase. Find the densities for each of these solvents in a handbook (see Technique 4).

   a. 1,1,1-Trichloroethane

   b. Hexane

6. A student prepares ethyl benzoate by the reaction of benzoic acid with ethanol using a sulfuric acid catalyst. The following compounds are found in the crude reaction mixture: ethyl benzoate (major component), benzoic acid, ethanol, and sulfuric acid. Using a handbook, obtain the solubility properties in water for each of these compounds (see Technique 4). Indicate how you would remove benzoic acid, ethanol, and sulfuric acid from ethyl benzoate. At some point in the purification, you should also use an aqueous sodium bicarbonate solution. Outline your procedure using a flowchart (see Section 12.12).

7. Calculate the weight of water that could be removed from a wet organic phase using 50.0 mg of magnesium sulfate. Assume that it gives the hydrate listed in Table 12.2.

8. Explain exactly what you would do when performing the following laboratory instructions; that is, write a short procedure.

   a. "Wash the organic layer with 1.0 mL of 1 *M* aqueous sodium bicarbonate."

   b. "Extract the aqueous layer three times with 1-mL portions of methylene chloride."

9. Just prior to drying an organic layer with a drying agent, you notice water droplets in the organic layer. What should you do next?

10. What should you do if there is some question about which layer is the organic one during an extraction procedure?

11. Saturated aqueous sodium chloride ($d = 1.2$ g/mL) is added to the following mixtures in order to dry the organic layer. Which layer is likely to be on the bottom in each case?

   a. Sodium chloride layer or a layer containing a high-density organic compound dissolved in methylene chloride ($d = 1.4$ g/mL)

   b. Sodium chloride layer or a layer containing a low-density organic compound dissolved in methylene chloride ($d = 1.1$ g/mL)

Physical Constants of Liquids: The Boiling Point and Density

PART A. BOILING POINTS AND THERMOMETER CORRECTION

13.1 The Boiling Point

As a liquid is heated, the vapor pressure of the liquid increases to the point at which it just equals the applied pressure (usually atmospheric pressure). At this point, the liquid is observed to boil. The normal boiling point is measured at 760 mm Hg (760 torr), or 1 atm. At a lower applied pressure, the vapor pressure needed for boiling is also lowered, and the liquid boils at a lower temperature. The relation between applied pressure and temperature of boiling for a liquid is determined by its vapor pressure–temperature behavior. Figure 13.1 is an idealization of the typical vapor pressure–temperature behavior of a liquid.

Because the boiling point is sensitive to pressure, it is important to record the barometric pressure when determining a boiling point if the determination is being conducted at an elevation significantly above or below sea level. Normal atmospheric variations may affect the boiling point, but they are usually of minor importance. However, if a boiling point is being monitored during the course of a vacuum distillation (Technique 16) that is being performed with an aspirator or a vacuum pump, the variation from the atmospheric value will be especially marked. In these cases, it is important to know the pressure as accurately as possible.

As a rule of thumb, the boiling point of many liquids drops about 0.5°C for a 10-mm decrease in pressure when in the vicinity of 760 mm Hg. At lower pressures, a 10°C drop in boiling point is observed for each halving of the pressure. For example, if the observed boiling point of a liquid is 150°C at 10 mm pressure, then the boiling point would be about 140°C at 5 mm Hg.

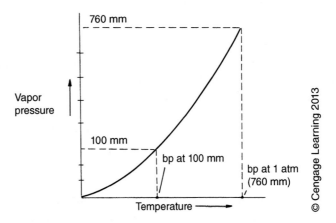

Figure 13.1
The vapor pressure–temperature curve for a typical liquid.

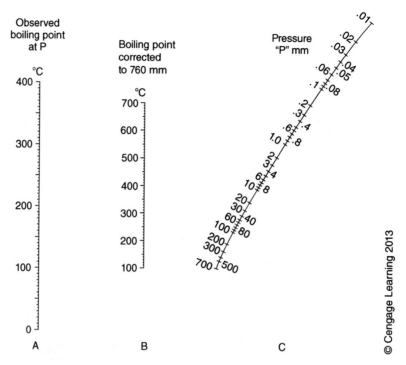

Figure 13.2

Pressure–temperature alignment nomograph. How to use the nomograph: Assume a reported boiling point of 100°C (column A) at 1 mm. To determine the boiling point at 18 mm, connect 100°C (column A) to 1 mm (column C) with a transparent plastic rule and observe where this line intersects column B (about 280°C). This value would correspond to the normal boiling point. Next, connect 280°C (column B) with 18 mm (column C) and observe where this intersects column A (151°C). The approximate boiling point will be 151°C at 18 mm. (Reprinted courtesy of EMD Chemicals, Inc.)

A more accurate estimate of the change in boiling point with a change of pressure can be made by using a nomograph. In Figure 13.2, a nomograph is given, and a method is described for using it to obtain boiling points at various pressures when the boiling point is known at some other pressure.

13.2 Determining the Boiling Point—Microscale and Macroscale Methods

Several experimental methods of determining boiling points are available. Selecting a method depends on how much liquid is available and the availability of specific apparatus. In either microscale or macroscale experiments in which 0.3–0.5 mL of liquid is available, the semimicroscale direct method is usually most reliable. If less material is available, it will be necessary to perform either the semimicroscale or microscale inverted capillary method. With practice, these methods can be reliable, too. With larger quantities in both microscale and macroscale experiments, the boiling point can also be observed while performing a distillation.

Semimicroscale Direct Method. The apparatus for this method is shown in Figure 13.3. With this method, the bulb of the thermometer can be immersed in vapor from the boiling liquid for a period long enough to allow it to equilibrate and give a good temperature reading. A 13-mm × 100-mm test tube works well in this procedure. Use 0.5 mL of liquid and a small, inert carborundum (black) boiling

Mercury Thermometer

Refluxing vapor

Boiling stone — } Boiling liquid

© Cengage Learning 2013

Figure 13.3
Macroscale method of determining the boiling point.

stone. This method works best with a partial immersion (76 mm) mercury thermometer (see Section 13.3). It is not necessary to perform a stem correction with this type of thermometer. This method also works well with a digital thermometer (see Section 13.4).

Place the bulb of the thermometer as close as possible to the boiling liquid without actually touching it. The best heating device is a hot plate with either an aluminum block or a sand bath.[1]

While you are heating the liquid, it is helpful to record the temperature at 1-minute intervals. This makes it easier to keep track of changes in the temperature and to know when the liquid has reached the boiling point. The liquid must boil vigorously, such that you see a reflux ring above the bulb of the thermometer and drops of liquid condensing on the sides of the test tube. Note that with some liquids, the reflux ring will be faint, and you must look closely to see it. The boiling point is reached when the temperature reading on the thermometer has remained constant at its highest observed value for 2–3 minutes. It is usually best to turn the heat control on the hot plate to a relatively high setting initially, especially if you are starting with a cold hot plate and aluminum block or sand bath. If the temperature begins to level off at a relatively low temperature (less than about 100°C) or if the reflux ring reaches the immersion ring on the thermometer, you should turn down the heat-control setting immediately.

Two problems can occur when you perform this boiling-point procedure. The first is much more common and occurs when the temperature appears to be leveling off at a temperature below the boiling point of the liquid. This is more likely to happen with a relatively high-boiling liquid (boiling points greater than about 150°C) or when the sample is not heated sufficiently. The best way to prevent this problem is to heat the sample more strongly. With high-boiling liquids, it may be helpful to wait for the temperature to remain constant for 3–4 minutes to make sure that you have reached the actual boiling point.

The second problem, which is rare, occurs when the liquid evaporates completely, and the temperature inside the dry test tube may rise higher than the actual boiling point of the liquid. This is more likely to happen with low-boiling liquids (boiling point less than 100°C) or if the temperature on the hot plate is set too high for too long. To check for this possibility, observe the amount of liquid remaining in the test tube as soon as you have finished with the procedure. If there is no liquid remaining, it is possible that the highest temperature you observed is greater than the boiling point of the liquid. In this case, you should repeat the boiling-point determination, heating the sample less strongly or using more sample.

Depending on the skill of the person performing this technique, boiling points may be slightly inaccurate. When experimental boiling points are inaccurate, it is more common for them to be lower than the literature value, and inaccuracies are more likely to occur for higher-boiling liquids. With higher-boiling liquids, the difference may be as much as 5°C. Carefully following the previous instructions will make it more likely that your experimental value will be close to the literature value.

With smaller amounts of material, you can carry out a microscale or semimicroscale determination of the boiling point by using the apparatus shown in Figure 13.4.

---

[1] *Note to the Instructor:* The aluminum block should have a hole drilled in it that goes all the way through the block and is just slightly larger than the outside diameter of the test tube. A sand bath can be conveniently prepared by adding 40 mL of sand to a 150-mL beaker or by using a heating mantle partially filled with sand. For additional comments about these heating methods, see the Instructor's Manual, Experiment 8, "Infrared Spectroscopy and Boiling-Point Determination."

Figure 13.4
Boiling-point determinations.

Semimicroscale Inverted Capillary Method. To carry out the semimicroscale determination, attach a piece of 5-mm glass tubing (sealed at one end) to a thermometer with a rubber band or a thin slice of rubber tubing. The liquid whose boiling point is being determined is introduced with a Pasteur pipette into this piece of tubing, and a short piece of melting-point capillary (sealed at one end) is dropped in with the open end down. The whole unit is then placed in a Thiele tube. The rubber band should be placed above the level of the oil in the Thiele tube; otherwise, the band may soften in the hot oil. When positioning the band, keep in mind that the oil will expand when heated. Next, the Thiele tube is heated in the same fashion as described in Technique 9, Section 9.6, for determining a melting point. Heating is continued until a rapid and continuous stream of bubbles emerges from the inverted capillary. At this point, you should stop heating. Soon, the stream of bubbles slows down and stops. When the bubbles stop, the liquid enters the capillary tube. The moment at which the liquid enters the capillary tube corresponds to the boiling point of the liquid, and the temperature is recorded.

Microscale Inverted Capillary Method. In microscale experiments, there often is too little product available to use the semimicroscale method just described. However, the method can be scaled down in the following manner. The liquid is placed in a 1-mm melting-point capillary tube to a depth of about 4–6 mm (see Figure 13.4B). Use a syringe or a Pasteur pipette that has had its tip drawn thinner to transfer the liquid into the capillary tube. It may be necessary to use a centrifuge to transfer the liquid to the bottom of the tube. Next, prepare an appropriately sized inverted capillary, or **bell.**

The easiest way to prepare a bell is to use a commercial micropipette, such as a 10-μL Drummond "microcap." These are available in vials of 50 or 100 microcaps and are inexpensive. To prepare the bell, cut the microcap in half with a file or scorer and then seal one end by inserting it a small distance into a flame, turning it on its axis until the opening closes.

If microcaps are not available, a piece of 1-mm open-end capillary tubing (same size as a melting-point capillary) can be rotated along its axis in a flame while being held horizontally. Use your index fingers and thumbs to rotate the tube; do not change the distance between your two hands while rotating. When the tubing is soft, remove it from the flame and pull it to a thinner diameter. When pulling, keep the tube straight by *moving both your hands and your elbows outward* by about 4 inches. Hold the pulled tube in place a few moments until it cools. Using the edge of a file or your fingernail, break out the thin center section. Seal one end of the thin section in the flame; then break it to a length that is about one and one-half times the height of your sample liquid (6–9 mm). Be sure the break is done squarely. Invert the bell (open end down), and place it in the capillary tube containing the sample liquid. Push the bell to the bottom with a fine copper wire if it adheres to the side of the capillary tube. A centrifuge may be used if you prefer. Figure 13.5 shows the construction method for the bell and the final assembly.

1. Rotate in flame until soft.
2. Remove from flame and pull.
3. Break pulled section out.
4. Seal one end.
5. Break to length.
6. Place bell in tube.

Several may be made at one time.

Figure 13.5
Construction of a microcapillary bell for microscale boiling-point determination.

Place the microscale assembly in a standard melting-point apparatus (or a Thiele tube if an electrical apparatus is not available) to determine the boiling point. Heating is continued until a rapid and continuous stream of bubbles emerges from the inverted capillary. At this point, stop heating. Soon, the stream of bubbles slows down and stops. When the bubbles stop, the liquid enters the capillary tube. The moment at which the liquid enters the capillary tube corresponds to the boiling point of the liquid, and the temperature is recorded.

Explanation of the Method. During the initial heating, the air trapped in the inverted bell expands and leaves the tube, giving rise to a stream of bubbles. When the liquid begins boiling, most of the air has been expelled; the bubbles of gas are due to the boiling action of the liquid. Once the heating is stopped, most of the vapor pressure left in the bell comes from the vapor of the heated liquid that seals its open end. There is always vapor in equilibrium with a heated liquid. If the temperature of the liquid is above its boiling point, the pressure of the trapped vapor will either exceed or equal the atmospheric pressure. As the liquid cools, its vapor pressure decreases. When the vapor pressure drops just below atmospheric pressure (just below the boiling point), the liquid is forced into the capillary tube.

Difficulties. Three problems are common to this method. The first arises when the liquid is heated so strongly that it evaporates or boils away. The second arises when the liquid is not heated above its boiling point before heating is discontinued. If the heating is stopped at any point below the actual boiling point of the sample, the liquid enters the bell *immediately*, giving an apparent boiling point that is too low. Be sure you observe a continuous stream of bubbles, too fast for individual bubbles to be distinguished, before lowering the temperature. Also be sure the bubbling action decreases slowly before the liquid enters the bell. If your melting-point apparatus has fine enough control and fast response, you can actually begin heating again and force the liquid out of the bell before it becomes completely filled with the liquid. This allows a second determination to be performed on the same sample. The third problem is that the bell may be so light that the bubbling action of the liquid causes the bell to move up the capillary tube. This problem can sometimes be solved by using a longer (heavier) bell or by sealing the bell so that a larger section of solid glass is formed at the sealed end of the bell.

When measuring temperatures above 150°C, thermometer errors can become significant. For an accurate boiling point with a high-boiling liquid, you may wish to apply a **stem correction** to the thermometer, as described in Section 13.3, or to calibrate the thermometer, as described in Technique 9, Section 9.9.

Microscale or Macroscale–Distillation Method. When you have large quantities of material, you can simply record the boiling point (or boiling range) as viewed on a thermometer while performing a simple distillation (see Technique 14). When this method is used to determine a boiling point, it is best to use a partial immersion mercury thermometer or a digital thermometer for more accurate readings.

13.3 Glass Thermometers and Stem Corrections

Three types of glass thermometers are available: bulb immersion, partial immersion (stem immersion), and total immersion. Bulb immersion thermometers are calibrated by the manufacturer to give correct temperature readings when only the bulb (not the rest of the thermometer) is placed in the medium to be measured. Partial immersion thermometers are calibrated to give correct temperature readings when they are immersed to a specified depth in the medium to be measured. Partial immersion thermometers are easily recognized because the manufacturer always scores a mark, or immersion ring, completely around the stem at the specified depth of immersion. The immersion ring is normally found below any of the temperature calibrations. Total immersion thermometers are calibrated when the entire thermometer is immersed in the medium to be measured. The three types of thermometer are often marked on the back (opposite side from the calibrations) by the words *bulb, immersion,* or *total,* but this may vary from one manufacturer to another.

Boiling-point determination and distillation are two techniques in which an accurate temperature reading may be obtained most easily with a partial immersion thermometer. A common immersion length for this type of thermometer is 76 mm. This length works well for these two techniques because the hot vapors are likely to surround the bottom of the thermometer up to a point fairly close to the immersion line. If a total immersion thermometer is used in these applications, a stem correction, which is described later, must be used to obtain an accurate temperature reading.

The liquid used in thermometers may be either mercury or a colored organic liquid such as an alcohol. Because mercury is highly poisonous and is difficult to clean up completely when a thermometer is broken, many laboratories now use non-mercury thermometers. When a highly accurate temperature reading is required, such as in a boiling-point determination or in some distillations, mercury thermometers may have an advantage over non-mercury thermometers for two reasons. Mercury has a lower coefficient of expansion than the liquids used in non-mercury thermometers. Therefore, a partial immersion mercury thermometer will give a more accurate reading when the thermometer is not immersed in the hot vapors exactly to the immersion line. In other words, the mercury thermometer is more forgiving. Furthermore, because mercury is a better conductor of heat, a mercury thermometer will respond more quickly to changes in the temperature of the hot vapors. If the temperature is read before the thermometer reading has stabilized, which is more likely to occur with a non-mercury thermometer, the temperature reading will be inaccurate.

Manufacturers design total immersion thermometers to read correctly only when they are immersed totally in the medium to be measured. The entire mercury thread must be covered. Because this situation is rare, a **stem correction** should be added to the observed temperature. This correction, which is positive, can be fairly large when high temperatures are being measured. Keep in mind, however, that if your thermometer has been calibrated for its desired use (such as described in Technique 9, Section 9.9 for a melting-point apparatus), a stem correction should not be necessary for any temperature within the calibration limits. You are most likely to want a stem correction when you are performing a distillation. If you determine a melting point or boiling point using an uncalibrated, total immersion thermometer, you will also want to use a stem correction.

When you wish to make a stem correction for a total immersion thermometer, the following formula may be used. It is based on the fact that the portion of the mercury thread in the stem is cooler than the portion immersed in the vapor or the heated area around the thermometer. The mercury will not have expanded in the cool stem to the same extent as in the warmed section of the thermometer. The equation used is

$$(0.000154)(T - t_1)(T - t_2) = \textbf{correction to be added to } T \textbf{ observed}$$

1. The factor 0.000154 is a constant, the coefficient of expansion for the mercury in the thermometer.

2. The term $T - t_1$ corresponds to the length of the mercury thread not immersed in the heated area. Use the temperature scale on the thermometer itself for this measurement rather than an actual length unit. T is the observed temperature, and t_1 is the *approximate* place where the heated part of the stem ends and the cooler part begins.

© Cengage Learning 2013

Figure 13.6
Measurement of a thermometer stem
correction during distillation.

3. The term $T - t_2$ corresponds to the difference between the temperature of the mercury in the vapor T and the temperature of the mercury in the air outside the heated area (room temperature). The term T is the observed temperature, and t_2 is measured by hanging another thermometer so the bulb is close to the stem of the main thermometer.

Figure 13.6 shows how to apply this method for a distillation. By the formula just given, it can be shown that high temperatures are more likely to require a stem correction and that low temperatures need not be corrected. The following sample calculations illustrate this point.

Example 1	Example 2
$T = 200°C$	$T = 100°C$
$t_1 = 0°C$	$t_1 = 0°C$
$t_2 = 35°C$	$t_2 = 35°C$
$(0.000154)(200)(165) = 5.1°$ stem correction	$(0.000154)(100)(65) = 1.0°$ stem correction
$200°C + 5°C = 205°C$ corrected temperature	$100°C + 1°C = 101°C$ corrected temperature

13.4 Digital Thermometers

Rather than using a glass thermometer to determine a boiling point or to monitor the temperature during a distillation, one can use a digital thermometer with a stainless steel temperature probe (see Figure 13.7). When a digital thermometer is used with the semimicroscale direct method of determining a boiling point (see Semimicroscale Direct Method in Section 13.2), the boiling point can usually be determined to within 2-3 degrees of the literature value. The temperature probe (or

Figure 13.7
Boiling point determination with a digital thermometer.

thermocouple) works only in a given temperature range. It is therefore important to select a probe that has a maximum temperature that is higher than the boiling points of the liquids that you will be measuring. See the Instructor's Manual, Experiment 7, Simple and Fractional Distillation, for more specific information about selecting an appropriate temperature probe.

An even better way to measure the temperature is to use the Vernier LabQuest unit, or the Vernier LabPro system, with a stainless steel temperature probe. The LabQuest is a handheld device that can be used as a stand-alone unit, while the LabPro is an interface unit that must be used with a computer and the associated LabPro software. As with the digital thermometers, the temperature probe used with these devices must also work in a range that exceeds the boiling points of the liquids you will be attempting to measure, Both of these systems provide a very accurate way of measuring the temperature. The data (temperature vs. time) are displayed either on the screen of the LabQuest unit or on a computer monitor (with the LabPro interface) while it is being collected. When performing a boiling point determination, the visual display of the temperature on the monitor makes it easy to know when the maximum temperature (the boiling point) has been reached.

Being able to see a graph of temperature vs. time when performing a distillation gives you a better sense of when the different liquids are distilling and makes it easier to control the distillation (see Technique 14, Section 14.5).

PART B. DENSITY

13.5 Density

Density is defined as mass per unit volume and is generally expressed in units of grams per milliliter (g/mL) for a liquid and grams per cubic centimeter (g/cm³) for a solid.

$$\text{Density} = \frac{\text{mass}}{\text{volume}} \quad \text{or} \quad D = \frac{M}{V}$$

In organic chemistry, density is most commonly used in converting the weight of liquid to a corresponding volume, or vice versa. It is often easier to measure a volume of a liquid than to weigh it. As a physical property, density is also useful for identifying liquids in much the same way that boiling points are used.

Although precise methods that allow the measurements of the densities of liquids at the microscale level have been developed, they are often difficult to perform. An approximate method for measuring densities can be found in using a 100-μL (0.100-mL) automatic pipette (Technique 5, Section 5.1). Clean, dry, and preweigh one or more conical vials (including their caps and liners) and record their weights. Handle these vials with a tissue to avoid getting your fingerprints on them. Adjust the automatic pipette to deliver 100 μL and fit it with a clean, new tip. Use the pipette to deliver 100 μL of the unknown liquid to each of your tared vials. Cap them so that the liquid does not evaporate. Reweigh the vials and use the weight of the 100 μL of liquid delivered to calculate a density for each case. It is recommended that from three to five determinations be performed, that the calculations be performed to three significant figures, and that all the calculations be averaged to obtain the final result. This determination of the density will be accurate to within two significant figures. Table 13.1 compares some literature values with those that could be obtained by this method.

Table 13.1 Densities determined by the automatic pipette method (g/mL)

Substance	BP	Literature	100 μL
Water	100	1.000	1.01
Hexane	69	0.660	0.66
Acetone	56	0.788	0.77
Dichloromethane	40	1.330	1.27
Diethyl ether	35	0.713	0.67

© Cengage Learning 2013

PROBLEMS

1. Using the pressure–temperature alignment chart in Figure 13.2, answer the following questions.

   a. What is the normal boiling point (at 760 mm Hg) for a compound that boils at 150°C at 10 mm Hg pressure?

   b. At what temperature would the compound in (a) boil if the pressure were 40 mm Hg?

    c. A compound was distilled at atmospheric pressure and had a boiling point of 285°C. What would be the approximate boiling range for this compound at 15 mm Hg?

2. Calculate the corrected boiling point for nitrobenzene by using the method given in Section 13.3. The boiling point was determined using an apparatus similar to that shown in Figure 13.3. Assume that a total immersion thermometer was used. The observed boiling point was 205°C. The reflux ring in the test tube just reached up to the 0°C mark on the thermometer. A second thermometer suspended alongside the test tube, at a slightly higher level than the one inside, gave a reading of 35°C.

3. Suppose that you had calibrated the thermometer in your melting-point apparatus against a series of melting-point standards. After reading the temperature and converting it using the calibration chart, should you also apply a stem correction? Explain.

4. The density of a liquid was determined by the automatic pipette method. A 100-μL automatic pipette was used. The liquid had a mass of 0.082 g. What was the density in grams per milliliter of the liquid?

5. During the microscale boiling-point determination (see Section 13.2, Microscale Inverted Capillary Method) of an unknown liquid, heating was discontinued at 154°C and the liquid immediately began to enter the inverted bell. Heating was begun again at once, and the liquid was forced out of the bell. Heating was again discontinued at 165°C, at which time a rapid stream of bubbles emerged from the bell. On cooling, the rate of bubbling gradually diminished until the liquid reached a temperature of 161°C and entered and filled the bell. Explain this sequence of events. What was the boiling point of the liquid?

Simple Distillation

Distillation is the process of vaporizing a liquid, condensing the vapor, and collecting the condensate in another container. This technique is useful for separating a liquid mixture when the components have different boiling points or when one of the components will not distill. It is one of the principal methods of purifying a liquid. Four basic distillation methods are available to the chemist: simple distillation, vacuum distillation (distillation at reduced pressure), fractional distillation, and steam distillation. This technique chapter will discuss simple distillation. Vacuum distillation will be discussed in Technique 16. Fractional distillation will be discussed in Technique 15, and steam distillation will be discussed in Technique 18.

14.1 The Evolution of Distillation Equipment

There are probably more types and styles of distillation apparatus than exist for any other technique in chemistry. Over the centuries, chemists have devised just about every conceivable design. The earliest known types of distillation apparatus were the **alembic** and the **retort** (Figure 14.1). They were used by alchemists in the Middle Ages and the Renaissance and probably even earlier by Arabic chemists. Most other distillation equipment has evolved as variations on these designs.

Figure 14.1 shows several stages in the evolution of distillation equipment as it relates to the organic laboratory. It is not intended to be a complete history; rather, it is representative. Up until recent years, equipment based on the retort design was common in the laboratory. Although the retort itself was still in use early in the twentieth century, it had evolved by that time into the distillation flask and water-cooled condenser combination. This early equipment was connected with corks. By 1958, most introductory laboratories were beginning to use "organic lab kits" that included glassware connected by standard-taper glass joints. The original lab kits contained large ⊺ 24/40 joints. Within a short time, they became smaller, with ⊺ 19/22 and even ⊺ 14/20 joints. These later kits are still being used today in many organic courses. Small-scale variations of these kits are also used today by chemical researchers, but they are too expensive to use in an introductory laboratory. Instead, the "microscale" equipment you are using in this course is coming into common use. This equipment has ⊺ 14/10 standard-taper joints, threaded outer joints with screwcap connectors, and an internal O-ring. The distillation apparatus in microscale kits is designed for work with small amounts of material, and it is different from the more traditional larger-scale equipment. It is perhaps more closely related to the alembic design than to that of the retort. Because both types of equipment are in use today, after we describe microscale equipment, we will also show the equivalent large-scale apparatus used to perform distillation.

14.2 Distillation Theory

In the traditional distillation of a pure substance, vapor rises from the distillation flask and comes into contact with a thermometer that records its temperature. The vapor then passes through a condenser, which reliquefies the vapor and passes it into the receiving flask. The temperature observed during the distillation of a **pure**

Figure 14.1

Some stages in the evolution of microscale distillation equipment from alchemical equipment (dates represent approximate time of popular use).

substance remains constant throughout the distillation so long as both vapor *and* liquid are present in the system (see Figure 14.2A). When a **liquid mixture** is distilled, often the temperature does not remain constant but increases throughout the distillation. The reason for this is that the composition of the vapor that is distilling varies continuously during the distillation (see Figure 14.2B).

For a liquid mixture, the composition of the vapor in equilibrium with the heated solution is different from the composition of the solution itself. This is shown in Figure 14.3, which is a phase diagram of the typical vapor–liquid relationship for a two-component system (A + B).

On this diagram, horizontal lines represent constant temperatures. The upper curve represents vapor composition, and the lower curve represents liquid composition. For any horizontal line (constant temperature), like that shown at *t*, the intersections of the line with the curves give the compositions of the liquid and the vapor that are in equilibrium with each other at that temperature. In the diagram, at temperature *t*, the intersection of the curve at X indicates that liquid of composition W will be in equilibrium with vapor of composition Z, which corresponds to the intersection at Y. Composition is given as a mole percentage of A and B in the mixture. Pure A, which boils at temperature t_A, is represented at the left. Pure B, which boils

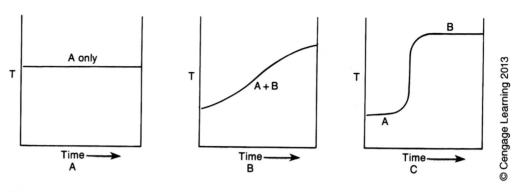

Figure 14.2

Three types of temperature behavior during a simple distillation. A. A single pure component. B. Two components of similar boiling points. C. Two components with widely differing boiling points. Good separations are achieved in A and C.

at temperature t_B, is represented on the right. For either pure A or pure B, the vapor and liquid curves meet at the boiling point. Thus, either pure A or pure B will distill at a constant temperature (t_A or t_B). Both the vapor and the liquid must have the same composition in either of these cases. This is not the case for mixtures of A and B.

A mixture of A and B of composition W will have the following behavior when heated. The temperature of the liquid mixture will increase until the boiling point of the mixture is reached. This corresponds to following line WX from W to X, the boiling point of the mixture t. At temperature t the liquid begins to vaporize, which corresponds to line XY. The vapor has the composition corresponding to Z. In other words, the first vapor obtained in distilling a mixture of A and B does not consist of pure A. It is richer in A than the original mixture but still contains a significant amount of the higher-boiling component B, even from the very beginning of the distillation. The result is that it is never possible to separate a mixture completely by a simple distillation. However, in two cases it is possible to get an acceptable separation into relatively pure components. In the first case, if the boiling points of A and B differ by a large amount (>100 degrees) and if the distillation is carried out carefully, it will be possible to get a fair separation of A and B. In the second case, if A contains a fairly small amount of B (<10%), a reasonable separation of A from B can be achieved. When the boiling-point differences are not large and when highly pure components are desired, it is necessary to perform a **fractional distillation.** Fractional distillation is described in Technique 15, in which the behavior during a simple distillation is also considered in detail. Note only that as vapor distills from the mixture of composition W (Figure 14.3), it is richer in A than is the solution. Thus, the composition of the material left behind in the distillation becomes richer in B (moves to the right from W toward pure B in the graph). A mixture of 90% B (dotted line on the right side in Figure 14.3) has a higher boiling point than at W. Hence, the temperature of the liquid in the distillation flask will increase during the distillation, and the composition of the distillate will change (as is shown in Figure 14.3B).

When two components that have a large boiling-point difference are distilled, the temperature

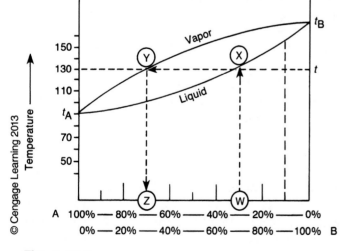

Figure 14.3

Phase diagram for a typical liquid mixture of two components.

remains constant while the first component distills. If the temperature remains constant, a relatively pure substance is being distilled. After the first substance distills, the temperature of the vapors rises, and the second component distills, again at a constant temperature. This is shown in Figure 14.2C. A typical application of this type of distillation might be an instance of a reaction mixture containing the desired component A (bp 140°C) contaminated with a small amount of undesired component B (bp 250°C) and mixed with a solvent such as diethyl ether (bp 36°C). The ether is removed easily at low temperature. Pure A is removed at a higher temperature and collected in a separate receiver. Component B can then be distilled, but it usually is left as a residue and not distilled. This separation is not difficult and represents a case where simple distillation might be used to advantage.

14.3 Microscale Equipment

Most large-scale distillation equipment requires the distilled liquid to travel a long distance from the distillation flask, through the condenser, to the receiving flask. When working at the microscale level, a long distillation path must be avoided. With small quantities of liquid, there are too many opportunities to lose all the sample. The liquid will adhere to, or wet, surfaces and get lost in every little nook and cranny of the system. A system with a long path also has a large volume, and a small amount of liquid may not produce enough vapor to fill it. Small-scale distillation requires a "short path" distillation. In order to make the distilling path as short as possible, the **Hickman head** has been adopted as the principal receiving device for most microscale distilling operations.

The Hickman Head. Two types of Hickman head (also called a Hickman "still") are shown in Figure 14.4. One of these variations has a convenient opening, or port, in the side, making removal of liquid that has collected in it easier. In operation, the liquid to be distilled is placed in a flask or vial attached to the bottom joint of the Hickman head and heated. If desired, you can attach a condenser to the top joint. Either a magnetic spin vane or a boiling stone is used to prevent bumping. Some typical assemblies are shown in Figures 14.5 and 14.7. The vapors of the heated liquid rise upward and are cooled and condensed on either the walls of the condenser or, if no condenser is used, on the inside walls of the Hickman head itself. As liquid drains downward, it collects in the circular well at the bottom of the still.

Collecting Fractions. The liquid that distills is called the **distillate.** Portions of the distillate collected during the course of a distillation are called **fractions.** A small fraction (usually discarded) collected before the distillation is begun in earnest is called a **forerun.** The well in a Hickman head can contain anywhere from 1 to 2 mL of liquid. In the style with the side port, fractions may be removed by opening the port and inserting a Pasteur pipette (Figure 14.6C). The unported head works equally well, but the head is emptied from the top by using a Pasteur pipette (Figure 14.6A). If a condenser or an internal thermometer is used, the distilling apparatus must be partially disassembled to remove liquid when the well fills. In some stills, the inner diameter of the head is small, and it is difficult to reach in at an angle with the pipette and make contact with the liquid. To remedy this problem, you may be able to use the longer (9-inch) Pasteur pipette instead of the shorter (5¾-inch) one. The longer pipette has a much longer narrow section (tip) and can adapt more effectively to the required angle. The disadvantage of the longer tip is that you are more likely to break it off inside the still. You may prefer to modify a short pipette by bending its tip slightly in a flame (Figure 14.6B).

Side port

© Cengage Learning 2013

A. Unported   B. Ported

Figure 14.4
The Hickman head.

Drying tube (optional)

Water condenser

→ H₂O

→ H₂O

Clamp

Hickman head

Spin vane

See caution in text

Aluminum block

© Cengage Learning 2013

Figure 14.5
Basic microscale distillation (external monitoring of temperature). Do not use a mercury thermometer.

Choice of Condenser. If you are careful (slow heating) or if the liquid to be distilled has a high boiling point, it may not be necessary to use a condenser with the Hickman head (Figure 14.7). In this case, the liquid being distilled must condense on the cooler sides of the head itself without any being lost through evaporation. If the liquid has a low boiling point or is very volatile, a condenser must be used. With very volatile liquids, a watercooled condenser must be used; however, an air-cooled condenser may suffice for less demanding cases. When using a water condenser, remember that water should enter the lower opening and exit from the upper one. If the hoses carrying the water in and out are connected in reverse fashion, the water jacket of the condenser will not fill completely.

Sealed Systems. Whenever you perform a distillation, be sure the system you are heating is not sealed off completely from the outside atmosphere. During a distillation, the air and vapors inside the system will both expand and contract. If pressure builds up inside a sealed system, the apparatus may explode. In performing a distillation, you should leave a small opening at the far end of the system. If water vapor could be harmful to the substances being distilled, a calcium chloride drying tube may be used to protect the system from moisture. Carefully examine each system discussed to see how an opening to the outside is provided.

External Monitoring of Temperature. The simple assembly using the Hickman head shown in Figure 14.5 does not monitor the temperature inside the apparatus. Instead, the temperature is monitored externally with a thermometer placed in an aluminum block.

CAUTION

You should not use a *mercury* thermometer with an aluminum block. If it breaks, the mercury will vaporize on the hot surface. Instead, use a non-mercury glass thermometer, a metal dial thermometer, or a digital electronic temperature measuring device.

External monitoring of the temperature has the disadvantage that the exact temperature at which liquid distills is never known. In many cases, this does not matter or is unavoidable, and the boiling point of the distilled liquid can be checked later by performing a microboiling-point determination (Technique 13, Section 13.2).

As a rule, there is at least a 15-degree difference in temperature between the temperature of the aluminum block or sand bath and that of the liquid in the heated distillation vial or flask. However, the magnitude of this difference cannot be relied on. Keep in mind that the liquid in the vial or flask may be at a different temperature than the vapor that is distilling. In many procedures in this text, the *approximate* temperature of the heating device will be given instead of the boiling point of the liquid involved. Because this method of monitoring the temperature is rather approximate, you will need to make the actual heater setting based on what is supposed to be occurring in the vial or flask.

Dismantling and using pipette

Open and
remove with
pipette

Hickman with side port

Cap

Side port

Open side
port and
remove with
pipette

Bend tip
if necessary

A   B   C

© Cengage Learning 2013

Figure 14.6
Removing fractions.

Internal Monitoring of Temperature. When you wish to monitor the actual temperature of a distillation, a thermometer must be placed inside the apparatus. Figures 14.7 and 14.8 show distillation assemblies that use an internal thermometer. The apparatus in Figure 14.7A represents the simplest possible distillation assembly. It does not use a condenser, and the thermometer is suspended from a clamp. It is possible to add either an air or a water condenser to this basic assembly (Figure 14.7B) and maintain internal monitoring of the temperature.

In the arrangement shown in Figure 14.8, a thermometer adapter is used. A thermometer adapter (Figure 14.9A) provides a convenient way of holding a thermometer in place. The Claisen head is used to provide an opening to the atmosphere, thereby avoiding a sealed system. With the Claisen head, a drying tube may be used to protect the system from atmospheric moisture.

If protection from atmospheric moisture is not required, the multipurpose adapter may be used. The multipurpose adapter (Figure 14.9B) replaces both the thermometer adapter and the Claisen head. With this adapter, the necessary opening to the atmosphere is provided by the side arm. The threaded joint holds the thermometer in place.

Carefully notice the position of the thermometer in Figures 14.7 and 14.8. The bulb of the thermometer must be placed in the stem of the Hickman head, *just below*

Figure 14.7
Basic microscale distillation (internal monitoring of temperature). Do not use a mercury thermometer.

the well, or it will not read the temperature correctly. The distillation temperature can be monitored most accurately by using a partial immersion mercury thermometer (see Technique 13, Section 13.3).

NOTE: It is good practice to monitor the temperature internally whenever possible.

Boiling Stones or Stirring. A boiling stone should be used during distillation in order to prevent bumping. As an alternative, the liquid being distilled may be rapidly stirred. A triangular spin vane of the correct size should be used when distilling from a conical vial, whereas a stirring bar should be used when distilling from a round-bottom flask.

Size of Distillation Flask. As a rule, the distillation flask or vial should not be filled to more than two thirds of its total capacity. This allows room for boiling and stirring action, and it prevents contamination of the distillate by bumping. A flask that is too large should also be avoided. With too large a flask, the **holdup** is excessive; the holdup is the amount of material that cannot distill because some vapor must fill the empty flask.

Figure 14.8
Basic microscale distillation using thermometer adapter
(internal monitoring of temperature).

Assembling the Apparatus. You should not grease the joints when assembling the apparatus. Ungreased joints seal well enough to allow you to perform a simple distillation. Stopcock grease can introduce a serious contaminant into your product.

Rate and Degree of Heating. Take care not to distill too quickly. If you vaporize liquid at a rate faster than it can be recondensed, some of your product may be lost by evaporation. On the other hand, you should not distill too slowly. This may also lead to loss of product because there is a longer period during which vapors can escape. Carefully examine your apparatus during distillation to monitor the position of either a reflux ring or a wet appearance on the surface of the glass. Either of these indicates the place at which condensation is occurring. The position at which condensation occurs should be well inside the Hickman head. Be sure that liquid is collecting in the well. If all the surfaces are shiny (wet) and there is no distillate, you are losing material.

NOTE: A slower rate of heating also helps to avoid bumping.

Figure 14.9
Two adapters.

If you are using a sand bath, material may be lost because the hot sand bath radiates too much heat upward and warms the Hickman still. If you believe this to be the case, it can often be remedied by placing a small square of aluminum foil over the top of the sand bath. Make a tear from one edge to the center of the foil to wrap it around the apparatus.

14.4 Semi-microscale and Macroscale Equipment

When you wish to distill quantities of liquid that are larger than 2–3 mL, different equipment is required. Most manufacturers of microscale equipment make two pieces of conventional distillation equipment sized to work with the ⊤ 14/10 microscale kit components. These two pieces, the **distillation head** and the **bent vacuum adapter,** are not provided in student microscale kits but must be purchased separately. Figure 14.10 shows a semimicroscale assembly using these components. Note that the bulb of the thermometer must be placed *below the side arm* if it is to be bathed in vapor and give a correct temperature reading. This apparatus assumes that a condenser is not necessary; however, you could easily insert one between the distilling head and the bent vacuum adapter. This insertion would produce a completely traditional distillation apparatus but would use microscale equipment. A distillation apparatus constructed from a "macroscale" organic laboratory kit is shown in Figure 14.11. This type of equipment is being used today in organic laboratories that have not converted to microscale. Electrically regulated **heating mantles** are often used with this equipment.

14.5 Using a Digital Thermometer

Rather than using a glass thermometer to monitor the temperature during a distillation, one can use a digital thermometer with a stainless steel temperature probe. The use of a digital thermometer for a semimicroscale distillation is illustrated in Figure 14.12. Digital thermometers may, of course, also be used in other styles of apparatus such as a standard distillation with a condenser or a microscale distillation. Technique 13, Section 13.4 discusses the use of digital thermometers, or the LabQuest and LabPro systems, in more detail.

Figure 14.10
Semimicroscale distillation (*requires special pieces).

Figure 14.11
Distillation with the standard macroscale organic lab kit.

Figure 14.12
Distillation using a digital thermometer.

PROBLEMS

1. Using Figure 14.3, answer the following questions.

   a. What is the molar composition of the vapor in equilibrium with a boiling liquid that has a composition of 60% A and 40% B?

   b. A sample of vapor has the composition 50% A and 50% B. What is the composition of the boiling liquid that produced this vapor?

2. Use an apparatus similar to that shown in Figure 14.10 and assume that the round-bottom flask holds 10 mL and that the Claisen head has an internal volume of about 2 mL in the vertical section. At the end of a distillation, vapor would fill this volume, but it could not be forced through the system. No liquid would remain in the distillation flask. Assuming this **holdup volume** of 12 mL, use the ideal gas law and assume a boiling point of 100°C (760 mm Hg) to calculate the number of microliters of liquid ($d = 0.9$ g/mL, $MW = 200$) that would recondense into the distillation flask on cooling.

3. Explain the significance of a horizontal line connecting a point on the lower curve with a point on the upper curve (such as line XY) in Figure 14.3.

4. Using Figure 14.3, determine the boiling point of a liquid having a molar composition of 50% A and 50% B.

5. What is the approximate difference between the temperature of a boiling liquid in a conical vial and the temperature read on an *external* thermometer when both are placed on an aluminum block?

6. Where should the thermometer bulb be located for internal monitoring in

    a. a distillation apparatus using a Hickman head?

    b. a large-scale distillation using a Claisen head with a water condenser placed beyond it?

7. Under what conditions can a good separation be achieved with a simple distillation?

Fractional Distillation, Azeotropes

Simple distillation, described in Technique 14, works well for most routine separation and purification procedures for organic compounds. When boiling-point differences of components to be separated are not large, however, **fractional distillation** must be used to achieve a good separation.

PART A. FRACTIONAL DISTILLATION

15.1 Differences between Simple and Fractional Distillation

When an ideal solution of two liquids, such as benzene (bp 80°C) and toluene (bp 110°C), is distilled by simple distillation, the first vapor produced will be enriched in the lower-boiling component (benzene). However, when that initial vapor is condensed and analyzed, the distillate will not be pure benzene. The boiling-point difference of benzene and toluene (30°C) is too small to achieve a complete separation by simple distillation. Following the principles outlined in Technique 14, Section 14.2, and using the vapor–liquid composition curve given in Figure 15.1, you can see what would happen if you started with an equimolar mixture of benzene and toluene.

Following the dashed lines shows that an equimolar mixture (50 mole % benzene) would begin to boil at about 91°C and, far from being 100% benzene, the distillate would contain about 74 mole % benzene and 26 mole % toluene. As the distillation continued, the composition of the undistilled liquid would move in the direction of A′ (there would be increased toluene due to removal of more benzene than toluene), and the corresponding vapor would contain a progressively smaller amount of benzene. In effect, the temperature of the distillation would continue to increase throughout the distillation (as in Technique 14, Figure 14.2B), and it would be impossible to obtain any fraction that consisted of pure benzene.

Suppose, however, that we are able to collect a small quantity of the first distillate that was 74 mole % benzene, and to redistill it. Using Figure 15.1, we can see that this liquid would begin to boil at about 84°C and would give an initial distillate containing 90 mole % benzene. If we were experimentally able to continue taking small fractions at the beginning of each distillation and redistill them, we would eventually reach a liquid with a composition of nearly 100 mole % benzene. However, because we only took a small amount of material at the beginning of each distillation, we would have lost most of the material we started with. To recapture a reasonable amount of benzene, we would have to process each of the fractions left behind in

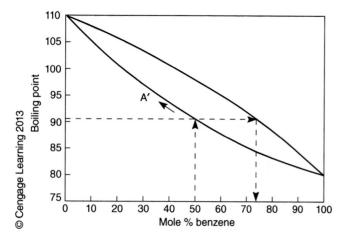

Figure 15.1
The vapor–liquid composition curve for mixtures of benzene and toluene.

326

the same way as our early fractions. As each of them was partially distilled, the material advanced would become progressively richer in benzene, whereas that left behind would become progressively richer in toluene. It would require thousands (maybe millions) of such microdistillations to separate benzene from toluene.

Obviously, the procedure just described would be very tedious; fortunately, it need not be performed in usual laboratory practice. **Fractional distillation** accomplishes the same result. You simply have to use a column inserted between the distillation flask and the receiver (Hickman head), as shown in Figure 15.2. This **fractionating column** is filled, or **packed,** with a suitable material such as a stainless steel sponge. This packing allows a mixture of benzene and toluene to be subjected continuously to many vaporization–condensation cycles as the material moves up the column. With each cycle within the column, the composition of the vapor is progressively enriched in the lower-boiling component (benzene). Nearly pure benzene (bp 80°C) finally emerges from the top of the column, condenses, and passes into the receiving head or flask. This process continues until all the benzene is removed. The distillation must be carried out slowly to ensure that numerous

© Cengage Learning 2013

Figure 15.2
Microscale apparatus for fractional distillation.

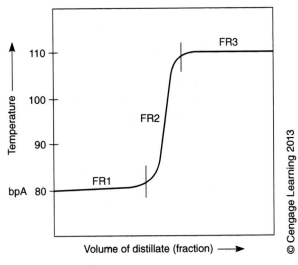

Figure 15.3
Temperature–distillate plot for fractional
distillation of a benzene–toluene mixture.

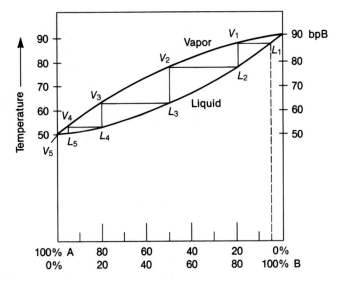

© Cengage Learning 2013

Figure 15.4
Phase diagram for a fractional distillation of an ideal
two-component system.

vaporization–condensation cycles occur. When nearly all the benzene has been removed, the temperature begins to rise, and a small amount of a second fraction,
which contains some benzene and toluene, may be collected. When the temperature reaches 110°C, the boiling point of pure toluene, the vapor is condensed and
collected as the third fraction. A plot of boiling point versus volume of condensate
(distillate) would resemble Figure 15.3. This separation would be much better than
that achieved by simple distillation (Figure 15.1).

**15.2 Vapor–Liquid
Composition
Diagrams**

A vapor–liquid composition-phase diagram like the one in Figure 15.4 can be used
to explain the operation of a fractionating column with an **ideal solution** of two
liquids, A and B. An ideal solution is one in which the two liquids are chemically
similar, miscible (mutually soluble) in all proportions, and do not interact. Ideal solutions obey **Raoult's Law.** Raoult's Law is explained in detail in Section 15.3.

The phase diagram relates the compositions of the boiling liquid (lower curve)
and its vapor (upper curve) as a function of temperature. Any horizontal line
drawn across the diagram (a constant-temperature line) intersects the diagram in
two places. These intersections relate the vapor composition to the composition
of the boiling liquid that produces that vapor. By convention, composition is expressed either in **mole fraction** or in **mole percentage.** The mole fraction is defined
as follows:

$$\text{Mole fraction A} = N_A = \frac{\text{moles A}}{\text{moles A} + \text{moles B}}$$

$$\text{Mole fraction B} = N_B = \frac{\text{moles B}}{\text{moles A} + \text{moles B}}$$

$$N_A + N_B = 1$$

$$\text{Mole percentage A} = N_A \times 100$$

$$\text{Mole percentage B} = N_B \times 100$$

The horizontal and vertical lines shown in Figure 15.4 represent the processes
that occur during a fractional distillation. Each of the **horizontal lines** (L_1V_1, L_2V_2,
etc.) represents the **vaporization** step of a given vaporization–condensation cycle

and represents the composition of the vapor in equilibrium with liquid at a given temperature. For example, at 63°C a liquid with a composition of 50% A (L_3 on the diagram) would yield vapor of composition 80% A (V_3 on diagram) at equilibrium. The vapor is richer in the lower-boiling component A than the original liquid was.

Each of the **vertical lines** (V_1L_2, V_2L_3, etc.) represents the **condensation** step of a given vaporization–condensation cycle. The composition does not change as the temperature drops on condensation. The vapor at V_3, for example, condenses to give a liquid (L_4 on the diagram) of composition 80% A with a drop in temperature from 63° to 53°C.

In the example shown in Figure 15.4, pure A boils at 50°C and pure B boils at 90°C. These two boiling points are represented at the left- and right hand edges of the diagram, respectively. Now consider a solution that contains only 5% of A but 95% of B. (Remember that these are *mole* percentages.) This solution is heated (following the dashed line) until it is observed to boil at L_1 (87°C). The resulting vapor has composition V_1 (20% A, 80% B). The vapor is richer in A than the original liquid, but it is by no means pure A. In a simple distillation apparatus, this vapor would be condensed and passed into the receiver in a very impure state. However, with a fractionating column in place, the vapor is condensed in the **column** to give liquid L_2 (20% A, 80% B). Liquid L_2 is immediately revaporized (bp 78°C) to give a vapor of composition V_2 (50% A, 50% B), which is condensed to give liquid L_3. Liquid L_3 is revaporized (bp 63°C) to give vapor of composition V_3 (80% A, 20% B), which is condensed to give liquid L_4. Liquid L_4 is revaporized (bp 53°C) to give a vapor of composition V_4 (95% A, 5% B). This process continues to V_5, which condenses to give nearly pure liquid A. The fractionating process follows the stepped lines in the figure downward and to the left.

As this process continues, all of liquid A is removed from the distillation flask or vial, leaving nearly pure B behind. If the temperature is raised, liquid B may be distilled as a nearly pure fraction. Fractional distillation will have achieved a separation of A and B, a separation that would have been nearly impossible with simple distillation. Notice that the boiling point of the liquid becomes lower each time it vaporizes. Because the temperature at the bottom of a column is normally higher than the temperature at the top, successive vaporizations occur higher and higher in the column as the composition of the distillate approaches that of pure A. This process is illustrated in Figure 15.5, where the composition of the liquids, their boiling points, and the composition of the vapors present are shown alongside the fractionating column.

Figure 15.5
Vaporization–condensation in a fractionation column.

$V_5 = 100\%$ A
$L_5 = 95\%$ A, bp 51°

$V_4 = 95\%$ A
$L_4 = 80\%$ A, bp 53°

$V_3 = 80\%$ A
$L_3 = 50\%$ A, bp 63°

$V_2 = 50\%$ A
$L_2 = 20\%$ A, bp 78°

$V_1 = 20\%$ A

$L_1 = 5\%$ A, bp 87°

© Cengage Learning 2013

15.3 Raoult's Law

Two liquids (A and B) that are miscible and that do not interact form an **ideal solution** and follow Raoult's Law. The law states that the partial vapor pressure of component A in the solution (P_A) equals the vapor pressure of pure A (P_A°) times its mole fraction (N_A) (Equation 1). A similar expression can be written for component B (Equation 2). The mole fractions N_A and N_B were defined in Section 15.2.

Partial vapor pressure of A in solution = $P_A = (P_A^\circ)(N_A)$ *[1]*

Partial vapor pressure of B in solution = $P_B = (P_B^\circ)(N_B)$ *[2]*

P_A° is the vapor pressure of pure A, independent of B. P_B° is the vapor pressure of B, independent of A. In a mixture of A and B, the partial vapor pressures are added to give the total vapor pressure above the solution (Equation 3). When the total pressure (sum of the partial pressures) equals the applied pressure, the solution boils.

$$P_{\text{total}} = P_A + P_B = P_A^{\circ}N_A + P_B^{\circ}N_B \qquad [3]$$

The composition of A and B in the vapor produced is given by Equations 4 and 5.

$$N_A(\text{vapor}) = \frac{P_A}{P_{\text{total}}} \qquad [4]$$

$$N_B(\text{vapor}) = \frac{P_B}{P_{\text{total}}} \qquad [5]$$

Several problems involving applications of Raoult's Law are illustrated in Figure 15.6. Note, particularly in the result from Equation 4, that the vapor is richer ($N_A = 0.67$) in the lower-boiling (higher vapor pressure) component A than it was before vaporization ($N_A = 0.50$). This proves mathematically what was described in Section 15.2.

The consequences of Raoult's Law for distillations are shown schematically in Figure 15.7. In Part A, the boiling points are identical (vapor pressures the same), and no separation is attained regardless of how the distillation is conducted. In Part B, a fractional distillation is required, whereas in Part C a simple distillation provides an adequate separation.

When a solid B (rather than another liquid) is dissolved in a liquid A, the boiling point is increased. In this extreme case, the vapor pressure of B is negligible, and the vapor will be pure A no matter how much solid B is added. Consider a solution of salt in water.

$$P_{\text{total}} = P_{\text{water}}^{\circ}N_{\text{water}} + P_{\text{salt}}^{\circ}N_{\text{salt}}$$

$$P_{\text{salt}}^{\circ} = 0$$

$$P_{\text{total}} = P_{\text{water}}^{\circ}N_{\text{water}}$$

A solution whose mole fraction of water is 0.7 will not boil at 100°C, because $P_{\text{total}} = (760)(0.7) = 532$ mm Hg and is less than atmospheric pressure. If the solution is heated to 110°C, it will boil because $P_{\text{total}} = (1085)(0.7) = 760$ mm Hg. Although the solution must be heated to 110°C to boil it, the vapor is pure water and has a boiling-point temperature of 100°C. (The vapor pressure of water at 110°C can be looked up in a handbook; it is 1085 mm Hg.)

Consider a solution at 100°C where $N_A = 0.5$ and $N_B = 0.5$.

1. What is the partial vapor pressure of A in the solution if the vapor pressure of pure A at 100°C is 1020 mm Hg?

   Answer: $P_A = P_A^{\circ}N_A = (1020)(0.5) = 510$ mm Hg

2. What is the partial vapor pressure of B in the solution if the vapor pressure of pure B at 100°C is 500 mm Hg?

   Answer: $P_B = P_B^{\circ}N_B = (500)(0.5) = 250$ mm Hg

3. Would the solution boil at 100°C if the applied pressure were 760 mm Hg?

   Answer: Yes. $P_{\text{total}} = P_A + P_B = (510 + 250) = 760$ mm Hg

4. What is the composition of the vapor at the boiling point?

   Answer: The boiling point is 100°C

   $$N_A(\text{vapor}) = \frac{P_A}{P_{\text{total}}} = 510/760 = 0.67$$

   $$N_B(\text{vapor}) = \frac{P_B}{P_{\text{total}}} = 250/760 = 0.33$$

Figure 15.6
Sample calculations with Raoult's Law.

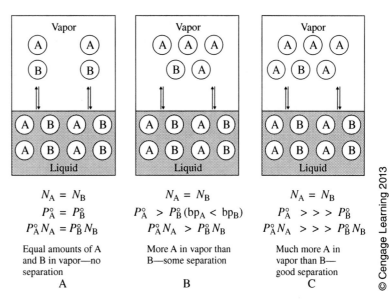

$$N_A = N_B$$
$$P_A^\circ = P_B^\circ$$
$$P_A^\circ N_A = P_B^\circ N_B$$

Equal amounts of A and B in vapor—no separation

A

$$N_A = N_B$$
$$P_A^\circ > P_B^\circ \, (bp_A < bp_B)$$
$$P_A^\circ N_A > P_B^\circ N_B$$

More A in vapor than B—some separation

B

$$N_A = N_B$$
$$P_A^\circ >>> P_B^\circ$$
$$P_A^\circ N_A >>> P_B^\circ N_B$$

Much more A in vapor than B— good separation

C

© Cengage Learning 2013

Figure 15.7
Consequences of Raoult's Law. (A) Boiling points (vapor pressures) are identical—no separation. (B) Boiling point somewhat lower for A than for B—requires fractional distillation. (C) Boiling point much lower for A than for B—simple distillation will suffice.

15.4 Column Efficiency

A common measure of the efficiency of a column is given by its number of **theoretical plates.** The number of theoretical plates in a column is related to the number of vaporization–condensation cycles that occur as a liquid mixture travels through it. Using the example mixture in Figure 15.4, if the first distillate (condensed vapor) had the composition at L_2 when starting with liquid of composition L_1, the column would be said to have *one theoretical plate.* This would correspond to a simple distillation, or one vaporization–condensation cycle. A column would have two theoretical plates if the first distillate had the composition at L_3. The two-theoretical-plate column essentially carries out "two simple distillations." According to Figure 15.4, *five theoretical plates* would be required to separate the mixture that started with composition L_1. Notice that this corresponds to the number of "steps" that need to be drawn in the figure to arrive at a composition of 100% A.

Most columns do not allow distillation in discrete steps, as indicated in Figure 15.4. Instead, the process is *continuous*, allowing the vapors to be continuously in contact with liquid of changing composition as they pass through the column. Any material can be used to pack the column as long as it can be wetted by the liquid and as long as it does not pack so tightly that vapor cannot pass.

The approximate relationship between the number of theoretical plates needed to separate an ideal two-component mixture and the difference in boiling points is given in Table 15.1. Notice that more theoretical plates are required as the boiling-point differences between the components decrease. For instance, a mixture of A (bp 130°C) and B (bp 166°C) with a boiling-point difference of 36°C would be expected to require a column with a minimum of five theoretical plates.

15.5 Types of Fractionating Columns and Packings

Several types of fractionating columns are shown in Figure 15.8. The Vigreux column, shown in Part A, has indentations that incline downward at angles of 45 degrees and are in pairs on opposite sides of the column. The projections into the column provide increased possibilities for condensation and for the vapor to

Table 15.1 Theoretical plates required to separate mixtures, based on boiling-point differences of components

Boiling-Point Difference	Number of Theoretical Plates
108	1
72	2
54	3
43	4
36	5
20	10
10	20
7	30
4	50
2	100

© Cengage Learning 2013

Packings

a
b
c
d

Small amount of
steel sponge if
needed

A Vigreux column

B Air condenser packed as a column
  a Glass tubing sections
  b Glass beads
  c Glass helices
  d Stainless steel sponge

© Cengage Learning 2013

Figure 15.8
Columns for fractional distillation.

equilibrate with the liquid. Vigreux columns are popular in cases where only a small number of theoretical plates are required. They are not very efficient (a 20-cm column might have only 2.5 theoretical plates), but they allow for rapid distillation and have a small **holdup** (the amount of liquid retained by the column). A column packed with a stainless steel sponge is a more effective fractionating column than a Vigreux column, but not by a large margin. Glass beads, or glass helices, can also be used as a packing material, and they have a slightly greater efficiency. The air condenser or the water condenser can be used as an improvised column if an actual fractionating column is unavailable. If a condenser is packed with glass beads, glass helices, or sections of glass tubing, the packing must be held in place by inserting a small plug of stainless steel sponge into the bottom of the condenser.

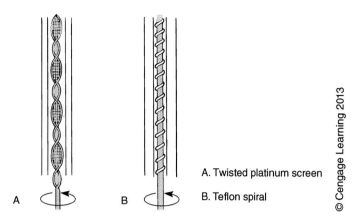

A. Twisted platinum screen

B. Teflon spiral

Figure 15.9
Bands for spinning-band columns.

Figure 15.10
A commercially available microscale spinning-band column.

The most effective type of column is the **spinning-band column.** In the most elegant form of this device, a tightly fitting, twisted platinum screen or a Teflon rod with helical threads is rotated rapidly inside the bore of the column (Figure 15.9). A spinning-band column that is available for microscale work is shown in Figure 15.10. This spinning-band column has a band about 2–3 cm in length and provides 4–5 theoretical plates. It can separate 1–2 mL of a mixture with a 30°C boiling-point difference. Larger research models of this spinning-band column can provide as many as 20 or 30 theoretical plates and can separate mixtures with a boiling-point difference of as little as 5–10°C.

Manufacturers of fractionating columns often offer them in a variety of lengths. Because the efficiency of a column is a function of its length, longer columns have more theoretical plates than shorter ones. It is common to express efficiency of a column in a unit called **HETP,** the **H**eight of a column that is **E**quivalent to one **T**heoretical **P**late. HETP is usually expressed in units of cm/plate. When the height of the column (in centimeters) is divided by this value, the total number of theoretical plates is specified.

15.6 Fractional Distillation: Methods and Practice

When a fractional distillation is performed, the column should be clamped in a vertical position. The distillation should be conducted as slowly as possible, but the rate of distillation should be steady enough to produce a constant temperature reading at the thermometer.

Many fractionating columns must be insulated so that temperature equilibrium is maintained at all times. Additional insulation will not be required for columns that have an evacuated outer jacket, but those that do not can benefit from being wrapped in insulation.

A microscale air condenser can be converted to a column by packing it with a piece of stainless steel sponge. The simplest form of insulation is Tygon tubing that has been split lengthwise. Select a piece with an inner diameter that just matches or is slightly smaller than the diameter of the fractionating column so that it will fit snugly.

> **CAUTION**
>
> **Cut the tubing to the correct length and then slit it with a sharp scissors. Do not use a razor blade or knife. Tygon tubing is difficult to cut; it is a nonslip substance and will "grab" even a single-edged razor blade in a way that can give you a nasty cut. See Experiment 6, page 52, for complete instructions.**

Glass wool and aluminum foil (shiny side in) are often used for insulation. You can wrap the column with glass wool and then use a wrapping of the aluminum foil to keep it in place. An especially effective method is to make an insulation blanket by placing a layer of glass wool or cotton between two rectangles of aluminum foil, placed shiny side in. The sandwich is bound together with duct tape. This blanket, which is reusable, can be wrapped around the column and held in place with twist ties or tape.

The **reflux ratio** is defined as the ratio of the number of drops of distillate that return to the distillation flask compared to the number of drops of distillate collected. In an efficient column, the reflux ratio should equal or exceed the number of theoretical plates. A high reflux ratio ensures that the column will achieve temperature equilibrium and achieve its maximum efficiency. This ratio is not easy to determine; in fact, it is impossible to determine when using a Hickman head, and it should not concern a beginning student. In some cases, the **throughput,** or **rate of takeoff,** of a column may be specified. This is expressed as the number of milliliters of distillate that can be collected per unit of time, usually as mL/min.

Microscale Apparatus. The apparatus shown in Figure 15.2 is the one you are most likely to use in the microscale laboratory. If your laboratory is one of the better-equipped ones, you may have access to spinning-band columns like those shown in Figure 15.10. The distillation temperature can be monitored most accurately by using a partial immersion mercury thermometer (see Technique 13, Section 13.3).

Macroscale Apparatus. Figure 15.11 illustrates a fractional distillation assembly that can be used for larger-scale distillations. It has a glass-jacketed column that is packed with a stainless steel sponge. This apparatus would be common in situations where quantities of liquid in excess of 10 mL were to be distilled.

Figure 15.11
Large-scale fractional distillation apparatus.

PART B. AZEOTROPES

15.7 Nonideal Solutions: Azeotropes

Some mixtures of liquids, because of attractions or repulsions between the molecules, do not behave ideally; they do not follow Raoult's Law. There are two types of vapor–liquid composition diagrams that result from this nonideal behavior: **minimum-boiling-point** and **maximum-boiling-point** diagrams. The minimum or maximum points in these diagrams correspond to a constant-boiling mixture called an **azeotrope.** An azeotrope is a mixture with a fixed composition that cannot be altered by either simple or fractional distillation. An azeotrope behaves as if it were a pure compound, and it distills from the beginning to the end of its distillation at a constant temperature, giving a distillate of constant (azeotropic) composition. The vapor in equilibrium with an azeotropic liquid has the same composition as the azeotrope. Because of this, an azeotrope is represented as a *point* on a vapor–liquid composition diagram.

A. Minimum-Boiling-Point Diagrams

A minimum-boiling-point azeotrope results from a slight incompatibility (repulsion) between the liquids being mixed. This incompatibility leads to a higher-than-expected combined vapor pressure from the solution. This higher combined vapor pressure brings about a lower boiling point for the mixture than is observed for the pure components. The most common two component mixture that gives a minimum-boiling-point azeotrope is the ethanol–water system shown in Figure 15.12. The azeotrope at V_3 has a composition of 96% ethanol–4% water and a boiling point of 78.1°C. This boiling point is not much lower than that of pure ethanol (78.3°C), but it means that it is impossible to obtain pure ethanol from the distillation of any ethanol–water mixture that contains more than 4% water. Even with the best fractionating column, you cannot obtain 100% ethanol. The remaining 4% of water can be removed by adding benzene and removing a different azeotrope, the ternary benzene–water–ethanol azeotrope (bp 65°C). Once the water is removed, the excess benzene is removed as an ethanol–benzene azeotrope (bp 68°C). The resulting material is free of water and is called "absolute" ethanol.

Figure 15.12
Ethanol–water minimum-boiling-point phase diagram.

The fractional distillation of an ethanol–water mixture of composition X can be described as follows. The mixture is heated (follow line XL_1) until it is observed to boil at L_1. The resulting vapor at V_1 will be richer in the lower-boiling component, ethanol, than the original mixture.[1] The condensate at L_2 is vaporized to give V_2. The process continues, following the lines to the right, until the azeotrope is obtained at V_3. The liquid that distills is not pure ethanol, but it has the azeotropic composition of 96% ethanol and 4% water, and it distills at 78.1°C. The azeotrope, which is richer in ethanol than the original mixture, continues to distill. As it distills, the percentage of water left behind in the distillation flask continues to increase. When all the ethanol has been distilled (as the azeotrope), pure water remains behind in the distillation flask, and it distills at 100°C.

If the azeotrope obtained by the preceding procedure is redistilled, it distills from the beginning to the end of the distillation at a constant temperature of 78.1°C as if it were a pure substance. There is no change in the composition of the vapor during the distillation.

Some common minimum-boiling azeotropes are given in Table 15.2. Numerous other azeotropes are formed in two- and three-component systems; such azeotropes are common. Water forms azeotropes with many substances; therefore, water must be carefully removed with **drying agents** whenever possible before compounds are distilled. Extensive azeotropic data are available in references such as the *Handbook of Chemistry and Physics.*[2]

Note that azeotropic combinations with water should be miscible or at least have a high degree of mutual solubility. If the water does not dissolve in the other component, or has low solubility, then the process becomes a steam distillation (see Technique 18).

B. Maximum-Boiling-Point Diagrams

A maximum-boiling-point azeotrope results from a slight attraction between the component molecules. This attraction leads to lower combined vapor pressure than

Table 15.2 Common minimum-boiling-point azeotropes

Azeotrope	Composition (Weight Percentage)	Boiling Poin (°C)
Ethanol–water	95.6% C_2H_5OH, 4.4% H_2O	78.17
Benzene–water	91.1% C_6H_6, 8.9% H_2O	69.4
Benzene–water–ethanol	74.1% C_6H_6, 7.4% H_2O, 18.5% C_2H_5OH	64.9
Methanol–carbon tetrachloride	20.6% CH_3OH, 79.4% CCl_4	55.7
Ethanol–benzene	32.4% C_2H_5OH, 67.6% C_6H_6	67.8
Methanol–toluene	72.4% CH_3OH, 27.6% $C_6H_5CH_3$	63.7
Methanol–benzene	39.5% CH_3OH, 60.5% C_6H_6	58.3
Cyclohexane–ethanol	69.5% C_6H_{12}, 30.5% C_2H_5OH	64.9
2-Propanol–water	87.8% $(CH_3)_2CHOH$, 12.2% H_2O	80.4
Butyl acetate–water	72.9% $CH_3COOC_4H_9$, 27.1% H_2O	90.7
Phenol–water	9.2% C_6H_5OH, 90.8% H_2O	99.5

© Cengage Learning 2013

[1] Keep in mind that this distillate is not pure ethanol but is an ethanol–water mixture.

[2] More examples of azeotropes, with their compositions and boiling points, can be found in the *CRC Handbook of Chemistry and Physics;* also in L. H. Horsley, ed., *Advances in Chemistry Series*, no. 116. Azeotropic Data, III (Washington, DC: American Chemical Society, 1973).

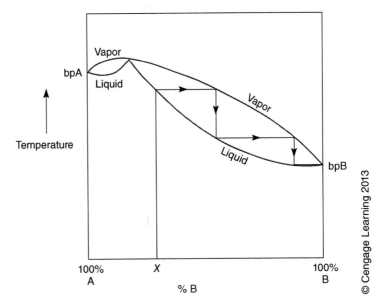

Figure 15.13
A maximum-boiling-point phase diagram.

Table 15.3 Maximum-boiling-point azeotropes

Azeotrope	Composition (Weight Percentage)	Boiling Point (°C)
Acetone–chloroform	20.0% CH_3COCH_3, 80.0% $CHCl_3$	64.7
Chloroform–methyl ethyl ketone	17.0% $CHCl_3$, 83.0% $CH_3COCH_2CH_3$	79.9
Hydrochloric acid	20.2% HCl, 79.8% H_2O	108.6
Acetic acid–dioxane	77.0% CH_3COCH, 23.0% $C_4H_8O_2$	119.5
Benzaldehyde–phenol	49.0% C_6H_5CHO, 51.0% C_6H_5OH	185.6

expected in the solution. The lower combined vapor pressures cause a higher boiling point than would be characteristic for the components. A two-component maximum-boiling-point azeotrope is illustrated in Figure 15.13. Because the azeotrope has a higher boiling point than any of the components, it will be concentrated in the distillation flask as the distillate (pure B) is removed. The distillation of a solution of composition X would follow to the right along the lines in Figure 15.13. Once the composition of the material remaining in the flask has reached that of the azeotrope, the temperature will rise, and the azeotrope will begin to distill. The azeotrope will continue to distill until all the material in the distillation flask has been exhausted.

Some maximum-boiling-point azeotropes are listed in Table 15.3. They are not nearly as common as minimum-boiling-point azeotropes.

C. Generalizations

There are some generalizations that can be made about azeotropic behavior. They are presented here without explanation, but you should be able to verify them by thinking through each case using the phase diagrams given. (Note that pure A is always to the left of the azeotrope in these diagrams, whereas pure B is to the right of the azeotrope.)

Minimum-boiling-point azeotropes

Initial Composition	Experimental Result
To left of azeotrope	Azeotrope distills first, pure A second
Azeotrope	Not separable
To right of azeotrope	Azeotrope distills first, pure B second

Maximum-boiling-point azeotropes

Initial Composition	Experimental Result
To left of azeotrope	Pure A distills first, azeotrope second
Azeotrope	Not separable
To right of azeotrope	Pure B distills first, azeotrope second

15.8 Azeotropic Distillation: Applications

There are many examples of chemical reactions in which the amount of product is low because of an unfavorable equilibrium. An example is the direct acid-catalyzed esterification of a carboxylic acid with an alcohol:

$$R-\overset{\overset{\displaystyle O}{\|}}{C}-OH + R-O-H \underset{}{\overset{H^+}{\rightleftharpoons}} R-\overset{\overset{\displaystyle O}{\|}}{C}-OR + H_2O$$

Because the equilibrium does not favor formation of the ester, it must be shifted to the right, in favor of the product, by using an excess of one of the starting materials. In most cases, the alcohol is the least expensive reagent and is the material used in excess. Isopentyl acetate (Experiment 13) and methyl salicylate (Experiment 46) are examples of esters prepared by using one of the starting materials in excess.

Another way of shifting the equilibrium to the right is to remove one of the products from the reaction mixture as it is formed. In the preceding example, water can be removed as it is formed by **azeotropic distillation.** A common large-scale method is to use the Dean–Stark water separator shown in Figure 15.14A. In this technique, an inert solvent, commonly benzene or toluene, is added to the reaction mixture contained in the round-bottom flask. The side arm of the water separator is also filled with this solvent. If benzene is used, as the mixture is heated under reflux, the benzene–water azeotrope (bp 69.4°C, Table 15.3) distills out of the flask.[3] When the vapor condenses, it enters the side arm directly below the condenser, and water separates from the benzene–water condensate; benzene and water mix as vapors, but they are not miscible as cooled liquids. Once the water (lower phase) separates from the benzene (upper phase), liquid benzene overflows from the side arm back into the flask. The cycle is repeated continuously until no more water forms in the side arm. You may calculate the weight of water that should theoretically be produced and compare this value with the amount of water collected in the side arm. Because the density of water is 1.0, the volume of water collected can be compared directly with the calculated amount, assuming 100% yield.

---

[3] Actually, with ethanol, a lower-boiling-point three-component azeotrope distills at 64.9°C (see Table 15.3). It consists of benzene–water–ethanol. Because some ethanol is lost in the azeotropic distillation, a large excess of ethanol is used in esterification reactions. The excess also helps shift the equilibrium to the right.

A. Dean–Stark trap
B. Improvised water separator

Figure 15.14
Large-scale water separators.

An improvised water separator, constructed from the components found in the traditional organic kit, is shown in Figure 15.14B. Although this requires the condenser to be placed in a nonvertical position, it works quite well.

At the microscale level, water separation can be achieved using a standard distillation assembly with a water condenser and a Hickman head (Figure 15.15). The side-ported variation of the Hickman head is the most convenient one to use for this purpose, but it is not essential. In this variation, you simply remove all the distillate (both solvent and water) several times during the course of the reaction. Use a Pasteur pipette to remove the distillate, as shown in Technique 14, Figure 14.6 Because both the solvent and water are removed in this procedure, it may be desirable to add more solvent from time to time, adding it through the condenser with a Pasteur pipette.

The most important consideration in using azeotropic distillation to prepare an ester (described above) is that the azeotrope containing water must have a **lower boiling point** than the alcohol used. With ethanol, the benzene–water azeotrope boils at a much lower temperature (69.4°C) than ethanol (78.3°C), and the technique previously described works well. With higher-boiling-point alcohols, azeotropic distillation works well because of the large boiling-point difference between the azeotrope and the alcohol.

With methanol (bp 65°C), however, the boiling point of the benzene–water azeotrope is actually *higher* by about 5°C, and methanol distills first. Thus, in esterifications involving methanol, a totally different approach must be taken. For example, you can mix the carboxylic acid, methanol, the acid catalyst, and 1,2-dichloroethane in a conventional reflux apparatus (Technique 7, Figure 7.6) without a water separator. During the reaction, water separates from the 1,2-dichloroethane because it is not

Solvent + water

Figure 15.15
Microscale water separator (both layers are removed).

© Cengage Learning 2013

miscible; however, the remainder of the components are soluble, so the reaction can continue. The equilibrium is shifted to the right by the "removal" of water from the reaction mixture.

Azeotropic distillation is also used in other types of reactions, such as ketal or acetal formation, and in enamine formation. The use of azeotropic distillation is illustrated in the formation of 2-acetylcyclohexanone (Experiment 43) via the enamine intermediate. Toluene is used in the azeotropic distillation of water. The Hickman head is used as a water separator.

Acetal formation

$$R-\overset{\overset{\text{O}}{\|}}{C}-H + 2\ ROH \underset{}{\overset{H^+}{\rightleftharpoons}} R-\underset{\underset{\text{OR}}{|}}{\overset{\overset{\text{OR}}{|}}{C}}-H + H_2O$$

Enamine formation

$$RCH_2-\underset{\underset{\text{O}}{\|}}{C}-CH_2R + \underset{\underset{\text{H}}{|}}{\overset{}{N}} \overset{H^+}{\rightleftharpoons} RCH=\underset{|}{C}-CH_2R + H_2O$$

© Cengage Learning 2013

PROBLEMS

1. In the accompanying chart are approximate vapor pressures for benzene and toluene at various temperatures.

Temp (°C)	*mm Hg*	*Temp (°C)*	*mm Hg*
Benzene 30	120	Toluene 30	37
40	180	40	60
50	270	50	95
60	390	60	140
70	550	70	200
80	760	80	290
90	1010	90	405
100	1340	100	560
		110	760

  a. What is the mole fraction of each component if 3.9 g of benzene C_6H_6 is dissolved in 4.6 g of toluene C_7H_8?

  b. Assuming that this mixture is ideal—that is, it follows Raoult's Law—what is the partial vapor pressure of benzene in this mixture at 50°C?

  c. Estimate to the nearest degree the temperature at which the vapor pressure of the solution equals 1 atm (bp of the solution).

  d. Calculate the composition of the vapor (mole fraction of each component) that is in equilibrium in the solution at the boiling point of this solution.

  e. Calculate the composition in weight percentage of the vapor that is in equilibrium with the solution.

2. Estimate how many theoretical plates are needed to separate a mixture that has a mole fraction of B equal to 0.70 (70% B) in Figure 15.4.

3. Two moles of sucrose are dissolved in 8 moles of water. Assume that the solution follows Raoult's Law and that the vapor pressure of sucrose is negligible. The boiling point of water is 100°C. The distillation is carried out at 1 atm (760 mm Hg).

  a. Calculate the vapor pressure of the solution when the temperature reaches 100°C.

  b. What temperature would be observed during the entire distillation?

  c. What would be the composition of the distillate?

  d. If a thermometer were immersed below the surface of the liquid of the boiling flask, what temperature would be observed?

4. Explain why the boiling point of a two-component mixture rises slowly throughout a simple distillation when the boiling-point differences are not large.

5. Given the boiling points of several known mixtures of A and B (mole fractions are known) and the vapor pressures of A and B in the pure state (P_A° and P_B°) at these same temperatures, how would you construct a boiling-point-composition phase diagram for A and B? Give a stepwise explanation.

6. Describe the behavior on distillation of a 98% ethanol solution through an efficient column. Refer to Figure 15.12.

7. Construct an approximate boiling-point-composition diagram for a benzene–methanol system. The mixture shows azeotropic behavior (see Table 15.3). Include on the graph the boiling points of pure benzene and pure methanol and the boiling point of the azeotrope. Describe the behavior on distillation of a mixture that is initially rich in benzene (90%) and then for a mixture that is initially rich in methanol (90%).

8. Construct an approximate boiling-point-composition diagram for an acetone–chloroform system, which forms a maximum boiling azeotrope (Table 15.4). Describe the behavior on distillation of a mixture that is initially rich in acetone (90%), and then describe the behavior of a mixture that is initially rich in chloroform (90%).

9. Two compounds have boiling points of 130 and 150°C. Estimate the number of theoretical plates needed to separate these substances in a fractional distillation.

10. A spinning-band column has an HETP of 0.25 in./plate. If the column has 12 theoretical plates, how long is it?

Vacuum Distillation, Manometers

Vacuum distillation (distillation at reduced pressure) is used for compounds that have high boiling points (above 200°C). Such compounds often undergo thermal decomposition at the temperatures required for their distillation at atmospheric pressure. The boiling point of a compound is lowered substantially by reducing the applied pressure. Vacuum distillation is also used for compounds that, when heated, might react with the oxygen present in air. It is also used when it is more convenient to distill at a lower temperature because of experimental limitations. For instance, a heating device may have difficulty heating to a temperature in excess of 250°C.

The effect of pressure on the boiling point is discussed more thoroughly in Technique 13, Section 13.1. A nomograph is given (Figure 13.2) that allows you to estimate the boiling point of a liquid at a pressure different from the one at which it is reported. For example, a liquid reported to boil at 200°C at 760 mm Hg would be expected to boil at 90°C at 20 mm Hg. This is a significant decrease in temperature, and it would be advantageous to use a vacuum distillation if any problems were to be expected. Counterbalancing this advantage, however, is the fact that separations of liquids of different boiling points may not be as effective with a vacuum distillation as with a simple distillation.

16.1 Microscale Methods

When working with glassware that is to be evacuated, you should wear safety glasses at all times. There is always danger of an implosion.

CAUTION

Safety glasses must be worn at all times during vacuum distillation.

It is a good idea to work in a hood when performing a vacuum distillation. If the experiment will involve high temperatures (> 220°C) for distillation or an extremely low pressure (< 0.1 mm Hg), for your own safety you should definitely work in a hood, behind a shield.

A basic apparatus similar to the one shown in Figure 16.1 may be used for microscale vacuum distillations. As is the case for simple distillation, this apparatus uses the Hickman head as a means to reduce the length of the vapor path. The major difference to be found when comparing this assembly to one for simple distillation (Technique 14, Figure 14.8) is that the opening to the atmosphere has been replaced by a connection to a vacuum source (top right-hand side). The usual sources of vacuum are the aspirator (Technique 8, Section 8.5), a mechanical vacuum pump, or a "house" vacuum line (one piped directly to the laboratory bench). The aspirator is probably the simplest of these sources and the vacuum source most likely to be available. However, if pressures below 10–20 mm Hg are required, a vacuum pump must be used.

Figure 16.1
Reduced-pressure microscale distillation (internal monitoring of temperature).

Assembling the Apparatus. When assembling an apparatus for vacuum distillation, it is important that all joints and connections be airtight. The joints in the newest microscale kits are standard-taper ground-glass joints, with a compression cap that contains an O-ring seal. Glassware that contains this type of compression joint will hold a vacuum quite easily. Under normal conditions, it is not necessary to grease these joints.

NOTE: Normally, you should not grease joints. It is necessary to grease the joints in a vacuum distillation only if you cannot achieve the desired pressure without using grease.

If you must grease joints, take care not to use too much grease. You are working with small quantities of liquid in a microscale distillation, and the grease can become a very serious contaminant if it oozes out the bottom of the joints into your system. Apply a small amount of grease (thin film) completely around the top of the *inner* joint; then mate the joints and turn them slightly to spread the grease evenly. If you have used the correct amount of grease, it will not ooze out the bottom; rather, the entire joint will appear clear and without striations or uncovered areas.

Make doubly sure that any connections to pressure tubing are tight. The pressure tubing itself should be relatively new and without cracks. If the tubing shows cracks when you stretch or bend it, it may be old and leak air into the system. Glass

A Thermometer adapters

A Regular thin-walled tubing

B Vacuum tubing

Figure 16.3
Comparison of tubing.

B Rubber stopper and glass tubing

Figure 16.2
Alternative vacuum connections.

tubing should fit securely into any rubber stoppers. If you can move the tubing up and down with only gentle force, it is too loose, and you should obtain a larger size. Check all glassware to be sure there are no cracks and that there are no chips in the standard-taper joints. Cracked glassware may break when evacuated.

Connecting to Vacuum. In Figure 16.1, the connection to vacuum has been made using a multipurpose adapter (see Technique 14, Figure 14.9B). If a multipurpose adapter is not available, an alternative method uses a Claisen head and two thermometer adapters (Figure. 16.2). If two thermometer adapters are not available, a #0 rubber stopper fitted with glass tubing can be used.

Whichever is used, the connection to the vacuum source is made using **pressure tubing.** Pressure tubing (also called vacuum tubing), unlike the more common thin-walled tubing used to carry water or gas, has heavy walls that will not collapse inward when it is evacuated. Compare the two types of tubing shown in Figure 16.3.

Water Trap. If an aspirator is used as a source of vacuum, a water trap must be placed between it and the distillation assembly. A commonly used type of water trap is shown at the bottom right of Figure 16.1. Variations in water pressure are to be expected when using an aspirator. If the pressure drops low enough, the vacuum in the system will draw water from the aspirator into the connecting line. The trap allows you to see this happening and take corrective action (prevent water from entering the distillation apparatus). The correct action for anything but a small amount of water is to "vent the system." This can be accomplished by opening the screw clamp at the top of the trap to let air into the system. When performing a vacuum distillation, you should also realize that the system should always be vented before stopping the aspirator. If you turn off the aspirator while the system is still under vacuum, water will be drawn into the connecting line and trap.

Manometer Connection. A Y-tube is shown in the line from the apparatus to the trap. This branching connection is optional but is required if you wish to monitor

To trap and vacuum source (See Figure 16.1)

© Cengage Learning 2013

Figure 16.4
Use of ebulliator tube instead of thermometer.

the actual pressure of the system using a manometer. The operation of manometers is discussed in Sections 16.7 and 16.8.

Thermometer Placement. If a thermometer is used, be sure that the bulb is placed in the stem of the Hickman head just below the well. If it is placed higher, it may not be surrounded by a constant stream of vapor from the material being distilled. If the thermometer is not exposed to a continuous stream of vapor, it may not reach temperature equilibrium. As a result, the temperature reading would be incorrect (low).

Preventing Bumpover. When a distillation flask is heated, there is always the possibility that the boiling action will become too vigorous (mainly due to superheating) and "bump" some of the undistilled liquid up into the Hickman head. The simplest way to prevent bumping is to stir the boiling liquid with a magnetic spin vane. Stirring rapidly will distribute the heat evenly, keep the boiling action smooth, and prevent bumping. Boiling stones cannot be used for this purpose in a vacuum distillation; they do not work in vacuum. In a conventional vacuum distillation (macroscale), it is customary to maintain smooth boiling action by using an **ebulliator tube.** The ebulliator tube agitates the boiling solution by providing a small, continuous stream of air bubbles. Figure 16.4 shows how a microscale vacuum distillation may be modified to use an ebulliator tube. The amount of air (rate of bubbles) provided by the ebulliator is adjusted by either tightening or loosening the screw clamp at the top. A Pasteur pipette makes an excellent ebulliator tube. As Figure 16.4 shows, the ebulliator tube replaces the thermometer. Hence, the ebulliator should be used only when internal monitoring of temperature is not required. In practice, although this method works satisfactorily, better results are obtained by stirring and distilling slowly.

NOTE: Heating slowly helps to avoid bumping.

16.2 Semi-microscale and Macroscale Equipment

A vacuum distillation apparatus using the components of the traditional organic laboratory kit is shown in Figure 16.5. It uses the ebulliator tube, the Claisen head, and a thermometer for internal temperature monitoring. A water condenser is shown, but with high-boiling liquids, this apparatus may be simplified by removing the water condenser. A special vacuum adapter allows connection to the manometer and vacuum source.

The Claisen head is used in larger-scale vacuum distillations because it allows the use of an ebulliator tube. The bend it provides in the distilling path helps to prevent bumpover. Because the Claisen head increases the holdup of the system, it cannot be used with very-small-scale distillations (<10 mL).

16.3 Stepwise Instructions for Microscale Vacuum Distillations

The following set of instructions is a step-by-step account of how to carry out a vacuum distillation. The microscale apparatus illustrated in Figure 16.1 will be used; however, the procedures apply to any vacuum distillation.

CAUTION

Safety glasses must be worn at all times during vacuum distillation.

Figure 16.5
Macroscale vacuum distillation using the standard organic laboratory kit.

A. Evacuating the Apparatus

1. Assemble the apparatus as shown in Figure 16.1. It should be held with a clamp attached to the top of the Hickman head and placed *above* the aluminum block.

NOTE: If you expect the temperature of the distillation to rise above 150°C, omit the threaded cap and O-ring between the conical vial and Hickman head. They will melt at high temperature.

---

2. If the sample contains solvent, concentrate the sample to be distilled in the conical vial (or round-bottom flask) that you are using. Use one of the solvent-removal methods discussed in Technique 7. If you have a large volume of solvent to evaporate and the sample does not fit in the conical vial, you must use an Erlenmeyer flask first and then transfer the sample to the conical vial. (Be sure to rinse the Erlenmeyer flask with a little solvent and then reevaporate in the conical vial.) As a rule, the distillation vial or flask should be no more than two-thirds full.

3. Attach the conical vial (or flask) to the apparatus and make sure all joints are sealed.

4. Turn the aspirator on to the maximum extent.

5. Close the screw clamp on the water trap very tightly. (If you are using an ebulliator tube as in Figure 16.4, you next regulate the rate of bubbling by adjusting the tightness of the screw clamp at the top of the tube.)

6. Using the manometer, observe the pressure. It may take a few minutes to remove any residual solvent and evacuate the system. If the pressure is not satisfactory, check all connections to see whether they are tight. (Readjust the ebulliator tube if necessary.)

NOTE: Do not proceed until you have a good vacuum.

B. Beginning Distillation

7. Lower the apparatus into the aluminum block and begin to heat. Place the external thermometer in the block now if you wish.

C A U T I O N

You should not use a *mercury* thermometer with an aluminum block. If it breaks, the mercury will vaporize on the hot surface. Instead, use a nonmercury glass thermometer, a metal dial thermometer, or a digital electronic temperature-measuring device.

---

8. Increase the temperature of the heat source until you begin to see distillate collect in the well of the Hickman head. (Observe very carefully; liquid may appear almost "magically" without any sign of boiling or any obvious reflux ring.)

9. If you are using a thermometer, record the temperature and pressure when distillate begins to appear. (If you are not using an internal thermometer, record the external temperature. If you have two thermometers, record both temperatures.)

C. Collecting a Fraction

10. To collect a fraction, raise the apparatus above the aluminum block and allow it to cool a bit before opening it.

11. Open the screw clamp on the water trap to allow air to enter the system. (If you are using an ebulliator tube, you also need to open the screw clamp at its *top immediately*, or the liquid in the distillation flask will be forced upward into it.)

12. Partially disassemble the apparatus and remove the fraction with a Pasteur pipette, as shown in Technique 14, Figure 14.6A. (If you have a Hickman head with a side port, you may simply open the side port to remove the fraction. This is shown in Figure 14.6C.)

NOTE: If you do not intend to collect a second fraction, go directly to steps 18–20.

---

13. Reassemble the apparatus (or close the side port) and tighten the clamp at the top of the ebulliator tube.

14. Tighten the screw clamp on the water trap and reestablish the desired pressure. If the pressure is not satisfactory, check all connections to make sure they are sealed.

15. Lower the apparatus back into the aluminum block and continue the distillation.

D. Shutdown

16. At the end of the distillation, raise the apparatus from the aluminum block and allow it to cool. Also let the aluminum block cool.

17. Open the screw clamp on the water trap first, and then immediately open the one at the top of the ebulliator tube.

18. Turn off the water at the aspirator. (Do not do this before step 17!)

19. Remove any distilled material by one of the methods shown in Figure 14.6.

20. Disassemble the apparatus and clean all glassware as soon as possible to prevent the joints from sticking.

NOTE: If you used grease, thoroughly clean all grease off the joints, or it will contaminate your samples in other procedures.

16.4 Rotary Fraction Collectors

With the types of apparatus we have discussed previously, the vacuum must be stopped to remove fractions when a new substance (fraction) begins to distill. Quite a few steps are required to perform this change, and it is quite inconvenient when there are several fractions to be collected. Two pieces of semimicroscale apparatus that are designed to alleviate the difficulty of collecting fractions while working under vacuum are shown in Figure 16.6. The collector, which is shown to the right, is sometimes called a "cow" because of its appearance. With these rotary fraction collecting devices, all you need to do is rotate the device to collect fractions.

16.5 Bulb-to-Bulb Distillation

The ultimate in microscale methods is to use a bulb-to-bulb distillation apparatus. This apparatus is shown in Figure 16.7. The sample to be distilled is placed in the

© Cengage Learning 2013

Figure 16.6
Rotary fraction collector.

Figure 16.7
Bulb-to-bulb distillation.

glass container attached to one of the arms of the apparatus. The sample is frozen solid, usually by using liquid nitrogen, but dry ice in 2-propanol or an ice–salt–water mixture may also be used. The coolant container shown in the figure is a **Dewar flask.** The Dewar flask has a double wall with the space between the walls evacuated and sealed. A vacuum is a very good thermal insulator, and there is little heat loss from the cooling solution.

After the sample is frozen, the entire apparatus is evacuated by opening the stopcock. When the evacuation is complete, the stopcock is closed, and the Dewar flask is removed. The sample is allowed to thaw, and then it is frozen again. This freeze–thaw–freeze cycle removes any air or gases that were trapped in the frozen sample. Next, the stopcock is opened to evacuate the system again. When the second evacuation is complete, the stopcock is closed, and the Dewar flask is moved to the other arm to cool the empty container. As the sample warms, it will vaporize, travel to the other side, and be frozen or liquefied by the cooling solution. This transfer of the liquid from one arm to the other may take quite a while, but no heating is required.

The bulb-to-bulb distillation is most effective when liquid nitrogen is used as coolant and when the vacuum system can achieve a pressure of 10^{-3} mm Hg or lower. This requires a vacuum pump; an aspirator cannot be used.

16.6 The Mechanical Vacuum Pump

The aspirator is not capable of yielding pressures below about 5 mm Hg. This is the vapor pressure of water at 0°C, and water freezes at this temperature. A more realistic value of pressure for an aspirator is about 20 mm Hg. When pressures below 20 mm Hg are required, a vacuum pump will have to be employed. Figure 16.8 illustrates a mechanical vacuum pump and its associated glassware. The vacuum pump operates on a principle similar to that of the aspirator, but the vacuum pump uses a high-boiling oil, rather than water, to remove air from the attached system. The oil used in a vacuum pump, a silicone oil or a high-molecular-weight hydrocarbon-based oil, has

Figure 16.8
A vacuum pump and its trap.

a very low vapor pressure, and very low system pressures can be achieved. A good vacuum pump, with new oil, can achieve pressures of 10^{-3} or 10^{-4} mm Hg. Instead of the oil being discarded as it is used, it is recycled continuously through the system.

A cooled trap is required when using a vacuum pump. This trap protects the oil in the pump from any vapors that may be present in the system. If vapors from organic solvents, or from the organic compounds being distilled, dissolve in the oil, the vapor pressure of the oil will increase, rendering it less effective. A special type of vacuum trap is illustrated in Figure 16.8. It is designed to fit into an insulated Dewar flask so that the coolant will last for a long period. At a minimum, this flask should be filled with ice water, but a dry ice–acetone mixture or liquid nitrogen is required to achieve lower temperatures and better protect the oil. Often, two traps are used; the first trap contains ice water and the second trap dry ice–acetone or liquid nitrogen. The first trap liquefies low-boiling vapors that might freeze or solidify in the second trap and block it.

16.7 The Closed-End Manometer

The principal device used to measure pressures in a vacuum distillation is the **closed-end manometer.** Two basic types are shown in Figures 16.9 and 16.10. The manometer shown in Figure 16.9 is widely used because it is relatively easy to construct. It consists of a U-tube that is closed at one end and mounted on a wooden support. You can construct the manometer from 9-mm glass capillary tubing and fill it, as shown in Figure 16.11.

CAUTION

Mercury is a very toxic metal with cumulative effects. Because mercury has a high vapor pressure, it must not be spilled in the laboratory. You must not touch it. Seek immediate help from an instructor in case of a spill or if you break a manometer. Spills must be cleaned immediately.

A small filling device is connected to the U-tube with pressure tubing. The U-tube is evacuated with a good vacuum pump; then the mercury is introduced by tilting the mercury reservoir.

Figure 16.9
A simple U-tube manometer.

Figure 16.11
Filling a U-tube manometer.

Figure 16.10
Commercial "stick" manometer.

NOTE: The entire filling operation should be conducted in a shallow pan in order to contain any spills that might occur.

Enough mercury should be added to form a column about 20 cm in total length. When the vacuum is interrupted by admitting air, the mercury is forced by atmospheric pressure to the end of the evacuated tube. The manometer is then ready for use. The constriction shown in Figure 16.11 helps to protect the manometer against breakage when the pressure is released. Be sure that the column of mercury is long enough to pass through this constriction.

When an aspirator or any other vacuum source is used, a manometer can be connected into the system. As the pressure is lowered, the mercury rises in the right tube and drops in the left tube until Δh corresponds to the approximate pressure of the system (see Figure 16.9).

$$\Delta h = (P_{\text{system}} - P_{\text{reference arm}}) = (P_{\text{system}} - 10^{-3}\text{mm Hg}) \approx P_{\text{system}}$$

A short piece of metric ruler or a piece of graph paper ruled in millimeter squares is mounted on the support board to allow Δh to be read. No addition or subtraction is necessary, because the reference pressure (created by the initial evacuation when filling) is approximately zero (10^{-3} mm Hg) when referred to readings in the 10- to 50-mm Hg range. To determine the pressure, count the number of millimeter squares beginning at the top of the mercury column on the left and continuing downward to the top of the mercury column on the right. This is the height difference Δh, and it gives the pressure in the system directly.

A commercial counterpart to the U-tube manometer is shown in Figure 16.10. With this manometer, the pressure is given by the difference in the mercury levels in the inner and outer tubes.

The manometers described here have a range of about 1–150 mm Hg in pressure. They are convenient to use when an aspirator is the source of vacuum. For high-vacuum systems (pressures below 1 mm Hg), a more elaborate manometer or an electronic measuring device must be used. These devices will not be discussed here.

16.8 Connecting and Using a Manometer

The most common use of a closed-end manometer is to monitor pressure during a reduced-pressure distillation. The manometer is placed in a vacuum distillation system, as shown in Figure 16.12. Generally, an aspirator is the source of vacuum. Both the manometer and the distillation apparatus should be protected by a trap from possible backups in the water line. Alternatives to the trap arrangements shown in Figure 16.12 appear in Figure 16.1. Notice in each case that the trap has a device (screw clamp or stopcock) for opening the system to the atmosphere. This is especially important in using a manometer because you should always make pressure changes slowly. If this is not done, there is a danger of spraying mercury throughout the system, breaking the manometer, or spurting mercury into the room. In the closed-end manometer, if the system is opened suddenly, the mercury rushes to the closed end of the U-tube. The mercury rushes with such speed and force that the end will be broken out of the manometer. Air should be admitted *slowly* by opening the valve cautiously. In a similar fashion, the valve should be closed slowly when the vacuum is being started, or mercury may be forcefully drawn into the system through the open end of the manometer.

If the pressure in a reduced-pressure distillation is lower than that desired, it is possible to adjust it by means of a **bleed valve.** The stopcock can serve this function in Figure 16.12 if it is opened only a small amount. In those systems with a screw clamp on the trap (Figure 16.1), remove the screw clamp from the trap valve and

Figure 16.12
Connecting a manometer to the system. To construct a "bleed," the needle valve may replace the stopcock.

attach the base of a Tirrill-style Bunsen burner. The needle valve in the base of the burner can be used to adjust precisely the amount of air that is admitted (bled) to the system and hence control the pressure.

PROBLEMS

1. Give some reasons that would lead you to purify a liquid by using vacuum distillation rather than by using simple distillation.

2. When using an aspirator as a source of vacuum in a vacuum distillation, do you turn off the aspirator before venting the system? Explain.

3. A compound was distilled at atmospheric pressure and had a boiling range of 310–325°C. What would be the approximate boiling range of this liquid if it were distilled under vacuum at 20 mm Hg?

4. Boiling stones generally do not work when a vacuum distillation is performed. What substitutes may be used?

5. What is the purpose of the trap that is used during a vacuum distillation performed with an aspirator?

Sublimation

In Technique 13, the influence of temperature on the change in vapor pressure of a liquid was considered (see Figure 13.1). It was shown that the vapor pressure of a liquid increases with temperature. Because the boiling point of a liquid occurs when its vapor pressure is equal to the applied pressure (normally atmospheric pressure), the vapor pressure of a liquid equals 760 mm Hg at its boiling point. The vapor pressure of a solid also varies with temperature. Because of this behavior, some solids can pass directly into the vapor phase without going through a liquid phase. This process is called **sublimation.** Because the vapor can be resolidified, the overall vaporization–solidification cycle can be used as a purification method. The purification can be successful only if the impurities have significantly lower vapor pressures than the material being sublimed.

17.1 Vapor-Pressure Behavior of Solids and Liquids

In Figure 17.1, vapor-pressure curves for solid and liquid phases for two different substances are shown. Along lines AB and DF, the sublimation curves, the solid and vapor are at equilibrium. To the left of these lines, the solid phase exists, and

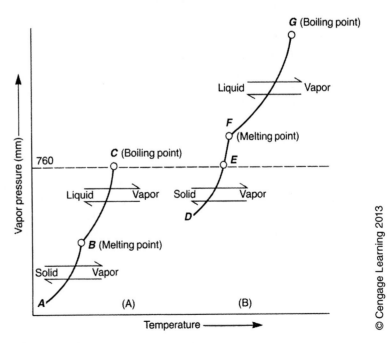

Figure 17.1
Vapor-pressure curves for solids and liquids. (A) Substance shows normal solid to liquid to gas transitions at 760 mm Hg pressure. (B) Substance shows a solid to gas transition at 760 mm Hg pressure.

© Cengage Learning 2013

355

to the right of these lines, the vapor phase is present. Along lines *BC* and *FG*, the liquid and vapor are at equilibrium. To the left of these lines, the liquid phase exists, and to the right, the vapor is present. The two substances vary greatly in their physical properties, as shown in Figure 17.1.

In the first case (Figure 17.1A), the substance shows normal change-of-state behavior on being heated, going from solid to liquid to gas. The dashed line, which represents an atmospheric pressure of 760 mm Hg, is located *above* the melting point *B* in Figure 17.1A. Thus, the applied pressure (760 mm Hg) is *greater* than the vapor pressure of the solid–liquid phase at the melting point. Starting at *A*, as the temperature of the solid is raised, the vapor pressure increases along *AB* until the solid is observed to melt at *B*. At *B* the vapor pressures of *both* the solid and liquid are identical. As the temperature continues to rise, the vapor pressure will increase along *BC* until the liquid is observed to boil at *C*. The description given is for the "normal" behavior expected for a solid substance. All three states (solid, liquid, and gas) are observed sequentially during the change in temperature.

In the second case (Figure 17.1B), the substance develops enough vapor pressure to vaporize completely at a temperature below its melting point. The substance shows a solid-to-gas transition only. The dashed line is now located *below* the melting point *F* of this substance. Thus, the applied pressure (760 mm Hg) is *less* than the vapor pressure of the solid–liquid phase at the melting point. Starting at *D*, the vapor pressure of the solid rises as the temperature increases along line *DF*. However, the vapor pressure of the solid reaches atmospheric pressure (point *E*) *before* the melting point at *F* is attained. Therefore, sublimation occurs at *E*. No melting behavior will be observed at atmospheric pressure for this substance. For a melting point to be reached and the behavior along line *FG* to be observed, an applied pressure greater than the vapor pressure of the substance at point *F* would be required. This could be achieved by using a sealed pressure apparatus.

The sublimation behavior just described is relatively rare for substances at atmospheric pressure. Several compounds exhibiting this behavior—carbon dioxide, perfluorocyclohexane, and hexachloroethane—are listed in Table 17.1. Notice that these compounds have vapor pressures *above* 760 mm Hg at their melting points. In other words, their vapor pressures reach 760 mm Hg below their melting points, and they sublime rather than melt. Anyone trying to determine the melting point of hexachloroethane at atmospheric pressure will see vapor pouring from the end of the melting-point tube! With a sealed capillary tube, the melting point of 186°C is observed.

Table 17.1 Vapor pressures of solids at their melting points

Compound	*Vapor Pressure of Solid at MP (mm Hg)*	*Melting Point (°C)*
Carbon dioxide	3876 (5.1 atm)	–57
Perfluorocyclohexane	950	59
Hexachloroethane	780	186
Camphor	370	179
Iodine	90	114
Naphthalene	7	80
Benzoic acid	6	122
p-Nitrobenzaldehyde	0.009	106

© Cengage Learning 2013

17.2 Sublimation Behavior of Solids

Sublimation is usually a property of relatively nonpolar substances that also have highly symmetrical structures. Symmetrical compounds have relatively high melting points and high vapor pressures. The ease with which a substance can escape from the solid state is determined by the strength of intermolecular forces. Symmetrical molecular structures have a relatively uniform distribution of electron density and a small dipole moment. A smaller dipole moment means a higher vapor pressure because of lower electrostatic attractive forces in the crystal.

Solids sublime if their vapor pressures are greater than atmospheric pressure at their melting points. Some compounds with the vapor pressures at their melting points are listed in Table 17.1. The first three entries in the table were discussed in Section 17.1. At atmospheric pressure they would sublime rather than melt, as shown in Figure 17.1B.

The next four entries in Table 17.1 (camphor, iodine, naphthalene, and benzoic acid) exhibit typical change-of-state behavior (solid, liquid, and gas) at atmospheric pressure, as shown in Figure 17.1A. These compounds sublime readily under reduced pressure, however. Vacuum sublimation is discussed in Section 17.3.

Compared with many other organic compounds, camphor, iodine, and naphthalene have relatively high vapor pressures at relatively low temperatures. For example, they have a vapor pressure of 1 mm Hg at 42, 39, and 53°C, respectively. Although this vapor pressure does not seem very large, it is high enough to lead, after a time, to **evaporation** of the solid from an open container. Mothballs (naphthalene and 1,4-dichlorobenzene) show this behavior. When iodine stands in a closed container over a period of time, you can observe movement of crystals from one part of the container to another.

Although chemists often refer to any solid–vapor transition as sublimation, the process just described for camphor, iodine, and naphthalene is really an **evaporation** of a solid. Strictly speaking, a sublimation point is like a melting point or a boiling point. It is defined as the point at which the vapor pressure of the solid *equals* the applied pressure. Many liquids readily evaporate at temperatures far below their boiling points. It is, however, much less common for solids to evaporate. Solids that readily sublime (evaporate) must be stored in sealed containers. When the melting point of such a solid is being determined, some of the solid may sublime and collect toward the open end of the melting-point tube while the rest of the sample melts. To solve the sublimation problem, one seals the capillary tube or rapidly determines the melting point. It is possible to use the sublimation behavior to purify a substance. For example, at atmospheric pressure, camphor can be readily sublimed, just below its melting point at 175°C. At 175°C the vapor pressure of camphor is 320 mm Hg. The vapor solidifies on a cool surface.

17.3 Vacuum Sublimation

Many organic compounds sublime readily under reduced pressure. When the vapor pressure of the solid equals the applied pressure, sublimation occurs, and the behavior is identical to that shown in Figure 17.1B. The solid phase passes directly into the vapor phase. From the data given in Table 17.1, you should expect camphor, naphthalene, and benzoic acid to sublime at or below the respective applied pressures of 370, 7, and 6 mm Hg. In principle, you can sublime *p*-nitrobenzaldehyde (last entry in the table), but it would not be practical because of the low applied pressure required.

17.4 Sublimation Methods

Sublimation can be used to purify solids. The solid is warmed until its vapor pressure becomes high enough for it to vaporize and condense as a solid on a cooled surface placed closely above. Several types of apparatus are illustrated in Figure 17.2. In each case, the cooled condensing surface is a tube filled with ice-cold water. The tube is filled from a beaker containing ice and water by using a Pasteur pipette. If the cooling water becomes warm before the sublimation is completed, the tube is emptied and refilled, once again by using a Pasteur pipette for these operations.

Figure 17.2
Sublimation apparatus.

A flame is the preferred heating device for a sublimation. The burner can be held by its cool base (not the hot barrel!) and moved up and down the sides of the thin-walled outer vial or tube to "chase" any solid that has formed on the sides toward the cold tube in the center. With an aluminum block, a ring of solid often forms on the inside walls of the apparatus just where it leaves the heating block. If this happens, using the aluminum collars will improve the situation considerably. When using a conical vial, use a thin-walled conical vial instead of a regular conical vial, because the thicker glass can shatter when heated by a flame.

Many solids do not develop enough vapor pressure at atmospheric pressure (760 mm Hg) to be purified by sublimation, but they frequently can be sublimed at reduced pressure. Thus, most sublimation equipment has provision for connection to an aspirator or other vacuum source. Reduction of pressure also helps to prevent thermal decomposition of substances that would require high temperatures to sublime at ordinary pressures.

Remember that while performing a sublimation, it is important to keep the temperature below the melting point of the solid. After sublimation, the material that has collected on the cooled surface is recovered by removing the central tube (cold-finger) from the apparatus. Take care in removing this tube to avoid dislodging the crystals that have collected. The deposit of crystals is scraped from the inner tube with a spatula. If reduced pressure has been used, the pressure must be released carefully to keep a blast of air from dislodging the crystals.

17.5 Advantages of Sublimation

One advantage of sublimation is that no solvent is used, and therefore none needs to be removed later. Sublimation also removes occluded material, such as molecules of solvent, from the sublimed substance. For instance, caffeine (sublimes at 178°C, melts at 236°C) absorbs water gradually from the atmosphere to form a hydrate. During sublimation, this water is lost, and anhydrous caffeine is obtained. If too much solvent is present in a sample to be sublimed, however, instead of becoming lost, it condenses on the cooled surface and thus interferes with the sublimation.

Sublimation is a faster method of purification than crystallization but not as selective. Similar vapor pressures are often a factor in dealing with solids that sublime; consequently, little separation can be achieved. For this reason, solids are far more often purified by crystallization. Sublimation is most effective in removing a volatile substance from a nonvolatile compound, particularly a salt or other inorganic material. Sublimation is also effective in removing highly volatile bicyclic or other symmetrical molecules from less volatile reaction products. Examples of volatile bicyclic compounds are borneol, isoborneol, and camphor.

PROBLEMS

1. Why is solid carbon dioxide called dry ice? How does it differ from solid water in behavior?
2. Under what conditions can you have *liquid* carbon dioxide?
3. A solid substance has a vapor pressure of 800 mm Hg at its melting point (80°C). Describe how the solid behaves as the temperature is raised from room temperature to 80°C while the atmospheric pressure is held constant at 760 mm Hg.
4. A solid substance has a vapor pressure of 100 mm Hg at the melting point (100°C). Assuming an atmospheric pressure of 760 mm Hg, describe the behavior of this solid as the temperature is raised from room temperature to its melting point.
5. A substance has a vapor pressure of 50 mm Hg at the melting point (100°C). Describe how you would experimentally sublime this substance.

Steam Distillation

The simple, vacuum, and fractional distillations described in Techniques 14, 15, and 16 are applicable to completely soluble (miscible) mixtures only. When liquids are *not* mutually soluble (immiscible), they can also be distilled, but with a somewhat different result. A mixture of immiscible liquids will boil at a lower temperature than the boiling points of any of the separate components as pure compounds. When steam is used to provide one of the immiscible phases, the process is called **steam distillation.** The advantage of this technique is that the desired material distills at a temperature below 100°C. Thus, if unstable or very high-boiling substances are to be removed from a mixture, decomposition is avoided. Because all gases mix, the two substances can mix in the vapor and codistill. Once the distillate is cooled, the desired component, which is not miscible, separates from the water. Steam distillation is used widely in isolating liquids from natural sources. It is also used in removing a reaction product from a tarry reaction mixture.

18.1 Differences between Distillation of Miscible and Immiscible Mixtures

Two liquids, A and B, that are mutually soluble (miscible), and that do not interact, form an ideal solution and follow Raoult's Law, as shown in Equation 1.

$$\textbf{Miscible Liquids} \qquad P_{total} = P_A^\circ N_A + P_B^\circ N_B \qquad [1]$$

Note that the vapor pressures of pure liquids P_A° and P_B° are not added directly to give the total pressure P_{total} but are reduced by the respective mole fractions N_A and N_B. The total pressure above a miscible or homogeneous solution will depend on P_A° and P_B° and also N_A and N_B. Thus, the composition of the vapor will also depend on *both* the vapor pressures and the mole fractions of each component.

$$\textbf{Immiscible Liquids} \quad P_{total} = P_A^\circ + P_B^\circ \qquad [2]$$

In contrast, when two mutually insoluble (immiscible) liquids are "mixed" to give a heterogeneous mixture, each exerts its own vapor pressure, independently of the other, as shown in Equation 2. The mole fraction term does not appear in this equation, because the compounds are not miscible. You simply add the vapor pressures of the pure liquids P_A° and P_B° at a given temperature to obtain the total pressure above the mixture. When the total pressure equals 760 mm Hg, the mixture boils. The composition of the vapor from an immiscible mixture, in contrast to the miscible mixture, is determined only by the vapor pressures of the two substances codistilling. Equation 3 defines the composition of the vapor from an immiscible mixture. Calculations involving this equation are given in Section 18.2.

$$\frac{\textbf{Moles A}}{\textbf{Moles B}} = \frac{P_A^\circ}{P_B^\circ} \qquad [3]$$

A mixture of two immiscible liquids boils at a lower temperature than the boiling points of either component. The explanation for this behavior is like that given

Miscible liquids   Immiscible liquids

$P_A^\circ = P_B^\circ$

Liquid: Moles A = B	Liquid: Moles A > B
Vapor: Moles A = B	Vapor: Moles A > B

$$P_T = P_A^\circ N_A + P_B^\circ N_B$$

P_T dependent upon amounts of A and B

A

$P_A^\circ = P_B^\circ$

Liquid: Moles A = B	Liquid: Moles A > B
Vapor: Moles A = B	Vapor: Moles A = B

$$P_T = P_A^\circ + P_B^\circ$$

P_T independent of amounts of A and B

B

Figure 18.1
Total pressure behavior for miscible and immiscible liquids. (A) Ideal miscible liquids follow Raoult's Law: P_T depends on the mole fractions and vapor pressures of A and of B. (B) Immiscible liquids do not follow Raoult's Law: P_T depends only on the vapor pressures of A and B.

for minimum-boiling-point azeotropes (Technique 15, Section 15.7). Immiscible liquids behave as they do because an extreme incompatibility between the two liquids leads to higher combined vapor pressures than Raoult's Law would predict. The higher combined vapor pressures cause a lower boiling point for the mixture than for either single component. Thus, you may think of steam distillation as a special type of azeotropic distillation in which the substance is completely insoluble in water.

The differences in behavior of miscible and immiscible liquids, where it is assumed that P_A° equals P_B°, are shown in Figure 18.1. Note that with miscible liquids, the composition of the vapor depends on the relative amounts of A and B present (Figure 18.1A). Thus, the composition of the vapor must change during a distillation. In contrast, the composition of the vapor with immiscible liquids is independent of the amounts of A and B present (Figure 18.1B). Hence, the vapor composition must remain *constant* during the distillation of such liquids, as predicted by Equation 3. Immiscible liquids act as if they were being distilled simultaneously from separate compartments, as shown in Figure 18.1B, even though in practice they are "mixed" during a steam distillation. Because all gases mix, they do give rise to a homogeneous vapor and codistill.

18.2 Immiscible Mixtures: Calculations

The composition of the distillate is constant during a steam distillation, as is the boiling point of the mixture. The boiling points of steam-distilled mixtures will always be below the boiling point of water (bp 100°C), as well as the boiling point of any of the other substances distilled. Some representative boiling points and compositions of steam distillates are given in Table 18.1. Note that the higher the boiling point of a pure substance, the more closely the temperature of the steam distillate approaches, but does not exceed, 100°C. This is a reasonably low temperature, and it avoids the decomposition that might result at high temperatures with a simple distillation.

For immiscible liquids, the molar proportions of two components in a distillate equal the ratio of their vapor pressures in the boiling mixture, as given in Equation 3. When Equation 3 is rewritten for an immiscible mixture involving water,

Equation 4 results. Equation 4 can be modified by substituting the relation moles = (weight/molecular weight) to give Equation 5.

$$\frac{\textbf{Moles substance}}{\textbf{Moles water}} = \frac{P^\circ_{\text{substance}}}{P^\circ_{\text{water}}} \qquad [4]$$

$$\frac{\textbf{Wt substance}}{\textbf{Wt water}} = \frac{(P^\circ_{\text{substance}})(\textbf{molecular weight}_{\text{substance}})}{(P^\circ_{\text{water}})(\textbf{molecular weight}_{\text{water}})} \qquad [5]$$

A sample calculation using this equation is given in Figure 18.2. Notice that the result of this calculation is very close to the experimental value given in Table 18.1.

18.3 Steam Distillation: Methods

Two methods for steam distillation are in general use in the laboratory: the **direct method** and the **live steam method.** In the first method, steam is generated *in situ* (in place) by heating a distillation flask containing the compound and water. In the second method, steam is generated outside and is passed into the distillation flask using an inlet tube.

Problem   How many grams of water must be distilled to steam-distill 1.55 g of 1-octanol from an aqueous solution? What will be the composition (wt %) of the distillate? The mixture distills at 99.4°C.

Answer   The vapor pressure of water at 99.4°C must be obtained from the *CRC Handbook* (= 744 mm Hg).

(a) Obtain the partial pressure of 1-octanol.

$$P^\circ_{\text{1-octanol}} = P_{\text{total}} - P^\circ_{\text{water}}$$
$$P^\circ_{\text{1-octanol}} = (760 - 744) = 16 \text{ mm Hg}$$

(b) Obtain the composition of the distillate.

$$\frac{\text{wt 1-octanol}}{\text{wt water}} = \frac{(16)(130)}{(744)(18)} = 0.155 \text{ g/g-water}$$

(c) Clearly, 10 g of water must be distilled.

$$(0.155 \text{ g/g-water})(10 \text{ g-water}) = 1.55 \text{ g 1-octanol}$$

(d) Calculate the **weight** percentages.

$$1\text{-octanol} = 1.55 \text{ g}/(10\text{g} + 1.55 \text{ g}) = 13.4\%$$
$$\text{water} = 10 \text{ g}/(10 \text{ g} + 1.55 \text{ g}) = 86.6\%$$

© Cengage Learning 2013

Figure 18.2
Sample calculations for a steam distillation.

Table 18.1 Boiling points and compositions of steam distillates

Mixture	Boiling Point of Pure Substance (°C)	Boiling Point of Mixture (°C)	Composition (% Water)
Benzene–water	80.1	69.4	8.9%
Toluene–water	110.6	85.0	20.2%
Hexane–water	69.0	61.6	5.6%
Heptane–water	98.4	79.2	12.9%
Octane–water	125.7	89.6	25.5%
Nonane–water	150.8	95.0	39.8%
1-Octanol–water	195.0	99.4	90.0%

© Cengage Learning 2013

A. Direct Method

Microscale. The direct method of steam distillation is the only one suitable for microscale reactions. Steam is produced in the conical vial or distillation flask (*in situ*) by heating water to its boiling point in the presence of the compound to be distilled. This method works well for small amounts of materials. A microscale steam distillation apparatus is shown in Figure 18.3. Water and the compound to be distilled are placed in the flask and heated. A stirring bar or a boiling stone should be used to prevent bumping. The vapors of the water and the desired compound codistill when they are heated. They are condensed and collect in the Hickman head. When the Hickman head fills, the distillate is removed with a Pasteur pipette and placed in another vial for storage. For the typical microscale experiment, it will be necessary to fill the well and remove the distillate three or four times. All these distillate fractions are placed in the same storage container. The efficiency in collecting the distillate can sometimes be improved if the inside walls of the Hickman head are rinsed several times into the well. A Pasteur pipette is used to perform the rinsing. Distillate is withdrawn from the well, and then it is used to wash the walls of the Hickman head all the way around the head. After the walls have been washed and when the well is full, the distillate can be withdrawn and transferred to the storage container. It may be necessary to add more water during the course of the distillation. More water is added (remove the condenser if used) through the center of the Hickman head by using a Pasteur pipette.

Semimicroscale. The apparatus shown in Technique 14, Figure 14.10, may also be used to perform a steam distillation at the microscale level or slightly above. This apparatus avoids the need to empty the collected distillate during the course of the distillation as is required when a Hickman head is used.

Macroscale. A larger-scale direct method steam distillation is illustrated in Figure 18.4. Although a heating mantle may be used, it is probably best to use a flame with this

Figure 18.3
Microscale steam distillation.

Figure 18.4
Macroscale direct steam distillation.

method because a large volume of water must be heated rapidly. A boiling stone must be used to prevent bumping. The separatory funnel allows more water to be added during the course of the distillation.

B. Live Steam Method

Macroscale. A large-scale steam distillation using the live steam method is shown in Figure 18.5. If steam lines are available in the laboratory, they may be attached directly to the steam trap (purge them first to drain water). If steam lines are not available, an external steam generator (see inset) must be prepared. The external generator usually will require a flame to produce steam at a rate fast enough for the distillation. When the distillation is first started, the clamp at the bottom of the steam trap is left open. The steam lines will have a large quantity of condensed water in them until they are well heated. When the lines become hot and condensation of steam ceases, the clamp may be closed. Occasionally, the clamp will have to be reopened to remove condensate. In this method, the steam agitates the mixture as it enters the bottom of the flask, and a stirrer or boiling stone is not required.

CAUTION

Hot steam can produce severe burns.

Sometimes it is helpful to heat the three-necked distilling flask with a heating mantle (or flame) to prevent excessive condensation at that point. Steam must be

Figure 18.5
Macroscale steam distillation using live steam.

admitted fast enough for you to see the distillate condensing as a milky white fluid in the condenser. The vapors that codistill will separate on cooling to give this cloudiness. When the condensate becomes clear, the distillation is near the end. The flow of water through the condenser should be faster than in other types of distillation to help cool the vapors. Make sure the vacuum adapter remains cool to the touch. An ice bath may be used to cool the receiving flask if desired. When the distillation is to be stopped, the screw clamp on the steam trap should be opened, and the steam inlet tube must be removed from the three-necked flask. If this is not done, liquid will back up into the tube and steam trap.

PROBLEMS

1. Calculate the weight of benzene codistilled with each gram of water and the percentage composition of the vapor produced during a steam distillation. The boiling point of the mixture is 69.4°C. The vapor pressure of water at 69.4°C is 227.7 mm Hg. Compare the result with the data in Table 18.1.

2. Calculate the approximate boiling point of a mixture of bromobenzene and water at atmospheric pressure. A table of vapor pressures of water and bromobenzene at various temperatures is given.

| | Vapor Pressures (mm Hg) | |
Temperature (°C)	Water	Bromobenzene
93	588	110
94	611	114
95	634	118
96	657	122
97	682	127
98	707	131
99	733	136

3. Calculate the weight of nitrobenzene that codistills (bp 99°C) with each gram of water during a steam distillation. You may need the data given in Problem 2.

4. A mixture of *p*-nitrophenol and *o*-nitrophenol can be separated by steam distillation. The *o*-nitrophenol is steam volatile, and the *para* isomer is not volatile. Explain. Base your answer on the ability of the isomers to form hydrogen bonds internally.

5. When another compound is mixed with water and distilled, how can you determine if it is a steam distillation or an azeotropic distillation?

Column Chromatography

The most modern and sophisticated methods of separating mixtures that the organic chemist has available all involve **chromatography.** Chromatography is defined as the separation of a mixture of two or more compounds or ions by distribution between two phases, one of which is stationary and the other moving. Various types of chromatography are possible, depending on the nature of the two phases involved: **solid–liquid** (column, thin-layer, and paper), **liquid–liquid** (high-performance liquid), and **gas–liquid** (vapor-phase) chromatographic methods are common.

All chromatography works on much the same principle as solvent extraction (Technique 12). Basically, the methods depend on the differential solubilities or adsorptivities of the substances to be separated relative to the two phases between which they are to be partitioned. In this chapter, column chromatography, a solid–liquid method, is considered. Thin-layer chromatography is examined in Technique 20; high-performance liquid chromatography is discussed in Technique 21; and gas chromatography, a gas–liquid method, is discussed in Technique 22.

19.1 Adsorbents

Column chromatography is a technique based on both adsorptivity and solubility. It is a solid–liquid phase-partitioning technique. The solid may be almost any material that does not dissolve in the associated liquid phase; the solids used most commonly are silica gel, $SiO_2 \cdot xH_2O$, also called silicic acid, and alumina, $Al_2O_3 \cdot xH_2O$. These compounds are used in their powdered or finely ground forms (usually 200 to 400 mesh).[1]

Most alumina used for chromatography is prepared from the impure ore bauxite $Al_2O_3 \cdot xH_2O + Fe_2O_3$. The bauxite is dissolved in hot sodium hydroxide and filtered to remove the insoluble iron oxides; the alumina in the ore forms the soluble amphoteric hydroxide $Al(OH)_4^-$. The hydroxide is precipitated by CO_2, which reduces the pH, as $Al(OH)_3$. When heated, the $Al(OH)_3$ loses water to form pure alumina Al_2O_3.

$$\text{Bauxite (crude)} \xrightarrow{\text{hot NaOH}} Al(OH)_4^-(aq) + Fe_2O_3(\text{insoluble})$$

$$Al(OH)_4^-(aq) + CO_2 \longrightarrow Al(OH)_3 + HCO_3^-$$

$$2\, Al(OH)_3 \xrightarrow{\text{heat}} Al_2O_3(s) + 3\, H_2O$$

Alumina prepared in this way is called **basic alumina** because it still contains some hydroxides. Basic alumina cannot be used for chromatography of compounds that are base sensitive. Therefore, it is washed with acid to neutralize the base,

---

[1] The term *mesh* refers to the number of openings per linear inch found in a screen. A large number refers to a fine screen (finer wires more closely spaced). When particles are sieved through a series of these screens, they are classified by the smallest mesh screen that they will pass through. Mesh 5 would represent a coarse gravel, and mesh 800 would be a fine powder.

giving **acid-washed alumina.** This material is unsatisfactory unless it has been washed with enough water to remove *all* the acid; on being so washed, it becomes the best chromatographic material, called **neutral alumina.** If a compound is acid-sensitive, either basic or neutral alumina must be used. You should be careful to ascertain what type of alumina is being used for chromatography. Silica gel is not available in any form other than that suitable for chromatography.

19.2 Interactions

If powdered or finely ground alumina (or silica gel) is added to a solution containing an organic compound, some of the organic compound will **adsorb** onto or adhere to the fine particles of alumina. Many kinds of intermolecular forces cause organic molecules to bind to alumina. These forces vary in strength according to their type. Nonpolar compounds bind to the alumina using only van der Waals forces. These are weak forces, and nonpolar molecules do not bind strongly unless they have extremely high molecular weights. The most important interactions are those typical of polar organic compounds. Either these forces are of the dipole–dipole type or they involve some direct interaction (coordination, hydrogen bonding, or salt formation). These types of interactions are illustrated in Figure 19.1, which for convenience shows only a portion of the alumina structure. Similar interactions occur with silica gel. The strengths of such interactions vary in the approximate order:

Salt formation > coordination > hydrogen-bonding > dipole–dipole > van der Waals

Strength of interaction varies among compounds. For instance, a strongly basic amine would bind more strongly than a weakly basic one (by coordination). In fact, strong bases and strong acids often interact so strongly that they *dissolve* alumina to some extent. You can use the following rule of thumb:

NOTE: The more polar the functional group, the stronger the bond to alumina (or silica gel).

A similar rule holds for solubility. Polar solvents dissolve polar compounds more effectively than nonpolar solvents; nonpolar compounds are dissolved best by nonpolar solvents. Thus, the extent to which any given solvent can wash an adsorbed compound from alumina depends almost directly on the relative polarity of the solvent. For example, although a ketone adsorbed on alumina might not be

Figure 19.1
Possible interactions of organic compounds with alumina.

Figure 19.2
Dynamic adsorption equilibrium.

removed by hexane, it might be removed completely by chloroform. For any adsorbed material, a kind of **distribution** equilibrium can be envisioned between the adsorbent material and the solvent. This is illustrated in Figure 19.2.

The distribution equilibrium is *dynamic*, with molecules constantly *adsorbing* from the solution and *desorbing* into it. The average number of molecules remaining adsorbed on the solid particles at equilibrium depends both on the particular molecule (RX) involved and the dissolving power of the solvent with which the adsorbent must compete.

19.3 Principle of Column Chromatographic Separation

The dynamic equilibrium mentioned previously, and the variations in the extent to which different compounds adsorb on alumina or silica gel, underlie a versatile and ingenious method for *separating* mixtures of organic compounds. In this method, the mixture of compounds to be separated is introduced onto the top of a cylindrical glass column (Figure 19.3) *packed,* or filled, with fine alumina particles (stationary solid phase). The adsorbent is continuously washed by a flow of solvent (moving phase) passing through the column.

Initially, the components of the mixture adsorb onto the alumina particles at the top of the column. The continuous flow of solvent through the column **elutes,** or washes, the solutes off the alumina and sweeps them down the column. The solutes (or materials to be separated) are called **eluates** or **elutants,** and the solvents are called **eluents.** As the solutes pass down the column to fresh alumina, new equilibria are established among the adsorbent, the solutes, and the solvent. The constant equilibration means that different compounds will move down the column at differing rates, depending on their relative affinity for the adsorbent on one hand and for the solvent on the other. Because the number of alumina particles is large, because they are closely packed, and because fresh solvent is being added continuously, the number of equilibrations between adsorbent and solvent that the solutes experience is enormous.

As the components of the mixture are separated, they begin to form moving bands (or zones), each band containing a single component. If the column is long enough and the other parameters (column diameter, adsorbent, solvent, and flow rate) are correctly chosen, the bands separate from one another, leaving gaps of pure solvent in between. As each band (solvent and solute) passes out the bottom of the column, it can be collected before the next band arrives. If the parameters mentioned are poorly chosen, the

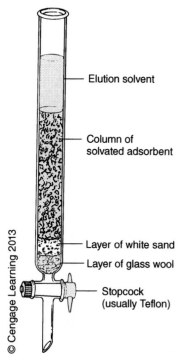

— Elution solvent

— Column of
  solvated adsorbent

— Layer of white sand
— Layer of glass wool

— Stopcock
  (usually Teflon)

Figure 19.3
Chromatographic column.

various bands either overlap or coincide, in which case either a poor separation or no separation at all is the result. A successful chromatographic separation is illustrated in Figure 19.4.

Figure 19.4

Sequence of steps in a chromatographic separation.

19.4 Parameters Affecting Separation

The versatility of column chromatography results from the many factors that can be adjusted. These include

1. Adsorbent chosen
2. Polarity of the solvents chosen
3. Size of the column (both length and diameter) relative to the amount of material to be chromatographed
4. Rate of elution (or flow)

By careful choosing of the conditions, almost any mixture can be separated. This technique has even been used to separate optical isomers. An optically active solid-phase adsorbent was used to separate the enantiomers.

Two fundamental choices for anyone attempting a chromatographic separation are the kind of adsorbent and the solvent system. In general, nonpolar compounds pass through the column faster than polar compounds because they have a smaller affinity for the adsorbent. If the adsorbent chosen binds all the solute molecules (both polar and nonpolar) strongly, they will not move down the column. On the other hand, if too polar a solvent is chosen, all the solutes (polar and nonpolar) may simply be washed through the column, with no separation taking place. The adsorbent and the solvent should be chosen so that neither is favored excessively in the equilibrium competition for solute molecules.[2]

A. Adsorbents

In Table 19.1, various kinds of adsorbents (solid phases) used in column chromatography are listed. The choice of adsorbent often depends on the types of compounds to be separated. Cellulose, starch, and sugars are used for polyfunctional plant and animal materials (natural products) that are very sensitive to acid–base interactions. Magnesium silicate is often used for separating acetylated sugars, steroids, and essential oils. Silica gel and Florisil are relatively mild toward most compounds and

Table 19.1 Solid adsorbents for column chromatography

Paper	
Cellulose	
Starch	
Sugars	
Magnesium silicate	Increasing strength of
Calcium sulfate	binding interactions
Silicic acid	toward polar compounds
Silica gel	
Florisil	
Magnesium oxide	
Aluminum oxide (alumina)*	
Activated charcoal (Norit)	

*Basic, acid-washed, and neutral.

© Cengage Learning 2013

---

[2] Often the chemist uses thin-layer chromatography (TLC), which is described in Technique 20, to arrive at the best choices of solvents and adsorbents for the best separation. The TLC experimentation can be performed quickly and with extremely small amounts (microgram quantities) of the mixture to be separated. This saves significant time and materials. Technique 20 describes this use of TLC.

are widely used for a variety of functional groups—hydrocarbons, alcohols, ketones, esters, acids, azo compounds, and amines. Alumina is the most widely used adsorbent and is obtained in the three forms mentioned in Section 19.1: acidic, basic, and neutral. The pH of acidic or acid-washed alumina is approximately 4. This adsorbent is particularly useful for separating acidic materials such as carboxylic acids and amino acids. Basic alumina has a pH of 10 and is useful in separating amines. Neutral alumina can be used to separate a variety of nonacidic and nonbasic materials.

The approximate strength of the various adsorbents listed in Table 19.1 is also given. The order is only approximate, and therefore it may vary. For instance, the strength, or separating abilities, of alumina and silica gel largely depend on the amount of water present. Water binds tightly to either adsorbent, taking up sites on the particles that could otherwise be used for equilibration with solute molecules. If one adds water to the adsorbent, it is said to have been **deactivated.** Anhydrous alumina or silica gel is said to be highly **activated.** High activity is usually avoided with these adsorbents. Use of the highly active forms of either alumina or silica gel, or of the acidic or basic forms of alumina, can often lead to molecular rearrangement or decomposition in certain types of solute compounds.

The chemist can select the degree of activity that is appropriate to carry out a particular separation. To accomplish this, highly activated alumina is mixed thoroughly with a precisely measured quantity of water. The water partially hydrates the alumina and thus reduces its activity. By carefully determining the amount of water required, the chemist can have available an entire spectrum of possible activities.

B. Solvents

In Table 19.2, some common chromatographic solvents are listed, along with their relative ability to dissolve polar compounds. Sometimes a single solvent can be found that will separate all the components of a mixture. Sometimes a mixture of solvents can be found that will achieve separation. More often, you must start elution with a nonpolar solvent to remove relatively nonpolar compounds from the column and then gradually increase the solvent polarity to force compounds of greater polarity to come down the column, or elute. The approximate order in

Table 19.2 Solvents (eluents) for chromatography

Petroleum ether	
Cyclohexane	
Carbon tetrachloride*	
Toluene	
Chloroform*	
Methylene chloride	Increasing polarity and
Diethyl ether	"solvent power" toward
Ethyl acetate	polar functional groups
Acetone	
Pyridine	
Ethanol	
Methanol	
Water	
Acetic acid ▼	

*Suspected carcinogens.

© Cengage Learning 2013

Table 19.3 Elution sequence for compounds

Hydrocarbons	Fastest (will elute with nonpolar solvent)
Olefins	
Ethers	
Halocarbons	
Aromatics	
Ketones	Order of elution
Aldehydes	
Esters	
Alcohols	
Amines	
Acids, strong bases ▼	Slowest (need a polar solvent)

© Cengage Learning 2013

which various classes of compounds elute by this procedure is given in Table 19.3. In general, nonpolar compounds travel through the column faster (elute first), and polar compounds travel more slowly (elute last). However, molecular weight is also a factor in determining the order of elution. A nonpolar compound of high molecular weight travels more slowly than a nonpolar compound of low molecular weight, and it may even be passed by some polar compounds.

Solvent polarity functions in two ways in column chromatography. First, a polar solvent will better dissolve a polar compound and move it down the column faster. Therefore, as already mentioned, one usually increases the polarity of the solvent during column chromatography to wash down compounds of increasing polarity. Second, as the polarity of the solvent increases, the solvent itself will displace adsorbed molecules from the alumina or silica and take their place on the column. Because of this second effect, a polar solvent will move *all* types of compounds, both polar and nonpolar, down the column at a faster rate than a nonpolar solvent.

When the polarity of the solvent has to be changed during a chromatographic separation, some precautions must be taken. Rapid changes from one solvent to another are to be avoided (especially when silica gel or alumina is involved). Usually, small percentages of a new solvent are mixed slowly into the one in use until the percentage reaches the desired level. If this is not done, the column packing often "cracks" as a result of the heat liberated when alumina or silica gel is mixed with a solvent. The solvent solvates the adsorbent, and the formation of a weak bond generates heat.

Solvent + alumina $\longrightarrow$ (alumina · solvent) + heat

Often, enough heat is generated locally to evaporate the solvent. The formation of vapor creates bubbles, which forces a separation of the column packing; this is called **cracking.** A cracked column does not produce a good separation, because it has discontinuities in the packing. The way in which a column is packed or filled is also very important in preventing cracking.

Certain solvents should be avoided with alumina or silica gel, especially with the acidic, basic, and highly active forms. For instance, with any of these adsorbents, acetone dimerizes via an aldol condensation to give diacetone alcohol. Mixtures of esters *transesterify* (exchange their alcoholic portions) when ethyl acetate or an alcohol is the eluent. Finally, the most active solvents (pyridine, methanol, water, and acetic acid) dissolve and elute some of the adsorbent itself. Generally, try to avoid going to solvents more polar than diethyl ether or methylene chloride in the eluent series (Table 19.2).

Table 19.4 Size of column and amount of adsorbent for typical sample sizes

Amount of Sample (g)	Amount of Adsorbent (g)	Column Diameter (mm)	Column Height (mm)
0.01	0.3	3.5	30
0.10	3.0	7.5	60
1.00	30.0	16.0	130
10.00	300.0	35.0	280

C. Column Size and Adsorbent Quantity

The column size and the amount of adsorbent must also be selected correctly to separate a given amount of sample well. As a rule of thumb, the amount of adsorbent should be 25 to 30 times, by weight, the amount of material to be separated by chromatography. Furthermore, the column should have a height-to-diameter ratio of about 8:1. Some typical relations of this sort are given in Table 19.4.

Note, as a caution, that the difficulty of the separation is also a factor in determining the size and length of the column to be used and the amount of adsorbent needed. Compounds that do not separate easily may require longer columns and more adsorbent than specified in Table 19.4. For easily separated compounds, a shorter column and less adsorbent may suffice.

D. Flow Rate

The rate at which solvent flows through the column is also significant in the effectiveness of a separation. In general, the time the mixture to be separated remains on the column is directly proportional to the extent of equilibration between stationary and moving phases. Thus, similar compounds eventually separate if they remain on the column long enough. The time a material remains on the column depends on the flow rate of the solvent. If the flow is too slow, however, the dissolved substances in the mixture may diffuse faster than the rate at which they move down the column. Then the bands grow wider and more diffuse, and the separation becomes poor.

19.5 Packing the Column: Typical Problems

The most critical operation in column chromatography is packing (filling) the column with adsorbent. The **column packing** must be evenly packed and free of irregularities, air bubbles, and gaps. As a compound travels down the column, it moves in an advancing zone, or **band.** It is important that the leading edge, or **front,** of this band be horizontal, or perpendicular to the long axis of the column. If two bands are close together and do not have horizontal band fronts, it is impossible to collect one band while completely excluding the other. The leading edge of the second band begins to elute before the first band has finished eluting. This condition can be seen in Figure 19.5. There are two main reasons for this problem. First, if the top surface edge of the adsorbent packing is not level, nonhorizontal bands result. Second, bands may be nonhorizontal if the column is not held in an exactly vertical position in both planes (front to back and side to side). When you are preparing a column, you must watch both these factors carefully.

Another phenomenon, called **streaming** or **channeling,** occurs when part of the band front advances ahead of the major part of the band. Channeling occurs if there are any cracks or irregularities in the adsorbent surface or any irregularities caused by air bubbles in the packing. A part of the advancing front moves ahead of the rest of the band by flowing through the channel. Two examples of channeling are shown in Figure 19.6.

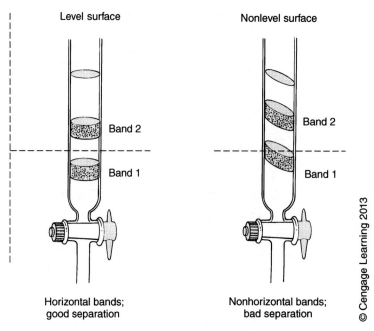

Figure 19.5
Comparison of horizontal and nonhorizontal band fronts.

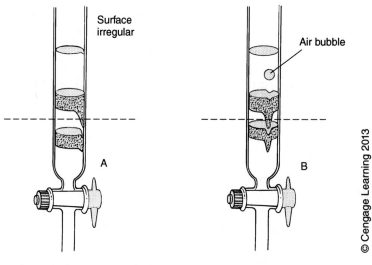

Figure 19.6
Channeling complications.

19.6 Packing the Column: Microscale Methods

The following methods are used to avoid problems resulting from uneven packing and column irregularities. These procedures should be followed carefully in preparing a chromatography column. Failure to pay close attention to the preparation of the column may well affect the quality of the separation.

Preparation of a column involves two distinct stages. In the first stage, a support base on which the packing will rest is prepared. This must be done so that the packing, a finely divided material, does not wash out of the bottom of the column. In the second stage, the column of adsorbent is deposited on top of the supporting base.

A. Preparing the Support Base

For microscale applications, select a Pasteur pipette (5¾-inch) and clamp it upright (vertically). To reduce the amount of solvent needed to fill the column, break off most of the tip of the pipette. Place a small ball of cotton in the pipette and tamp it into position using a glass rod or a piece of wire. Take care not to plug the column totally by tamping the cotton too hard. The correct position of the cotton is shown in Figure 19.7. A microscale chromatography column is packed by one of the dry pack methods described in Part B of this section.

B. Depositing the Adsorbent

Dry Pack Method 1. To fill a microscale column, fill the Pasteur pipette (with the cotton plug, prepared as described in Section A) about half full with solvent. Using a microspatula, add the solid adsorbent slowly to the solvent in the column. As you add the solid, tap the column *gently* with a pencil, a finger, or a glass rod. The tapping promotes even settling and mixing and gives an evenly packed column free of air bubbles. As the adsorbent is added, solvent flows out of the Pasteur pipette. Because the adsorbent must not be allowed to dry during the packing process, you must use a means of controlling the solvent flow. If a piece of small-diameter plastic tubing is available, it can be fitted over the narrow tip of the Pasteur pipette. The flow rate can then be controlled using a screw clamp. A simple approach to controlling the flow rate is to use a finger over the top of the Pasteur pipette, much as you control the flow of liquid in a volumetric pipette. Continue adding the adsorbent slowly, with constant tapping, until the level of the adsorbent has reached the desired level. As you pack the column, be careful not to let the column run dry. The final column should appear as shown in Figure 19.7.

Dry Pack Method 2. An alternative dry pack method for microscale columns is to fill the Pasteur pipette with *dry* adsorbent, without any solvent. Position a plug of cotton in the bottom of the Pasteur pipette. The desired amount of adsorbent is added slowly, and the pipette tapped constantly, until the level of adsorbent has reached the desired height. Figure 19.7 can be used as a guide to judge the correct height of the column of adsorbent. When the column is packed, added solvent is allowed to percolate through the adsorbent until the entire column is moistened. The solvent is not added until just before the column is to be used.

NOTE: This method is not recommended for use with silica gel or for experiments where a careful separation is required.

This method is useful when the adsorbent is alumina, but it does not produce satisfactory results with silica gel. Even with alumina, poor separations can arise due to uneven packing, air bubbles, and cracking, especially if a solvent that has a highly exothermic heat of solvation is used.

19.7 Packing the Column: Semi-microscale and Macroscale Methods

As with microscale columns, the procedures described in this section should be followed carefully in preparing a semimicroscale or conventional-scale chromatography column. Failure to pay close attention to the details of these procedures may adversely affect the quality of the separation.

Figure 19.7
Microscale chromatography column.

— Solvent

— Solid adsorbent

— Cotton

© Cengage Learning 2013

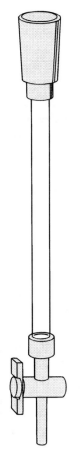

Figure 19.8
Commercial
semimicroscale
chromatography
column. (The
column is shown
equipped with an
optional solvent
reservoir.)

Again, preparation of a column involves two distinct stages: preparing the support base and filling the column with adsorbent.

A. Preparing the Support Base

Semimicroscale Columns. An alternative apparatus for small-scale column chromatography is a commercial column, such as the one shown in Figure 19.8. This type of column is made of glass and has a solvent-resistant plastic stopcock at the bottom.[3] The stopcock assembly contains a filter disc to support the adsorbent column. An optional upper fitting, also made of solvent-resistant plastic, serves as a solvent reservoir. The column shown in Figure 19.8 is equipped with the solvent reservoir. This type of column is available in a variety of lengths, ranging from 100 to 300 mm. Because the column has a built-in filter disc, it is not necessary to prepare a support base before the adsorbent is added.

Macroscale Columns. For large-scale applications, clamp a chromatography column upright (vertically). The column (Figure 19.3) is a piece of cylindrical glass tubing with a stopcock attached at one end. The stopcock usually has a Teflon plug because stopcock grease (used on glass plugs) dissolves in many of the organic solvents used as eluents. Stopcock grease in the eluent will contaminate the eluates.

Instead of a stopcock, attach a piece of flexible tubing to the bottom of the column, with a screw clamp used to stop or regulate the flow (Figure 19.9). When a screw clamp is used, care must be taken that the tubing used is not dissolved by the solvents that will pass through the column during the experiment. Rubber, for instance, dissolves in chloroform, benzene, methylene chloride, toluene, or tetrahydrofuran (THF). Tygon tubing dissolves (actually, the plasticizer is removed) in many solvents, including benzene, methylene chloride, chloroform, ether, ethyl acetate, toluene, and THF. Polyethylene tubing is the best choice for use at the end of a column because it is inert with most solvents.

Next, the column is partially filled with a quantity of solvent, usually a nonpolar solvent like hexane, and a support for the finely divided adsorbent is prepared in the following way. A loose plug of glass wool is tamped down into the bottom of the column with a long glass rod until all entrapped air is forced out as bubbles. Take care not to plug the column totally by tamping the glass wool too hard. A small layer of clean white sand is formed on top of the glass wool by pouring sand into the column. The column is tapped to level the surface of the sand. Any sand adhering to the side of the column is washed down with a small quantity of solvent. The sand forms a base that supports the column of adsorbent and prevents it from washing through the stopcock. The column is packed in one of two ways: by the slurry method or by the dry pack method.

B. Depositing the Adsorbent

Slurry Method. The slurry method is not recommended as a microscale method for use with Pasteur pipettes. On a very small scale, it is too difficult to pack the column with the slurry without losing the solvent before the packing has been completed. Microscale columns should be packed by the dry pack method, as described in Section 19.6.

In the slurry method, the adsorbent is packed into the column as a mixture of a solvent and an undissolved solid. The slurry is prepared in a separate container

---

[3] *Note to the Instructor:* With certain organic solvents, we have found that the "solvent-resistant" plastic stopcock may tend to dissolve! We recommend that instructors test their equipment with the solvent that they intend to use before the start of the laboratory class.

Figure 19.9
Tubing with screw clamp to regulate solvent flow on a chromatography column.

(Erlenmeyer flask) by adding the solid adsorbent, a little at a time, to a quantity of the solvent. This order of addition (adsorbent added to solvent) should be followed strictly because the adsorbent solvates and liberates heat. If the solvent is added to the adsorbent, it may boil away almost as fast as it is added due to heat evolved. This will be especially true if ether or another low-boiling solvent is used. When this happens, the final mixture will be uneven and lumpy. Enough adsorbent is added to the solvent, and mixed by swirling the container, to form a thick but flowing slurry. The container should be swirled until the mixture is homogenous and relatively free of entrapped air bubbles.

For a standard-sized column, the procedure is as follows. When the slurry has been prepared, the column is filled about half full with solvent, and the stopcock is opened to allow solvent to drain slowly into a large beaker. The slurry is mixed by swirling and is then poured in portions into the top of the draining column (a wide-necked funnel may be useful here). Be sure to swirl the slurry thoroughly before each addition to the column. The column is tapped constantly and *gently* on the side during the pouring operation with the fingers or with a pencil fitted with a rubber stopper. A short piece of large-diameter pressure tubing may also be used for tapping. The tapping promotes even settling and mixing and gives an evenly packed column free of air bubbles. Tapping is continued until all the material has settled, showing a well-defined level at the top of the column. Solvent from the collecting beaker may be re-added to the slurry if it becomes too thick to be poured into the column at one time. In fact, the collected solvent should be cycled through the column several times to ensure that settling is complete and that the column is firmly packed. The downward flow of solvent tends to compact the adsorbent. You should take care never to let the column "run dry" during packing. There should always be solvent on top of the absorbent column.

Dry Pack Method 1. In the first of the dry pack methods introduced here, the column is filled with solvent and allowed to drain *slowly*. The dry adsorbent is added, a little at a time, while the column is tapped gently with a pencil, finger, or glass rod.

Semimicroscale Columns. The procedure to fill a commercial semimicroscale column is essentially the same as that used to fill a Pasteur pipette (Section 19.6). The commercial column has the advantage that it is much easier to control the flow of solvent from the column during the filling process, because the stopcock can be adjusted appropriately. It is not necessary to use a cotton plug or to deposit a layer of sand before adding the adsorbent. The presence of the fritted disc at the base of the column acts to prevent adsorbent from escaping from the column.

Macroscale Columns. A plug of cotton is placed at the base of the column, and an even layer of sand is formed on top. The column is filled about half full with solvent, and the solid adsorbent is added carefully from a beaker while the solvent is allowed to flow slowly from the column. As the solid is added, the column is tapped as described for the slurry method in order to ensure that the column is packed evenly. When the column has the desired length, no more adsorbent is added. This method also produces an evenly packed column. Solvent should be cycled through this column (for macroscale applications) several times before each use. The same portion of solvent that has drained from the column during the packing is used to cycle through the column.

Dry Pack Method 2. In this method, the column is filled with dry adsorbent without any solvent. When the desired amount of adsorbent has been added, solvent is allowed to percolate through the column.

Semimicroscale Columns. The Dry Pack Method 2 is similar to that described for Pasteur pipettes (Section 19.6), except that the plug of cotton is not required. The flow rate of solvent through the column can be controlled using the stopcock, which is part of the column assembly (see Figure 19.8).

Macroscale Columns. Macroscale columns can also be packed by a dry pack method that is similar to the microscale methods described in Section 19.6. The disadvantages described for the microscale method also apply to the macroscale method. This method is not recommended for use with silica gel or alumina, because the combination leads to uneven packing, air bubbles, and cracking, especially if a solvent that has a highly exothermic heat of solvation is used.

19.8 Applying the Sample to the Column

The solvent (or solvent mixture) used to pack the column is normally the least polar elution solvent that can be used during chromatography. The compounds to be chromatographed are not highly soluble in the solvent. If they were, they would probably have a greater affinity for the solvent than for the adsorbent and would pass right through the column without equilibrating with the stationary phase.

The first elution solvent, however, is generally not a good solvent to use in preparing the sample to be placed on the column. Because the compounds are not highly soluble in nonpolar solvents, it takes a large amount of the initial solvent to dissolve the compounds, and it is difficult to get the mixture to form a narrow band on top of the column. A narrow band is ideal for an optimum separation of components. For the best separation, therefore, the compound is applied to the top of the column undiluted if it is a liquid or in a *very small* amount of highly polar solvent if it is a solid. Water must not be used to dissolve the initial sample being chromatographed, because it reacts with the column packing.

In adding the sample to the column, use the following procedure. Lower the solvent level to the top of the adsorbent column by draining the solvent from the column. Add the sample (either a pure liquid or a solution) to form a small layer on top of the adsorbent. A Pasteur pipette is convenient for adding the sample to the column. Take care not to disturb the surface of the adsorbent. This is best accomplished by touching the pipette to the inside of the glass column and slowly draining it so as to allow the sample to spread into a thin film, which slowly descends to cover the entire adsorbent surface. Drain the pipette close to the surface of the adsorbent. When all the sample has been added, drain this small layer of liquid into the column until the top surface of the column *just begins* to dry. Then add a small layer of the chromatographic solvent carefully with a Pasteur pipette, again being careful not to disturb the surface. Drain this small layer of solvent into the column until the top surface of the column just dries. Add another small layer of fresh solvent, if necessary, and repeat the process until it is clear that the sample is strongly adsorbed on the top of the column. If the sample is colored and the fresh layer of solvent acquires some of this color, the sample has not been properly adsorbed. Once the sample has been properly applied, you can protect the level surface of the adsorbent by carefully filling the top of the column with solvent and sprinkling clean, white sand into the column so as to form a small protective layer on top of the adsorbent. For microscale applications, this layer of sand is not required.

Separations are often better if the sample is allowed to stand a short time on the column before elution. This allows a true equilibrium to be established. In columns that stand for too long, however, the adsorbent often compacts or even swells, and the flow can become annoyingly slow. Diffusion of the sample to widen the bands also becomes a problem if a column is allowed to stand over an extended period. For small-scale chromatography, using Pasteur pipettes, there is no stopcock, and it is not possible to stop the flow. In this case, it is not considered necessary to allow the column to stand.

19.9 Elution Techniques

Solvents for analytical and preparative chromatography should be pure reagents. Commercial-grade solvents often contain small amounts of residue, which remains when the solvent is evaporated. For normal work, and for relatively easy separations that take only small amounts of solvent, the residue usually presents few problems. For large-scale work, commercial-grade solvents may have to be redistilled before use. This is especially true for hydrocarbon solvents, which tend to have more residue than other solvent types. Most of the experiments in this laboratory manual have been designed to avoid this particular problem.

One usually begins elution of the products with a nonpolar solvent, such as hexane or petroleum ether. The polarity of the elution solvent can be increased gradually by adding successively greater percentages of either ether or toluene (for instance, 1, 2, 5, 10, 15, 25, 50, 100%) or some other solvent of greater solvent power (polarity) than hexane. The transition from one solvent to another should not be too rapid in most solvent changes. If the two solvents to be changed differ greatly in their heats of solvation in binding to the adsorbent, enough heat can be generated to crack the column. Ether is especially troublesome in this respect because it has both a low boiling point and a relatively high heat of solvation. Most organic compounds can be separated on silica gel or alumina using hexane–ether or hexane–toluene combinations for elution and following these by pure methylene chloride. Solvents of greater polarity are usually avoided for the various reasons mentioned previously. In microscale work, the usual procedure is to use only one solvent for the chromatography.

The flow of solvent through the column should not be too rapid or the solutes will not have time to equilibrate with the adsorbent as they pass down the column. If the rate of flow is too low or stopped for a period, diffusion can become a problem—the solute band will diffuse, or spread out, in all directions. In either of these cases, separation will be poor. As a general rule (and only an approximate one), most macroscale columns are run with flow rates ranging from 5 to 50 drops of effluent per minute; a steady flow of solvent is usually avoided. Microscale columns made from Pasteur pipettes do not have a means of controlling the solvent flow rate, but commercial microscale columns are equipped with stopcocks. The solvent flow rate in this type of column can be adjusted in a manner similar to that used with larger columns. To avoid diffusion of the bands, do not stop the column and do not set it aside overnight.

19.10 Reservoirs

For microscale chromatography, the portion of the Pasteur pipette above the adsorbent is used as a reservoir of solvent. Fresh solvent, as needed, is added by means of another Pasteur pipette. When it is necessary to change solvent, the new solvent is also added in this manner. In some cases, the chromatography may proceed too slowly; the rate of solvent flow can be accelerated by attaching a rubber dropper bulb to the top of the Pasteur pipette column and squeezing *gently*. The additional air pressure forces the solvent through the column more rapidly. If this technique is used, however, care must be taken to remove the rubber bulb from the column before releasing it. Otherwise, air may be drawn up through the bottom of the column, destroying the column packing.

When large quantities of solvent are used in a chromatographic separation, it is often convenient to use a solvent reservoir to forestall having to add small portions of fresh solvent continually. The simplest type of reservoir, a feature of many columns, is created by fusing the top of the column to a round-bottom flask (Figure 19.10A). If

Figure 19.10
Various types of solvent-reservoir arrangements for chromatographic columns.

the column has a standard-taper joint at its top, a reservoir can be created by joining a standard-taper separatory funnel to the column (Figure 19.10B). In this arrangement, the stopcock is left open, and no stopper is placed in the top of the separatory funnel. A third common arrangement is shown in Figure 19.10C. A separatory funnel is filled with solvent; its stopper is wetted with solvent and put *firmly* in place. The funnel is inserted into the empty filling space at the top of the chromatographic column, and the stopcock is opened. Solvent flows out of the funnel, filling the space at the top of the column until the solvent level is well above the outlet of the separatory funnel. As solvent drains from the column, this arrangement automatically refills the space at the top of the column by allowing air to enter through the stem of the separatory funnel. Some microscale columns, such as that shown in Figure 19.8, are equipped with a solvent reservoir that fits onto the top of the column. It functions just like the reservoirs described in this section.

19.11 Monitoring the Column

It is a happy instance when the compounds to be separated are colored. The separation can then be followed visually and the various bands collected separately as they elute from the column. For the majority of organic compounds, however, this lucky circumstance does not exist, and other methods must be used to determine the positions of the bands. The most common method of following a separation of colorless compounds is to collect **fractions** of constant volume in preweighed

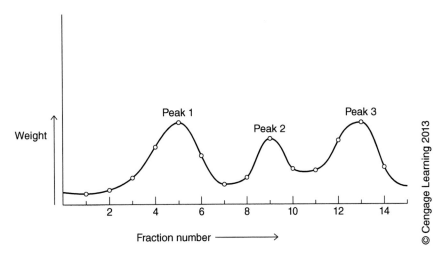

Figure 19.11
Typical elution graph.

flasks, to evaporate the solvent from each fraction, and to reweigh the flask plus any residue. A plot of fraction number versus the weight of the residues after evaporation of solvent gives a plot like that in Figure 19.11. Clearly, fractions 2 through 7 (Peak 1) may be combined as a single compound, and so can fractions 8 through 11 (Peak 2) and 12 through 15 (Peak 3). The size of the fractions collected (1, 10, 100, or 500 mL) depends on the size of the column and the ease of separation.

Another common method of monitoring the column is to mix an inorganic phosphor into the adsorbent used to pack the column. When the column is illuminated with an ultraviolet light, the adsorbent treated in this way fluoresces. However, many solutes have the ability to **quench** the fluorescence of the indicator phosphor. In areas in which solutes are present, the adsorbent does not fluoresce, and a dark band is visible. In this type of column, the separation can also be followed visually.

Thin-layer chromatography is often used to monitor a column. This method is described in Technique 20 (Section 20.10). Several sophisticated instrumental and spectroscopic methods, which we shall not detail, can also monitor a chromatographic separation.

19.12 Tailing

When a single solvent is used for elution, an elution curve (weight versus fraction) like that shown as a solid line in Figure 19.12 is often observed. An ideal elution curve is shown by dashed lines. In the nonideal curve, the compound is said to be **tailing.** Tailing can interfere with the beginning of a curve or a peak of a second component and lead to a poor separation. One way to avoid this is to increase the polarity of the solvent constantly while eluting. In this way, at the tail of the peak, where the solvent polarity is increasing, the compound will move slightly faster than at the front and allow the tail to squeeze forward, forming a more nearly ideal band.

19.13 Recovering the Separated Compounds

In recovering each of the separated compounds of a chromatographic separation when they are solids, the various correct fractions are combined and evaporated. If the combined fractions contain sufficient material, they may be purified by recrystallization. If the compounds are liquids, the correct fractions are combined, and the solvent is evaporated. If sufficient material has been collected, liquid samples can be purified by distillation. The combination of chromatography–crystallization or

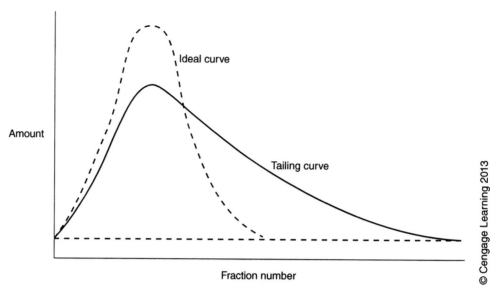

Figure 19.12
Elution curves: One ideal and one that "tails."

chromatography–distillation usually yields very pure compounds. For microscale applications, the amount of sample collected is too small to allow a purification by crystallization or distillation. The samples that are obtained after the solvent has been evaporated are considered to be sufficiently pure, and no additional purification is attempted.

19.14 Decolorization by Column Chromatography

A common outcome of organic reactions is the formation of a product that is contaminated by highly colored impurities. Very often these impurities are highly polar, and they have a high molecular weight, as well as being colored. The purification of the desired product requires that these impurities be removed. Section 11.7 of Technique 11 details methods of decolorizing an organic product. In most cases, these methods involve the use of a form of activated charcoal, or Norit.

An alternative, which is applied conveniently in microscale experiments, is to remove the colored impurity by column chromatography. Because of the polarity of the impurities, the colored components are strongly adsorbed on the stationary phase of the column, and the less polar desired product passes through the column and is collected.

Microscale decolorization of a solution on a chromatography column requires that a column be prepared in a Pasteur pipette, using either alumina or silica gel as the adsorbent (Section 19.6). The sample to be decolorized is diluted to the point where crystallization within the column will not take place, and it is then passed through the column in the usual manner. The desired compound is collected as it exits the column, and the excess solvent is removed by evaporation (Technique 7, Section 7.10).

19.15 Gel Chromatography

The stationary phase in gel chromatography consists of a cross-linked polymeric material. Molecules are separated according to their *size* by their ability to penetrate a sieve-like structure. Molecules permeate the porous stationary phase as they move down the column. Small molecules penetrate the porous structure more easily than large ones. Thus, the large molecules move through the column faster than the smaller ones and elute first. The separation of molecules by gel chromatography is depicted in Figure 19.13. With adsorption chromatography using materials

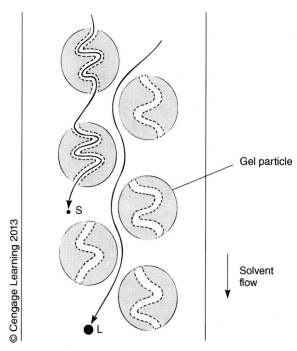

Figure 19.13

Gel chromatography: Comparison of the paths of large (L) and small (S) molecules through the column during the same interval.

such as alumina or silica, the order is usually the reverse. Small molecules (of low molecular weight) pass through the column *faster* than large molecules (of high molecular weight) because large molecules are more strongly attracted to the polar stationary phase.

Equivalent terms used by chemists for the gel-chromatography technique are **gel filtration** (biochemistry term), **gel-permeation chromatography** (polymer chemistry term), and **molecular sieve chromatography. Size-exclusion chromatography** is a general term for the technique, and it is perhaps the most descriptive term for what occurs on a molecular level.

Sephadex is one of the most popular materials for gel chromatography. It is widely used by biochemists for separating proteins, nucleic acids, enzymes, and carbohydrates. Most often, water or aqueous solutions of buffers are used as the moving phase. Chemically, Sephadex is a polymeric carbohydrate that has been cross-linked. The degree of cross-linking determines the size of the "holes" in the polymer matrix. In addition, the hydroxyl groups on the polymer can adsorb water, which causes the material to swell. As it expands, "holes" are created in the matrix. Several different gels are available from manufacturers, each with its own set of characteristics. For example, a typical Sephadex gel, such as G-75, can separate molecules in the molecular weight (MW) range 3000 to 70,000. Assume for the moment that one has a four-component mixture containing compounds with molecular weights of 10,000, 20,000, 50,000, and 100,000. The 100,000-MW compound would pass through the column first because it cannot penetrate the polymer matrix. The 50,000-, 20,000-, and 10,000-MW compounds penetrate the matrix to various degrees and would be separated. The molecules would elute in the order given (decreasing order of molecular weights). The gel separates on the basis of molecular size and configuration, rather than molecular weight.

Sephadex LH-20 has been developed for nonaqueous solvents. Some of the hydroxyl groups have been alkylated, and thus the material can swell under both aqueous and nonaqueous conditions (it now has "organic" character). This material can be used with several organic solvents, such as alcohol, acetone, methylene chloride, and aromatic hydrocarbons.

Another type of gel is based on a polyacrylamide structure (Bio-Gel P and Poly-Sep AA). A portion of a polyacrylamide chain is shown here:

$$-CH_2-CH-CH_2-C-CH_2-CH-$$
$$\qquad\;\; | \qquad\qquad | \qquad\qquad |$$
$$\qquad C=O \qquad C=O \qquad C=O$$
$$\qquad\;\; | \qquad\qquad | \qquad\qquad |$$
$$\qquad NH_2 \qquad NH_2 \qquad NH_2$$

Gels of this type can also be used in water and some polar organic solvents. They tend to be more stable than Sephadex, especially under acidic conditions. Polyacrylamides can be used for many biochemical applications involving macromolecules. For separating synthetic polymers, cross-linked polystyrene beads (copolymer of styrene and divinylbenzene) find common application. Again, the beads are swollen before use. Common organic solvents can be used to elute the polymers. As with other gels, the higher-molecular-weight compounds elute before the lower-molecular-weight compounds.

19.16 Flash Chromatography

One of the drawbacks to column chromatography is that, for large-scale preparative separations, the time required to complete a separation may be very long. Furthermore, the resolution that is possible for a particular experiment tends to deteriorate as the time for the experiment grows longer. This latter effect arises because the bands of compounds that move very slowly through a column tend to "tail."

A technique that can be useful in overcoming these problems has been developed. This technique, called **flash chromatography,** is actually a simple modification of ordinary column chromatography. In flash chromatography, the adsorbent is packed into a relatively short glass column, and air pressure is used to force the solvent through the adsorbent.

The apparatus used for flash chromatography is shown in Figure 19.14. The glass column is fitted with a Teflon stopcock at the bottom to control the flow rate of solvent. A plug of glass wool is placed in the bottom of the column to act as a support for the adsorbent. A layer of sand may also be added on top of the glass wool. The column is filled with adsorbent using the dry pack method. When the column has been filled, a fitting is attached to the top of the column, and the entire apparatus is connected to a source of high-pressure air or nitrogen. The fitting is designed so that the pressure applied to the top of the column can be adjusted precisely. The source of the high-pressure air is often a specially adapted air pump.

A typical column would use silica gel adsorbent (particle size = 40 to 63 μm) packed to a height of 5 inches in a glass column of 20-mm diameter. The pressure applied to the column would be adjusted to achieve a solvent flow rate such that the solvent level in the column would decrease by about 2 in./min. This system would be appropriate to separate the components of a 250-mg sample.

Figure 19.14
Apparatus for flash chromatography.

Labels: Bleed valve; High-pressure air; Teflon stopcock

© Cengage Learning 2013

The high-pressure air forces the solvent through the column of adsorbent at a rate that is much greater than what would be achieved if the solvent flowed through the column under the force of gravity. Because the solvent is caused to flow faster, the time required for substances to pass through the column is reduced. By itself, simply applying air pressure to the column might reduce the clarity of the separation because the components of the mixture would not have time to establish themselves into distinctly separate bands. However, in flash chromatography, you can use a much finer adsorbent than would be used in ordinary chromatography. With a much smaller particle size for the adsorbent, the surface area is increased, and the resolution possible thereby improves.

A simple variation on this idea does not use air pressure. Instead, the lower end of the column is inserted into a stopper, which is fitted into the top of a suction flask. Vacuum is applied to the system, and the vacuum acts to draw the solvent through the adsorbent column. The overall effect of this variation is similar to that obtained when air pressure is applied to the top of the column.

REFERENCES

Deyl, Z.; Macek, K.; Janák, J. *Liquid Column Chromatography*. Elsevier: Amsterdam, 1975.

Heftmann, E. *Chromatography*, 3rd ed. Van Nostrand Reinhold: New York, 1975.

Jacobson, B. M. An Inexpensive Way to Do Flash Chromatography. *Journal of Chemical Education, 65* (May 1988): 459.

Still, W. C.; Kahn, M.; Mitra, A Rapid Chromatographic Technique for Preparative Separations with Moderate Resolution. *Journal of Organic Chemistry, 43* (1978): 2923.

PROBLEMS

1. A sample was placed on a chromatography column. Methylene chloride was used as the eluting solvent. No separation of the components in the sample was observed. What must have been happening during this experiment? How would you change the experiment to overcome this problem?

2. You are about to purify an impure sample of naphthalene by column chromatography. What solvent should you use to elute the sample?

3. Consider a sample that is a mixture composed of biphenyl, benzoic acid, and benzyl alcohol. Predict the order of elution of the components in this mixture. Assume that the chromatography uses a silica column, and the solvent system is based on cyclohexane, with an increasing proportion of methylene chloride being added as a function of time.

4. An orange compound was added to the top of a chromatography column. Solvent was added immediately, with the result that the entire volume of solvent in the solvent reservoir turned orange. No separation could be obtained from the chromatography experiment. What went wrong?

5. A yellow compound, dissolved in methylene chloride, is added to a chromatography column. The elution is begun using petroleum ether as the solvent. After 6 L of solvent have passed through the column, the yellow band still has not traveled down the column appreciably. What should be done to make this experiment work better?

6. You have 0.50 g of a mixture that you wish to purify by column chromatography. How much adsorbent should you use to pack the column? Estimate the appropriate column diameter and height.

7. In a particular sample, you wish to collect the component with the *highest* molecular weight as the *first* fraction. What chromatographic technique should you use?

8. A colored band shows an excessive amount of tailing as it passes through the column. What can you do to rectify this problem?

9. How would you monitor the progress of a column chromatography when the sample is colorless? Describe at least two methods.

Thin-Layer Chromatography

Thin-layer chromatography (TLC) is a very important technique for the rapid separation and qualitative analysis of small amounts of material. It is ideally suited for the analysis of mixtures and reaction products in microscale experiments. The technique is closely related to column chromatography. In fact, TLC can simply be considered column chromatography in reverse, with the solvent ascending the adsorbent, rather than descending. Because of this close relationship to column chromatography, and because the principles governing the two techniques are similar, Technique 19, on column chromatography, should be read first.

20.1 Principles of Thin-Layer Chromatography

Like column chromatography, TLC is a solid–liquid partitioning technique. However, the moving liquid phase is not allowed to percolate down the adsorbent; it is caused to ascend a thin layer of adsorbent coated onto a backing support. The most typical backing is a glass plate, but other materials are also used. A thin layer of the adsorbent is spread onto the plate and allowed to dry. A coated and dried plate of glass is called a **thin-layer plate** or a **thin-layer slide.** (The reference to *slide* comes about because microscope slides are often used to prepare small thin-layer plates.) When a thin-layer plate is placed upright in a vessel that contains a shallow layer of solvent, the solvent ascends the layer of adsorbent on the plate by capillary action.

In TLC, the sample is applied to the plate before the solvent is allowed to ascend the adsorbent layer. The sample is usually applied as a small spot near the base of the plate; this technique is often referred to as **spotting.** The plate is spotted by repeated applications of a sample solution from a small capillary pipette. When the filled pipette touches the plate, capillary action delivers its contents to the plate, and a small spot is formed.

As the solvent ascends the plate, the sample is partitioned between the moving liquid phase and the stationary solid phase. During this process, you are **developing,** or **running,** the thin-layer plate. In development, the various components in the applied mixture are separated. The separation is based on the many equilibrations the solutes experience between the moving and the stationary phases. (The nature of these equilibrations was thoroughly discussed in Technique 19, Sections 19.2 and 19.3.) As in column chromatography, the least polar substances advance faster than the most polar substances. A separation results from the differences in the rates at which the individual components of the mixture advance upward on the plate. When many substances are present in a mixture, each has its own characteristic solubility and adsorptivity properties, depending on the functional groups in its structure. In general, the stationary phase is strongly polar and strongly binds polar substances. The moving liquid phase is usually less polar than the adsorbent and most easily dissolves substances that are less polar or even nonpolar. Thus, substances that are the most polar travel slowly upward, or not at all, and nonpolar substances travel more rapidly if the solvent is sufficiently nonpolar.

When the thin-layer plate has been developed, it is removed from the developing tank and allowed to dry until it is free of solvent. If the mixture that was originally spotted on the plate was separated, there will be a vertical series of spots on the plate. Each spot corresponds to a separate component or compound from the original mixture. If the components of the mixture are colored substances, the various spots will be clearly visible after development. More often, however, the "spots" will not be visible because they correspond to colorless substances. If spots are not apparent, they can be made visible only if a **visualization method** is used. Often, spots can be seen when the thin-layer plate is held under ultraviolet light; the ultraviolet lamp is a common visualization method. Also common is the use of iodine vapor. The plates are placed in a chamber containing iodine crystals and left to stand for a short time. The iodine reacts with the various compounds adsorbed on the plate to give colored complexes that are clearly visible. Because iodine often changes the compounds by reaction, the components of the mixture cannot be recovered from the plate when the iodine method is used. (Other methods of visualization are discussed in Section 20.7.)

20.2 Commercially Prepared TLC Plates

The most convenient type of TLC plate is prepared commercially and sold in a ready-to-use form. Many manufacturers supply glass plates precoated with a durable layer of silica gel or alumina. More conveniently, plates are also available that have either a flexible plastic backing or an aluminum backing. The most common types of commercial TLC plates are composed of plastic sheets that are coated with silica gel and polyacrylic acid, which serves as a binder. A fluorescent indicator may be mixed with the silica gel. The indicator renders the spots due to the presence of compounds in the sample visible under ultraviolet light (see Section 20.7). Although these plates are relatively expensive when compared with plates prepared in the laboratory, they are far more convenient to use, and they provide more consistent results. The plates are manufactured quite uniformly. Because the plastic backing is flexible, they have the additional advantage that the coating does not flake off the plates easily. The plastic sheets (usually 8 in. by 8 in. square) can also be cut with a pair of scissors or paper cutter to whatever size may be required.

If the package of commercially prepared TLC plates has been opened previously, or if the plates have not been purchased recently, they should be dried before use. Dry the plates by placing them in an oven at 100°C for 30 minutes, and store them in a desiccator until they are to be used.

20.3 Preparation of Thin-Layer Slides and Plates

Commercially prepared plates (Section 20.2) are the most convenient to use, but if you must prepare your own slides or plates, this section gives the directions for preparing them. The two adsorbent materials used most often for TLC are alumina G (aluminum oxide) and silica gel G (silicic acid). The G designation stands for gypsum (calcium sulfate). Calcined gypsum, $CaSO_4 \cdot \frac{1}{2}H_2O$, is better known as plaster of Paris. When exposed to water or moisture, gypsum sets in a rigid mass, $CaSO_4 \cdot 2H_2O$, which binds the adsorbent together and to the glass plates used as a backing support. In the adsorbents used for TLC, about 10–13% by weight of gypsum is added as a binder. The adsorbent materials are otherwise like those used in column chromatography; the adsorbents used in column chromatography have a larger particle size, however. The material for thin-layer work is a fine powder. The small particle size, along with the added gypsum, makes it impossible to use silica gel G or alumina G for column work. In a column, these adsorbents generally set so rigidly that solvent virtually stops flowing through the column.

A. Microscope Slide TLC Plates

For qualitative work such as identifying the number of components in a mixture or trying to establish that two compounds are identical, small TLC plates made from microscope slides are especially convenient. Coated microscope slides are easily made by dipping the slides into a container holding a slurry of the adsorbent material. Although numerous solvents can be used to prepare a slurry, methylene chloride is probably the best choice. It has the two advantages of low boiling point (40°C) and inability to cause the adsorbent to set or form lumps. The low boiling point means that it is not necessary to dry the coated slides in an oven. Its inability to cause the gypsum binder to set means that slurries made with it are stable for several days. The layer of adsorbent formed is fragile, however, and must be treated carefully. For this reason, some people prefer to add a small amount of methanol to the methylene chloride to enable the gypsum to set more firmly. The methanol solvates the calcium sulfate much as water does. More durable plates can be made by dipping plates into a slurry prepared from water. These plates must be oven-dried before use. Also, a slurry prepared from water must be used soon after its preparation. If it is not, it begins to set and form lumps. Thus, an aqueous slurry must be prepared immediately before use; it cannot be used after it has stood for any length of time. For microscope slides, a slurry of silica gel G in methylene chloride is not only convenient but also adequate for most purposes.

Preparing the Slurry. The slurry is most conveniently prepared in a 4-oz wide-mouthed screw-cap jar. About 3 mL of methylene chloride are required for each gram of silica gel G. For a smooth slurry without lumps, the silica gel should be added to the solvent while the mixture is being either stirred or swirled. Adding solvent to the adsorbent usually causes lumps to form in the mixture. When the addition is complete, the cap should be placed on the jar tightly and the jar shaken vigorously to ensure thorough mixing. The slurry may be stored in the tightly capped jar until it is to be used. More methylene chloride may have to be added to replace evaporation losses.

CAUTION

Avoid breathing silica dust or methylene chloride, prepare and use the slurry in a hood, and avoid getting methylene chloride or the slurry mixture on your skin. Wear protective gloves.

Preparing the Slides. If new microscope slides are available, you can use them without any special treatment. However, it is more economical to reuse or recycle microscope slides. Wash the slides with soap and water, rinse with water, and then rinse with 50% aqueous methanol. Allow the plates to dry thoroughly on paper towels. They should be handled by the edges because fingerprints on the plate surface will make it difficult for the adsorbent to bind to the glass.

Coating the Slides. The slides are coated with adsorbent by dipping them into the container of slurry. You can coat two slides simultaneously by sandwiching them together before dipping them in the slurry.

NOTE: Perform the coating operation under a hood.

The use of nitrile gloves is recommended.

Two are dipped at one time

Screw-cap jar filled with slurry (capped and shaken vigorously before dipping slides)

© Cengage Learning 2013

Figure 20.1
Dipping slides to coat them.

Shake the slurry vigorously just before dipping the slides. Because the slurry settles on standing, it should be mixed in this way before each set of slides is dipped. The depth of the slurry in the jar should be about 3 inches, and the plates should be dipped into the slurry until only about 0.25 inches at the top remains uncoated. The dipping operation should be performed smoothly. The plates may be held at the top (see Figure 20.1), where they will not be coated. They are dipped into the slurry and withdrawn with a slow and steady motion. The dipping operation takes about 2 seconds. Some practice may be required to get the correct timing. After dipping, replace the cap on the jar and hold the plates for a minute until most of the solvent has evaporated. Separate the plates and place them on paper towels to complete the drying. The plates should have an even coating; there should be no streaks and no thin spots where glass shows through the adsorbent. The plates should not have a thick and lumpy coating.

Two conditions cause thin and streaked plates. First, the slurry may not have been mixed thoroughly before the dipping operation; the adsorbent might then have settled to the bottom of the jar, and the thin slurry at the top would not have coated the slides properly. Second, the slurry simply may not have been thick enough; more silica gel G must then be added to the slurry until the consistency is correct. If the slurry is too thick, the coating on the plates will be thick, uneven, and lumpy. To correct this, dilute the slurry with enough solvent to achieve the proper consistency.

Plates with an unsatisfactory coating may be wiped clean with a paper towel and redipped. Take care to handle the plates only from the top or by the sides to avoid getting fingerprints on the glass surface.

B. Larger Thin-Layer Plates

For separations involving large amounts of material, or for difficult separations, it may be necessary to use larger thin-layer plates. Plates with dimensions up to 20–25 cm^2 are common. With larger plates, it is desirable to have a more durable coating, and a water slurry of the adsorbent should be used to prepare them. If silica gel is used, the slurry should be prepared in the ratio of about 1 g silica gel G to each 2 mL of water. The glass plate used for the thin-layer plate should be washed, dried, and placed on a sheet of newspaper. Place two strips of masking tape along two edges of the plate. Use more than one layer of masking tape if a thicker coating is desired on the plate. A slurry is prepared, shaken well, and poured along one of the untaped edges of the plate.

NOTE: Observe the same precautions stated for Microscope Slide TLC Plates.

A heavy piece of glass rod, long enough to span the taped edges, is used to level and spread the slurry over the plate. While the rod is resting on the tape, it is pushed

Figure 20.2
Preparing a large plate.

along the plate from the end at which the slurry was poured toward the opposite end of the plate. This is illustrated in Figure 20.2. After the slurry is spread, the masking tape strips are removed, and the plates are dried in a 110°C oven for about 1 hour. Plates of 10–25 cm² are easily prepared by this method. Larger plates present more difficulties. Many laboratories have a commercially manufactured spreading machine that makes the entire operation simpler.

20.4 Sample Application: Spotting the Plates

Preparing a Micropipette

To apply the sample that is to be separated to the thin-layer plate, one uses a micropipette. A micropipette is easily made from a short length of thin-walled capillary tubing like that used for melting-point determinations, but open at both ends. The capillary tubing is heated at its midpoint with a microburner and rotated until it is soft. When the tubing is soft, the heated portion of the tubing is drawn out until a constricted portion of tubing 4–5 cm long is formed. After cooling, the constricted portion of tubing is scored at its center with a file or scorer and broken. The two halves yield two capillary micropipettes. Figure 20.3 shows how to make such pipettes.

① Rotate in flame until soft.
② Remove from flame and pull.
③ Score lightly in center of pulled section.
④ Break in half to give two pipettes.

Figure 20.3
Construction of two capillary micropipettes.

Spotting the Plate

To apply a sample to the plate, begin by placing about 1 mg of a solid test substance, or one drop of a liquid test substance, in a small container such as a watch glass or a test

Figure 20.4
Spotting the plate with a drawn capillary pipette.

tube. Dissolve the sample in a few drops of a volatile solvent. Acetone or methylene chloride is usually a suitable solvent. If a solution is to be tested, it can often be used directly. The small capillary pipette, prepared as described, is filled by dipping the pulled end into the solution to be examined. Capillary action fills the pipette. Empty the pipette by touching it *lightly* to the thin-layer plate at a point about 1 cm from the bottom (Figure 20.4). The spot must be high enough that it does not dissolve in the developing solvent. It is important to touch the plate very lightly and not to gouge a hole in the adsorbent. When the pipette touches the plate, the solution is transferred to the plate as a small spot. The pipette should be touched to the plate *very briefly* and then removed. If the pipette is held to the plate, its entire contents will be delivered to the plate. Only a small amount of material is needed. It is often helpful to blow gently on the plate as the sample is applied. This helps to keep the spot small by evaporating the solvent before it can spread out on the plate. The smaller the spot formed, the better the separation obtainable. If needed, additional material can be applied to the plate by repeating the spotting procedure. You should repeat the procedure with several small amounts, rather than apply one large amount. The solvent should be allowed to evaporate between applications. If the spot is not small (about 2 mm in diameter), a new plate should be prepared. The capillary pipette may be used several times if it is rinsed between uses. It is repeatedly dipped into a small portion of solvent to rinse it and touched to a paper towel to empty it.

As many as three spots may be applied to a microscope-slide TLC plate. Each spot should be about 1 cm from the bottom of the plate, and all spots should be evenly spaced, about 1 cm apart. The spots should be positioned at least 1 cm from the edges of the plate. Due to diffusion, spots often increase in diameter as the plate is developed. To keep spots containing different materials from merging and to avoid confusing the samples, do not place more than three spots on a single plate. Larger plates can accommodate many more samples.

20.5 Developing (Running) TLC Plates

Preparing a Development Chamber

A convenient development chamber for microscope-slide TLC plates can be made from a 4-oz wide-mouthed jar. An alternative development chamber can be constructed from a beaker, using aluminum foil to cover the opening. The inside of the jar or beaker should be lined with a piece of filter paper, cut so that it does not quite extend around the inside of the jar. A small vertical opening (2–3 cm) should be left in the filter paper for observing the development. Before development, the filter paper inside the jar or beaker should be thoroughly moistened with the development solvent. The solvent-saturated liner helps to keep the chamber saturated with solvent vapors, thereby speeding the development. Once the liner is saturated, the level of solvent in the bottom of the development chamber is adjusted to a depth of about 5 mm, and the chamber is capped (or covered with aluminum foil) and set aside until it is to be used. A correctly prepared development chamber (with slide in place) is shown in Figure 20.5.

Developing the TLC Plate

Once the spot has been applied to the thin-layer plate and the solvent has been selected (see Section 20.5), the plate is placed in the chamber for development. The

Plate does not touch
the filter paper

Filter paper liner in jar
(should be completely moistened by solvent)

Solvent front travels up slide
by capillary action

Spot must be *above* solvent level
(small amount of solvent, 5 mL)

© Cengage Learning 2013

Figure 20.5
Development chamber with thin-layer plate undergoing
development.

plate must be placed in the chamber carefully so that none of the coated portion touches the filter paper liner. In addition, the solvent level in the bottom of the chamber must not be above the spot that was applied to the plate, or the spotted material will dissolve in the pool of solvent instead of undergoing chromatography. Once the plate has been placed correctly, replace the cap on the developing chamber and wait for the solvent to advance up the plate by capillary action. This generally occurs rapidly, and you should watch carefully. As the solvent rises, the plate becomes visibly moist. When the solvent has advanced to within 5 mm of the end of the coated surface, the plate should be removed, and the position of the solvent front should be marked *immediately* by scoring the plate along the solvent line with a *pencil*. The solvent front must not be allowed to travel beyond the end of the coated surface. The plate should be removed before this happens. The solvent will not actually advance beyond the end of the plate, but spots allowed to stand on a completely moistened plate on which the solvent is not in motion expand by diffusion. Once the plate has dried, any visible spots should be outlined on the plate with a pencil. If no spots are apparent, a visualization method (Section 20.7) may be needed.

20.6 Choosing a Solvent for Development

The development solvent used depends on the materials to be separated. You may have to try several solvents before a satisfactory separation is achieved. Because microscope slides can be prepared and developed rapidly, an empirical choice is usually not hard to make. A solvent that causes all the spotted material to move with the solvent front is too polar. One that does not cause any of the material in the spot to move is not polar enough. As a guide to the relative polarity of solvents, consult Table 19.2 in Technique 19. Figure 20.6 shows three TLC plates run with different solvents. As can be seen, if the solvent is too polar, the spots tend to run near the top of the plate, and the separation is poor. If the solvent is not sufficiently polar, the spots do not travel very far; again, the separation is poor. The ideal solvent choice allows the spots to travel well up the plate but allows for a clean separation.

Methylene chloride and toluene are solvents of intermediate polarity and good choices for a wide variety of functional groups to be separated. For hydrocarbon materials, good first choices are hexane, petroleum ether (ligroin), or toluene. Hexane or petroleum ether with varying proportions of toluene or ether give

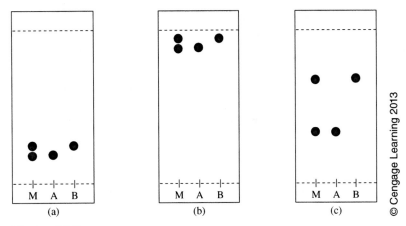

Figure 20.6
TLC plates showing the effects of solvent polarity on a separation.
The three spots on each plate are indicated by M for a two-component mixture, A for a standard sample of substance A, and B for a standard sample of substance B. (a) Solvent of low polarity: poor separation. (b) Solvent of high polarity: poor separation. (c) Solvent of intermediate polarity: clean separation.

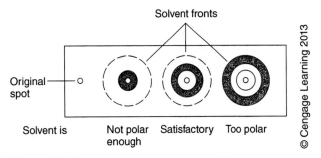

Figure 20.7
Concentric ring method of testing solvents.

solvent mixtures of moderate polarity that are useful for many common functional groups. Polar materials may require ethyl acetate, acetone, or methanol.

A rapid way to determine a good solvent is to apply several sample spots to a single plate. The spots should be placed a minimum of 1 cm apart. A capillary pipette is filled with a solvent and gently touched to one of the spots. The solvent expands outward in a circle. The solvent front should be marked with a pencil. A different solvent is applied to each spot. As the solvents expand outward, the spots expand as concentric rings. From the appearance of the rings, you can judge approximately the suitability of the solvent. Several types of behavior experienced with this method of testing are shown in Figure 20.7.

20.7 Visualization Methods

It is fortunate when the compounds separated by TLC are colored because the separation can be followed visually. More often than not, however, the compounds are colorless. In that case, the separated materials must be made visible by some reagent or some method that makes the separated compounds visible. Reagents that give rise to colored spots are called **visualization reagents.** Methods of viewing that make the spots apparent are **visualization methods.**

The visualization reagent used most often is iodine. Iodine reacts with many organic materials to form complexes that are either brown or yellow. In this visualization method, the developed and dried TLC plate is placed in a 4-oz wide-mouth screw-cap jar along with a few crystals of iodine. The jar is capped and gently warmed on a steam bath or a hot plate at low heat. The jar fills with iodine vapors, and the spots begin to appear. When the spots are sufficiently intense, the plate is removed from the jar and the spots are outlined with a pencil. The spots are not permanent. Their appearance results from the formation of complexes the iodine makes with the organic substances. As the iodine sublimes off the plate, the spots fade. Hence, they should be marked immediately. Nearly all compounds except saturated hydrocarbons and alkyl halides form complexes with iodine. The intensities of the spots do not accurately indicate the amount of material present, except in the crudest way.

A more convenient variation on this method is to combine 50 grams of silica gel with about 200 mg of iodine crystals in an 8-oz. jar.[1] Rotate the jar periodically to disperse the iodine. Making certain that the TLC plate is completely dry, immerse it in the silica gel-iodine mixture and close the lid tightly. Rotate the jar to ensure that the TLC plate is completely covered. After one or two minutes, remove the plate from the jar using forceps. Be careful not to inhale the powder!

The second most common method of visualization is by an ultraviolet (UV) lamp. Under UV light, compounds often look like bright spots on the plate. This often suggests the structure of the compound: Certain types of compounds shine very brightly under UV light because they fluoresce.

Another method that provides good results involves adding a fluorescent indicator to the adsorbent used to coat the plates. A mixture of zinc and cadmium sulfides is often used. When treated in this way and held under UV light, the entire plate fluoresces. However, dark spots appear on the plate where the separated compounds are seen to quench this fluorescence.

In addition to the preceding methods, several chemical methods are available that either destroy or permanently alter the separated compounds through reaction. Many of these methods are specific for particular functional groups.

Alkyl halides can be visualized if a dilute solution of silver nitrate is sprayed on the plates. Silver halides are formed. These halides decompose if exposed to light, giving rise to dark spots (free silver) on the TLC plate.

Most organic functional groups can be made visible if they are charred with sulfuric acid. Concentrated sulfuric acid is sprayed on the plate, which is then heated in an oven at 110°C to complete the charring. Permanent spots are thus created.

Colored compounds can be prepared from colorless compounds by making derivatives before spotting them on the plate. An example of this is the preparation of 2,4-dinitrophenylhydrazones from aldehydes and ketones to produce yellow and orange compounds. You may also spray the 2,4-dinitrophenylhydrazine reagent on the plate after the ketones or aldehydes have separated. Red and yellow spots form where the compounds are located. Other examples of this method are using ferric chloride for visualizing phenols and using bromocresol green for detecting carboxylic acids. Chromium trioxide, potassium dichromate, and potassium permanganate can be used for visualizing compounds that are easily oxidized. *p*-Dimethylaminobenzaldehyde easily detects amines. Ninhydrin reacts with amino acids to make them visible. Numerous other methods and reagents available from various supply outlets are specific for certain types of functional groups. These visualize only the class of compounds of interest.

---

[1]The authors are grateful to Prof. Amanda Murphy for suggesting this method. It is best to prepare the jar at least one day in advance of class period to allow the iodine to disperse evenly throughout the silica gel. The silica gel should be evenly stained with iodine. When the mixture is first prepared, the silica gel will appear pink, but it will turn to a rusty orange color over time.

20.8 Preparative Plates

If you use large plates (Section 20.3B), materials can be separated, and the separated components can be recovered individually from the plates. Plates used in this way are called **preparative plates.** For preparative plates, a thick layer of adsorbent is generally used. Instead of being applied as a spot or a series of spots, the mixture to be separated is applied as a line of material about 1 cm from the bottom of the plate. As the plate is developed, the separated materials form bands. After development, you can observe the separated bands, usually by UV light, and outline the zones in pencil. If the method of visualization is destructive, most of the plate is covered with paper to protect it, and the reagent is applied only at the extreme edge of the plate.

Once the zones have been identified, the adsorbent in those bands is scraped from the plate and extracted with solvent to remove the adsorbed material. Filtration removes the adsorbent, and evaporation of the solvent gives the recovered component from the mixture.

20.9 The R_f Value

Thin-layer chromatography conditions include

1. Solvent system
2. Adsorbent
3. Thickness of the adsorbent layer
4. Relative amount of material spotted

Under an established set of such conditions, a given compound always travels a fixed distance relative to the distance the solvent front travels. This ratio of the distance the compound travels to the distance the solvent travels is called the **R_f value.** The symbol R_f stands for "retardation factor," or "ratio-to-front," and it is expressed as a decimal fraction:

$$R_f = \frac{\text{distance traveled by substance}}{\text{distance traveled by solvent front}}$$

When the conditions of measurement are completely specified, the R_f value is constant for any given compound, and it corresponds to a physical property of that compound.

The R_f value can be used to identify an unknown compound, but like any other identification based on a single piece of data, the R_f value is best confirmed with some additional data. Many compounds can have the same R_f value, just as many compounds have the same melting point.

It is not always possible, in measuring an R_f value, to duplicate exactly the conditions of measurement another researcher has used. Therefore, R_f values tend to be of more use to a single researcher in one laboratory than they are to researchers in different laboratories. The only exception to this is when two researchers use TLC plates from the same source, as in commercial plates, or know the *exact* details of how the plates were prepared. Nevertheless, the R_f value can be a useful guide. If exact values cannot be relied on, the relative values can provide another researcher with useful information about what to expect. Anyone using published R_f values will find it a good idea to check them by comparing them with standard substances whose identity and R_f values are known.

To calculate the R_f value for a given compound, measure the distance that the compound has traveled from the point at which it was originally spotted. For spots that are not too large, measure to the center of the migrated spot. For large spots, the measurement should be repeated on a new plate, using less material. For spots that show tailing, the measurement is made to the "center of gravity" of the spot. This first distance measurement is then divided by the distance the solvent front has traveled from the same original spot. A sample calculation of the R_f values of two compounds is illustrated in Figure 20.8.

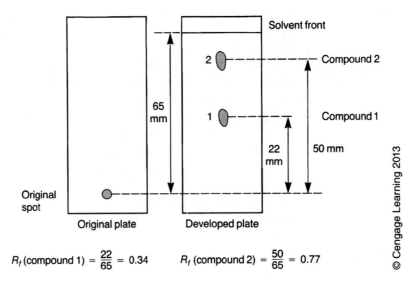

$$R_f \text{ (compound 1)} = \frac{22}{65} = 0.34 \qquad R_f \text{ (compound 2)} = \frac{50}{65} = 0.77$$

Figure 20.8
Sample calculation of R_f values.

20.10 Thin-Layer Chromatography Applied in Organic Chemistry

Thin-layer chromatography has several important uses in organic chemistry. It can be used in the following applications:

1. To establish that two compounds are identical
2. To determine the number of components in a mixture
3. To determine the appropriate solvent for a column-chromatographic separation
4. To monitor a column-chromatographic separation
5. To check the effectiveness of a separation achieved on a column, by crystallization or by extraction
6. To monitor the progress of a reaction

In all these applications, TLC has the advantage that only small amounts of material are necessary. Material is not wasted. With many of the visualization methods, less than a tenth of a microgram (10^{-7} g) of material can be detected. On the other hand, samples as large as a milligram may be used. With preparative plates that are large (about 9 in. on a side) and have a relatively thick coating of adsorbent (>500 μm), it is often possible to separate from 0.2 to 0.5 g of material at one time. The main disadvantage of TLC is that volatile materials cannot be used, because they evaporate from the plates.

Thin-layer chromatography can establish that two compounds suspected to be identical are in fact identical. Simply spot both compounds side by side on a single plate and develop the plate. If both compounds travel the same distance on the plate (have the same R_f value), they are probably identical. If the spot positions are not the same, the compounds are definitely not identical. It is important to spot compounds *on the same plate*. This is especially important with hand-dipped microscope slides. Because they vary widely from plate to plate, no two plates have exactly the same thickness of adsorbent. If you use commercial plates, this precaution is not necessary, although it is nevertheless a good idea.

Thin-layer chromatography can establish whether a sample is a single substance or a mixture. A single substance gives a single spot no matter what solvent is used to develop the plate. On the other hand, the number of components in a mixture can be established by trying various solvents on a mixture. A word of caution should be given. It may be difficult, in dealing with compounds of very similar properties, isomers for example, to find a solvent that will separate the mixture. Inability to achieve a separation is not absolute proof that a sample is a single pure substance. Many compounds can be separated only by *multiple developments* of the TLC slide with a fairly nonpolar solvent. In this method, you remove the plate after the first development and allow it to dry. After being dried, it is placed in the chamber again and developed once more. This effectively doubles the length of the slide. At times, several developments may be necessary.

When a mixture is to be separated, you can use TLC to choose the best solvent to separate it if column chromatography is contemplated. You can try various solvents on a plate coated with the same adsorbent as will be used in the column. The solvent that resolves the components best will probably work well on the column. These small-scale experiments are quick, use very little material, and save time that would be wasted by attempting to separate the entire mixture on the column. Similarly, TLC plates can **monitor** a column. A hypothetical situation is shown in Figure 20.9.

A solvent was found that would separate the mixture into four components (A–D). A column was run using this solvent, and 11 fractions of 15 mL each were collected. Thin-layer analysis of the various fractions showed that Fractions 1–3 contained Component A; Fractions 4–7, Component B; Fractions 8–9, Component C; and Fractions 10–11, Component D. A small amount of cross-contamination was observed in Fractions 3, 4, 7, and 9.

In another TLC example, a researcher found a product from a reaction to be a mixture. It gave two spots, A and B, on a TLC slide. After the product was crystallized, the crystals were found by TLC to be pure A, whereas the mother liquor was found to have a mixture of A and B. The crystallization was judged to have purified A satisfactorily.

Finally, it is often possible to monitor the progress of a reaction by TLC. At various points during a reaction, samples of the reaction mixture are taken and subjected to TLC analysis. An example is given in Figure 20.10. In this case, the desired reaction was the conversion of A to B. At the beginning of the reaction (0 hr), a TLC slide was prepared that was spotted with pure A, pure B, and the reaction mixture. Similar slides were prepared at 0.5, 1, 2, and 3 hours after the start of the reaction. The slides showed that the reaction was complete in 2 hours. When the reaction was run longer than 2 hours, a new compound, side product C, began to appear. Thus, the optimum reaction time was judged to be 2 hours.

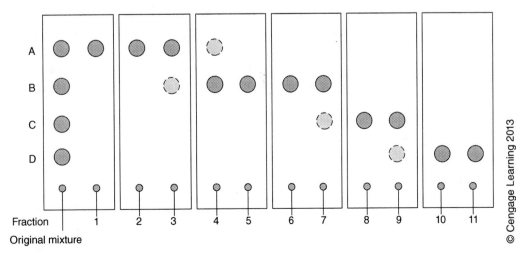

Figure 20.9

Monitoring a column.

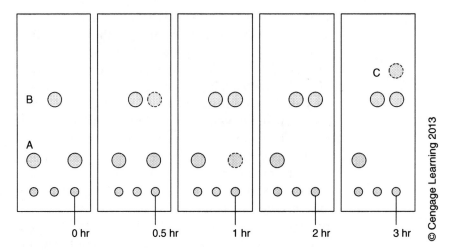

© Cengage Learning 2013

Figure 20.10
Monitoring a reaction.

20.11 Paper Chromatography

Paper chromatography is often considered to be related to thin-layer chromatography. The experimental techniques are somewhat like those of TLC, but the principles are more closely related to those of extraction. Paper chromatography is actually a liquid–liquid partitioning technique, rather than a solid–liquid technique. For paper chromatography, a spot is placed near the bottom of a piece of high-grade filter paper (Whatman No. 1 is often used). Then the paper is placed in a developing chamber. The development solvent ascends the paper by capillary action and moves the components of the spotted mixture upward at differing rates. Although paper consists mainly of pure cellulose, the cellulose itself does not function as the stationary phase. Rather, the cellulose absorbs water from the atmosphere, especially from an atmosphere saturated with water vapor. Cellulose can absorb up to about 22% of water. It is this water adsorbed on the cellulose that functions as the stationary phase. To ensure that the cellulose is kept saturated with water, many development solvents used in paper chromatography contain water as a component. As the solvent ascends the paper, the compounds are partitioned between the stationary water phase and the moving solvent. Because the water phase is stationary, the components in a mixture that are most highly water-soluble, or those that have the greatest hydrogen-bonding capacity, are the ones that are held back and move most slowly. Paper chromatography applies mostly to highly polar compounds or to those that are polyfunctional. The most common use of paper chromatography is for sugars, amino acids, and natural pigments. Because filter paper is manufactured consistently, R_f values can often be relied on in paper chromatographic work. However, R_f values are customarily measured from the leading edge (top) of the spot—not from its center, as is customary in TLC.

PROBLEMS

1. A student spots an unknown sample on a TLC plate and develops it in dichloromethane solvent. Only one spot, for which the R_f value is 0.95, is observed. Does this indicate that the unknown material is a pure compound? What can be done to verify the purity of the sample?

2. You and another student were each given an unknown compound. Both samples contained colorless material. You each used the same brand of commercially prepared TLC plate and developed the plates using the same solvent.

Each of you obtained a single spot of $R_f = 0.75$. Were the two samples necessarily the same substance? How could you prove unambiguously that they were identical using TLC?

3. Consider a sample that is a mixture composed of biphenyl, benzoic acid, and benzyl alcohol. The sample is spotted on a TLC plate and developed in a dichloromethane–cyclohexane solvent mixture. Predict the *relative* R_f values for the three components in the sample. *Hint*: See Table 19.3.

4. Calculate the R_f value of a spot that travels 5.7 cm, with a solvent front that travels 13 cm.

5. A student spots an unknown sample on a TLC plate and develops it in pentane solvent. Only one spot, for which the R_f value is 0.05, is observed. Is the unknown material a pure compound? What can be done to verify the purity of the sample?

6. A *colorless* unknown substance is spotted on a TLC plate and developed in the correct solvent. The spots do not appear when visualization with a UV lamp or iodine vapors is attempted. What could you do in order to visualize the spots if the compound is

   a. An alkyl halide

   b. A ketone

   c. An amino acid

   d. A sugar

High-Performance Liquid Chromatography (HPLC)

The separation that can be achieved is greater if the column packing used in column chromatography is made more dense by using an adsorbent that has a smaller particle size. The solute molecules encounter a much larger surface area on which they can be adsorbed as they pass through the column packing. At the same time, the solvent spaces between the particles are reduced in size. As a result of this tight packing, equilibrium between the liquid and solid phases can be established rapidly with a fairly short column, and the degree of separation is markedly improved. The disadvantage of making the column packing more dense is that the solvent flow rate becomes very slow or even stops. Gravity is not strong enough to pull the solvent through a tightly packed column.

A recently developed technique can be applied to obtain much better separations with tightly packed columns. A pump forces the solvent through the column packing. As a result, solvent flow rate is increased and the advantage of better separation is retained. This technique, called **high-performance liquid chromatography (HPLC)**, is becoming widely applied to problems where separations by ordinary column chromatography are unsatisfactory. Because the pump often provides pressures in excess of 1000 pounds per square inch (psi), this method is also known as **high-pressure liquid chromatography**. High pressures are not required, however, and satisfactory separations can be achieved with pressures as low as 100 psi.

The basic design of an HPLC instrument is shown in Figure 21.1. The instrument contains the following essential components:

1. Solvent reservoir
2. Solvent filter and degasser
3. Pump
4. Pressure gauge
5. Sample injection system
6. Column
7. Detector
8. Amplifier and electronic controls
9. Chart recorder

There may be other variations on this simple design. Some instruments have heated ovens in order to maintain the column at a specified temperature, fraction collectors, and microprocessor-controlled data-handling systems. Additional filters for the solvent and sample may also be included. You may find it interesting to compare this schematic diagram with that shown in Technique 22 (Figure 22.2) for a gas-chromatography instrument. Many of the essential components are common to both types of instruments.

Solvent reservoir

Pressure gauge

Sample injector

Column

Filter

Pump

Reference detector

Sample detector

Amplifier

Recorder

© Cengage Learning 2013

Figure 21.1
Schematic diagram of a high-performance liquid chromatograph.

21.1 Adsorbents and Columns

The most important factor to consider when choosing a set of experimental conditions is the nature of the material packed into the column. You must also consider the size of the column that will be selected. The chromatography column is generally packed with silica or alumina adsorbents. Unlike column chromatography, however, the adsorbents used for HPLC have a much smaller particle size. Typically, particle size ranges from 5 to 20 μm in diameter for HPLC; it is on the order of 100 μm for column chromatography.

The adsorbent is packed into a column that can withstand the elevated pressures typical of this type of experiment. Generally, the column is constructed of stainless steel, although some columns that are constructed of a rigid polymeric material ("PEEK" —Poly Ether Ether Ketone) are available commercially. A strong column is required to withstand the high pressures that may be used. The columns are fitted with stainless steel connectors, which ensure a pressure-tight fit between the tubing that connects the column to the other components of the instrument.

Columns that fulfill a large number of specialized purposes are available. In this chapter, we consider only the four important types of columns. These are

1. Normal-phase chromatography
2. Reversed-phase chromatography
3. Ion-exchange chromatography
4. Size-exclusion chromatography

In most types of chromatography, the adsorbent is more polar that the mobile phase. For example, the solid packing material, which may be either silica or alumina, has a stronger affinity for polar molecules than does the solvent. As a result, the molecules in the sample adhere strongly to the solid phase, and their progress down the column is much slower than the rate at which solvent moves through the column. The time required for a substance to move through the column can be altered by changing the polarity of the solvent. In general, as the solvent becomes more polar, the faster substances move through the column. This type of behavior is known as **normal-phase chromatography**. In HPLC, you inject a sample onto a normal-phase column and elute it by varying the polarity of the solvent, much as you do with ordinary column chromatography. Disadvantages of normal-phase chromatography are that retention times tend to be long, and bands have a tendency to "tail."

These disadvantages can be ameliorated by selecting a column in which the solid support is *less polar* than the moving solvent phase. This type of chromatography is known as **reversed-phase chromatography.** In this type of chromatography, the silica column packing is treated with alkylating agents. As a result, nonpolar alkyl groups are bonded to the silica surface, making the adsorbent nonpolar. The alkylating agents that are used most commonly can attach methyl ($—CH_3$), octyl ($—C_8H_{17}$), or octadecyl ($—C_{18}H_{37}$) groups to the silica surface. The latter variation, where an 18-carbon chain is attached to the silica, is the most popular. This type of column is known as a **C-18 column**. The bonded alkyl groups have an effect similar to that which would be produced by an extremely thin organic solvent layer coating the surface of the silica particles. The interactions that take place between the substances dissolved in the solvent and the stationary phase thus become more like those observed in a liquid-liquid extraction. The solute particles distribute themselves between the two "solvents"—that is, between the moving solvent and the organic coating on the silica. The longer the chains of the alkyl groups that are bonded to the silica, the more effective the alkyl groups are as they interact with solute molecules.

Reversed-phase chromatography is widely used because the rate at which solute molecules exchange between moving phase and stationary phase is rapid, which means that substances pass through the column relatively quickly. Furthermore, problems arising from the "tailing" of peaks are reduced. A disadvantage of this type of column, however, is that the chemically bonded solid phases tend to decompose. The organic groups are slowly hydrolyzed from the surface of the silica, which leaves a normal silica surface exposed. Thus, the chromatographic process that takes place on the column slowly shifts from a reversed-phase to a normal-phase separation mechanism.

Another type of solid support that is sometimes used in reversed-phase chromatography is organic polymer beads. These beads present a surface to the moving phase that is largely organic in nature.

For solutions of ions, select a column that is packed with an ion-exchange resin. This type of chromatography is known as **ion-exchange chromatography**. The ion-exchange resin that is chosen can be either an anion-exchange resin or a cation-exchange resin, depending upon the nature of the sample being examined.

A fourth type of column is known as a **size-exclusion column** or a **gel-filtration column**. The interaction that takes place on this type of column is similar to that described in Technique 19, Section 19.15.

21.2 Column Dimensions

The dimensions of the column that you use depend upon the application. For analytical applications, a typical column is constructed of tubing that has an inside diameter of between 4 and 5 mm, although analytical columns with inside diameters of 1 or 2 mm are also available. A typical analytical column has a length of about 7.5 to 30 cm. This type of column is suitable for the separation of a 0.1- to 5-mg sample. With columns of smaller diameter, it is possible to perform an analysis with samples smaller than 1 *micro*gram.

High-performance liquid chromatography is an excellent analytical technique, but the separated compounds may also be isolated. The technique can be used for preparative experiments. Just as in column chromatography, the fractions can be collected into individual receiving containers as they pass through the column. The solvents can be evaporated from these fractions, allowing you to isolate separated components of the original mixture. Samples that range in size from 5 to 100 mg can be separated on a semipreparative, or **semiprep**, column. The dimensions of a semiprep column are typically 8 mm inside diameter and 10 cm in length. A semiprep column is a practical choice when you wish to use the same column for both analytical and preparative separations. A semiprep column is small enough to provide reasonable sensitivity in analyses, but it is also capable of handling moderate-size samples when you need to isolate the components of a mixture. Even larger samples can be separated using a **preparative column**. This type of column is useful when you wish to collect the components of a mixture and then use the pure samples for additional study (e.g., for a subsequent chemical reaction or for spectroscopic analysis). A preparative column may be as large as 20 mm in inside diameter and 30 cm in length. A preparative column can handle samples as large as 1 g per injection.

21.3 Solvents

The choice of solvent used for an HPLC separation depends on the type of chromatographic process selected. For a normal-phase separation, the solvent is selected based on its polarity. The criteria described in Technique 19, Section 19.4B, are used. A solvent of very low polarity might be pentane, petroleum ether, hexane, or carbon tetrachloride; a solvent of very high polarity might be water, acetic acid, methanol, or 1-propanol. For a reversed-phase experiment, a less polar solvent causes solutes to migrate *faster*. For example, for a mixed methanol-water solvent, as the percentage of methanol in the solvent increases (solvent becomes less polar), the time required to elute the components of a mixture from a column decreases. The behavior of solvents as eluents in a reversed-phase chromatography would be the reverse of the order shown in Table 19.2 (Technique 19).

If a single solvent (or solvent mixture) is used for the entire separation, the chromatogram is said to be **isochratic**. Special electronic devices are available with HPLC instruments that allow you to program changes in the solvent composition from the beginning to the end of the chromatography. These are called **gradient elution systems**. With gradient elution, the time required for a separation may be shortened considerably.

The need for pure solvents is especially acute with HPLC. The narrow bore of the column and the very small particle size of the column packing require that solvents be particularly pure and free of insoluble residue. In most cases, the solvents must be filtered through ultrafine filters and **degassed** (have dissolved gases removed) before they can be used.

The solvent gradient is chosen so that the eluting power of the solvent increases over the duration of the experiment. The result is that components of the mixture that tend to move very slowly through the column are caused to move faster as the eluting power of the solvent gradually increases. The instrument can be programmed to change the composition of the solvent following a linear gradient or a nonlinear gradient, depending on the specific requirements of the separation.

21.4 Detectors

A flow-through **detector** must be provided to determine when a substance has passed through the column. In most applications, the detector detects either the change in index of refraction of the liquid as its composition changes or the presence of solute by its absorption of ultraviolet or visible light. The signal generated by the detector is amplified and treated electronically in a manner similar to that found in gas chromatography (Technique 22, Section 22.6).

A detector that responds to changes in the index of refraction of the solution may be considered the most universal of the HPLC detectors. The refractive index of the liquid passing through the detector changes slightly, but significantly, as the liquid changes from pure solvent to a liquid where the solvent contains some type of organic solute. This change in refractive index can be detected and compared to the refractive index of pure solvent. The difference in index values is then recorded as a peak on a chart. A disadvantage of this type of detector is that it must respond to very small changes in refractive index. As a result, the detector tends to be unstable and difficult to balance.

When the components of the mixture have some type of absorption in the ultraviolet or visible regions of the spectrum, a detector that is adjusted to detect absorption at a particular wavelength of light can be used. This type of detector is much more stable, and the readings tend to be more reliable. Unfortunately, many organic compounds do not absorb ultraviolet light, and this type of detector cannot be used.

21.5 Presentation of Data

The data produced by an HPLC instrument appear in the form of a chart, where detector response is the vertical axis and time is represented on the horizontal axis. These are recorded on a continuously moving strip of chart paper, although they may also be observed in graphic form on a computer display. In virtually all respects, the form of the data is identical to that produced by a gas chromatograph; in fact, in many cases, the data-handling system for the two types of instruments is essentially identical. To understand how to analyze the data from an HPLC instrument, read Sections 22.12 and 22.13 in Technique 22.

REFERENCE

Rubinson, K. A. *Chemical Analysis.* Little, Brown and Co: Boston, 1987. Chapter 14, Liquid Chromatography.

PROBLEMS

1. For a mixture of biphenyl, benzoic acid, and benzyl alcohol, predict the order of elution and describe any differences that you would expect for a normal-phase HPLC experiment (in hexane solvent) compared with a reversed-phase experiment (in tetrahydrofuran-water solvent).
2. How would the *gradient elution program* differ between normal-phase and reversed-phase chromatography?

Gas Chromatography

Gas chromatography is one of the most useful instrumental tools for separating and analyzing organic compounds that can be vaporized without decomposition. Common uses include testing the purity of a substance and separating the components of a mixture. The relative amounts of the components in a mixture may also be determined. In some cases, gas chromatography can be used to identify a compound. In microscale work, it can also be used as a preparative method to isolate pure compounds from a small amount of a mixture.

Gas chromatography resembles column chromatography in principle, but it differs in three respects. First, the partitioning processes for the compounds to be separated are carried out between a **moving gas phase** and a **stationary liquid phase.** (Recall that in column chromatography the moving phase is a liquid and the stationary phase is a solid adsorbent.) A second difference is that the temperature of the gas system can be controlled because the column is contained in an insulated oven. And third, the concentration of any given compound in the gas phase is a function of its vapor pressure only. Because gas chromatography separates the components of a mixture primarily on the basis of their vapor pressures (or boiling points), this technique is also similar in principle to fractional distillation. In microscale work, it is sometimes used to separate and isolate compounds from a mixture; fractional distillation would normally be used with larger amounts of material.

Gas chromatography (GC) is also known as **vapor-phase chromatography** (VPC) and as **gas–liquid partition chromatography** (GLPC). All three names, as well as their indicated abbreviations, are often found in the literature of organic chemistry. In reference to the technique, the last term, GLPC, is the most strictly correct and is preferred by most authors.

22.1 The Gas Chromatograph

The apparatus used to carry out a gas–liquid chromatographic separation is generally called a **gas chromatograph.** A typical student-model gas chromatograph, the GOW-MAC model 69-350, is illustrated in Figure 22.1. A schematic block diagram of a basic gas chromatograph is shown in Figure 22.2. The basic elements of the apparatus are apparent. In short, the sample is injected into the chromatograph, and it is immediately vaporized in a heated injection chamber and introduced into a moving stream of gas, called the **carrier gas**. The vaporized sample is then swept into a column filled with particles coated with a liquid adsorbent. The column is contained in a temperature-controlled oven. As the sample passes through the column, it is subjected to many gas–liquid partitioning processes, and the components are separated. As each component leaves the column, its presence is detected by an electrical detector that generates a signal that is recorded on a strip chart recorder.

Many modern instruments are also equipped with a microprocessor, which can be programmed to change parameters, such as the temperature of the oven, while a mixture is being separated on a column. With this capability, it is possible to optimize the separation of components and to complete a run in a relatively short time.

405

Figure 22.1
Gas chromatograph.

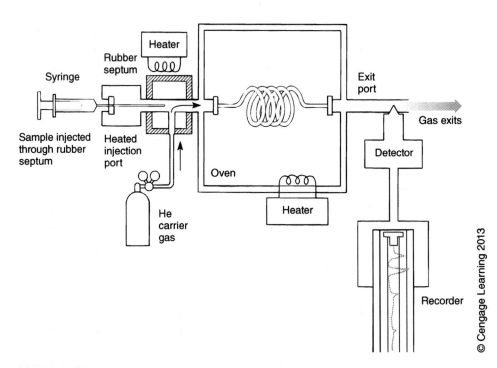

Figure 22.2
Schematic diagram of a gas chromatograph.

22.2 The Column   The heart of the gas chromatograph is the column. There are two types in common use: packed and capillary columns.

Packed Columns. These columns are usually constructed of stainless steel tubing with diameters of 1/8 in. (3 mm) or 1/4 in. (6 mm) and lengths of from 4 to 12 feet. The column is packed with a liquid or low-melting solid as the **stationary phase** distributed on a solid **support material.** The stationary phase must be relatively nonvolatile, that is, it should have a low vapor pressure and a high boiling point. Some typical stationary phases used with packed columns are listed in Table 22.1. Typical support materials are shown in Table 22.2. The most common support material consists of diatomaceous earth (Chromosorb).

Packed columns are bought from commercial sources or may sometimes be made in the laboratory by researchers. Basically, you dissolve one of the stationary phases listed in Table 22.1 in methylene chloride. Then you add the support material to the solution followed by removal of the solvent on a rotary evaporator (see Technique 7, Section 7.11, and Figure 7.19). The evaporation process evenly distributes the stationary phase onto the support material and yields a dry solid. In the final step, the solid, consisting of the stationary phase coated on the support

Table 22.1 Typical Stationary Phases

	Type	Composition	Maximum Temperature (°C)	Typical Use
Apiezons (L, M, N, etc.)	Hydrocarbon greases (varying MW)	Hydrocarbon mixtures	250–300	Hydrocarbons
SE-30	Methyl silicone rubber	Like silicone oil, but cross-linked	350	General applications
DC-200	Silicone oil $(R=CH_3)$	$R_3Si-O-\left[\begin{array}{c} R \\ \| \\ Si-O \\ \| \\ R \end{array}\right]_n SiR_3$	225	Aldehydes, ketones, halocarbons
DC-710	Silicone oil $(R=CH_3)$ $(R=C_6H_5)$	$\left[\begin{array}{c} R' \\ \| \\ Si-O \\ \| \\ R \end{array}\right]_n -$	300	General applications
Carbowaxes (400–20*M*)	Polyethylene glycols (varying chain lengths)	Polyether $HO-(CH_2CH_2-O)_n-CH_2CH_2OH$	Up to 250	Alcohols, ethers, halocarbons
DEGS	Diethylene glycol succinate	Polyester $\left[CH_2CH_2-O-\overset{\displaystyle O}{\underset{\|}{C}}-(CH_2)_2-\overset{\displaystyle O}{\underset{\|}{C}}-O\right]_n$	200	General applications

Increasing polarity →

Table 22.2 Typical Solid Supports

Crushed firebrick	Chromosorb T
Nylon beads	(Teflon beads)
Glass beads	Chromosorb P
Silica	(pink diatomaceous earth,
Alumina	high absorptivity, pH 6–7)
Charcoal	Chromosorb W
Molecular sieves	(white diatomaceous earth,
	medium absorptivity, pH 8–10)
	Chromosorb G
	(like the above,
	low absorptivity, pH 8.5)

© Cengage Learning 2013

material, is packed into the stainless steel tubing as evenly as possible. After plugging the ends of the tubing with glass wool to prevent the solid from coming out, the tubing is rolled into a coil that will fit into the oven of the gas chromatograph with the two ends connected to the gas entrance and exit ports (see Figure 22.2).

The selection of the packed column depends on the application. If one wants to separate nonpolar compounds that vary only by boiling point, one often uses one of the polydimethyl siloxanes (methyl silicones) columns such as SE-30 or DC-200. For more polar compounds, chemists will select a silicone column that has attached methyl and phenyl groups on the silicone polymer (DC-710). Separating even more polar compounds calls for a polyethylene glycol (Carbowax) column or a column packed with diethylene glycol succinate (DEGS). Chemists will need to carefully note the maximum temperature that can be employed with the columns (Table 22.1). Above the specified temperature, the liquid phase itself will begin to "bleed" off the column.

Packed columns are cheaper to buy and can separate larger quantities of material than capillary columns. Packed columns, however, are not as efficient in separating materials, especially with compounds with very similar polarities or boiling points.

Capillary Columns. Many gas chromatographs sold today use capillary columns rather than packed columns. Capillary columns are made of very thin fused-silica with an inner diameter of about 0.25 mm. Typically the columns are very long, often 25 meters up to 100 meters in length. The stationary phase is coated as a film on the inner surface with a thickness of about 0.25 μm. The film is bonded to the silica and cross-linked to improve thermal stability and to help prevent bleeding of the stationary phase from the column. Most of the capillary columns do not have any support material in them.

The liquid stationary phases used with capillary columns are similar to those used in packed columns. The most common stationary phases are polysiloxanes (silicones) that contain various substituents that modify the polarity of the phase. Polydimethyl siloxane (methyl silicone) is nonpolar. Replacing methyl groups with increasing numbers of phenyl substituents increases the polarity of the silicone. For example, J&W DB-1, or a similar stationary phase sold by other companies,[1] has the same properties as methyl silicone (SE-30 or DC-200) and is used with nonpolar

---

[1] Many companies supply capillary columns: J&W (Alltech), Supelco, HP, Chrompack, and Quadrex are some of the suppliers. Comparison of chemical compositions, polarities, and applications may be made by consulting: http://www.quadrexcorp.com/2009/index.htm (accessed April 23, 2011).

compounds that separate by boiling point differences. For other applications, a J&W DB-5 may be used. This silicone consists of a material with 95% methyl and 5% phenyl substituents on the silicone. A DB-17 column has 50% phenyl groups replacing methyl groups, and would have a medium polarity (similar to DC-710). J&W DB-wax is used to separate much more polar compounds and is similar to diethylene glycols (Carbowax). Chiral capillary columns are also available that can separate enantiomers (Section 22.8).

Because of the length and small diameter of capillary columns, there is increased interaction between the compounds in the mixture and the stationary phase. Capillary columns are, therefore, much more efficient in separating compounds with similar properties than with packed columns, but only if a dilute solution of a mixture of compounds is injected into the column. In order to obtain a satisfactory separation, you must dissolve about 1 drop of a mixture in about 2 mL of a solvent such as methylene chloride or pentane. *About 1 μL* of this dilute sample is injected onto the column. In contrast, 1 to 10 μL of an undiluted sample can often be analyzed on a packed column without overloading the column. These expensive capillary columns must be purchased from commercial companies specializing in their manufacture. Sensible researchers would never try to make their own capillary columns!

In the final step, the liquid-phase-coated support material is packed into the tubing as evenly as possible. The tubing is bent or coiled so that it fits into the oven of the gas chromatograph with its two ends connected to the gas entrance and exit ports.

Selection of a liquid phase usually revolves about two factors. First, most of them have an upper temperature limit above which they cannot be used. Above the specified limit of temperature, the liquid phase itself will begin to "bleed" off the column. Second, the materials to be separated must be considered. For polar samples, it is usually best to use a polar liquid phase; for nonpolar samples, a nonpolar liquid phase is indicated. The liquid phase performs best when the substances to be separated *dissolve* in it.

Most researchers today buy packed columns from commercial sources, rather than pack their own. A wide variety of types and lengths is available. Alternatives to packed columns are Golay or glass capillary columns of diameters 0.1–0.2 mm. With these columns, no solid support is required, and the liquid is coated directly on the inner walls of the tubing. Liquid phases commonly used in glass capillary columns are similar in composition to those used in packed columns. They include DB-1 (similar to SE-30), DB-17 (similar to DC-710), and DB-WAX (similar to Carbowax 20M). The length of a capillary column is usually very long, typically 50–100 ft. Because of the length and small diameter, there is increased interaction between the sample and the stationary phase. Gas chromatographs equipped with these small-diameter columns are able to separate components more effectively than instruments using larger packed columns.

22.3 Principles of Separation

After a column is selected and installed, the carrier gas (usually helium, argon, or nitrogen) is allowed to flow through the column supporting the liquid phase. The mixture of compounds to be separated is introduced into the carrier gas stream, where its components are equilibrated (or partitioned) between the moving gas phase and the stationary liquid phase (Figure 22.3). The latter is held stationary because it is adsorbed onto the surfaces of the support material.

The sample is introduced into the gas chromatograph by a microliter syringe. It is injected as a liquid or as a solution through a rubber septum into a heated chamber, called the **injection port,** where it is vaporized and mixed with the carrier gas.

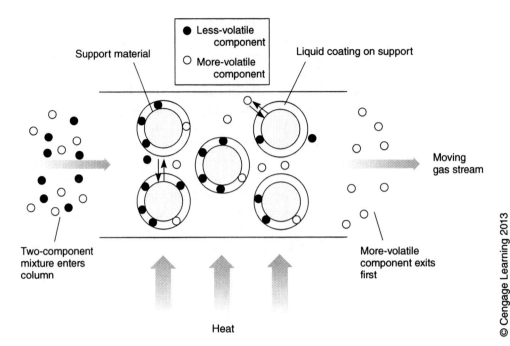

Figure 22.3
The separation process.

As this mixture reaches the column, which is heated in a controlled oven, it begins to equilibrate between the liquid and gas phases. The length of time required for a sample to move through the column is a function of how much time it spends in the vapor phase and how much time it spends in the liquid phase. The more time it spends in the vapor phase, the faster it gets to the end of the column. In most separations, the components of a sample have similar solubilities in the liquid phase. Therefore, the time the different compounds spend in the vapor phase is primarily a function of the vapor pressure, and the more volatile component arrives at the end of the column first, as illustrated in Figure 22.3. By selecting the correct temperature of the oven and the correct liquid phase, the compounds in the injected mixture travel through the column at different rates and are separated.

22.4 Factors Affecting Separation

Several factors determine the rate at which a given compound travels through a gas chromatograph. First of all, compounds with low boiling points will generally travel through the gas chromatograph faster than compounds of higher boiling points. This is because the column is heated, and low-boiling compounds always have higher vapor pressures than compounds of higher boiling point. In general, therefore, for compounds with the same functional group, the higher the molecular weight, the longer the retention time. For most molecules, the boiling point increases as the molecular weight increases. If the column is heated to a temperature that is too high, however, the entire mixture to be separated is flushed through the column at the same rate as the carrier gas, and no equilibration takes place with the liquid phase. On the other hand, at too low a temperature, the mixture dissolves in the liquid phase and never revaporizes. Thus, it is retained on the column.

The second factor, the rate of flow of the carrier gas, is important. The carrier gas must not move so rapidly that molecules of the sample in the vapor phase cannot equilibrate with those dissolved in the liquid phase. This may result in poor separation between components in the injected mixture. If the rate of flow is too slow, however, the bands broaden significantly, leading to poor resolution (see Section 22.8).

The third factor is the choice of liquid phase used in the column. The molecular weights, functional groups, and polarities of the component molecules in the mixture to be separated must be considered when a liquid phase is being chosen. One generally uses a different type of material for hydrocarbons, for instance, than for esters. The materials to be separated should *dissolve* in the liquid. The useful temperature limit of the liquid phase selected must also be considered.

The fourth factor, the length of the column, is also important. Compounds that resemble one another closely, in general, require longer columns than dissimilar compounds. Many kinds of isomeric mixtures fit into the "difficult" category. The components of isomeric mixtures are so much alike that they travel through the column at very similar rates. You need a longer column, therefore, to take advantage of any differences that may exist.

22.5 Advantages of Gas Chromatography

All factors that have been mentioned must be adjusted by the chemist for any mixture to be separated. Considerable preliminary investigation is often required before a mixture can be separated successfully into its components by gas chromatography. Nevertheless, the advantages of the technique are many.

First, many mixtures can be separated by this technique when no other method is adequate. Second, as little as 1–10 μL (1 μL$=10^{-6}$L) of a mixture can be separated by this technique. This advantage is particularly important when working at the microscale level. Third, when gas chromatography is coupled with an electronic recording device (see following discussion), the amount of each component present in the separated mixture can be estimated quantitatively.

The range of compounds that can be separated by gas chromatography extends from gases, such as oxygen (bp $-$ 183°C) and nitrogen (bp $-$ 196°C), to organic compounds with boiling points over 400°C. The only requirement for the compounds to be separated is that they have an appreciable vapor pressure at a temperature at which they can be separated and that they be thermally stable at this temperature.

22.6 Monitoring the Column (The Detector)

To follow the separation of the mixture injected into the gas chromatograph, it is necessary to use an electrical device called a **detector.** Two types of detectors in common use are the **thermal conductivity detector (TCD)** and the **flame-ionization detector (FID).**

The thermal conductivity detector is simply a hot wire placed in the gas stream at the column exit. The wire is heated by constant electrical voltage. When a steady stream of carrier gas passes over this wire, the rate at which it loses heat and its electrical conductance have constant values. When the composition of the vapor stream changes, the rate of heat flow from the wire, and hence its resistance, changes. Helium, which has a higher thermal conductivity than most organic substances, is a common carrier gas. Thus, when a substance elutes in the vapor stream, the thermal conductivity of the moving gases will be lower than with helium alone. The wire then heats up, and its resistance decreases.

A typical TCD operates by difference. Two detectors are used: one exposed to the actual effluent gas and the other exposed to a reference flow of carrier gas only. To achieve this situation, a portion of the carrier gas stream is diverted *before* it enters the injection port. The diverted gas is routed through a reference column into which no sample has been admitted. The detectors mounted in the sample and reference columns are arranged so as to form the arms of a Wheatstone bridge circuit, as shown in Figure 22.4. As long as the carrier gas alone flows over both detectors, the circuit is in balance. However, when a sample elutes from the sample column, the bridge circuit becomes unbalanced, creating an electrical signal. This signal can

Figure 22.4
Typical thermal conductivity detector.

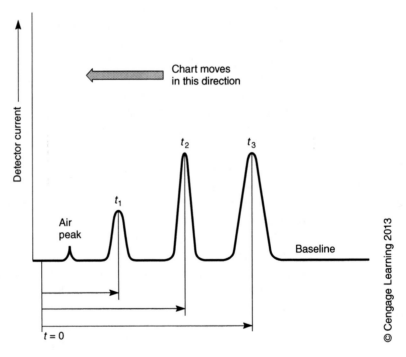

Figure 22.5
Typical chromatogram.

be amplified and used to activate a strip chart recorder. The recorder is an instrument that plots, by means of a moving pen, the unbalanced bridge current versus time on a continuously moving roll of chart paper. This record of detector response (current) versus time is called a **chromatogram.** A typical gas chromatogram is illustrated in Figure 22.5. Deflections of the pen are called **peaks.**

When a sample is injected, some air (CO_2, H_2O, N_2, and O_2) is introduced along with the sample. The air travels through the column almost as rapidly as the carrier gas; as it passes the detector, it causes a small pen response, thereby giving a peak,

Vent

Flame

To amplifier

Air

H₂

Column
effluent

© Cengage Learning 2013

Figure 22.6
Flame-ionization detector.

called the **air peak.** At later times (t_1, t_2, t_3), the components also give rise to peaks on the chromatogram as they pass out of the column and past the detector.

In a flame-ionization detector, the effluent from the column is directed into a flame produced by the combustion of hydrogen, as illustrated in Figure 22.6. As organic compounds burn in the flame, ion fragments are produced that collect on the ring above the flame. The resulting electrical signal is amplified and sent to a recorder in a similar manner to a TCD, except that an FID does not produce an air peak. The main advantage of the FID is that it is more sensitive and can be used to analyze smaller quantities of sample. Also, because an FID does not respond to water, a gas chromatograph with this detector can be used to analyze aqueous solutions. Two disadvantages are that it is more difficult to operate and the detection process destroys the sample. Therefore, an FID gas chromatograph cannot be used to do preparative work, which is often desired in the microscale laboratory.

22.7 Retention Time

The period following injection that is required for a compound to pass through the column is called the **retention time** of that compound. For a given set of constant conditions (flow rate of carrier gas, column temperature, column length, liquid phase, injection port temperature, carrier), the retention time of any compound is always constant (much like the R_f value in thin-layer chromatography, as described in Technique 20, Section 20.9). The retention time is measured from the time of injection to the time of maximum pen deflection (detector current) for the component being observed. This value, when obtained under controlled conditions, can identify a compound by a direct comparison of it with values for known compounds determined under the same conditions. For easier measurement of retention times, most strip chart recorders are adjusted to move the paper at a rate that corresponds to time divisions calibrated on the chart paper. The retention times (t_1, t_2, t_3) are indicated in Figure 22.5 for the three peaks illustrated.

Most modern gas chromatographs are attached to a "data station," which uses a computer or a microprocessor to process the data. With these instruments, the chart often does not have divisions. Instead, the computer prints the retention time, usually to the nearest 0.01 minute, above each peak.

22.8 Chiral Stationary Phases

A recent innovation in gas chromatography is to use chiral adsorbent materials to achieve separations of stereoisomers. The interaction between a particular stereoisomer and the chiral adsorbent may be different from the interaction between the opposite stereoisomer and the same chiral adsorbent. As a result, retention times for the two stereoisomers are likely to be sufficiently different to allow for a clean separation. The interactions between a chiral substance and the chiral adsorbent will include hydrogen-bonding and dipole-dipole attraction forces, although other properties may also be involved. One enantiomer should interact more strongly with the adsorbent than its opposite form. Thus, one enantiomer should pass through the gas chromatography column more slowly than its opposite form.

The ability of chiral adsorbents to separate stereoisomers is rapidly finding many useful applications, particularly in the synthesis of pharmaceutical agents. The biological activity of chiral substances often depends upon their stereochemistry because the living body is a highly chiral environment. A large number of pharmaceutical compounds have two enantiomeric forms that in many cases show significant differences in their behavior and activity. The ability to prepare enantiomerically pure drugs is very important because these pure substances are much more potent (and often have fewer side effects) than their racemic analogues.

Another type of stationary phase in gas chromatography is based on molecules such as the **cyclodextrins.** With these materials, the discrimination between enantiomers depends on the interactions between the stereoisomers and the chiral cavity that is formed within these materials. Because enantiomers differ in shape, they will fit differently within the chiral cavity. The result will be that the enantiomers will pass through the cyclodextrin stationary phase at different rates, thus leading to a separation.

The cyclodextrins owe their specificity to their structure, which is based on polymers of D-(+)-glucose. The hydroxyl groups of the glucose have been alkylated, so that the cavity is relatively nonpolar. The exterior hydroxyl groups of the cyclodextrins have also been substituted with *tert*-butyldimethylsilyl groups. The result is a material that can also utilize differences in hydrogen-bonding and dipole—dipole interactions to separate stereoisomers.

The structure of one important cyclodextrin-based chiral adsorbent is shown in Figure 22.7. Gas chromatography using this chiral adsorbent as a stationary phase has been used to separate a wide variety of stereoisomers. In one recent publication,

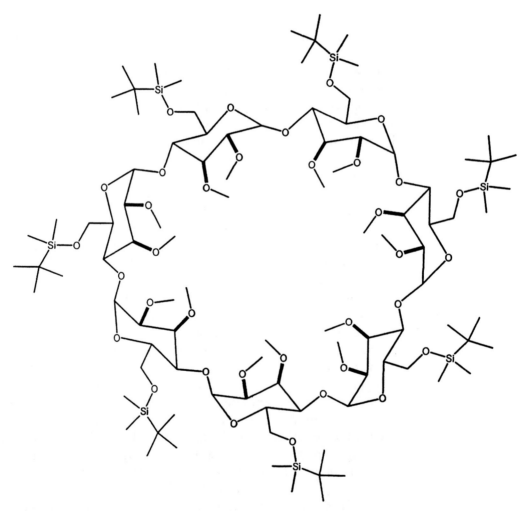

© Cengage Learning 2013

Figure 22.7
Cyclodextrin derivative used as a chiral adsorbent in gas chromatography.

this method was used to isolate a pure sample of (S)-(+)-2-methyl-4-octanol, a male-specific compound released by the sugarcane weevil, *Sphenophorus levis*.[2]

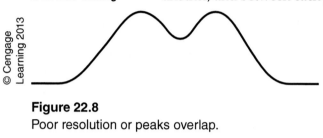

(S)-(+)-2-Methyl-4-octanol

© Cengage Learning 2013

22.9 Poor Resolution and Tailing

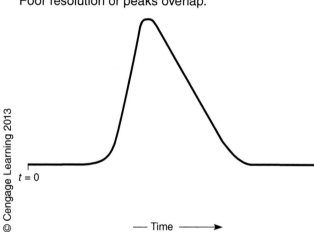

Figure 22.8
Poor resolution or peaks overlap.

t = 0

— Time ——→

Figure 22.9
Tailing.

© Cengage Learning 2013

The peaks in Figure 22.5 are well **resolved**. That is, the peaks are separated from one another, and between each pair of adjacent peaks the tracing returns to the **baseline**. In Figure 22.8, the peaks overlap, and the resolution is not good. Poor resolution is often caused by using too much sample, too high a column temperature, too short a column, a liquid phase that does not discriminate well between the two components, a column with too large a diameter, or, in short, almost any wrongly adjusted parameter. When peaks are poorly resolved, it is more difficult to determine the relative amount of each component. Methods for determining the relative percentages of each component are given in Section 22.12.

Another desirable feature illustrated by the chromatogram in Figure 22.5 is that each peak is symmetrical. A common example of an unsymmetrical peak is one in which **tailing** has occurred, as shown in Figure 22.9. Tailing usually results from injecting too much sample into the gas chromatograph. Another cause of tailing occurs with polar compounds, such as alcohols and aldehydes. These compounds may be temporarily adsorbed on column walls or areas of the support material that are not adequately coated by the liquid phase. Therefore, they do not leave in a band, and tailing results.

22.10 Qualitative Analysis

A disadvantage of the gas chromatograph is that it gives no information whatever about the identities of the substances it has separated. The little information it does provide is given by the retention time. It is hard to reproduce this quantity from day to day, however, and exact duplications of separations performed last month may be difficult to make this month. It is usually necessary to **calibrate** the column each time it is used. That is, you must run pure samples of all known and suspected components of a mixture individually, just before chromatographing the mixture, to obtain the retention time of each known compound. As an alternative, each suspected component can be added, one by one, to the unknown mixture while the operator looks to see which peak has its intensity increased relative to the unmodified mixture. Another solution is to *collect* the components individually as they emerge from the gas chromatograph. Each component can then be identified by other means, such as by infrared or nuclear magnetic resonance spectroscopy or by mass spectrometry.

[2] Zarbin, P. H. G.; Princival, J. L.; dos Santos, A. A.; de Oliveira, A. R. M. Synthesis of (S)-(+)-2-Methyl-4-octanol: Male-Specific Compound Released by Sugarcane Weevil *Sphenophorus levis*. *Journal of the Brazilian Chemical Society*. 15 (**2004**): 331–334.

22.11 Collecting the Sample

For gas chromatography with a thermal conductivity detector, it is possible to collect samples that have passed through the column. One method uses a gas-collection tube (see Figure 22.10), which is included in most microscale glassware kits. A collection tube is joined to the exit port of the column by inserting the ℸ5/5 inner joint into a metal adapter, which is connected to the exit port. When a sample is eluted from the column in the vapor state, it is cooled by the connecting adapter and the gas-collection tube and condenses in the collection tube. The gas-collection tube is removed from the adapter when the recorder indicates that the desired sample has completely passed through the column. After the first sample has been collected, the process can be repeated with another gas-collection tube.

To isolate the liquid, the tapered joint of the collection tube is inserted into a 0.1-mL conical vial, which has a ℸ5/5 outer joint. The assembly is placed into a test tube, as illustrated in Figure 22.11. During centrifugation, the sample is forced into the bottom of the conical vial. After the apparatus is disassembled, the liquid can be removed from the vial with a syringe for a boiling-point determination or analysis by infrared spectroscopy. If a determination of the sample weight is desired, the empty conical vial and cap should be tared and reweighed after the liquid has been collected. It is advisable to dry the gas collection tube and the conical vial in an oven before use to prevent contamination by water or other solvents used in cleaning this glassware.

Another method for collecting samples is to connect a cooled trap to the exit port of the column. A simple trap, suitable for microscale work, is illustrated in Figure 22.12. Suitable coolants include ice water, liquid nitrogen, or

Figure 22.10
Gas-chromatography
collection tube.

Rubber septum cap with a hole cut in the center

If the septum cap fits snugly in the test tube, it is not necessary to fold the top part of the septum cap over the lip of the test tube.

1.5-cm × 12.5-cm Test tube

Cotton

© Cengage Learning 2013

Figure 22.11
Gas-chromatography collection tube
and 0.1-mL conical vial.

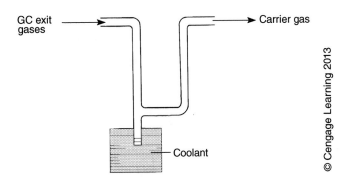

Figure 22.12
Collection trap.

dry ice–acetone. For instance, if the coolant is liquid nitrogen (bp − 196°C) and the carrier gas is helium (bp − 269°C), compounds boiling above the temperature of liquid nitrogen generally are condensed or trapped in the small tube at the bottom of the U-shaped tube. The small tube is scored with a file just below the point where it is connected to the larger tube, the tube is broken off, and the sample is removed for analysis. To collect each component of the mixture, you must change the trap after each sample is collected.

22.12 Quantitative Analysis

The area under a gas-chromatograph peak is proportional to the amount (moles) of compound eluted. Hence, the molar percentage composition of a mixture can be approximated by comparing relative peak areas. This method of analysis assumes that the detector is equally sensitive to all compounds eluted and that it gives a linear response with respect to amount. Nevertheless, it gives reasonably accurate results.

The simplest method of measuring the area of a peak is by geometrical approximation, or triangulation. In this method, you multiply the height h of the peak above the baseline of the chromatogram by the width of the peak at half of its height $w_{1/2}$. This is illustrated in Figure 22.13. The baseline is approximated by drawing a line between the two side arms of the peak. This method works well only if the peak is symmetrical. If the peak has tailed or is unsymmetrical, it is best to cut out the peaks with scissors and weigh the pieces of paper on an **analytical balance**. Because the weight per area of a piece of good chart paper is reasonably constant from place to place, the ratio of the areas is the same as the ratio of the weights. To obtain a percentage composition for the mixture, first add all the peak areas (weights). Then, to calculate the percentage of any component in the mixture, divide its individual area by the total area and multiply the result by 100. A sample calculation is illustrated in Figure 22.14. If peaks overlap (see Figure 22.8), either the gas-chromatographic conditions must be readjusted to achieve better resolution of the peaks or the peak shape must be estimated.

Approximate area = $h ¥ w_{1/2}$

Figure 22.13
Triangulation of a peak.

There are various instrumental means, which are built into recorders, of detecting the amounts of each sample automatically. One method uses a separate pen that produces a trace that integrates the area under each peak. Another method employs an electronic device that automatically prints out the area under each peak and the percentage composition of the sample.

Figure 22.14
Sample percentage composition calculation.

Most modern data stations label the top of each peak with its retention time in minutes. When the trace is completed, the computer prints a table of all the peaks with their retention times, areas, and the percentage of the total area (sum of all the peaks) that each peak represents. Some caution should be used with these results because the computer often does not include smaller peaks and occasionally does not resolve narrow peaks that are so close together that they overlap. If the trace has several peaks and you would like the ratio of only two of them, you will have to determine their percentages yourself using only their two areas or instruct the instrument to integrate only these two peaks.

For the experiments in this textbook, we have assumed that the detector is equally sensitive to all compounds eluted. Compounds with different functional groups or with widely varying molecular weights, however, produce different responses with both TCD and FID gas chromatographs. With a TCD, the responses are different because not all compounds have the same thermal conductivity. Different compounds analyzed with an FID gas chromatograph also give different responses because the detector response varies with the type of ions produced. For both types of detectors, it is possible to calculate a **response factor** for each compound in a mixture. Response factors are usually determined by making up an equimolar mixture of two compounds, one of which is considered to be the reference. The mixture is separated on a gas chromatograph, and the relative percentages are calculated using one of the methods described previously. From these percentages you can determine a response factor for the compound being compared to the reference. If you do this for all the components in a mixture, you can then use these correction factors to make more accurate calculations of the relative percentages for the compounds in the mixture.

To illustrate how response factors are determined, consider the following example. An equimolar mixture of benzene, hexane, and ethyl acetate is prepared and analyzed using a flame-ionization gas chromatograph. The peak areas obtained are

> Hexane 831158
> Ethyl acetate 1449695
> Benzene 966463

In most cases, benzene is taken as the standard, and its response factor is defined to be equal to 1.00. Calculation of the response factors for the other components of the test mixture proceeds as follows:

Hexane	831158/966463 = 0.86
Ethyl acetate	1449695/966463 = 1.50
Benzene	966463/966463 = 1.00 (by definition)

Notice that the response factors calculated in this example are molar response factors. It is necessary to correct these values by the relative molecular weights of each substance to obtain weight response factors.

When you use a flame-ionization gas chromatograph for quantitative analysis, it is first necessary to determine the response factors for each component of the mixture being analyzed, as just shown. For a quantitative analysis, it is likely that you will have to convert molar response factors into weight response factors. Next, the chromatography experiment using the unknown samples is performed. The observed peak areas for each component are corrected using the response factors in order to arrive at the correct weight percentage of each component in the sample. The application of response factors to correct the original results of a quantitative analysis will be illustrated in the following section.

22.13 Treatment of Data: Chromatograms Produced by Modern Data Stations

A. Gas Chromatograms and Data Tables

Most modern gas chromatography instruments are equipped with computer-based data stations. Interfacing the instrument with a computer allows the operator to display and manipulate the results in whatever manner might be desired. The operator thus can view the output in a convenient form. The computer can display the actual gas chromatogram and display the integration results. It can even display the result of two experiments simultaneously, making a comparison of parallel experiments convenient.

Figure 22.15 shows a gas chromatogram of a mixture of hexane, ethyl acetate, and benzene. The peaks corresponding to each substance can be seen; the peaks are labeled with their respective retention times. We can also see that there is a very small amount of an unspecified impurity, with a retention time of about 3.4 minutes.

	Retention Time (minutes)
Hexane	2.959
Ethyl acetate	3.160
Benzene	3.960

Figure 22.16 shows part of the printed output that accompanies the gas chromatogram. It is this information that is used in the quantitative analysis of the mixture. According to the printout, the first peak has a retention time of 2.954 minutes (the difference between the retention times that appear as labels on the graph and those that appear in the data table are not significant). The computer has also determined the area under this peak (422,373 counts). Finally, the computer has calculated the percentage of the first substance (hexane) by determining the total area

Chart Speed = 15.96 cm/min   Attenuation = 1573   Zero Offset = 9%
Start Time = 2.860 min   End Time = 4.100 min   Min/Tick = 1.00

Figure 22.15
A sample gas chromatogram obtained from a data station.

of all the peaks in the chromatogram (1,227,054 counts) and dividing that into the area for the hexane peak. The result is displayed as 34.4217%. In a similar manner, the data table shows the retention times and peak areas for the other two peaks in the sample, along with a determination of the percentage of each substance in the mixture.

B. Application of Response Factors

If the detector responded with equal sensitivity to each of the components of the mixture, the data table shown in Figure 22.16 would contain the complete quantitative analysis of the sample. Unfortunately, as we have seen (Section 22.12), gas chromatography detectors respond more sensitively to some substances than they do to others. To correct for this discrepancy, it is necessary to apply corrections that are based on the **response factors** for each component of the mixture.

The method for determining the response factors was introduced in Section 22.12. In this section, we will see how this information is applied in order to obtain a correct

```
Run Mode        : Analysis
Peak Measurement: Peak Area
Calculation Type: Percent
```

Peak No.	Peak Name	Result ()	Ret. Time (min)	Time Offset (min)	Area (counts)	Sep. Code	Width 1/2 (sec)	Status Codes
1		34.4217	2.954	0.000	422373	BB	1.0	
2		16.6599	3.155	0.000	204426	BB	1.2	
3		48.9184	3.954	0.000	600255	BB	1.6	
	Totals:	100.0000		0.000	1227054			

Total Unidentified Counts :   1227054 counts

Detected Peaks: 8   Rejected Peaks: 5   Identified Peaks: 0

Multiplier: 1   Divisor: 1   Unidentified Peak Factor: 0

Baseline Offset: 1 microVolts

Noise (used): 28 microVolts — monitored before this run

Manual injection

****

Figure 22.16
A data table to accompany the gas chromatogram shown in Figure 22.15.

analysis. This example should serve to demonstrate the procedure for correcting raw gas chromatography results when response factors are known. According to the data table, the reported peak area for the first (hexane) peak is 422,373 counts. The response factor for hexane was previously determined to be 0.86. The area of the hexane peak is thus corrected as follows:

$$422,373/0.86 = 491,000$$

Notice that the calculated result has been adjusted to reflect a reasonable number of significant figures.

The areas for the other peaks in the gas chromatogram are corrected in a similar manner:

Hexane	422,373/0.86 =	491,000
Ethyl acetate	204,426/1.50 =	136,000
Benzene	600,255/1.00 =	600,000
Total peak area		1,227,000

Using these corrected areas, the true percentages of each component can be easily determined:

		Composition
Hexane	491,000/1,227,000	40.0%
Ethyl acetate	136,000/1,227,000	11.1%
Benzene	600,000/1,227,000	48.9%
Total		100.0%

C. Determination of Relative Percentages of Components in a Complex Mixture

In some circumstances, one may wish to determine the relative percentages of two components when the mixture being analyzed may be more complex and may contain more than two components. Examples of this situation might include the analysis of a reaction product where the laboratory worker might be interested in the relative percentages of two isomeric products when the sample might also contain peaks arising from the solvent, unreacted starting material, or some other product or impurity.

The example provided in Figures 22.15 and 22.16 can be used to illustrate the method of determining the relative percentages of some, but not all, of the components in the sample. Assume we are interested in the relative percentages of hexane and ethyl acetate in the sample but not in the percentage of benzene, which may be a solvent or an impurity. We know from the previous discussion that the *corrected* relative areas of the two peaks of interest are as follows:

	Relative Area
Hexane	491,000
Ethyl acetate	136,000
Total	627,000

We can determine the relative percentages of the two components simply by dividing the area of each peak by the total area of the two peaks:

		Percentage
Hexane	491,000/627,000	78.3%
Ethyl acetate	136,000/627,000	21.7%
Total		100.0%

22.14 Gas Chromatography— Mass Spectrometry (GC–MS)

A variation on gas chromatography is **gas chromatography-mass spectrometry**, also known as **GC–MS**. In this technique, a gas chromatograph is coupled to a mass spectrometer (see Technique 28). In effect, the mass spectrometer acts as a detector. The gas stream emerging from the gas chromatograph is admitted through a valve into a tube, where it passes over the sample inlet system of the mass spectrometer. Some of the gas stream is thus admitted into the ionization chamber of the mass spectrometer.

The molecules in the gas stream are converted into ions in the ionization chamber, and thus the gas chromatogram is actually a plot of time versus **ion current**, a measure of the number of ions produced. At the same time that the molecules are converted into ions, they are also accelerated and passed through the **mass analyzer** of the instrument. The instrument, therefore, determines the mass spectrum of each fraction eluting from the gas chromatography column.

A drawback of this method involves the need for rapid scanning by the mass spectrometer. The instrument must determine the mass spectrum of each component in the mixture before the next component exits from the column so that the spectrum of one substance is not contaminated by the spectrum of the next fraction.

Because high-efficiency capillary columns are used in the gas chromatograph, in most cases compounds are completely separated before the gas stream is analyzed. The typical GC-MS instrument has the capability of obtaining at least one scan per second in the range of 10–300 amu. Even more scans are possible if a narrow range of masses is analyzed. Using capillary columns, however, requires the user to take particular care to ensure that the sample does not contain any particles that might obstruct the flow of gases through the column. For this reason, the sample is carefully filtered through a very fine filter before the sample is injected into the chromatograph.

With a GC–MS system, a mixture can be analyzed and results obtained that resemble very closely those shown in Figures 22.15 and 22.16. A library search on each component of the mixture can also be conducted. The data stations of most instruments contain a library of standard mass spectra in their computer memory. If the components are known compounds, they can be identified tentatively by a comparison of their mass spectrum with the spectra of compounds found in the computer library. In this way, a "hit list" can be generated that reports on the probability that the compound in the library matches the known substance. A typical printout from a GC–MS instrument will list probable compounds that fit the mass spectrum of the component, the names of the compounds, their CAS Nos. (see Technique 29, Section 29.11), and a "quality" or "confidence" number. This last number provides an estimate of how closely the mass spectrum of the component matches the mass spectrum of the substance in the computer library.

A variation on the GC–MS technique includes coupling a Fourier transform infrared spectrometer (FT–IR) to a gas chromatograph. The substances that elute from the gas chromatograph are detected by determining their infrared spectra rather than their mass spectra. A new technique that also resembles GC–MS is **high-performance liquid chromatography–mass spectrometry (HPLC–MS)**. An HPLC instrument is coupled through a special interface to a mass spectrometer. The substances that elute from the HPLC column are detected by the mass spectrometer, and their mass spectra can be displayed, analyzed, and compared with standard spectra found in the computer library built into the instrument.

PROBLEMS

1. **a.** A sample consisting of 1-bromopropane and 1-chloropropane is injected into a gas chromatograph equipped with a nonpolar column. Which compound has the shorter retention time? Explain your answer.

   b. If the same sample were run several days later with the conditions as nearly the same as possible, would you expect the retention times to be identical to those obtained the first time? Explain.

2. Using triangulation, calculate the percentage of each component in a mixture composed of two substances, A and B. The chromatogram is shown in Figure 22.17.

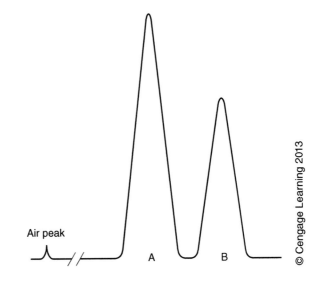

Figure 22.17
A chromatogram for problem 2.

Air peak

A

B

© Cengage Learning 2013

3. Make a photocopy of the chromatogram in Figure 22.17. Cut out the peaks and weigh them on an analytical balance. Use the weights to calculate the percentage of each component in the mixture. Compare your answer to what you calculated in problem 2.

4. What would happen to the retention time of a compound if the following changes were made?

   a. Decrease the flow rate of the carrier gas

   b. Increase the temperature of the column

   c. Increase the length of the column

Polarimetry

23.1 Nature of Polarized Light

Light has a dual nature because it shows properties of both waves and particles. The wave nature of light can be demonstrated by two experiments: polarization and interference. Of the two, polarization is the more interesting to organic chemists because they can take advantage of polarization experiments to learn something about the structure of an unknown molecule.

Ordinary white light consists of wave motion in which the waves have a variety of wavelengths and vibrate in all possible planes perpendicular to the direction of propagation. Light can be made to be **monochromatic** (of one wavelength or color) by using filters or special light sources. Frequently, a sodium lamp (sodium D line = 5893 Å) is used. Although the light from this lamp consists of waves of only one wavelength, the individual light waves still vibrate in all possible planes perpendicular to the beam. If we imagine that the beam of light is aimed directly at the viewer, ordinary light can be represented by showing the edges of the planes oriented randomly around the path of the beam, as on the left side of Figure 23.1.

A Nicol prism, which consists of a specially prepared crystal of Iceland spar (or calcite), has the property of serving as a screen that can restrict the passage of light waves. Waves that are vibrating in one plane are transmitted; those in all other planes are rejected (either refracted in another direction or absorbed). The light that passes through the prism is called **plane-polarized light,** and it consists of waves that vibrate in only one plane. A beam of plane-polarized light aimed directly at the viewer can be represented by showing the edges of the plane oriented in one particular direction, as on the right side of Figure 23.1.

Iceland spar has the property of **double refraction;** that is, it can split, or doubly refract, an entering beam of ordinary light into two separate emerging beams of light. Each of the two emerging beams (labeled A and B in Figure 23.2) has only a single plane of vibration, and the plane of vibration in beam A is perpendicular to the plane of beam B. In other words, the crystal has separated the incident beam of

Figure 23.1
Ordinary versus plane-polarized light.

© Cengage Learning 2013

Beam A   Beam B

Figure 23.2
Double refraction.

© Cengage Learning 2013

425

ordinary light into two beams of plane-polarized light, with the plane of polarization of beam A perpendicular to the plane of beam B.

To generate a single beam of plane-polarized light, one can take advantage of the double-refracting property of Iceland spar. A Nicol prism, invented by the Scottish physicist William Nicol, consists of two crystals of Iceland spar cut to specified angles and cemented by Canada balsam. This prism transmits one of the two beams of plane-polarized light while reflecting the other at a sharp angle so that it does not interfere with the transmitted beam. Plane-polarized light can also be generated by a Polaroid filter, a device invented by E. H. Land, an American physicist. Polaroid filters consist of certain types of crystals embedded in transparent plastic and capable of producing plane-polarized light.

After passing through a first Nicol prism, plane-polarized light can pass through a second Nicol prism, but only if the second prism has its axis oriented so that it is *parallel* to the incident light's plane of polarization. Plane-polarized light is *absorbed* by a Nicol prism that is oriented so that its axis is *perpendicular* to the incident light's plane of polarization. These situations can be illustrated by the picket-fence analogy, as shown in Figure 23.3. Plane-polarized light can pass through a fence whose slats are oriented in the proper direction but is blocked out by a fence whose slats are oriented perpendicularly.

An **optically active substance** is one that interacts with polarized light to rotate the plane of polarization through some angle α. Figure 23.4 illustrates this phenomenon.

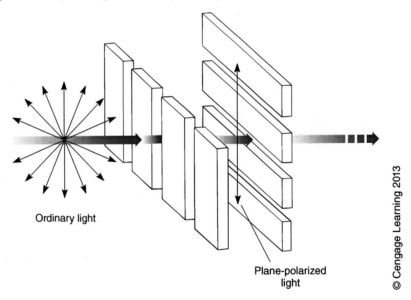

Ordinary light

Plane-polarized light

© Cengage Learning 2013

Figure 23.3
The picket-fence analogy.

Incident light

Sample cell

Transmitted light

α

© Cengage Learning 2013

Figure 23.4
Optical activity.

23.2 The Polarimeter　　An instrument called a **polarimeter** is used to measure the extent to which a substance interacts with polarized light. A schematic diagram of a polarimeter is shown in Figure 23.5. The light from the source lamp is polarized by being passed through a fixed Nicol prism, called a **polarizer.** This light passes through the sample, with which it may or may not interact to have its plane of polarization rotated in one direction or the other. A second, rotatable Nicol prism, called the **analyzer,** is adjusted to allow the maximum amount of light to pass through. The number of degrees and the direction of rotation required for this adjustment are measured to give the observed rotation α.

So that data determined by several persons under different conditions can be compared, a standardized means of presenting optical rotation data is necessary. The most common way of presenting such data is by recording the **specific rotation** $[\alpha]_{\lambda}^{t}$, which has been corrected for differences in concentration, cell path length, temperature, solvent, and wavelength of the light source. The equation defining the specific rotation of a compound in solution is

$$[\alpha]_{\lambda}^{t} = \frac{\alpha}{cl}$$

where α = observed rotation in degrees, c = concentration in grams per milliliter of solution, l = length of sample tube in decimeters, λ = wavelength of light (usually indicated as "D," for the sodium D line), and t = temperature in degrees Celsius. For pure liquids, the density d of the liquid in grams per milliliter replaces c in the preceding formula. You may occasionally want to compare compounds of different molecular weights, so a **molecular rotation,** based on moles instead of grams, is more convenient than a specific rotation.

The molecular rotation M_{λ}^{t} is derived from the specific rotation $[\alpha]_{\lambda}^{t}$ by

$$M_{\lambda}^{t} = \frac{[\alpha]_{\lambda}^{t} \times \text{Molecular weight}}{100}$$

Usually, measurements are made at 25°C with the sodium D line as a light source; consequently, specific rotations are reported as $[\alpha]_{D}^{25}$.

Polarimeters that are now available incorporate electronics to determine the angle of rotation of chiral molecules. These instruments are essentially automatic. The only real difference between an automatic polarimeter and a manual one is that a light detector replaces the eye. No visual observation of any kind is made with an automatic instrument. A microprocessor adjusts the analyzer until the light reaching the detector is at a minimum. The angle of rotation is displayed digitally in an LCD window, including the sign of rotation. The simplest instrument is equipped with a sodium lamp that gives rotations based on the sodium D line (589 nm). More

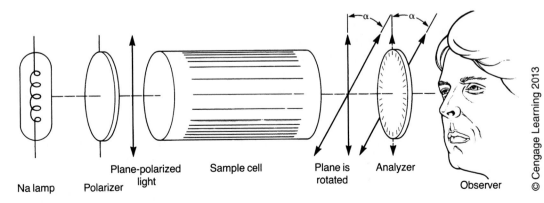

Na lamp　　Polarizer　Plane-polarized light　　Sample cell　　Plane is rotated　　Analyzer　　Observer

© Cengage Learning 2013

Figure 23.5
Schematic diagram of a polarimeter.

expensive instruments use a tungsten lamp and filters so that wavelengths can be varied over a range of values. Using the latter instrument, a chemist can observe rotations at different wavelengths.

23.3 Sample Preparation: The Sample Cell

Figure 23.6
Two modern polarimetry cells (Rudolph Research).

It is important for the solution whose optical rotation is to be determined to contain no suspended particles of dust, dirt, or undissolved material that might disperse the incident polarized light. Therefore, you must clean the sample cell carefully, and your sample must be free of suspended particles. You must also prevent the presence of any air bubbles in the bore when you fill the cell. Most cells have a stem in the center or an area at one end of the cell where the diameter of the tube is increased. These features are designed to help you catch any bubbles in an area that is above the path that the light takes through the main bore.

Two modern **polarimetry cells** are shown in Figure 23.6. In the first case, the cell is filled until the liquid completely fills the bore and a small portion of the center stem. Then, if one gently rocks the cell back and forth along its axis, bubbles will rise and collect in the stem where they are above the light path. A stopper is placed in the stem when you are finished. In the second case, the cell is filled vertically, and the end is screwed on. Bubbles are trapped at the raised end when the cell is turned horizontally.

Sample cells are available in various lengths, with 0.5 dm and 1.0 dm being the most common. A typical 0.5-dm cell holds about 3–5 mL of solution, but many companies sell **microcells** that have a very narrow-diameter bore and require much less solution. Polarimeter cells are quite expensive because the windows must be made out of quartz rather than ordinary glass. Be sure to handle them carefully and to avoid getting fingerprints on the end windows because this will also disperse the polarized light.

With liquid samples, it is often possible to use the **neat** (undiluted) liquid as your sample. In this case, the concentration of the sample is just the density of the liquid (g/mL). If you have a solid sample or if you have too little of a liquid to fill the cell, you will have to either dissolve or dilute the sample with a solvent. In this case, you must weigh (grams) the amount of material you use and divide by the total volume (mL) to obtain the concentration in g/mL. Water, methanol, and ethanol are the best solvents to use because they are unlikely to attack the cell you are using. Many cells have rubber parts or use a cement to attach the windows to the ends of the bore. Rubber and cements will often dissolve in stronger solvents such as acetone or methylene chloride, thereby damaging the cell. Check with your instructor before using any solvent stronger than water, methanol, or ethanol. These are also the preferred solvents to use for cleaning the cells.

23.4 Operation of the Polarimeter

A. The Zeiss Polarimeter, a Classic Instrument

The procedures given here are for the operation of the Zeiss polarimeter (Figure 23.7), a classic analog instrument with a circular scale and a sodium lamp. Many other older models of polarimeter are operated in a similar fashion.

Before taking any measurements, turn on the sodium lamp and wait 5–10 minutes for the lamp to warm up and stabilize. After the warm-up period is complete, you should make an initial check of the instrument by taking a zero reading with a sample cell filled only with solvent. If the zero reading does not correspond with the zero-degree (0°) calibration mark, then the difference in readings must be used to correct all subsequent readings.

To take the zero measurement, place the polarimeter cell with the sample in the sloped cradle or rack inside the instrument. If you are using a cell with an enlarged end, that end must be placed at the high end of the cradle, making sure that no

Figure 23.7
The Zeiss polarimeter.

bubbles are in the bore of the cell. After closing the cover and while watching through the eyepiece, turn the analyzer knob or ring until the proper angle of the analyzer is reached (the angle that allows no light to pass through the instrument). Most analog instruments, including the Zeiss polarimeter, are of the split-field type. When you look upward through the eyepiece, you see a circle split into three sectors (Figure 23.8), with the center sector either lighter or darker than those on either side. The analyzer prism is rotated until all of the sectors are matched in intensity, usually the darker color (see Figure 23.8). This is called the **null** reading.

When you look downward in the eyepiece, you see the value of the angle through which the plane of the polarized light has been rotated (if any) indicated on a vernier degree scale (Figure 23.9). Some polarimeters, such as the original Rudolph polarimeter, have instead a large circular scale, like a halo, attached directly to the knob you turn.

After determining the zero setting on the blank solution, place the polarimeter cell containing your sample into the polarimeter and measure the observed angle of rotation in the same way as described for the zero measurement. Be sure to record not only the numerical value of the reading but also the direction of rotation. Also record the solvent, temperature, and concentration, as these are also critical to the measurement. Rotations clockwise are due to dextrorotatory substances and are indicated by the "+" sign. Rotations counterclockwise are due to levorotatory substances and are indicated by the "−" sign. You should take several readings, including readings for which the value was approached from both sides. In other words, where the actual reading might be +75°, first approach this reading upward from somewhere between 0° and 75°; on the next measurement, approach the null from an angle greater than 75°. Duplicating readings, approaching the observed rotation from both sides, and averaging the readings reduce the error.

If you are not sure whether you have a dextrorotatory or a levorotatory substance, you can make this determination by halving the concentration of your compound, reducing the length of the cell by half, or reducing the intensity of the light. The confusion between dextrorotatory and levorotatory arises because you are reading a circular scale. The null reading can be approached from either direction (clockwise or counterclockwise), starting from zero (see Figure 23.10). For instance, is your null at + 120°, or is it at −240°? Both readings are at the same point on the scale. Figure 23.10 shows that by reducing the concentration, the cell length, or the light intensity in half (any one of these), the reading will change, and it will move in a different direction for levorotatory substances than for dextrorotatory substances. The direction of rotation is most often determined by making measurements at different dilutions.

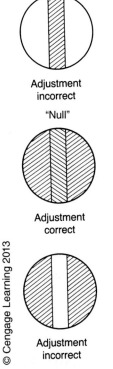

Adjustment
incorrect

"Null"

Adjustment
correct

Adjustment
incorrect

Figure 23.8
Image field sectors
in the polarimeter.

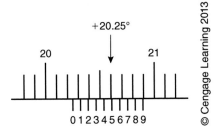

+20.25°

20   21

0 1 2 3 4 5 6 7 8 9

Figure 23.9
The vernier degree scale seen in the lower field
of the Zeiss polarimeter.

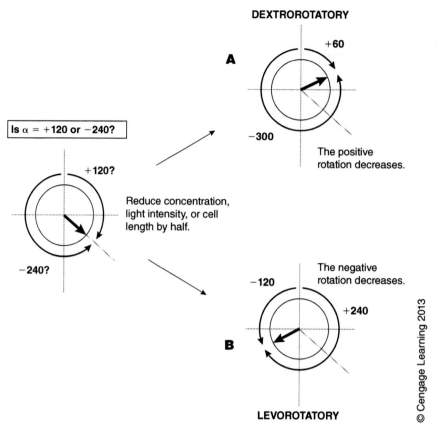

Figure 23.10
How to determine the direction of rotation. This diagram shows the
effect on observed rotation if you reduce by half the concentration
of the compound, the light intensity, or the length of the cell. By this
method, it is easy to determine if the compound is dextrorotatory
(A) or levorotatory (B).

Once you have determined the value and direction of the observed rotation α,
you must correct it by the zero value and then use the formulas in Section 23.2 to
convert it to the specific rotation $[\alpha]_D$. The specific rotation is always reported as a
function of temperature, indicating the wavelength by "D" if a sodium lamp was
used, and the solvent and concentration used are reported. For example:

$$[\alpha]_D = +43.8 \ (c = 7.5 \ \text{g}/100 \ \text{mL, in absolute ethanol})$$

B. The Modern Digital Polarimeter

A modern digital polarimeter, such as the one shown in Figure 23.11, is much easier
to operate than the older analog instruments. The modern instrument will store the
zero reading for you, subtract it from every subsequent reading automatically, determine the direction of rotation, and calculate the specific rotation from the reading
obtained on your sample. When finished, it can print everything on a sheet of paper
for you to take with you. In a typical instrument, you first determine the zero reading
and then store it in electronic memory. Once the zero reading is determined, you place
your sample in the instrument. The instrument automatically finds the null angle and
the direction of rotation and displays it on an LED readout. The instrument approaches
the null several times to be sure of its reading and determines the direction of rotation

Figure 23.11
The Autopol IV (Rudolph Research), a modern digital polarimeter.

by reducing the intensity of the light. It can do this several ways. One common method is to attenuate (reduce) the incident light intensity of the beam of polarized light and see what effect this has on the angle of rotation. Even a digital polarimeter, however, cannot extract a reading from a poor sample, such as one that is cloudy, has a bubble, or has suspended solid material. A good sample is still your responsibility.

23.5 Optical Purity

When you prepare a sample of an enantiomer by a resolution method, the sample is not always 100% of a single enantiomer. It frequently is contaminated by residual amounts of the opposite stereoisomer. If you know the amount of each enantiomer in a mixture, you can calculate the **optical purity.** Some chemists prefer to use the term **enantiomeric excess (ee)** rather than optical purity. The two terms can be used interchangeably. The percentage enantiomeric excess or optical purity is calculated as follows:

$$\% \text{ Optical purity} = \frac{\text{moles one enantiomer} - \text{moles of other enantiomer}}{\text{total moles of both enantiomers}} \times 100$$

$$\% \text{ Optical purity} = \% \text{ enantiomeric excess (ee)}$$

Often, it is difficult to apply the previous equation because you do not know the exact amount of each enantiomer present in a mixture. It is far easier to calculate the optical purity (ee) by using the observed specific rotation of the mixture and dividing it by the specific rotation of the pure enantiomer. Values for the pure enantiomers can sometimes be found in literature sources.

$$\% \text{ Optical purity} = \% \text{ enantiomeric excess} = \frac{\text{observed specific rotation}}{\text{specific rotation of pure enantiomer}} \times 100$$

This latter equation holds true only for mixtures of two chiral molecules that are mirror images of each other (enantiomers). If some other chiral substance is present in the mixture as an impurity, then the actual optical purity will deviate from the value calculated.

In a racemic (±) mixture, there is no excess enantiomer, and the optical purity (enantiomeric excess) is zero; in a completely resolved material, the optical purity (enantiomeric excess) is 100%. A compound that is $x\%$ optically pure contains $x\%$ of one enantiomer and $(100 - x)\%$ of a racemic mixture.

Once the optical purity (enantiomeric excess) is known, the relative percentages of each of the enantiomers can be calculated easily. If the predominant form in the impure, optically active mixture is assumed to be the (+) enantiomer, the percentage of the (+) enantiomer is

$$\left[x + \left(\frac{100 - x}{2} \right) \right]\%$$

and the percentage of the (−) enantiomer is $[(100 − x)/2]\%$. The relative percentages of (+) and (−) forms in a partially resolved mixture of enantiomers can be calculated as shown next. Consider a partially resolved mixture of camphor enantiomers. The specific rotation for pure (+)-camphor is $+43.8°$ in absolute ethanol, but the mixture shows a specific rotation of $+26.3°$.

$$\text{Optical purity} = \frac{+26.3°}{+43.8°} \times 100 = 60\% \text{ optically pure}$$

$$\% \ (+) \text{ enantiomer} = 60 + \left(\frac{100 − 60}{2}\right) = 80\%$$

$$\%(−) \text{ enantiomer} = \left(\frac{100 − 60}{2}\right) = 20\%$$

Notice that the difference between these two calculated values equals the optical purity or enantiomeric excess.

PROBLEMS

1. Calculate the specific rotation of a substance that is dissolved in a solvent (0.4 g/mL) and that has an observed rotation of −10° as determined with a 0.5-dm cell.

2. Calculate the observed rotation for a solution of a substance (2.0 g/mL) that is 80% optically pure. A 2-dm cell is used. The specific rotation for the optically pure substance is +20°.

3. What is the optical purity of a partially racemized product if the calculated specific rotation is −8° and the pure enantiomer has a specific rotation of −10°? Calculate the percentage of each of the enantiomers in the partially racemized product.

Refractometry

The **refractive index** is a useful physical property of liquids. Often, a liquid can be identified from a measurement of its refractive index. The refractive index can also provide a measure of the purity of the sample being examined. This is accomplished by comparing the experimentally measured refractive index with the value reported in the literature for an ultrapure sample of the compound. The closer the measured sample's value to the literature value, the purer the sample.

24.1 The Refractive Index

The refractive index has as its basis the fact that light travels at a different velocity in condensed phases (liquids, solids) than in air. The refractive index n is defined as the ratio of the velocity of light in air to the velocity of light in the medium being measured:

$$n = \frac{V_{air}}{V_{liquid}} = \frac{\sin \theta}{\sin \phi}$$

It is not difficult to measure the ratio of the velocities experimentally. It corresponds to ($\sin \theta / \sin \phi$), where θ is the angle of incidence for a beam of light striking the surface of the medium and ϕ is the angle of refraction of the beam of light *within* the medium. This is illustrated in Figure 24.1.

The refractive index for a given medium depends on two variable factors. First, it is *temperature* dependent. The density of the medium changes with temperature; hence, the speed of light in the medium also changes. Second, the refractive index is *wavelength* dependent. Beams of light with different wavelengths are refracted to different extents in the same medium and give different refractive indices for that medium. It is usual to report refractive indices measured at 20°C, with a sodium discharge lamp as the source of illumination. The sodium lamp gives off yellow light of 589-nm wavelength, the so-called sodium D line. Under these conditions, the refractive index is reported in the following form:

$$n_D^{20} = 1.4892$$

The superscript indicates the temperature, and the subscript indicates that the sodium D line was used for the measurement. If another wavelength is used for the determination, the D is replaced by the appropriate value, usually in nanometers (1 nm $= 10^{-9}$ m).

Notice that the hypothetical value reported has four decimal places. It is easy to determine the refractive index to within several parts in 10,000. Therefore, n_D is a very accurate physical constant for a given substance and can be used for identification. However, it is sensitive to even small amounts of impurity in the substance measured. Unless the substance is purified *extensively,* you will not usually be able to reproduce the last two decimal

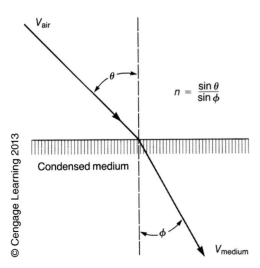

$$n = \frac{\sin \theta}{\sin \phi}$$

V_{air}

Condensed medium

V_{medium}

© Cengage Learning 2013

Figure 24.1
The refractive index

places given in a handbook or other literature source. Typical organic liquids have refractive index values between 1.3400 and 1.5600.

24.2 The Abbé Refractometer

The instrument used to measure the refractive index is called a **refractometer.** Although many styles of refractometer are available, by far the most common instrument is the Abbé refractometer. This style of refractometer has the following advantages:

1. White light may be used for illumination; the instrument is compensated, however, so that the index of refraction obtained is actually that for the sodium D line.
2. The prisms can be temperature controlled.
3. Only a small sample is required (a few drops of liquid using the standard method or about 5 μL using a modified technique).

A common type of Abbé refractometer is shown in Figure 24.2.

The optical arrangement of the refractometer is complex; a simplified diagram of the internal workings is given in Figure 24.3. The letters *A, B, C,* and *D* label corresponding parts in both Figures 24.2 and 24.3. A complete description of refractometer optics is too difficult to attempt here, but Figure 24.3 gives a simplified diagram of the essential operating principles.

Using the standard method, introduce the sample to be measured between the two prisms. If it is a free-flowing liquid, it may be introduced into a channel along the side of the prisms, injected from a Pasteur pipette. If it is a viscous sample, the prisms must be opened (they are hinged) by lifting the upper one; a few drops of liquid are applied to the lower prism with a Pasteur pipette or a wooden applicator. If a Pasteur pipette is used, take care not to touch the prisms because they become scratched easily. When the prisms are closed, the liquid should spread evenly to

Figure 24.2
Abbé refractometer (Bausch and Lomb Abbé 3L).

© Cengage Learning 2013

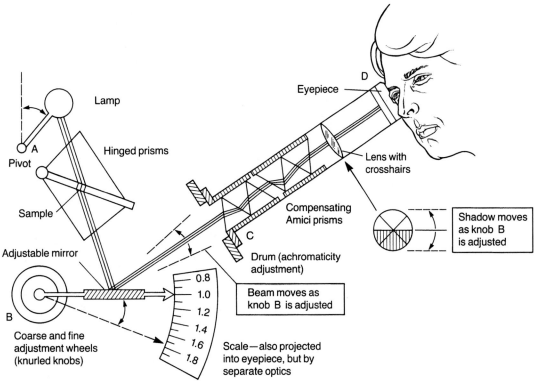

Figure 24.3
Simplified diagram of a refractometer.

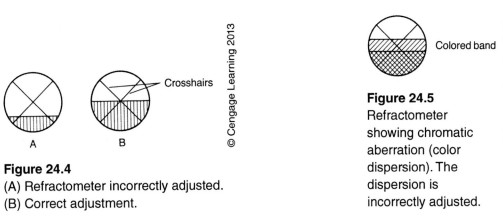

Figure 24.4
(A) Refractometer incorrectly adjusted.
(B) Correct adjustment.

Figure 24.5
Refractometer showing chromatic aberration (color dispersion). The dispersion is incorrectly adjusted.

make a thin film. With highly volatile samples, the remaining operations must be performed rapidly. Even when the prisms are closed, evaporation of volatile liquids can readily occur.

Next, turn on the light and look into the eyepiece *D*. The hinged lamp is adjusted to give the maximum illumination to the visible field in the eyepiece. The light rotates at pivot *A*.

Rotate the coarse and fine adjustment knobs at *B* until the dividing line between the light and dark halves of the visual field coincides with the center of the crosshairs (Figure 24.4). If the crosshairs are not in sharp focus, adjust the eyepiece to focus them. If the horizontal line dividing the light and dark areas appears as a colored band, as in Figure 24.5, the refractometer shows **chromatic aberration** (color dispersion). This can be adjusted with knob *C* drum (Figure 24.3). This knurled knob rotates a series of prisms, called Amici prisms, that color-compensate the refractometer and cancel out dispersion. Adjust the knob to give a sharp, uncolored division between the light and dark segments. When you have adjusted everything correctly (as in Figure 24.4B), read the refractive index. In the instrument described here, press a small button on the left side of the housing to make the scale visible in the eyepiece. In other refractometers, the scale is visible at all times, frequently through a separate eyepiece.

Occasionally, the refractometer will be so far out of adjustment that it may be difficult to measure the refractive index of an unknown. When this happens, it is wise to place a pure sample of known refractive index in the instrument, set the scale to the correct value of refractive index, and adjust the controls for the sharpest line possible. Once this is done, it is easier to measure an unknown sample. It is especially helpful to perform this procedure prior to measuring the refractive index of a highly volatile sample.

NOTE: There are many styles of refractometer, but most have adjustments similar to those described here.

In the procedure just described, several drops of liquid are required to obtain the refractive index. In some experiments, you may not have enough sample to use this standard method. It is possible to modify the procedure so that a reasonably accurate refractive index can be obtained on about 5 μL of liquid. Instead of placing the sample directly onto the prism, you apply the sample to a small piece of lens paper. The lens paper can be conveniently cut with a handheld paper punch,[1] and the paper disc (0.6-cm diameter) is placed in the center of the bottom prism of the refractometer. To avoid scratching the prism, use forceps or tweezers with plastic tips to handle the disc. About 5 μL of liquid is carefully placed on the lens paper using a microliter syringe. After closing the prisms, adjust the refractometer as described previously and read the refractive index. With this method, the horizontal line dividing the light and dark areas may not be as sharp as it is in the absence of the lens paper. It may also be impossible to eliminate color dispersion completely. Nonetheless, the refractive index values determined by this method are usually within 10 parts in 10,000 of the values determined by the standard procedure.

24.3 Cleaning the Refractometer

In using the refractometer, you should always remember that if the prisms are scratched, the instrument will be ruined.

NOTE: Do not touch the prisms with any hard object.

This admonition includes Pasteur pipettes and glass rods.

When measurements are completed, the prisms should be cleaned with ethanol or petroleum ether. Moisten *soft* tissues with the solvent and wipe the prisms *gently.* When the solvent has evaporated from the prism surfaces, the prisms should be locked together. The refractometer should be left with the prisms closed to avoid collection of dust in the space between them. The instrument should also be turned off when it is no longer in use.

24.4 The Digital Refractometer

Today, there are modern digital refractometers available that determine the refractive index of a liquid electronically (Figure 24.6). Once the instrument has been calibrated, it is only necessary to place a drop of your liquid between the prisms (see

---

[1] In order to cut the lens paper more easily, place several sheets between two pieces of heavier paper, such as that used for file folders.

© Cengage Learning 2013

Figure 24.6
The Rudolph J-series, a modern digital refractometer. To make a measurement, place the sample on the lower prism (see the inset) and close the lid.

the inset in Figure 24.6), close the lid, and read the display. The instrument can make temperature corrections and store the values of your readings in its microprocessor memory. Once again, these instruments must be treated with respect, taking care not to scratch the prisms and to clean them after use.

24.5 Temperature Corrections

Most refractometers are designed so that circulating water at a constant temperature can maintain the prisms at 20°C. If this temperature-control system is not used or if the water is not at 20°C, a temperature correction must be made. Although the magnitude of the temperature correction may vary from one class of compound to another, a value of 0.00045 per degree Celsius is a useful approximation for most substances. The index of refraction of a substance *decreases* with *increasing* temperature. Therefore, add the correction to the observed n_D value for temperatures higher than 20°C and subtract it for temperatures lower than 20°C. For example, the reported n_D value for nitrobenzene is 1.5529. One would observe a value at 25°C of 1.5506. The temperature correction would be made as follows:

$$n_D^{20} = 1.5506 + 5(0.00045) = 1.5529$$

PROBLEMS

1. A solution consisting of isobutyl bromide and isobutyl chloride is found to have a refractive index of 1.3931 at 20°C. The refractive indices at 20°C of isobutyl bromide and isobutyl chloride are 1.4368 and 1.3785, respectively. Determine the molar composition (in percent) of the mixture by assuming a linear relation between the refractive index and the molar composition of the mixture.

2. The refractive index of a compound at 16°C is found to be 1.3982. Correct this refractive index to 20°C.

Infrared Spectroscopy

Almost any compound having covalent bonds, whether organic or inorganic, will be found to absorb frequencies of electromagnetic radiation in the infrared region of the spectrum. The infrared region of the electromagnetic spectrum lies at wavelengths longer than those associated with visible light, which includes wavelengths from approximately 400 nm to 800 nm (1 nm = 10^{-9} m), but at wavelengths shorter than those associated with radio waves, which have wavelengths longer than 1 cm. For chemical purposes, we are interested in the *vibrational* portion of the infrared region. This portion includes radiations with wavelengths (λ) between 2.5 μm and 15 μm (1 μm = 10^{-6} m). The relation of the infrared region to other regions included in the electromagnetic spectrum is illustrated in Figure 25.1.

As with other types of energy absorption, molecules are excited to a higher energy state when they absorb infrared radiation. The absorption of the infrared radiation is, like other absorption processes, a quantized process. Only selected frequencies (energies) of infrared radiation are absorbed by a molecule. The absorption of infrared radiation corresponds to energy changes on the order of 8–40 kJ/mole (2–10 kcal/mole). Radiation in this energy range corresponds to the range encompassing the stretching and bending vibrational frequencies of the bonds in most covalent molecules. In the absorption process, those frequencies of infrared radiation that match the natural vibrational frequencies of the molecule in question are absorbed, and the energy absorbed increases the *amplitude* of the vibrational motions of the bonds in the molecule.

Most chemists refer to the radiation in the vibrational infrared region of the electromagnetic spectrum by units called **wavenumbers** ($\bar{\nu}$). Wavenumbers are expressed in reciprocal centimeters (cm^{-1}) and are easily computed by taking the reciprocal of the wavelength (λ) expressed in centimeters. This unit has the advantage, for those performing calculations, of being directly proportional to energy. Thus, the vibrational infrared region of the spectrum extends from about 4000 cm^{-1} to 650 cm^{-1} (or wavenumbers).

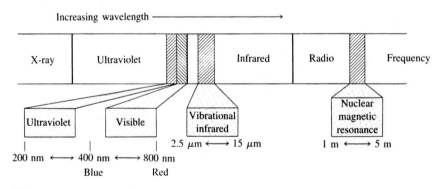

Figure 25.1
A portion of the electromagnetic spectrum showing the relation of vibrational infrared radiation to other types of radiation.

Wavelengths (μm) and wavenumbers (cm⁻¹) can be interconverted by the following relationships:

$$\text{cm}^{-1} = \frac{1}{(\mu m)} \times 10,000$$

$$\mu m = \frac{1}{(\text{cm})^{-1}} \times 10,000$$

PART A. SAMPLE PREPARATION AND RECORDING THE SPECTRUM

25.1 Introduction

To determine the infrared spectrum of the compound, one must place the compound in a sample holder or cell. In infrared spectroscopy, this immediately poses a problem. Glass, quartz, and plastics absorb strongly throughout the infrared region of the spectrum (any compound with covalent bonds usually absorbs) and cannot be used to construct sample cells. Ionic substances must be used in cell construction. Metal halides (sodium chloride, potassium bromide, silver chloride) are commonly used for this purpose.

Sodium Chloride Cells. Single crystals of sodium chloride are cut and polished to give plates that are transparent throughout the infrared region. These plates are then used to fabricate cells that can be used to hold *liquid* samples. Because sodium chloride is water soluble, samples must be *dry* before a spectrum can be obtained. In general, sodium chloride plates are preferred for most applications involving liquid samples. Potassium bromide plates may also be used in place of sodium chloride.

Silver Chloride Cells. Cells may be constructed of silver chloride. These plates may be used for *liquid* samples that contain small amounts of water, because silver chloride is water-insoluble. However, because water absorbs in the infrared region, as much water as possible should be removed, even when using silver chloride. Silver chloride plates must be stored in the dark. They darken when exposed to light, and they cannot be used with compounds that have an amino functional group. Amines react with silver chloride.

Solid Samples. The easiest way to hold a *solid* sample in place is to dissolve the sample in a volatile organic solvent, place several drops of this solution on a salt plate, and allow the solvent to evaporate. This dry film method can be used only with modern FT-IR spectrometers. The other methods described here can be used with both FT-IR and dispersion spectrometers. A solid sample can also be held in place by making a potassium bromide pellet that contains a small amount of dispersed compound. A solid sample may also be suspended in mineral oil, which absorbs only in specific regions of the infrared spectrum. Another method is to dissolve the solid compound in an appropriate solvent and place the solution between two sodium chloride or silver chloride plates.

ATP Accessory. Modern FT-IR instruments now offer an attenuated total reflectance (ATR) accessory along with the typical transmittance module. The ATR method provides a powerful sampling technique that virtually eliminates sample preparation with both liquids and solids, thus leading to a dramatic improvement in throughput in the teaching laboratory. Although manufacturers offer multiple crystal options, the diamond ATR offers the best option for maximum durability in the organic teaching laboratory. With the ATR accessory, one simply places a small amount of a liquid or solid directly on the diamond without any previous preparation. The spectrum obtained with an ATR FT-IR is nearly identical to that obtained with an FT-IR operating in the transmittance mode. One may observe some differences in the relative intensities of the peaks, but the peak position in wavenumbers is identical in both modes.[1] ATR FT-IR does not require a clear sample that allows light to pass through the sample such as is common with transmittance instruments. There are some limitations with a diamond ATR instrument. Some materials such as coating on metal and very dark samples do not analyze satisfactorily, but there are few other limitations.

25.2 Liquid Samples—NaCl Plates

The simplest method of preparing the sample, if it is a liquid, is to place a thin layer of the liquid between two sodium chloride plates that have been ground flat and polished. This is the method of choice when you need to determine the infrared spectrum of a pure liquid. A spectrum determined by this method is referred to as a **neat** spectrum. No solvent is used. The polished plates are expensive because they are cut from a large, single crystal of sodium chloride. Salt plates break easily, and they are water soluble.

Preparing the Sample. Obtain two sodium chloride plates and a holder from the desiccator where they are stored. Moisture from fingers will mar and occlude the polished surfaces. Samples that contain water will destroy the plates.

NOTE: The plates should be touched only on their edges. Be certain to use a sample that is dry or free from water.

Add 1 or 2 drops of the liquid to the surface of one plate and then place the second plate on top.[2] The pressure of this second plate causes the liquid to spread out and form a thin capillary film between the two plates. As shown in Figure 25.2, set the plates between the bolts in a holder and place the metal ring carefully on the salt plates. Use the hex nuts to hold the salt plates in place.

NOTE: Do not overtighten the nuts or the salt plates will cleave or split.

Tighten the nuts firmly, but do not use any force to turn them. Spin them with the fingers until they stop; then turn them just another fraction of a full turn, and they will be tight enough. If the nuts have been tightened carefully, you should observe a *transparent film of sample* (a uniform wetting of the surface). If a thin film has not been obtained, either loosen one or more of the hex nuts and adjust them so that a uniform film is obtained or add more sample.

The thickness of the film obtained between the two plates is a function of two factors: (1) the amount of liquid placed on the first plate (1 drop, 2 drops, and so on), and (2) the pressure used to hold the plates together. If more than 1 or 2 drops of liquid have been used, the amount will probably be too much, and the resulting

---

[1] Shuttlefield, J.D.; Grassian, V.H. ATR-FTIR in the Undergraduate Chemistry Laboratory, Part 1: "Fundamentals and Examples". *Journal of Chemical Education, 85,* (**2008**): 279–281.

[2] Use a Pasteur pipette or a short length of microcapillary tubing. If you use the microcapillary tubing, it can be filled by touching it into the liquid sample. When you touch it (lightly) to the salt plate, it will empty. Be careful not to scratch the plate.

Figure 25.2
Salt plates and holder.

spectrum will show strong absorptions that are off the scale of the chart paper. Only enough liquid to wet both surfaces is needed.

If the sample has a very low viscosity, the capillary film may be too thin to produce a good spectrum. Another problem you may find is that the liquid is so volatile that the sample evaporates before the spectrum can be determined. In these cases, you may need to use the silver chloride plates discussed in Section 25.3 or a solution cell described in Section 25.6. Often, you can obtain a reasonable spectrum by assembling the cell quickly and running the spectrum before the sample runs out of the salt plates or evaporates.

Determining the Infrared Spectrum. Slide the holder into the slot in the sample beam of the spectrophotometer. Determine the spectrum according to the instructions provided by your instructor. In some cases, your instructor may ask you to calibrate your spectrum. If this is the case, refer to Section 25.8.

Cleaning and Storing the Salt Plates. Once the spectrum has been determined, demount the holder and rinse the salt plates with methylene chloride (or *dry* acetone). (Keep the plates away from water!) Use a soft tissue, moistened with the solvent, to wipe the plates. If some of your compound remains on the plates, you may observe a shiny surface. Continue to clean the plates with solvent until no more compound remains on the surfaces of the plates.

CAUTION

Avoid direct contact with methylene chloride. Return the salt plates and holder to the desiccator for storage.

25.3 Liquid Samples—AgCl Plates

The minicell shown in Figure 25.3 may also be used with liquids.[3] The cell assembly consists of a two-piece threaded body, an O-ring, and two silver chloride plates. The plates are flat on one side, and there is a circular depression (0.025 mm or 0.10 mm deep) on the other side of the plate. An advantage of using silver chloride plates is that they may be used with wet samples or solutions. A disadvantage is that silver chloride darkens when exposed to light for extended periods. Silver chloride plates also scratch more easily than salt plates and react with amines.

Preparing the Sample. Silver chloride plates should be handled in the same way as salt plates. Unfortunately, they are smaller and thinner (about like a contact lens) than salt plates, and care must be taken not to lose them! Remove them from the light-tight container with care. It is difficult to tell which side of the plate has the slight circular depression. Your instructor may have etched a letter on each plate to indicate which side is the flat one. To determine the infrared spectrum of a pure liquid (neat spectrum), select the flat side of each silver chloride plate. Insert the O-ring into the cell body as shown in Figure 25.3, place the plate into the cell body with the flat surface up, and add 1 drop or less of liquid to the plate.

NOTE: Do not use amines with AgCl plates.

Place the second plate on top of the first with the flat side down. The orientation of the silver chloride plates is shown in Figure 25.4A. This arrangement is used to obtain a capillary film of your sample. Screw the top of the minicell into the body of

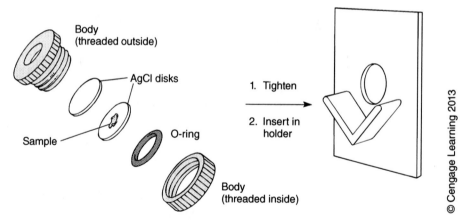

Figure 25.3
AgCl minicell liquid sample cell and V-mount holder.

A. Capillary film   B. 0.10-mm Path length   C. 0.20-mm Path length

Figure 25.4
Path-length variations for AgCl plates.

---

[3] The Wilks Mini-Cell liquid sample holder is available from the Foxboro Company, 151 Woodward Avenue, South Norwalk, CT 06856. We recommend the AgCl cell windows with 0.10-mm depression rather than the 0.025-mm depression.

the cell so that the silver chloride plates are held firmly together. A tight seal forms because AgCl deforms under pressure.

Other combinations may be used with these plates. For example, you may vary the sample path length by using the orientations shown in Figures 25.4B and C. If you add your sample and the 0.10-mm depression of one plate and cover it with the flat side of the other one, you obtain a path length of 0.10 mm (see Figure 25.4B). This arrangement is useful for analyzing volatile or low-viscosity liquids. Placement of the two plates with their depressions toward each other gives a path length of 0.20 mm (see Figure 25.4C). This orientation may be used for a solution of a solid (or liquid) in carbon tetrachloride (see Section 25.6B).

Determining the Spectrum. Slide the V-mount holder shown in Figure 25.3 into the slot on the infrared spectrophotometer. Set the cell assembly in the V-mount holder and determine the infrared spectrum of the liquid.

Cleaning and Storing the AgCl Plates. Once the spectrum has been determined, the cell assembly holder should be demounted and the AgCl plates rinsed with methylene chloride or acetone. Do not use tissue to wipe the plates, because they scratch easily. AgCl plates are light sensitive. Store the plates in a light-tight container.

25.4 Solid Samples—Dry Film

A simple method for determining the infrared spectrum of a solid sample is the dry film method. This method is easier than the other methods described here, it does not require any specialized equipment, and the spectra are excellent.[4] The disadvantage is that the dry film method can be used only with modern FT-IR spectrometers.

To use this method, place about 5 mg of your solid sample in a small, clean test tube. Add about 5 drops of methylene chloride (or diethyl ether, pentane, or dry acetone), and stir the mixture to dissolve the solid. Using a Pasteur pipette (not a capillary tube), place several drops of the solution on the face of a salt plate. Allow the solvent to evaporate; a uniform deposit of your product will remain as a dry film coating the salt plate. Mount the salt plate on a V-shaped holder in the infrared beam. Note that only one salt plate is used; the second salt plate is not used to cover the first. Once the salt plate is positioned properly, you may determine the spectrum in the normal manner. With this method, it is *very important* that you clean your material off the salt plate. When you are finished, use methylene chloride or dry acetone to clean the salt plate.

25.5 Solid Samples—Other Methods

The methods described in this section can be used with both FT-IR and dispersion spectrometers.

A. Attenuated Total Reflectance (ATR)

Preparation of solid samples for analysis by infrared analysis has tended to be much more labor intensive than analysis of liquids. The traditional methods involve preparation of a KBr pellet or a Nujol mull described in sections 25.5 B and 25.5 C. The use of an attenuated total reflectance accessory with an FT-IR instrument has dramatically improved the preparation time previously required. One simply places a small amount of a solid on the instrument. For these laboratories equipped with this accessory, it is strongly recommended for analysis of both solids and liquids (Section 25.1).

[4] Feist, P. L. Sampling Techniques for Organic Solids in IR Spectroscopy: Thin Solid Films as the Method of Choice in Teaching Laboratories. *Journal of Chemical Education, 78* (**2001**): 351.

Figure 25.5
Making a KBr pellet with a handpress.

© Cengage Learning 2013

B. KBr Pellets

One method of preparing a solid sample is to make a **potassium bromide (KBr) pellet.** When KBr is placed under pressure, it melts, flows, and seals the sample into a solid solution, or matrix. Because potassium bromide does not absorb in the infrared spectrum, a spectrum can be obtained on a sample without interference.

Preparing the Sample. Remove the agate mortar and pestle from the desiccator for use in preparing the sample. (Take care of them; they are expensive.) Grind 1 mg (0.001 g) of the solid sample for 1 minute in the agate mortar. At this point, the particle size will become so small that the surface of the solid appears shiny. Add 80 mg (0.080 g) of *powdered* KBr and grind the mixture for about 30 seconds with the pestle. Scrape the mixture into the middle with a spatula and grind the mixture again for about 15 seconds. This grinding operation helps to mix the sample thoroughly with the KBr. You should work as rapidly as possible because KBr absorbs water. The sample and KBr must be finely ground, or the mixture will scatter the infrared radiation excessively. Using your spatula, heap the mixture in the center of the mortar. Return the bottle of potassium bromide to the desiccator where it is stored when it is not in use.

The sample and potassium bromide should be weighed on an analytical balance the first few times that a pellet is prepared. After some experience, you can estimate these quantities quite accurately by eye.

Making a Pellet Using a KBr Handpress. Two methods are commonly used to prepare KBr pellets. The first method uses the handpress apparatus shown in Figure 25.5.[5] Remove the die set from the storage container. Take extreme care to avoid scratching the polished surfaces of the die set. Place the anvil with the shorter die pin (lower anvil in Figure 25.5) on a bench. Slip the collar over the pin. Remove about one fourth of your KBr mixture with a spatula and transfer it into the collar. The powder may not cover the head of the pin completely, but do not be concerned about this. Place the anvil with the longer die pin into the collar so that the die pin comes into contact with the sample. Never press the die set unless it contains a sample.

Lift the die set carefully by holding onto the lower anvil so that the collar stays in place. If you are careless with this operation, the collar may move enough to allow the powder to escape. Open the handle of the handpress slightly, tilt the press back a bit, and insert the die set into the press. Make sure that the die set is seated against the side wall of the chamber. Close the handle. It is imperative that the die set be seated against the side wall of the chamber so that the die is centered in the chamber. Pressing the die in an off-centered position can bend the anvil pins.

With the handle in the closed position, rotate the pressure dial so that the upper ram of the handpress just touches the upper anvil of the die assembly. Tilt the unit back so that the die set does not fall out of the handpress. Open the handle and rotate the pressure dial clockwise about one-half turn. Slowly compress the KBr

[5]The KBr Quick Press unit is available from Wilmad Glass Company, Inc., Route 40 and Oak Road, Buena, NJ 08310.

Figure 25.6
Making a KBr pellet with a
minipress.

mixture by closing the handle. The pressure should be no greater than that exerted by a very firm handshake. Do not apply excessive pressure or the dies may be damaged. If in doubt, rotate the pressure dial counterclockwise to lower the pressure. If the handle closes too easily, open the handle, rotate the pressure dial clockwise, and compress the sample again. Compress the sample for about 60 seconds.

After this time, tilt the unit back so that the die set does not fall out of the handpress. Open the handle and carefully remove the die set from the unit. Turn the pressure dial counterclockwise about one full turn. Pull the die set apart and inspect the KBr pellet. Ideally, the pellet should appear clear like a piece of glass, but usually it will be translucent or somewhat opaque. There may be some cracks or holes in the pellet. The pellet will produce a good spectrum, even with imperfections, as long as light can travel through the pellet. Clean the dies using the procedure outlined below, in "Cleaning and Storing the Equipment."

Making a Pellet with a KBr Minipress. The second method of preparing a pellet uses the minipress apparatus shown in Figure 25.6. Obtain a ground KBr mixture as described in "Preparing the Sample" and transfer a portion of the finely ground powder (usually not more than half) into a die that compresses it into a translucent pellet. As shown in Figure 25.6, the die consists of two stainless steel bolts and a threaded barrel. The bolts have their ends ground flat. To use this die, screw one of the bolts into the barrel, but not all the way; leave one or two turns. Carefully add the powder with a spatula into the open end of the partly assembled die and tap it lightly on the benchtop to give an even layer on the face of the bolt. While keeping the barrel upright, carefully screw the second bolt into the barrel until it is finger tight. Insert the head of the bottom bolt into the hexagonal hole in a plate bolted to the benchtop. This plate keeps the head of one bolt from turning. The top bolt is tightened with a torque wrench to compress the KBr mixture. Continue to turn the torque wrench until you hear a loud click (the ratchet mechanism makes softer clicks) or until you reach the appropriate torque value (20 ft-lb). If you tighten the bolt beyond this point, you may twist the head off one of the bolts. Leave the die under pressure for about 60 seconds; then reverse the ratchet on the torque wrench or pull the torque wrench in the opposite direction to open the assembly. When the two bolts are loose, hold the barrel horizontally and carefully remove the two bolts. You should observe a clear or translucent KBr pellet in the center of the barrel. Even if the pellet is not totally transparent, you should be able to obtain a satisfactory spectrum as long as light passes through the pellet.

Determining the Infrared Spectrum. To obtain the spectrum, slide the holder appropriate for the type of die that you are using into the slot on the infrared spectrophotometer. Set the die containing the pellet in the holder so that the sample is centered in the optical path. Obtain the infrared spectrum. If you are using a double-beam instrument, you may be able to compensate (at least partially) for a marginal pellet by placing a wire screen or attenuator in the reference beam, thereby balancing the lowered transmittance of the pellet. An FT-IR instrument will automatically deal with the low intensity if you select the "autoscale" option.

Problems with an Unsatisfactory Pellet. If the pellet is unsatisfactory (too cloudy to pass light), one of several things may have been wrong:

1. The KBr mixture may not have been ground finely enough, and the particle size may be too big. The large particle size creates too much light scattering.
2. The sample may not be dry.

3. Too much sample may have been used for the amount of KBr taken.
4. The pellet may be too thick; that is, too much of the powdered mixture was put into the die.
5. The KBr may have been "wet" or have acquired moisture from the air while the mixture was being ground in the mortar.
6. The sample may have a low melting point. Low-melting solids not only are difficult to dry, but also melt under pressure. You may need to dissolve the compound in a solvent and run the spectrum in solution (see Section 25.6).

Cleaning and Storing the Equipment. After you have determined the spectrum, punch the pellet out of the die with a wooden applicator stick (a spatula should not be used as it may scratch the dies). Remember that the polished faces of the die set must not be scratched, or they become useless. After the pellet has been punched out, wash all parts of the die set or minipress with warm water. Then rinse the parts with acetone and dry them using a Kimwipe. Check with your instructor to see if there are additional instructions for cleaning the die set. Return the dies to the storage container. Wash the mortar and pestle with water, dry them carefully with paper towels, and return them to the desiccator. Return the KBr powder to its desiccator.

C. Nujol Mulls

If an adequate KBr pellet cannot be obtained or if the solid is insoluble in a suitable solvent, the spectrum of a solid may be determined as a **Nujol mull.** In this method, finely grind about 5 mg of the solid sample in an agate mortar with a pestle. Then add 1 or 2 drops of Nujol mineral oil (white) and grind the mixture to a very fine dispersion. The solid is not dissolved in the Nujol; it is actually a suspension. This mull is then placed between two salt plates using a rubber policeman. Mount the salt plates in the holder in the same way as for liquid samples (see Section 25.2).

Nujol is a mixture of high-molecular-weight hydrocarbons. Hence, it has absorptions in the C—H stretch and CH_2 and CH_3 bending regions of the spectrum (Figure 25.7). Clearly, if Nujol is used, no information can be obtained in these portions of the spectrum. In interpreting the spectrum, you must ignore these Nujol peaks. It is important to label the spectrum immediately after it was determined,

Figure 25.7
Infrared spectrum of Nujol (mineral oil).

noting that it was determined as a Nujol mull. Otherwise, you might forget that the C—H peaks belong to Nujol and not to the dispersed solid.

25.6 Solid Samples—Solution Spectra

A. Method A—Solution Between Salt (NaCl) Plates

For substances that are soluble in carbon tetrachloride, a quick and easy method for determining the spectra of solids is available. Dissolve as much solid as possible in 0.1 mL of carbon tetrachloride. Place 1 or 2 drops of the solution between sodium chloride plates in precisely the same manner as used for pure liquids (see Section 25.2). The spectrum is determined as described for pure liquids using salt plates (see Section 25.2). You should work as quickly as possible. If there is a delay, the solvent will evaporate from between the plates before the spectrum is recorded. Because the spectrum contains the absorptions of the solute superimposed on the absorptions of carbon tetrachloride, it is important to remember that any absorption that appears near 800 cm^{-1} may be due to the stretching of the C—Cl bond of the solvent. Information contained to the right of about 900 cm^{-1} is not usable in this method. There are no other interfering bands for this solvent (see Figure 25.8), and any other absorptions can be attributed to your sample. Chloroform solutions should not be studied by this method because the solvent has too many interfering absorptions (see Figure 25.9).

CAUTION

Carbon tetrachloride is a hazardous solvent. Work under the hood!

Carbon tetrachloride, besides being toxic, is suspected of being a carcinogen. Despite the health problems associated with its use, there is no suitable alternative solvent for infrared spectroscopy. Other solvents have too many interfering infrared absorption bands. Handle carbon tetrachloride carefully to minimize the adverse health effects. The spectroscopic-grade carbon tetrachloride should be stored in a glass-stoppered bottle in a hood. A Pasteur pipette should be attached to the bottle, possibly by storing it in a test tube taped to the side of the bottle. All sample preparation should be conducted in a hood. Rubber or plastic gloves should be worn.

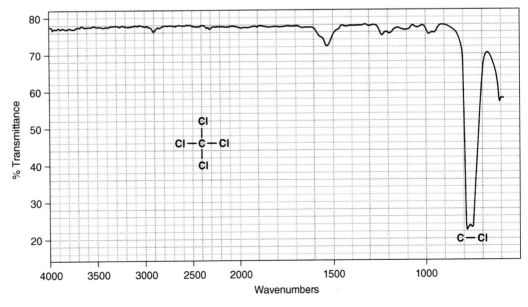

© Cengage Learning 2013

Figure 25.8
Infrared spectrum of carbon tetrachloride.

Figure 25.9
Infrared spectrum of chloroform.

The cells should also be cleaned in the hood. All carbon tetrachloride used in preparing samples should be disposed of in an appropriately marked waste container.

B. Method B—AgCl Minicell

The AgCl minicell described in Section 25.3 may be used to determine the infrared spectrum of a solid dissolved in carbon tetrachloride. Prepare a 5–10% solution (5–10 mg in 0.1 mL) in carbon tetrachloride. If it is not possible to prepare a solution of this concentration because of low solubility, dissolve as much solid as possible in the solvent. Following the instructions given in Section 25.3, position the AgCl plates as shown in Figure 25.4C to obtain the maximum possible path length of 0.20 mm. When the cell is tightened firmly, the cell will not leak.

As indicated in method A, the spectrum will contain the absorptions of the dissolved solid superimposed on the absorptions of carbon tetrachloride. A strong absorption appears near 800 cm^{-1} for the C—Cl stretch in the solvent. No useful information may be obtained for the sample to the right of about 900 cm^{-1}, but other bands that appear in the spectrum will belong to your sample. Read the safety material provided in method A. Carbon tetrachloride is toxic, and it should be used under a hood.

NOTE: Care should be taken in cleaning the AgCl plates. Because AgCl plates scratch easily, they should not be wiped with tissue. Rinse them with methylene chloride and keep them in a dark place. Amines will destroy the plates.

C. Method C—Solution Cells (NaCl)

The spectra of solids may also be determined in a type of permanent sample cell called a **solution cell.** (The infrared spectra of liquids may also be determined in this cell.) The solution cell, shown in Figure 25.10, is made from two salt plates, mounted with a Teflon spacer between them to control the thickness of the sample. The top sodium chloride plate has two holes drilled in it so that the sample can be introduced into the cavity between the two plates. These holes are extended

Figure 25.10
A solution cell.

through the face plate by two tubular extensions designed to hold Teflon plugs, which seal the internal chamber and prevent evaporation. The tubular extensions are tapered so that a syringe body (Luer lock without a needle) will fit snugly into them from the outside. The cells are thus filled from a syringe; usually, they are held upright and filled from the bottom entrance port.

These cells are expensive, and you should try either method A or B before using solution cells. If you do need them, obtain your instructor's permission and receive instruction before using the cells. The cells are purchased in matched pairs, with identical path lengths. Dissolve a solid in a suitable solvent, usually carbon tetrachloride, and add the solution to one of the cells (**sample cell**) as described in the previous paragraph. The pure solvent, identical to that used to dissolve the solid, is placed in the other cell (**reference cell**). The spectrum of the solvent is subtracted from the spectrum of the solution (not always completely), and a spectrum of the solute is thus provided. For the solvent compensation to be as exact as possible and to avoid contamination of the reference cell, it is essential that one cell be used as a reference and that the other cell be used as a sample cell without ever being interchanged. After the spectrum is determined, it is important to clean the cells by flushing them with clean solvent. They should be dried by passing dry air through the cell.

Solvents most often used in determining infrared spectra are carbon tetrachloride (see Figure 25.8), chloroform (see Figure 25.9), and carbon disulfide (see Figure 25.11). A 5–10% solution of solid in one of these solvents usually gives a good spectrum. Carbon tetrachloride and chloroform are suspected carcinogens; however, because there are no suitable alternative solvents, these compounds must be used in infrared spectroscopy. The procedure outlined above for carbon tetrachloride should be followed. This procedure serves equally well for chloroform.

Figure 25.11
Infrared spectrum of carbon disulfide.

NOTE: Before you use the solution cells, you must obtain the instructor's permission and instruction on how to fill and clean the cells.

25.7 Recording the Spectrum

The instructor will describe how to operate the infrared spectrophotometer, because the controls vary considerably, depending on the manufacturer, model of the instrument, and type. For example, some instruments involve pushing only a few buttons, whereas others use a more complicated computer interface system.

In all cases, it is important that the sample, the solvent, the type of cell or method used, and any other pertinent information be written on the spectrum immediately after the determination. This information may be important, and it is easily forgotten if not recorded. You may also need to calibrate the instrument (see Section 25.8).

25.8 Calibration

For some instruments, the frequency scale of the spectrum must be calibrated so that you know the position of each absorption peak precisely. You can recalibrate by recording a very small portion of the spectrum of polystyrene over the spectrum of your sample. The complete spectrum of polystyrene is shown in Figure 25.12. The most important of these peaks is at 1603 cm^{-1}; other useful peaks are at 2850 cm^{-1} and 906 cm^{-1}. After you record the spectrum of your sample, substitute a thin film of polystyrene for the sample cell and record the tips (not the entire spectrum) of the most important peaks over the sample spectrum.

It is always a good idea to calibrate a spectrum when the instrument uses chart paper with a preprinted scale. It is difficult to align the paper properly so that the scale matches the absorption lines precisely. You often need to know the precise values for certain functional groups (for example, the carbonyl group). Calibration is essential in these cases.

With computer-interfaced instruments, the instrument does not need to be calibrated. With this type of instrument, the spectrum and scale are printed on blank

Figure 25.12
Infrared spectrum of polystyrene (thin film).

paper at the same time. The instrument has an internal calibration that ensures that the positions of the absorptions are known precisely and that they are placed at the proper positions on the scale. With this type of instrument, it is often possible to print a list of the locations of the major peaks as well as to obtain the complete spectrum of your compound.

PART B. INFRARED SPECTROSCOPY

25.9 Uses of the Infrared Spectrum

Because every type of bond has a different natural frequency of vibration and because the same type of bond in two different compounds is in a slightly different environment, no two molecules of different structure have exactly the same infrared absorption pattern, or **infrared spectrum.** Although some of the frequencies absorbed in the two cases might be the same, in no case of two different molecules will their infrared spectra (the patterns of absorption) be identical. Thus, the infrared spectrum can be used to identify molecules much as a fingerprint can be used to identify people. Comparing the infrared spectra of two substances thought to be identical will establish whether or not they are in fact identical. If the infrared spectra of two substances coincide peak for peak (absorption for absorption), in most cases, the substances are identical.

A second and more important use of the infrared spectrum is that it gives structural information about a molecule. The absorptions of each type of bond (N—H, C—H, O—H, C—X, C=O, C—O, C—C, C=C, C≡C, C≡N, and so on) are regularly found only in certain small portions of the vibrational infrared region. A small range of absorption can be defined for each type of bond. Outside this range, absorptions will normally be due to some other type of bond. Thus, for instance, any absorption in the range 3000 ± 150 cm^{-1} will almost always be due to the presence of a CH bond in the molecule; an absorption in the range 1700 ± 100 cm^{-1} will normally be due to the presence of a C=O bond (carbonyl group) in the molecule. The same type of range applies to each type of bond. The way these are spread out over the vibrational infrared is illustrated schematically in Figure 25.13. It is a good idea to remember this general scheme for future convenience.

© Cengage Learning 2013

Figure 25.13
Approximate regions in which various common types of bonds absorb.
(Bending, twisting, and other types of bond vibration have been omitted for
clarity.)

25.10 Modes of Vibration

The simplest types, or **modes,** of vibrational motion in a molecule that are **infrared active,** that is, give rise to absorptions, are the stretching and bending modes.

C—H   Stretching   Bending

© Cengage Learning 2013

Other, more complex types of stretching and bending are also active, however. To introduce several words of terminology, the normal modes of vibration for a methylene group are shown below.

In any group of three or more atoms—at least two of which are identical—there are *two* modes of stretching or bending: the symmetric mode and asymmetric mode. Examples of such groupings are —CH₃, —CH₂—, —NO₂, —NH₂, and anhydrides (CO)₂O. For the anhydride, owing to asymmetric and symmetric modes of stretch, this functional group gives *two* absorptions in the C═O region. A similar phenomenon is seen for amino groups, where primary amines usually have *two* absorptions in the NH stretch region, whereas secondary amines R₂NH have only one absorption peak. Amides show similar bands. There are two strong N═O stretch peaks for a nitro group, which are caused by asymmetric and symmetric stretching modes.

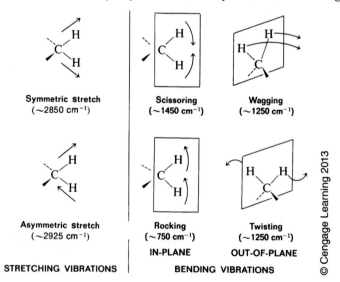

Symmetric stretch (~2850 cm⁻¹)

Asymmetric stretch (~2925 cm⁻¹)

STRETCHING VIBRATIONS

Scissoring (~1450 cm⁻¹)

Wagging (~1250 cm⁻¹)

Rocking (~750 cm⁻¹)

Twisting (~1250 cm⁻¹)

IN-PLANE   OUT-OF-PLANE

BENDING VIBRATIONS

© Cengage Learning 2013

25.11 What to Look for in Examining Infrared Spectra

The instrument that determines the absorption spectrum for a compound is called an **infrared spectrophotometer.** The spectrophotometer determines the relative strengths and positions of all the absorptions in the infrared region and

Figure 25.14
Infrared spectrum of methyl isopropyl ketone (neat liquid, salt plates).

plots this information on a piece of paper. This plot of absorption intensity versus wavenumber or wavelength is referred to as the **infrared spectrum** of the compound. A typical infrared spectrum, that of methyl isopropyl ketone, is shown in Figure 25.14.

The strong absorption in the middle of the spectrum corresponds to C=O, the carbonyl group. Note that the C=O peak is quite intense. In addition to the characteristic position of absorption, the **shape** and **intensity** of this peak are also unique to the C=O bond. This is true for almost every type of absorption peak; both shape and intensity characteristics can be described, and these characteristics often make it possible to distinguish the peak in a confusing situation. For instance, to some extent both C=O and C=C bonds absorb in the same region of the infrared spectrum:

$$C=O \; 1850\text{–}1630 \text{ cm}^{-1}$$

$$C=C \; 1680\text{–}1620 \text{ cm}^{-1}$$

However, the C=O bond is a strong absorber, whereas the C=C bond generally absorbs only weakly. Hence, a trained observer would not normally interpret a strong peak at 1670 cm^{-1} to be a carbon–carbon double bond or a weak absorption at this frequency to be due to a carbonyl group.

In Figure 25.14, notice that the very strong C=O peak at 1710 cm^{-1} leads to a very weak overtone at twice the C=O frequency (3420 cm^{-1}). As is often the case, very strong bands may yield a weaker peak at twice the frequency of the main band.

The shape of a peak often gives a clue to its identity as well. Thus, although the NH and OH regions of the infrared overlap,

$$OH \; 3650\text{–}3200 \text{ cm}^{-1}$$

$$NH \; 3500\text{–}3300 \text{ cm}^{-1}$$

NH usually gives a **sharp** absorption peak (absorbs a very narrow range of frequencies), and OH, when it is in the NH region, usually gives a **broad** absorption peak. Primary amines give *two* absorptions in this region, whereas alcohols give only one.

Therefore, while you are studying the sample spectra in the pages that follow, you should also notice shapes and intensities. They are as important as the frequency at which an absorption occurs, and you must train your eye to recognize these features. In the literature of organic chemistry, you will often find absorptions referred to as strong (s), medium (m), weak (w), broad, or sharp. The author is trying to convey some idea of what the peak looks like without actually drawing the spectrum. Although the intensity of an absorption often provides useful information about the identity of a peak, be aware that the relative intensities of all of the peaks in the spectrum are dependent on the amount of sample that is used and the sensitivity setting of the instrument. Therefore, the *actual* intensity of a particular peak may vary from spectrum to spectrum, and you must pay attention to *relative* intensities.

25.12 Correlation Charts and Tables

To extract structural information from infrared spectra, you must know the frequencies or wavelengths at which various functional groups absorb. Infrared **correlation tables** present as much information as is known about where the various functional groups absorb. The books listed at the end of this chapter present extensive lists of correlation tables. Sometimes, the absorption information is given in a chart, called a **correlation chart.** A simplified correlation table is given in Table 25.1.

Although you may think assimilating the mass of data in Table 25.1 will be difficult, it is not if you make a modest start and then gradually increase your familiarity with the data. An ability to interpret the fine details of an infrared spectrum will follow. This is most easily accomplished by first establishing the broad visual patterns of Figure 25.13 firmly in mind. Then, as a second step, a "typical absorption value" can be memorized for each of the functional groups in this pattern. This value will be a single number that can be used as a pivot value for the memory. For instance, start with a simple aliphatic ketone as a model for all typical carbonyl compounds. The typical aliphatic ketone has a carbonyl absorption of 1715 ± 10 cm^{-1}. Without worrying about the variation, memorize 1715 cm^{-1} as the base value for carbonyl absorption. Then learn the extent of the carbonyl range and the visual pattern of how the different kinds of carbonyl groups are arranged throughout this region. See, for instance, Figure 25.27, which gives typical values for carbonyl compounds. Also learn how factors such as ring size (when the functional group is contained in a ring) and conjugation affect the base values (that is, in which direction the values are shifted). Learn the trends—always remembering the base value (1715 cm^{-1}). It might prove useful as a beginning to memorize the base values in Table 25.2 for this approach. Notice that there are only eight values.

25.13 Analyzing a Spectrum (or What You Can Tell at a Glance)

In analyzing the spectrum of an unknown, concentrate first on establishing the presence (or absence) of a few major functional groups. The most conspicuous peaks are C=O, O—H, N—H, C—O, C=C, C≡C, C≡N, and NO$_2$. If they are present, they give immediate structural information. Do not try to analyze in detail the CH absorptions near 3000 cm^{-1}; almost all compounds have these absorptions. Do not worry about subtleties of the exact type of environment in which the functional group is found. A checklist of the important gross features follows:

1. Is a carbonyl group present?

Table 25.1 A Simplified Correlation Table

	Type of Vibration		Frequency (cm^{-1})	Intensity[a]
C—H	Alkanes	(stretch)	3000–2850	s
	—CH$_3$	(bend)	1450 and 1375	m
	—CH$_2$$^-$	(bend)	1465	m
	Alkenes	(stretch)	3100–3000	m
		(bend)	1700–1000	s
	Aromatics	(stretch)	3150–3050	s
		(out-of-plane bend)	1000–700	s
	Alkyne	(stretch)	ca. 3300	s
	Aldehyde		2900–2800	w
			2800–2700	w
C—C	Alkane	Not interpretatively useful		
C=C	Alkene		1680–1600	m–w
	Aromatic		1600–1400	m–w
C≡C	Alkyne		2250–2100	m–w
C=O	Aldehyde		1740–1720	s
	Ketone (acyclic)		1725–1705	s
	Carboxylic acid		1725–1700	s
	Ester		1750–1730	s
	Amide		1700–1640	s
	Anhydride		ca. 1810	s
			ca. 1760	s
C—O	Alcohols, ethers, esters, carboxylic acids		1300–1000	s
O—H	Alcohol, phenols			
	Free		3650–3600	m
	H-Bonded		3400–3200	m
	Carboxylic acids		3300–2500	m
N—H	Primary and secondary amines		ca. 3500	m
C≡N	Nitriles		2260–2240	m
N=O	Nitro (R—NO$_2$)		1600–1500	s
			1400–1300	s
C—X	Fluoride		1400–1000	s
	Chloride		800–600	s
	Bromide, iodide		<600	s

[a]s, strong; m, medium; w, weak.

Table 25.2 Base Values for Absorptions of Bonds

O—H	3400 cm^{-1}	C≡C	2150 cm^{-1}
N—H	3500 cm^{-1}	C=O	1715 cm^{-1}
C—H	3000 cm^{-1}	C=C	1650 cm^{-1}
C≡N	2250 cm^{-1}	C—O	1100 cm^{-1}

© Cengage Learning 2013

The C=O group gives rise to a strong absorption in the region 1820–1600 cm^{-1}. The peak is often the strongest in the spectrum and of medium width. You can't miss it.

2. If C=O is present, check the following types. (If it is absent, go to item 3.)

Acids	Is O—H also present?
	Broad absorption near 3300–2500 cm^{-1} (usually overlaps C—H).
Amides	Is N—H also present?
	Medium absorption near 3500 cm^{-1}, sometimes a double peak, equivalent halves.
Esters	Is C—O also present?
	Medium intensity absorptions near 1300–1000 cm^{-1}.
Anhydrides	Have *two* C=O absorptions near 1810 and 1760 cm^{-1}.
Aldehydes	Is aldehyde C—H present?
	Two weak absorptions near 2850 cm^{-1} and 2750 cm^{-1} on the right side of C—H absorptions.
Ketones	The preceding five choices have been eliminated.

3. If C=O is absent

Alcohols	Check for O—H.
or Phenols	*Broad* absorption near 3600–3300 cm^{-1}.
	Confirm this by finding C—O near 1300–1000 cm^{-1}.
Amines	Check for N—H.
	Medium absorption(s) near 3500 cm^{-1}.
Ethers	Check for C—O (and absence of O—H)
	near 1300–1000 cm^{-1}.

4. Double bonds or aromatic rings or both

C=C is a *weak* absorption near 1650 cm^{-1}.

Medium to strong absorptions in the region 1650–1450 cm^{-1} often imply an aromatic ring.

Confirm the above by consulting the C—H region.

Aromatic and vinyl C—H occur to the left of 3000 cm^{-1} (aliphatic C—H occurs to the right of this value).

5. Triple bonds   C≡N is a medium, sharp absorption near 2250 cm^{-1}.

C≡C is a weak but sharp absorption near 2150 cm^{-1}.

Check also for acetylenic C—H near 3300 cm^{-1}.

6. Nitro groups   *Two* strong absorptions near 1600–1500 cm^{-1} and 1390–1300 cm^{-1}.

7. Hydrocarbons   None of the above is found.

Main absorptions are in the C—H region near 3000 cm^{-1}.

Very simple spectrum, only other absorptions are near 1450 cm^{-1} and 1375 cm^{-1}.

The beginning student should resist the idea of trying to assign or interpret *every* peak in the spectrum. You simply will not be able to do this. Concentrate first on learning the principal peaks and recognizing their presence or absence. This is best done by carefully studying the illustrative spectra in the section that follows.

NOTE: In describing the shifts of absorption peaks or their relative positions, we have used the phrases "to the left" and "to the right." This was done to simplify descriptions of peak positions. The meaning is clear because all spectra are conventionally presented left to right from 4000 − 600 cm^{-1}.

25.14 Survey of the Important Functional Groups

A. Alkanes

The spectrum is usually simple, with a few peaks.

C—H   Stretch occurs around 3000 cm^{-1}.

    1. In alkanes (except strained ring compounds), absorption always occurs to the right of 3000 cm^{-1}.

    2. If a compound has vinylic, aromatic, acetylenic, or cyclopropyl hydrogens, the CH absorption is to the left of 3000 cm^{-1}.

CH$_2$ Methylene groups have a characteristic absorption at approximately 1450 cm^{-1}.

CH$_3$ Methyl groups have a characteristic absorption at approximately 1375 cm^{-1}.

C—C   Stretch—not interpretatively useful—has many peaks.

The spectrum of decane is shown in Figure 25.15.

B. Alkenes

=C—H   Stretch occurs to the left of 3000 cm^{-1}.

=C—H   Out-of-plane (oop) bending occurs at 1000–650 cm^{-1}.

    The C—H oop absorptions often allow you to determine the type of substitution pattern on the double bond, according to the number of absorptions and their positions. The correlation chart in Figure 25.16 shows the positions of these bands.

C=C   Stretch 1675–1600 cm^{-1}, often weak.

    Conjugation moves C=C stretch to the right.

    Symmetrically substituted bonds, as in 2,3-dimethyl-2-butene, do not absorb in the infrared region (no dipole change). Highly substituted double bonds are often vanishingly weak in absorption.

Figure 25.15

Infrared spectrum of decane (neat liquid, salt plates).

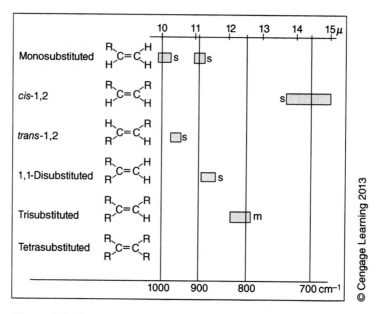

Figure 25.16
The C—H out-of-plane bending vibrations for substituted alkenes.

Figure 25.17
Infrared spectrum of 4-methylcyclohexene (neat liquid, salt plates).

The spectra of 4-methylcyclohexene and styrene are shown in Figures 25.17 and 25.18.

C. Aromatic Rings

=C—H   Stretch is always to the left of 3000 cm^{-1}.

=C—H   Out-of-plane oop bending occurs at 900 to 690 cm^{-1}.

Figure 25.18
Infrared spectrum of styene (neat liquid, salt plates).

The C—H oop absorptions often allow you to determine the type of ring substitution by their numbers, intensities, and positions. The correlation chart in Figure 25.19A indicates the positions of these bands.

The patterns are generally reliable—they are most reliable for rings with alkyl substituents and least reliable for polar substituents.

Ring Absorptions (C═C). There are often four sharp absorptions that occur in pairs at 1600 cm^{-1} and 1450 cm^{-1} and are characteristic of an aromatic ring. See, for example, the spectra of anisole (Figure 25.23), benzonitrile (Figure 25.26), and methyl benzoate (Figure 25.35).

There are many weak combination and overtone absorptions that appear between 2000 cm^{-1} and 1667 cm^{-1}. The relative shapes and numbers of these peaks can be used to determine whether an aromatic ring is monosubstituted or di-, tri-, tetra-, penta-, or hexa-substituted. Positional isomers can also be distinguished. Because the absorptions are weak, these bands are best observed by using neat liquids or concentrated solutions. If the compound has a high-frequency carbonyl group, this absorption overlaps the weak overtone bands, so no useful information can be obtained from analyzing this region. The various patterns that are obtained in this region are shown in Figure 25.19B.

The spectra of styrene and *o*-dichlorobenzene are shown in Figures 25.18 and 25.20.

D. Alkynes

≡C—H   Stretch is usually near 3300 cm^{-1}, sharp peak.

C≡C   Stretch is near 2150 cm^{-1}, sharp peak.

Conjugation moves C≡C stretch to the right.

Disubstituted or symmetrically substituted triple bonds give either no absorption or weak absorption.

A

B

© Cengage Learning 2013

Figure 25.19
(A) The C—H out-of-plane bending vibrations for substituted benzenoid compounds. (B) The 2000–1667 cm⁻¹ region for substituted benzenoid compounds. (From Dyer, J.R. *Applications of Absorption Spectroscopy of Organic Compounds*, Prentice Hall: Englewood Cliffs, NJ, 1965.)

© Cengage Learning 2013

Figure 25.20
Infrared spectrum of *o*-dichlorobenzene (neat liquid, salt plates).

E. Alcohols and Phenols

O—H   Stretch is a sharp peak at 3650–3600 cm^{-1} if no hydrogen bonding takes place. (This is usually observed only in dilute solutions.)

                If there is hydrogen bonding (usual in neat or concentrated solutions), the absorption is *broad* and occurs more to the right at 3500–3200 cm^{-1}, sometimes overlapping C—H stretch absorptions.

C—O   Stretch is usually in the range of 1300–1000 cm^{-1}.

                Phenols are like alcohols. The 2-naphthol shown in Figure 25.21 has some molecules hydrogen bonded and some free. The spectrum of 4-methylcyclohexanol is shown in Figure 25.22. This alcohol, which was determined neat, would also have had a free OH spike to the left of this hydrogen-bonded band if it had been determined in dilute solution.

F. Ethers

C—O   The most prominent band is due to C—O stretch at 1300–1000 cm^{-1}. Absence of C═O and O—H bands is required to be sure the C—O stretch is not due to an alcohol or ester. Phenyl and vinyl ethers are found in the left portion of the range, aliphatic ethers in the right. (Conjugation with the oxygen moves the absorption to the left.)

    The spectrum of anisole is shown in Figure 25.23.

G. Amines

N—H   Stretch occurs in the range of 3500–3300 cm^{-1}.

                Primary amines have *two* bands typically 30 cm^{-1} apart.

                Secondary amines have one band, often vanishingly weak.

                Tertiary amines have no NH stretch.

Figure 25.21

Infrared spectrum of 2-naphthol showing both free and hydrogen-bonded OH (CHCl$_3$ solution).

Figure 25.22
Infrared spectrum of 4-methylcyclohexanol (neat liquid, salt plates).

Figure 25.23
Infrared spectrum of anisole (neat liquid, salt plates).

C—N   Stretch is weak and occurs in the range of 1350–1000 cm⁻¹.

N—H   Scissoring bending mode occurs in the range of 1640–1560 cm⁻¹ (broad).

An oop bending absorption can sometimes be observed at about 800 cm⁻¹.

The spectrum of *n*-butylamine is shown in Figure 25.24.

Figure 25.24
Infrared spectrum of *n*-butylamine (neat liquid, salt plates).

H. Nitro Compounds

N=O   Stretch is usually two strong bands at 1600–1500 cm^{-1} and 1390–1300 cm^{-1}.

The spectrum of nitrobenzene is shown in Figure 25.25.

I. Nitriles

C≡N   Stretch is a sharp absorption near 2250 cm^{-1}.

Conjugation with double bonds or aromatic rings moves the absorption to the right.

The spectrum of benzonitrile is shown in Figure 25.26.

J. Carbonyl Compounds

The carbonyl group is one of the most strongly absorbing groups in the infrared region of the spectrum. This is mainly due to its large dipole moment. It absorbs in a variety of compounds (aldehydes, ketones, acids, esters, amides, anhydrides, and acid chlorides) in the range of 1850–1650 cm^{-1}. In Figure 25.27, the normal values for the various types of carbonyl groups are compared. In the sections that follow, each type is examined separately.

K. Aldehydes

C=O   Stretch at approximately 1725 cm^{-1} is normal.

Aldehydes *seldom* absorb to the left of this value.

Conjugation moves the absorption to the right.

C—H   Stretch, aldehyde hydrogen (—CHO), consists of *weak* bands at about 2750 cm^{-1} and 2850 cm^{-1}. Note that the CH stretch in alkyl chains does not usually extend this far to the right.

The spectrum of an unconjugated aldehyde, nonanal, is shown in Figure 25.28, and the conjugated aldehyde, benzaldehyde, is shown in Figure 25.29.

© Cengage Learning 2013

Figure 25.25
Infrared spectrum of nitrobenzene (neat liquid, salt plates).

© Cengage Learning 2013

Figure 25.26
Infrared spectrum of benzonitrile (neat liquid, salt plates).

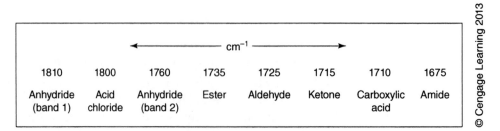

© Cengage Learning 2013

Figure 25.27
Normal base values for the C=O stretching vibrations for carbonyl groups.

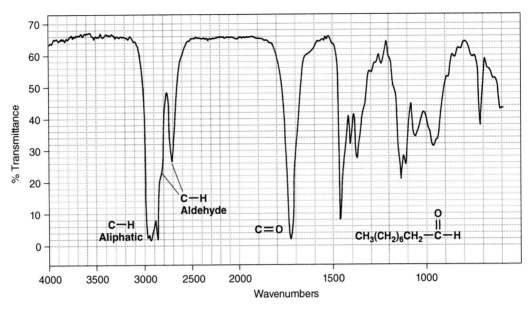

Figure 25.28
Infrared spectrum of nonanal (neat liquid, salt plates).

Figure 25.29
Infrared spectrum of benzaldehyde (neat liquid, salt plates).

L. Ketones

C=O   Stretch at approximately at 1715 cm^{-1} is normal.

Conjugation moves the absorption to the right.

Ring strain moves the absorption to the left in cyclic ketones (see Figure 25.30).

The spectra of methyl isopropyl ketone and mesityl oxide are shown in Figures 25.14 and 25.31. The spectrum of camphor, shown in Figure 25.32, has a carbonyl group that has been shifted to a higher frequency because of ring strain (1745 cm^{-1}).

Figure 25.30
Effects of conjugation and ring strain on carbonyl frequencies in ketones.

Figure 25.31
Infrared spectrum of mesityl oxide (neat liquid, salt plates).

M. Acids

O—H   Stretch, usually *very broad* (strongly hydrogen-bonded) at 3300–2500 cm^{-1}, often interferes with C—H absorptions.

C=O   Stretch, broad, 1730–1700 cm^{-1}.

Conjugation moves the absorption to the right.

C—O   Stretch, in the range of 1320–1210 cm^{-1}, is strong.

The spectrum of benzoic acid is shown in Figure 25.33.

Figure 25.32
Infrared spectrum of camphor (KBr pellet).

Figure 25.33
Infrared spectrum of benzoic acid (KBr pellet).

$$\text{N. Esters } \left(\text{R}{-}\overset{\overset{\text{O}}{\|}}{\text{C}}{-}\text{OR}' \right)$$

C=O   Stretch occurs at about 1735 cm^{-1} in normal esters.

                1. Conjugation in the R part moves the absorption to the right.

                2. Conjugation with the O in the R′ part moves the absorption to the left.

                3. Ring strain (lactones) moves the absorption to the left.

C—O   Stretch, two bands or more, one stronger than the others, is in the
           range of 1300–1000 cm^{-1}.

The spectrum of an unconjugated ester, isopentyl acetate, is shown in Figure 25.34 (C=O appears at 1740 cm^{-1}). A conjugated ester, methyl benzoate, is shown in Figure 25.35 (C=O appears at 1720 cm^{-1}).

Figure 25.34
Infrared spectrum of isopentyl acetate (neat liquid, salt plates).

Figure 25.35
Infrared spectrum of methyl benzoate (neat liquid, salt plates).

O. Amides

C=O	Stretch is at approximately 1700–1640 cm^{-1}.
	Conjugation and ring size (lactams) have the usual effects.
N—H	Stretch (if monosubstituted or unsubstituted) is at 3500–3100 cm^{-1}.
	Unsubstituted amides have two bands (—NH$_2$) in this region.
N—H	Bending around 1640–1550 cm^{-1}.

The spectrum of benzamide is shown in Figure 25.36.

Figure 25.36
Infrared spectrum of benzamide (solid phase, KBr).

Figure 25.37
Infrared spectrum of *cis*-norbornene-5,6-*endo*-dicarboxylic anhydride (KBr pellet).

P. Anhydrides

C=O   Stretch always has *two* bands: 1830–1800 cm^{-1} and 1775–1740 cm^{-1}.

Unsaturation moves the absorptions to the right.

Ring strain (cyclic anhydrides) moves the absorptions to the left.

C—O   Stretch is at 1300–900 cm^{-1}. The spectrum of *cis*-norbornene-5,6-*endo*-dicarboxylic anhydride is shown in Figure 25.37.

Q. Acid Chlorides

C=O   Stretch occurs in the range 1810–1775 cm^{-1} in unconjugated
          chlorides. Conjugation lowers the frequency to 1780–1760 cm^{-1}.

C—O   Stretch occurs in the range 730–550 cm^{-1}.

R. Halides

It is often difficult to determine either the presence or the absence of a halide in a compound by infrared spectroscopy. The absorption bands cannot be relied on, especially if the spectrum is being determined with the compound dissolved in CCl$_4$ or CHCl$_3$ solution.

C—F   Stretch, 1350–960 cm^{-1}.

C—Cl   Stretch, 850–500 cm^{-1}.

C—Br   Stretch, to the right of 667 cm^{-1}.

C—I   Stretch, to the right of 667 cm^{-1}.

The spectra of the solvents, carbon tetrachloride and chloroform, are shown in Figures 25.8 and 25.9, respectively.

REFERENCES

Bellamy, L. J. *The Infra-Red Spectra of Complex Molecules*, 3rd ed.; Methuen: New York, **1975**.

Colthup, N. B.; Daly, L. H.; Wiberly, S. E. *Introduction to Infrared and Raman Spectroscopy*, 3rd ed. Academic Press: San Diego, CA, **1990**.

Dyer, J. R. *Applications of Absorption Spectroscopy of Organic Compounds*; Prentice-Hall: Englewood Cliffs, NJ, **1965**.

Lin-Vien, D.; Colthup, N. B.; Fateley, W. G.; Grasselli, J. G. *Infrared and Raman Characteristic Frequencies of Organic Molecules*; Academic Press: San Diego, CA, **1991**.

Nakanishi, K.; Soloman, P. H. *Infrared Absorption Spectroscopy*, 2nd ed.; Holden-Day: San Francisco, **1977**.

Pavia, D. L.; Lampman, G. M.; Kriz, G. S.; Vyryan, J. R. *Introduction to Spectroscopy: A Guide for Students of Organic Chemistry*, 4th ed. Brooks/Cole: Belmont, CA, **2008**.

Silverstein, R. M.; Webster, F. X.; Kiemle, D. J. *Spectrometric Identification of Organic Compounds*, 7th ed.; Wiley & Sons: New York, **2005**.

PROBLEMS

1. Comment on the suitability of running the infrared spectrum under each of the following conditions. If there is a problem with the conditions given, provide a suitable alternative method.

   a. A neat spectrum of liquid with a boiling point of 150°C is determined using salt plates.

   b. A neat spectrum of a liquid with a boiling point of 35°C is determined using salt plates.

   c. A KBr pellet is prepared with a compound that melts at 200°C.

   d. A KBr pellet is prepared with a compound that melts at 30°C.

   e. A solid aliphatic hydrocarbon compound is determined as a Nujol mull.

f. Silver chloride plates are used to determine the spectrum of aniline.

g. Sodium chloride plates are selected to run the spectrum of a compound that contains some water.

2. Indicate how you could distinguish between the following pairs of compounds by using infrared spectroscopy.

a.
$$CH_3CH_2CH_2\overset{\overset{\displaystyle O}{\|}}{C}-H \qquad\qquad CH_3CH_2\overset{\overset{\displaystyle O}{\|}}{C}CH_3$$

b.

c.
$$CH_3CH_2\overset{\overset{\displaystyle H}{|}}{N}CH_2CH_3 \qquad\qquad CH_3CH_2CH_2CH_2NH_2$$

d.
$$CH_3CH_2\overset{\overset{\displaystyle O}{\|}}{C}OCH_2CH_3 \qquad\qquad CH_3CH_2\overset{\overset{\displaystyle O}{\|}}{C}CH_2OCH_3$$

e.
$$CH_3CH_2\overset{\overset{\displaystyle O}{\|}}{C}OH \qquad\qquad CH_3CH_2CH_2OH$$

f.

g. $CH_3CH_2CH=CH_2 \qquad\qquad CH_3CH=CHCH_3$ (trans)

h. $CH_3CH_2CH_2C\equiv CH \qquad\qquad CH_3CH_2CH_2CH=CH_2$

i.

j. $CH_3CH_2CH_2CH_2\overset{\overset{\displaystyle O}{\|}}{C}-OH \qquad\qquad CH_3CH_2CH_2\overset{\overset{\displaystyle O}{\|}}{C}OCH_3$

k. $CH_3CH_2CH_2CH_2CH_3 \qquad\qquad CH_2=CHCH_2CH_2CH_2CH_3$

l. $CH_3CH_2CH_2CH_2C\equiv CH \qquad\qquad CH_3CH_2CH_2C\equiv CCH_3$

Nuclear Magnetic Resonance Spectroscopy (Proton NMR)

Nuclear magnetic resonance (NMR) spectroscopy is an instrumental technique that allows the number, type, and relative positions of certain atoms in a molecule to be determined. This type of spectroscopy applies only to those atoms that have nuclear magnetic moments because of their nuclear spin properties. Although many atoms meet this requirement, hydrogen atoms ($_1^1H$) are of the greatest interest to the organic chemist. Atoms of the ordinary isotopes of carbon ($_6^{12}C$) and oxygen ($_8^{16}O$) do not have nuclear magnetic moments, and ordinary nitrogen atoms ($_7^{14}N$), although they do have magnetic moments, generally fail to show typical NMR behavior for other reasons. The same is true of the halogen atoms, except for fluorine ($_9^{19}F$), which does show active NMR behavior. Of the atoms mentioned here, the hydrogen nucleus ($_1^1H$) and carbon-13 nucleus ($_6^{13}C$) are the most important to organic chemists. Proton (^1H) NMR is discussed here and carbon (^{13}C) NMR is described in Technique 27.

Nuclei of NMR-active atoms placed in a magnetic field can be thought of as tiny bar magnets. In hydrogen, which has two allowed nuclear spin states ($+\frac{1}{2}$ and $-\frac{1}{2}$), either the nuclear magnets of individual atoms can be aligned with the magnetic field (spin $+\frac{1}{2}$), or they can be opposed to it (spin $-\frac{1}{2}$). A slight majority of the nuclei are aligned with the field, because this spin orientation constitutes a slightly lower-energy spin state. If radio-frequency waves of the appropriate energy are supplied, nuclei aligned with the field can absorb this radiation and reverse their direction of spin or become reoriented so that the nuclear magnet opposes the applied magnetic field (see Figure 26.1).

The frequency of radiation required to induce spin conversion is a direct function of the strength of the applied magnetic field. When a spinning hydrogen nucleus is placed in a magnetic field, the nucleus begins to process with angular frequency ω, much like a child's toy top. This precessional motion is depicted in Figure 26.2. The angular frequency of nuclear precession ω increases as the strength of the applied magnetic field is increased. The radiation that must be supplied to induce spin conversion in a hydrogen nucleus of spin $+\frac{1}{2}$ must have a frequency that just matches the angular precessional frequency ω. This is called the resonance condition, and spin conversion is said to be a resonance process.

Figure 26.1
The NMR absorption process.

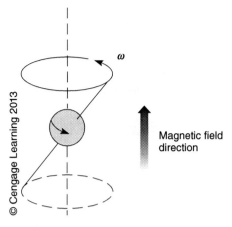

Figure 26.2

Precessional motion of a spinning nucleus in an applied magnetic field.

Magnetic field direction

© Cengage Learning 2013

For the average proton (hydrogen atom), if a magnetic field of approximately 1.4 tesla is applied, radio-frequency radiation of 60 MHz is required to induce a spin transition.[1] Fortunately, the magnetic field strength required to induce the various protons in a molecule to absorb 60-MHz radiation varies from proton to proton within the molecule and is a sensitive function of the immediate *electronic* environment of each proton. The proton nuclear magnetic resonance spectrometer supplies a basic radio-frequency radiation of 60 MHz to the sample being measured and *increases* the strength of the applied magnetic field over a range of several parts per million from the basic field strength. As the field increases, various protons come into resonance (absorb 60-MHz energy), and a resonance signal is generated for each proton. An NMR spectrum is a plot of the strength of the magnetic field versus the intensity of the absorptions. A typical 60-MHz NMR spectrum is shown in Figure 26.3.

Modern FT-NMR instruments produce the same type of NMR spectrum just described, even though they do it by a different method. See your lecture textbook for a discussion of the differences between classic CW instruments and modern FT-NMR instruments. Fourier transform spectrometers operating at magnetic field strengths of at least 7.1 tesla and at spectrometer frequencies of 300 MHz and above allow chemists to obtain both the proton and carbon NMR spectra on the same sample.

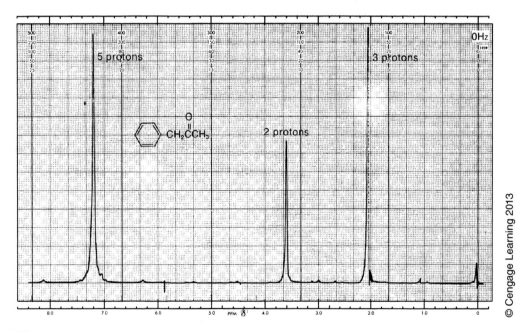

Figure 26.3

Nuclear magnetic resonance spectrum of phenylacetone (the absorption peak at the far right is caused by the added reference substance tetramethylsilane).

---

[1] Most modern instruments (FT-NMR instruments) use higher fields than described here and operate differently. The classical 60-MHz continuous wave (CW) instrument is used here as a simple example.

PART A. PREPARING A SAMPLE FOR NMR SPECTROSCOPY

The NMR sample tubes used in most instruments are approximately 0.5 cm × 18 cm in overall dimension and are fabricated of uniformly thin glass tubing. These tubes are very fragile and expensive, so care must be taken to avoid breaking the tubes.

CAUTION

NMR tubes are made out of very thin glass and break easily. Never place the cap on tightly, and take special care when removing it.

To prepare the solution, you must first choose the appropriate solvent. The solvent should not have NMR absorption peaks of its own; that is, it should contain no protons. Carbon tetrachloride (CCl_4) fits this requirement and can be used in some instruments. However, because FT-NMR spectrometers require deuterium to stabilize (lock) the field, organic chemists usually use deuterated chloroform ($CDCl_3$) as a solvent. This solvent dissolves most organic compounds and is relatively inexpensive. You can use this solvent with any NMR instrument. You should not use normal chloroform $CHCl_3$ because the solvent contains a proton. Deuterium ^2H does not absorb in the proton region and is thus "invisible," or not seen, in the proton NMR spectrum. Use deuterated chloroform to dissolve your sample, unless you are instructed to use another solvent, such as deuterated derivatives of water, acetone, or dimethylsulfoxide.

26.1 Routine Sample Preparation Using Deuterated Chloroform

1. Most organic liquids and low-melting solids will dissolve in deuterated chloroform. However, you should first determine whether your sample will dissolve in ordinary $CHCl_3$ before using the deuterated solvent. If your sample does not dissolve in chloroform, consult your instructor about a possible alternative solvent, or consult Section 26.2.

CAUTION

Chloroform, deuterated chloroform, and carbon tetrachloride are all toxic solvents. In addition, they may be carcinogenic substances.

2. If you are using an FT–NMR spectrometer, add 30 mg (0.030 g) of your liquid or solid sample to a tared conical vial or test tube. Use a Pasteur pipette to transfer a liquid or a spatula to transfer a solid. Non-FT instruments usually require a more concentrated solution in order to obtain an adequate spectrum. Typically, a 10–30% sample concentration (weight/weight) is used.
3. Transfer about 0.5 mL of the deuterated chloroform with a clean, dry Pasteur pipette to your sample. Swirl the test tube or conical vial to help dissolve the sample. At this point, the sample should have completely dissolved. Add a little more solvent, if necessary, to dissolve the sample fully.
4. Transfer the solution to the NMR tube using a clean, dry Pasteur pipette. Be careful when transferring the solution to avoid breaking the edge of the fragile NMR tube. It is best to hold the NMR tube and the container with the solution in the same hand when making the transfer.
5. Once the solution has been transferred to the NMR tube, use a clean pipette to add enough deuterated chloroform to bring the total solution height to about 50 mm (see Figure 26.4). In some cases, you will need to add a small amount

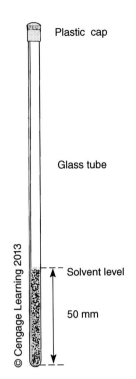

Plastic cap

Glass tube

Solvent level

50 mm

Figure 26.4
An NMR sample tube.

of tetramethylsilane (TMS) as a reference substance (see Section 26.3). Check with your instructor to see if you need to add TMS to your sample. Deuterated chloroform has a small amount of $CHCl_3$ impurity, which gives rise to a low-intensity peak in the NMR spectrum at 7.27 parts per million (ppm). This impurity may also help you to "reference" your spectrum.

6. Cap the NMR tube. Do this firmly but not too tightly. If you jam the cap on, you may have trouble removing it later without breaking the end off of the very thin glass tube. Make sure that the cap is on straight. Invert the NMR tube several times to mix the contents.

7. You are now ready to record the NMR spectrum of your sample. Insert the NMR tube into its holder and adjust its depth by using the gauge provided to you.

Cleaning the NMR Tube

1. Carefully uncap the tube so that you do not break it. Turn the tube upside down and hold it vertically over a beaker. Shake the tube up and down gently so that its contents empty into the beaker.

2. Partially refill the NMR tube with acetone using a Pasteur pipette. Carefully replace the cap and invert the tube several times to rinse it.

3. Remove the cap and drain the tube as before. Place the open tube upside down in a beaker with a Kimwipe or paper towel placed in the bottom of the beaker. Leave the tube standing in this position for at least one laboratory period so that the acetone completely evaporates. Alternatively, you may place the beaker and NMR tube in an oven for at least 2 hours. If you need to use the NMR tube before the acetone has fully evaporated, attach a piece of pressure tubing to the tube and pull a vacuum with an aspirator. After several minutes, the acetone should have fully evaporated. Because acetone contains protons, you must not use the NMR tube until the acetone has evaporated completely.[2]

4. Once the acetone is evaporated, place the clean tube and its cap (do not cap the tube) in its storage container and place it in your desk. The storage container will prevent the tube from being crushed.

Health Hazards Associated With NMR Solvents

Carbon tetrachloride, chloroform (and chloroform-d), and benzene (and benzene-d_6) are hazardous solvents. Besides being highly toxic, they are suspected carcinogens. In spite of these health problems, these solvents are commonly used in NMR spectroscopy. Deuterated acetone may be a safer alternative. These solvents are used because they contain no protons and are excellent solvents for most organic compounds. Therefore, you must learn to handle these solvents with great care to minimize the hazard. These solvents should be stored either under a hood or in septum-capped bottles. If the bottles have screw caps, a pipette should be attached to each bottle. A recommended way of attaching the pipette is to store it in a test tube taped to the side of the bottle. Septum-capped bottles can be used only by withdrawing the solvent with a hypodermic syringe that has been designated solely for this use. All samples should be prepared under a hood, and solutions should be disposed of in an appropriately designated waste container that is stored under the hood. Wear rubber or plastic gloves when preparing or discarding samples.

---

[2] If you can't wait to be sure all acetone has evaporated, you may rinse the tube once or twice with a *very small* amount of $CDCl_3$ before using it.

26.2 Nonroutine Sample Preparation

Some compounds do not dissolve readily in $CDCl_3$. A commercial solvent called Unisol will often dissolve the difficult cases. Unisol is a mixture of $CDCl_3$ and DMSO-d_6. Deuterated acetone may also dissolve more polar substances.

With highly polar substances, you may find that your sample will not dissolve in deuterated chloroform or Unisol. If this is the case, you may be able to dissolve the sample in deuterium oxide D_2O. Spectra determined in D_2O often show a small peak at about 5 ppm because of OH impurity. If the sample compound has acidic hydrogens, they may *exchange* with D_2O, leading to the appearance of an OH peak in the spectrum and the *loss* of the original absorption from the acidic proton, owing to the exchanged hydrogen. In many cases, this will also alter the splitting patterns of a compound.

Many solid carboxylic acids do not dissolve in $CDCl_3$ or even D_2O. In such cases, add a small piece of sodium metal to about 1 mL of D_2O. The acid is then dissolved in this solution. The resulting basic solution enhances the solubility of the carboxylic acid. In such a case, the hydroxyl proton of the carboxylic acid cannot be observed in the NMR spectrum because it exchanges with the solvent. A large DOH peak is observed, however, due to the exchange and the H_2O impurity in the D_2O solvent.

When the above solvents fail, other special solvents can be used. Acetone, acetonitrile, dimethylsulfoxide, pyridine, benzene, and dimethylformamide can be used if you are not interested in the region or regions of the NMR spectrum in which they give rise to absorption. The deuterated (but expensive) analogs of these compounds are also used in special instances (for example, acetone-d_6, dimethylsulfoxide-d_6, dimethylformamide-d_7, and benzene-d_6). If the sample is not sensitive to acid, trifluoroacetic acid (which has no protons with $\delta < 12$) can be used. You must be aware that these solvents often lead to chemical shift values different from those determined in CCl_4 or $CDCl_3$. Variations of as much as 0.5–1.0 ppm have been observed. In fact, it is sometimes possible, by switching to pyridine, benzene, acetone, or dimethylsulfoxide as solvents, to separate peaks that overlap when CCl_4 or $CDCl_3$ solutions are used.

26.3 Reference Substances

To provide the internal reference standard, TMS must be added to the sample solution. This substance has the formula $(CH_3)_4Si$. By universal convention, the chemical shifts of the protons in this substance are defined as 0.00 ppm. The spectrum should be shifted so that the TMS signal appears at this position on precalibrated paper.

The concentration of TMS in the sample should range from 1% to 3%. Some people prefer to add 1 to 2 drops of TMS to the sample just before determining the spectrum. Because TMS has 12 equivalent protons, not much of it needs to be added. A Pasteur pipette or a syringe may be used for the addition. It is far easier to have available in the laboratory a prepared solvent that already contains TMS. Deuterated chloroform and carbon tetrachloride often have TMS added to them. Because TMS is highly volatile (bp 26.5°C), such solutions should be stored, tightly stoppered, in a refrigerator. Tetramethylsilane itself is best stored in a refrigerator as well.

Tetramethylsilane does not dissolve in D_2O. For spectra determined in D_2O, a different internal standard, sodium 2,2-dimethyl-2-silapentane-5-sulfonate, must be used. This standard is water soluble and gives a resonance peak at 0.00 ppm.

$$CH_3-\underset{\underset{CH_3}{|}}{\overset{\overset{CH_3}{|}}{Si}}-CH_2-CH_2-CH_2-SO_3^-\,Na^+$$

Sodium 2,2-dimethyl-2-silapentane-5-sulfonate (DSS)

© Cengage Learning 2013

PART B. NUCLEAR MAGNETIC RESONANCE (¹H NMR)

26.4 The Chemical Shift

The differences in the applied field strengths at which the various protons in a molecule absorb 60-MHz radiation are extremely small. The different absorption positions amount to a difference of only a few parts per million (ppm) in the magnetic field strength. Because it is experimentally difficult to measure the precise field strength at which each proton absorbs to less than one part in a million, a technique has been developed whereby the *difference* between two absorption positions is measured directly. A standard reference substance is used to achieve this measurement, and the positions of the absorptions of all other protons are measured relative to the values for the reference substance. The reference substance that has been universally accepted is **tetramethylsilane** $(CH_3)_4Si$, which is also called TMS. The proton resonances in this molecule appear at a higher field strength than the proton resonances in most other molecules, and all the protons of TMS have resonance at the same field strength.

To give the position of absorption of a proton, a quantitative measurement, a parameter called the **chemical shift** (δ), has been defined. One δ unit corresponds to a one-ppm change in the magnetic field strength. To determine the chemical shift value for the various protons in a molecule, the operator determines an NMR spectrum of the molecule with a small quantity of TMS added directly to the sample. That is, both spectra are determined *simultaneously*. The TMS absorption is adjusted to correspond to the $\delta = 0$ ppm position on the recording chart, which is calibrated in δ units, and the $\delta = 0$ values of the absorption peaks for all other protons can be read directly from the chart.

Because the NMR spectrometer increases the magnetic field as the pen moves from left to right on the chart, the TMS absorption appears at the extreme right edge of the spectrum ($\delta = 0$ ppm) or at the *upfield* end of the spectrum. The chart is calibrated in δ units (or ppm), and most other protons absorb at a lower field strength (or *downfield*) from TMS.

The shift from TMS for a given proton depends on the strength of the applied magnetic field. In an applied field of 1.41 tesla, the resonance of a proton is approximately 60 MHz, whereas in an applied field of 2.35 tesla (23,500 gauss), the resonance appears at approximately 100 MHz. The ratio of the resonance frequencies is the same as the ratio of the two field strengths:

$$\frac{100 \text{ MHz}}{60 \text{ MHz}} = \frac{2.35 \text{ Tesla}}{1.41 \text{ Tesla}} = \frac{23,500 \text{ Gauss}}{14,100 \text{ Gauss}} = \frac{5}{3}$$

Hence, for a given proton, the shift (in hertz) from TMS is five-thirds larger in the 100-MHz range than in the 60-MHz range. This can be confusing for workers trying to compare data if they have spectrometers that differ in the strength of the applied magnetic field. The confusion is easily overcome by defining a new parameter that is independent of field strength—for instance, by dividing the shift in hertz of a given proton by the frequency in megahertz of the spectrometer with which the shift value was obtained. In this manner, a field-independent measure called the **chemical shift** (δ) is obtained:

$$\delta = \frac{(\text{shift in Hz})}{(\text{spectrometer frequency in MHz})} \tag{1}$$

The chemical shift in δ units expresses the amount by which a proton resonance is shifted from TMS, in parts per million (ppm), of the spectrometer's basic operating frequency. Values of δ for a given proton are always the same, irrespective of whether the measurement was made at 60 MHz, 100 MHz, or 300 MHz. For instance, at 60 MHz, the shift of the protons in CH_3Br is 162 Hz from TMS; at 100 MHz, the shift is 270 Hz; and at 300 MHz, the shift is 810 Hz. However, all three correspond to the same value of $\delta = 2.70$ ppm:

$$\delta = \frac{162 \text{ Hz}}{60 \text{ MHz}} = \frac{270 \text{ Hz}}{100 \text{ MHz}} = \frac{810 \text{ Hz}}{300 \text{ MHz}} = 2.70 \text{ ppm}$$

26.5 Chemical Equivalence—Integrals

All of the protons in a molecule that are in chemically identical environments often exhibit the same chemical shift. Thus, all of the protons in TMS or all of the protons in benzene, cyclopentane, or acetone have their own respective resonance values all at the same δ value. Each compound gives rise to a single absorption peak in its NMR spectrum. The protons are said to be **chemically equivalent.** On the other hand, molecules that have sets of protons that are chemically distinct from one another may give rise to an absorption peak from each set.

Molecules giving rise to one
NMR absorption peak—all
protons chemically equivalent

Molecules giving rise to two
NMR absorption peaks—two
different sets of chemically
equivalent protons

© Cengage Learning 2013

The NMR spectrum given in Figure 26.3 is that of phenylacetone, a compound having *three* chemically distinct types of protons:

You can immediately see that the NMR spectrum furnishes valuable information on this basis alone. In fact, the NMR spectrum not only can distinguish how many types of protons a molecule has, but also can reveal *how many* of each type are contained within the molecule.

In the NMR spectrum, the area under each peak is proportional to the number of hydrogens generating that peak. Hence, in the case of phenylacetone, the area ratio of the three peaks is 5:2:3, the same as the ratio of the numbers of each type of hydrogen. The NMR spectrometer can electronically "integrate" the area under each peak. It does this by tracing over each peak a vertically rising line, which rises in height by an amount proportional to the area under the peak. Shown in Figure 26.5 is an NMR spectrum of benzyl acetate, with each of the peaks integrated in this way.

It is important to note that the height of the integral line does not give the absolute number of hydrogens; it gives the *relative* numbers of each type of hydrogen. For a given integral to be of any use, there must be a second integral to which it is referred. The benzyl acetate case provides a good example of this. The first integral rises for 55.5 divisions on the chart paper, the second for 22.0 divisions, and the third for 32.5 divisions. These numbers are relative and give the *ratios* of the

Figure 26.5
Determination of the integral ratios for benzyl acetate.

various types of protons. You can find these ratios by dividing each of the larger numbers by the smallest number:

$$\frac{55.5 \text{ div}}{22.0 \text{ div}} = 2.52 \quad \frac{22.0 \text{ div}}{22.0 \text{ div}} = 1.00 \quad \frac{32.5 \text{ div}}{22.0 \text{ div}} = 1.48$$

Thus, the number ratio of the protons of each type is 2.52:1.00:1.48. If you assume that the peak at 5.1 ppm is really caused by two hydrogens and that the integrals are slightly in error (this can be as much as 10%), then you can arrive at the true ratios by multiplying each figure by 2 and rounding off; we then get 5:2:3. Clearly, the peak at 7.3 ppm, which integrates for 5, arises from the resonance of the aromatic ring protons, and the peak at 2.0 ppm, which integrates for 3, is caused by the methyl protons. The two-proton resonance at 5.1 ppm arises from the benzyl protons. Notice then that the integrals give the simplest ratios, but not necessarily the true ratios, of the number of protons in each type.

In addition to the rising integral line, modern instruments usually give digitized numerical values for the integrals. Like the heights of the integral lines, these digitized integral values are not absolute but relative, and they should be treated as explained in the preceding paragraph. These digital values are also not exact; like the integral lines, they have the potential for a small degree of error (up to 10%). Figure 26.6 is an example of an integrated spectrum of benzyl acetate determined on a 300-MHz pulsed FT–NMR instrument. The digitized values of the integrals appear under the peaks.

Figure 26.6

An integrated spectrum of benzyl acetate determined on a 300-MHz FT-NMR.

26.6 Chemical Environment and Chemical Shift

If the resonance frequencies of all protons in a molecule were the same, NMR would be of little use to the organic chemist. However, not only do different types of protons have different chemical shifts but they also have a value of chemical shift that characterizes the type of proton they represent. Every type of proton has only a limited range of δ values over which it gives resonance. Hence, the numerical value of the chemical shift for a proton indicates the *type of proton* originating the signal, just as the infrared frequency suggests the type of bond or functional group. Notice, for instance, that the aromatic protons of both phenylacetone (see Figure 26.3) and benzyl acetate (see Figure 26.5) have resonance near 7.3 ppm and that both methyl groups attached directly to a carbonyl group have a resonance of approximately 2.1 ppm. Aromatic protons characteristically have resonance near 7–8 ppm, and acetyl groups (the methyl protons) have their resonance near 2 ppm. These values of chemical shift are diagnostic. Notice also how the resonance of the benzyl (—CH2—) protons comes at a higher value of chemical shift (5.1 ppm) in benzyl acetate than in phenylacetone (3.6 ppm). Being attached to the electronegative element, oxygen, these protons are more deshielded (see Section 26.7) than the protons in phenylacetone. A trained chemist would have readily recognized the probable presence of the oxygen by the chemical shift shown by these protons.

It is important to learn the ranges of chemical shifts over which the most common types of protons have resonance. Figure 26.7 is a correlation chart that contains the most essential and frequently encountered types of protons. Table 26.1 lists the chemical shift ranges for selected types of protons. For the beginner, it is often difficult to memorize a large body of numbers relating to chemical shifts and proton types. However, this needs to be done only approximately. It is more important to "get a feel" for the regions and the types of protons than to know a string of actual numbers. To do this, study Figure 26.7 carefully.

The values of chemical shift given in Figure 26.7 and in Table 26.1 can be easily understood in terms of two factors: local diamagnetic shielding and anisotropy. These two factors are discussed in Sections 26.7 and 26.8.

Figure 26.7

A simplified correlation chart for proton chemical shift values.

Table 26.1 Approximate Chemical Shift Ranges (ppm) for Selected Types of Protons

R—CH₃		0.7–1.3	R–N–C–H	2.2–2.9
R—CH₂—R		1.2–1.4		
R₃CH		1.4–1.7	R–S–C–H	2.0–3.0
R–C=C–C–H		1.6–2.6	I–C–H	2.0–4.0
R–C–C–H, H–C–C–H (O)		2.1–2.4	Br–C–H	2.7–4.1
RO–C–C–H, HO–C–C–H (O)		2.1–2.5	Cl–C–H	3.1–4.1
			R–S–O–C–H (O,O)	ca. 3.0
N≡C–C–H		2.1–3.0	RO–C–H, HO–C–H	3.2–3.8
⟨benzene⟩–C–H		2.3–2.7	R–C–O–C–H (O)	3.5–4.8
R–C≡C–H		1.7–2.7	O₂N–C–H	4.1–4.3
R–S–H	var	1.0–4.0ᵃ	F–C–H	4.2–4.8
R–N–H	var	0.5–4.0ᵃ		
R–O–H	var	0.5–5.0ᵃ	R–C=C–H	4.5–6.5
⟨benzene⟩–O–H	var	4.0–7.0ᵃ	⟨benzene⟩–H	6.5–8.0
⟨benzene⟩–N–H	var	3.0–5.0ᵃ	R–C–H (O)	9.0–10.0
R–C–N–H (O)	var	5.0–9.0ᵃ	R–C–OH (O)	11.0–12.0

Note: For those hydrogens shown as —C—H, if that hydrogen is part of a methyl group (CH₃), the shift is generally at the low end of the range given; if the hydrogen is in a methylene group (—CH₂—), the shift is intermediate; and if the hydrogen is in a methine group (—CH—), the shift is typically at the high end of the range given.

ᵃThe chemical shift of these groups is variable, depending on the chemical environment in the molecule and on concentration, temperature, and solvent.

Table 26.2 Dependence of Chemical Shift of CH_3X on the Element X

Compound CH_3X	CH_3F	CH_3OH	CH_3Cl	CH_3Br	CH_3I	CH_4	$(CH_3)_4Si$
Element X	F	O	Cl	Br	I	H	Si
Electronegativity of X	4.0	3.5	3.1	2.8	2.5	2.1	1.8
Chemical shift (ppm)	4.26	3.40	3.05	2.68	2.16	0.23	0

Table 26.3 Substitution Effects

	$CHCl_3$	CH_2Cl_2	CH_3Cl	$—CH_2Br$	$—CH_2—CH_2Br$	$—CH_2—CH_2CH_2Br$
δ (ppm)	7.27	5.30	3.05	3.3	1.69	1.25

Note: Values apply to underlined hydrogens.

26.7 Local Diamagnetic Shielding

The trend of chemical shifts that is easiest to explain is that involving electronegative elements substituted on the same carbon to which the protons of interest are attached. The chemical shift simply increases as the electronegativity of the attached element increases. This is illustrated in Table 26.2 for several compounds of the type CH_3X.

Multiple substituents have a stronger effect than a single substituent. The influence of the substituent drops off rapidly with distance. An electronegative element has little effect on protons that are more than three carbons away from it. These effects are illustrated in Table 26.3.

Electronegative substituents attached to a carbon atom, because of their electron-withdrawing effects, reduce the valence electron density around the protons attached to that carbon. These electrons *shield* the proton from the applied magnetic field. This effect, called **local diamagnetic shielding,** occurs because the applied magnetic field induces the valence electrons to circulate. This circulation generates an induced magnetic field, which *opposes* the applied field. This is illustrated in Figure 26.8. Electronegative substituents on carbon reduce the local diamagnetic shielding in the vicinity of the attached protons because they reduce the electron density around those protons. Substituents that produce this effect are said to *deshield* the proton. The greater the electronegativity of the substituent, the more the deshielding of the protons and, hence, the greater the chemical shift of those protons.

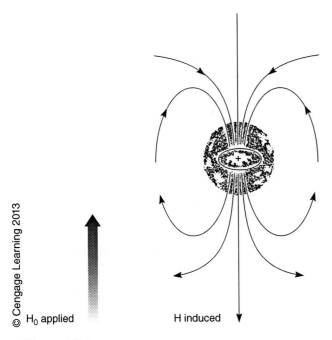

H_0 applied   H induced

Figure 26.8
Local diamagnetic shielding of a photon due to its valence electrons.

26.8 Anisotropy

Figure 26.7 clearly shows that several types of protons have chemical shifts not easily explained by a simple consideration of the electronegativity of the attached groups. Consider, for instance, the protons of benzene or other aromatic systems. Aryl protons generally have a chemical shift that is as large as that for the proton of chloroform. Alkenes, alkynes, and aldehydes also have protons whose resonance values are not in line with the expected magnitude of any electron-withdrawing effects. In each of these cases, the effect is due to the presence of an unsaturated

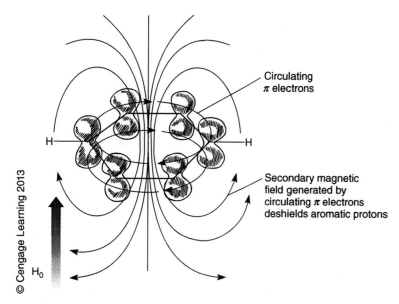

Figure 26.9
Diamagnetic anisotropy in benzene.

system (π electrons) in the vicinity of the proton in question. In benzene, for example, when the π electrons in the aromatic ring system are placed in a magnetic field, they are induced to circulate around the ring. This circulation is called a **ring current.** Moving electrons (the ring current) generate a magnetic field much like that generated in a loop of wire through which a current is induced to flow. The magnetic field covers a spatial volume large enough to influence the shielding of the benzene hydrogens. This is illustrated in Figure 26.9. The benzene hydrogens are deshielded by the **diamagnetic anisotropy** of the ring. An applied magnetic field is nonuniform (anisotropic) in the vicinity of a benzene molecule because of the labile electrons in the ring that interact with the applied field. Thus, a proton attached to a benzene ring is influenced by *three* magnetic fields: the strong magnetic field applied by the magnets of the NMR spectrometer and two weaker fields, one due to the usual shielding by the valence electrons around the proton and the other due to the anisotropy generated by the ring system electrons. It is this anisotropic effect that gives the benzene protons a greater chemical shift than is expected. These protons just happen to lie in a **deshielding** region of this anisotropic field. If a proton were placed in the center of the ring rather than on its periphery, the proton would be shielded because the field lines would have the opposite direction.

All groups in a molecule that have π electrons generate secondary anisotropic fields. In acetylene, the magnetic field generated by induced circulation of π electrons has a geometry such that the acetylene hydrogens are **shielded.** Hence, acetylenic hydrogens come at a higher field than expected. The shielding and deshielding regions due to the various π electron functional groups have characteristic shapes and directions; they are illustrated in Figure 26.10. Protons falling within the cones are shielded, and those falling outside the conical areas are deshielded. Because the magnitude of the anisotropic field diminishes with distance, beyond a certain distance anisotropy has essentially no effect.

26.9 Spin–Spin Splitting (n + 1 Rule)

We have already considered how the chemical shift and the integral (peak area) can give information about the numbers and types of hydrogens contained in a molecule. A third type of information available from the NMR spectrum is derived from spin–spin splitting. Even in simple molecules, each type of proton rarely gives a single resonance peak. For instance, in 1,1,2-trichloroethane there are two chemically distinct types of hydrogen:

$$Cl-\underset{\underset{Cl}{|}}{\overset{\overset{\textcircled{H}}{|}}{C}}-\textcircled{CH_2}-Cl$$

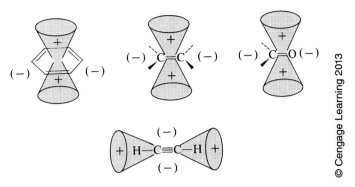

Figure 26.10
Anisotropy caused by the presence of π electrons in some common multiple-bond systems.

Figure 26.11
NMR spectrum of 1,1,2-trichlorethane.

From information given thus far, you would predict *two* resonance peaks in the NMR spectrum of 1,1,2-trichloroethane with an area ratio (integral ratio) of 2:1. In fact, the NMR spectrum of this compound has *five* peaks. A group of three peaks (called a *triplet*) exists at 5.77 ppm, and a group of two peaks (called a *doublet*) is found at 3.95 ppm. The spectrum is shown in Figure 26.11. The methine (CH) resonance (5.77 ppm) is split into a triplet, and the methylene resonance (3.95 ppm) is split into a doublet. The area under the three triplet peaks is *one*, relative to an area of *two* under the two doublet peaks.

This phenomenon is called **spin–spin splitting.** Empirically, spin–spin splitting can be explained by the "$n + 1$ rule." Each type of proton "senses" the number of equivalent protons (n) on the carbon atom or atoms next to the one to which it is bonded, and its resonance peak is split into $n + 1$ components.

Let's examine the case at hand, 1,1,2-trichloroethane, using the $n + 1$ rule. First, the lone methine hydrogen is situated next to a carbon bearing two methylene protons. According to the rule, it has two equivalent neighbors ($n = 2$) and is split into $n + 1 = 3$ peaks (a triplet). The methylene protons are situated next to a carbon bearing only one methine hydrogen. According to the rule, they have one neighbor ($n = 1$) and are split into $n + 1 = 2$ peaks (a doublet).

The spectrum of 1,1,2-trichloroethane can be explained easily by the interaction, or coupling, of the spins of protons on adjacent carbon atoms. The position of absorption of proton H_a is affected by the spins of protons H_b and H_c attached to the neighboring (adjacent) carbon atom. If the spins of these protons are aligned with the applied magnetic field, the small magnetic field generated by their nuclear spin properties will augment the strength of the field experienced by the first-mentioned proton H_a. The proton H_a will thus be *deshielded*. If the spins of H_b and H_c are opposed to the applied field, they will decrease the field experienced by proton H_a. It will then be *shielded*. In each of these situations, the absorption position of H_a will be altered. Among the many molecules in the solution, you will find all the various possible spin combinations for H_b and H_c; hence, the NMR spectrum of the molecular solution will give *three* absorption peaks (a triplet) for H_a because H_b and H_c have three different possible spin combinations (Figure 26.12). By a similar analysis, it can be seen that protons H_b and H_c should appear as a doublet.

Some common splitting patterns that can be predicted by the $n + 1$ rule and that are frequently observed in a number of molecules are shown in Figure 26.13. Notice particularly the last entry, where *both* methyl groups (six protons in all) function as a unit and split the methine proton into a septet ($6 + 1 = 7$).

26.10 The Coupling Constant

The quantitative amount of spin–spin interaction between two protons can be defined by the **coupling constant**. The spacing between the component peaks in a single multiplet is called the coupling constant J. This distance is measured on the same scale as the chemical shift and is expressed in hertz (Hz).

Coupling constants for protons on adjacent carbon atoms have magnitudes of from about 6 Hz to 8 Hz (see Table 26.4). You should expect to see a coupling constant in this range for compounds where there is free rotation about a single bond. Because three bonds separate protons from each other on adjacent carbon atoms, we label these coupling constants as ^3J. For example, the coupling constant for the

Figure 26.12

Analysis of spin–spin splitting pattern for 1,1,2-trichloroethane.

Figure 26.13
Some common splitting patterns.

compound shown in Figure 26.11 would be written as $^3J = 6$ Hz. The boldfaced lines in the following diagram show how the protons on adjacent carbon atoms are three bonds away from each other.

In compounds where there is a C = C double bond, free rotation is restricted. In compounds of this kind, we often find two types of ^3J coupling constants: $^3J_{trans}$ and $^3J_{cis}$. These coupling constants vary in value as shown in Table 26.4, but $^3J_{trans}$ is

Table 26.4 Representative Coupling Constants and Approximate Values (Hz)

almost always larger than $^3J_{cis}$. The magnitudes of these ^3Js often provide important structural clues. You can distinguish, for example, between a *cis* alkene and a *trans* alkene on the basis of the observed coupling constants for the two vinyl protons on disubstituted alkenes. Most of the coupling constants shown in the first column of Table 26.4 are three-bond couplings, but you will notice that there is a two-bond (^2J) coupling constant listed. These protons that are bonded to a common carbon atom are often referred to as *geminal* protons and can be labeled as $^2J_{gem}$. Notice that the coupling constants for *geminal* protons are quite small for alkenes. The ^2J couplings are observed only when the protons on a methylene group are in a different environment (see Section 26.11). The following structure shows the various types of couplings that you observe for protons on a C = C double bond in a typical alkene, vinyl acetate. The spectrum for this compound is described in detail in Section 26.11.

Vinyl acetate

© Cengage Learning 2013

Longer-range couplings that occur over four or more bonds are observed in some alkenes and also in aromatic compounds. Thus, in Table 26.4, we see that it is possible to observe a small H—H coupling ($^4J = 0$–3 Hz) occurring over four bonds in an alkene. In an aromatic compound, you often observe a small but measurable coupling between *meta* protons that are four bonds away from each other ($^4J = 1$–4 Hz). Couplings over five bonds are usually quite small, with values close to 0 Hz. The long-range couplings are usually observed only in *unsaturated* compounds. The spectra of saturated compounds are often more easily interpreted because they usually have only three bond couplings. Aromatic compounds are discussed in detail in Section 26.13.

26.11 Magnetic Equivalence

In the example of spin–spin splitting in 1,1,2-trichloroethane (Figure 26.11), notice that the two protons H_b and H_c, which are attached to the same carbon atom, do not split one another. They behave as an integral group. Actually, the two protons H_b and H_c *are* coupled to one another; however, for reasons we cannot explain fully here, protons that are attached to the same carbon and both of which have the same chemical shift do not show spin–spin splitting. Another way of stating this is that protons coupled to the same extent to *all* other protons in a molecule do not show spin–spin splitting. Protons that have the same chemical shift and are coupled equivalently to all other protons are magnetically equivalent and do not show spin–spin splitting. Thus, in 1,1,2-trichloroethane (see Figure 26.11), protons H_b and H_c have the same value of δ and are coupled by the same value of J to proton H_a. They are magnetically equivalent, and $^2J_{gem} = 0$.

It is important to differentiate magnetic equivalence and chemical equivalence. Note the following two compounds.

Figure 26.14
NMR spectrum of vinyl acetate.

In the cyclopropane compound, the two geminal hydrogens H_A and H_B are chemically equivalent; however, they are not magnetically equivalent. Proton H_A is on the same side of the ring as the two halogens. Proton H_B is on the same side of the ring as the two methyl groups. Protons H_A and H_B will have different chemical shifts, will couple to one another, and will show spin–spin splitting. Two doublets will be seen for H_A and H_B. For cyclopropane rings, $^2J_{gem}$ is usually around 5 Hz.

The general vinyl structure (alkene) shown in the previous figure and the specific example of vinyl acetate shown in Figure 26.14 are examples of cases in which the methylene protons H_A and H_B are nonequivalent. They appear at different chemical shift values and will split each other. This coupling constant, $^2J_{gem}$, is usually small with vinyl compounds (about 2 Hz).

The spectrum of vinyl acetate is shown in Figure 26.14. H_C appears downfield at about 7.3 ppm because of the electronegativity of the attached oxygen atom. This proton is split by H_B into a doublet ($^3J_{trans} = {}^3J_{BC} = 15$ Hz), and then each leg of the doublet is split by H_A into a doublet ($^3J_{cis} = {}^3J_{AC} = 7$ Hz). Notice that the $n+1$ rule is applied individually to each adjacent proton. The pattern that results is usually referred to as a doublet of doublets (dd). The graphic analysis shown in Figure 26.15 should help you understand the pattern obtained for proton H_C.

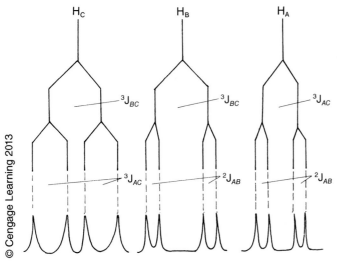

Figure 26.15
Analysis of the splittings in vinyl acetate.

Now look at the pattern shown in Figure 26.14 for proton H_B at 4.85 ppm. It is also a doublet of doublets. Proton H_B is split by proton H_C into a doublet ($^3J_{trans} = {}^3J_{BC} = 15$ Hz), and then each leg of the doublet is split by the geminal proton H_A into doublets ($^2J_{gem} = {}^2J_{AB} = 2$ Hz).

Proton H_A, shown in Figure 26.14, appears at 4.55 ppm. This pattern is also a doublet of doublets. Proton H_A is split by proton H_C into a doublet ($^3J_{cis} = {}^3J_{AC} = 7$ Hz), and then each leg of the doublet is split by the geminal proton H_B into doublets ($^2J_{gem} = ^2J_{AB} = 2$ Hz). For each proton shown in Figure 26.14, the NMR spectrum must be analyzed graphically, splitting by splitting. This complete graphic analysis is shown in Figure 26.15.

26.12 Spectra at Higher Field Strength

Occasionally, the 60-MHz spectrum of an organic compound, or a portion of it, is almost undecipherable because the chemical shifts of several groups of protons are all very similar. In these cases, all the proton resonances occur in the same area of the spectrum, and peaks often overlap so extensively that individual peaks and splittings cannot be extracted. One way to simplify such a situation is to use a spectrometer that operates at a higher frequency. Although both 60-MHz and 100-MHz instruments are still in use, it is becoming increasingly common to find instruments operating at much higher fields and with spectrometer frequencies 300, 400, or 500 MHz.

Although NMR coupling constants do not depend on the frequency or the field strength of operation of the NMR spectrometer, chemical shifts in hertz depend on these parameters. This circumstance can often be used to simplify an otherwise undecipherable spectrum. Suppose, for instance, that a compound contained three multiplets derived from groups of protons with very similar chemical shifts. At 60 MHz, these peaks might overlap, as illustrated in Figure 26.16, and simply give an unresolved envelope of absorption. It turns out that the $n + 1$ rule fails to make the proper predictions when chemical shifts are similar for the protons in a molecule. The spectral patterns that result are said to be **second order,** and what you end up seeing is an amorphous blob of unrecognizable patterns!

Figure 26.16 also shows the spectrum of the same compound at two higher frequencies (100 MHz and 300 MHz). When the spectrum is redetermined at a higher frequency, the coupling constants (J) do not change, but the chemical shifts in *hertz* (not ppm) of the proton groups (H_A, H_B, H_C) responsible for the multiplets do increase. It is important to realize, however, that the chemical shift in *ppm* is a constant, and it will not change when the frequency of the spectrometer is increased (see equation 1 in Section 26.4).

Figure 26.16

A comparison of the spectrum of a compound with overlapping multiplets at 60 MHz, with spectra of the same compound also determined at 100 MHz and 300 MHz.

Notice that at 300 MHz, the individual multiplets are cleanly separated and resolved. At high frequency, the chemical shift differences of each proton increase, resulting in more clearly recognizable patterns (that is, triplets, quartets, and so on) and less overlap of proton patterns in the spectrum. At high frequency, the chemical shift differences are large, and the $n + 1$ rule will more likely correctly predict the patterns. Thus, it is a clear advantage to use NMR spectrometers operating at high frequency (300 MHz or above) because the resulting spectra are more likely to provide nonoverlapped and well-resolved peaks. When the protons in a spectrum follow the $n + 1$ rule, the spectrum is said to be **first order.** The result is that you will obtain a spectrum with much more recognizable patterns, as shown in Figure 26.16.

26.13 Aromatic Compounds—Substituted Benzene Rings

Phenyl rings are so common in organic compounds that it is important to know a few facts about NMR absorptions in compounds that contain them. In general, the ring protons of a benzenoid system have resonance near 7.3 ppm; however, electron-withdrawing ring substituents (for example, nitro, cyano, carboxyl, or carbonyl) move the resonance of these protons downfield (larger ppm values), and electron-donating ring substituents (for example, methoxy or amino) move the resonance of these protons upfield (smaller ppm values). Table 26.5 shows these trends for a series of symmetrically *p*-disubstituted benzene compounds. The *p*-disubstituted compounds were chosen because their two planes of symmetry render all of the hydrogens equivalent. Each compound gives only one aromatic peak (a singlet) in the proton NMR spectrum. Later, you will see that some positions are affected more strongly than others in systems with substitution patterns different from this one.

In the sections that follow, we will attempt to cover some of the most important types of benzene ring substitution. In some cases, it will be necessary to examine sample spectra taken at both 60 MHz and 300 MHz. Many benzenoid rings show second-order splittings at 60 MHz, but are essentially first order at 300 MHz.

A. Monosubstituted Rings

Alkylbenzenes. In monosubstituted benzenes in which the substituent is neither a strongly electron-withdrawing nor a strongly electron-donating group, all the ring protons give rise to what appears to be a *single resonance* when the spectrum is determined at 60 MHz. This is a particularly common occurrence in alkyl-substituted benzenes. Although the protons *ortho, meta,* and *para* to the substituent are not chemically equivalent, they generally give rise to a single unresolved absorption peak. A possible explanation is that the chemical shift differences, which should be

Table 26.5 Proton Chemical Shifts in p-disubstituted Benzene Compounds

Substituent X	δ (ppm)	
—OCH₃	6.80	Electron-donating (shielding)
—OH	6.60	
—NH₂	6.36	
—CH₃	7.05	
—H	7.32	
—COOH	8.20	Electron-withdrawing (deshielding)
—NO₂	8.48	

© Cengage Learning 2013

Figure 26.17
The aromatic ring portions of the ¹H NMR spectra of ethylbenzene at (A) 60 MHz and (B) 300 MHz.

small in any event, are somehow eliminated by the presence of the ring current, which tends to equalize them. All of the protons are nearly equivalent under these conditions. The NMR spectra of the aromatic portions of alkylbenzene compounds are good examples of this type of circumstance. Figure 26.17A is the 60-MHz ¹H spectrum of ethylbenzene.

The 300-MHz spectrum of ethylbenzene, shown in Figure 26.17B, presents quite a different picture. With the increased frequency shifts at 300 MHz, the nearly equivalent (at 60 MHz) protons are neatly separated into two groups. The *ortho* and *para* protons appear upfield from the *meta* protons. The splitting pattern is clearly second order.

Electron-Donating Groups. When electron-donating groups are attached to the ring, the ring protons are not equivalent, even at 60 MHz. A highly activating substituent such as methoxy clearly increases the electron density at the *ortho* and *para* positions of the ring (by resonance) and helps to give these protons greater shielding than those in the *meta* positions and, thus, a substantially different chemical shift.

At 60 MHz, this chemical shift difference results in a complicated second-order splitting pattern for anisole (methoxybenzene), but the protons do fall clearly into two groups, the *ortho/para* protons and the *meta* protons. The 60-MHz NMR spectrum of the aromatic portion of anisole (see Figure 26.18A) has a complex multiplet for the *o,p,* protons (integrating for three protons) that is upfield from the *meta* protons

(A)   (B)

Figure 26.18
The aromatic ring portions of the ^{1}H NMR spectra of anisole at (A) 60 MHz and (B) 300 MHz.

Figure 26.19
Anisotropic deshielding of the ortho protons of benzaldehyde.

(integrating for two protons), with a clear distinction (gap) between the two types. Aniline (aminobenzene) provides a similar spectrum, also with a 3:2 split, owing to the electron-releasing effect of the amino group.

The 300-MHz spectrum of anisole (see Figure 26.18B) shows the same separation between the *ortho/para* hydrogens (upfield) and the *meta* hydrogens (downfield). However, because the actual shift in Hertz between the two types of hydrogens is greater, there is less second-order interaction and the lines in the pattern are sharper at 300 MHz. In fact, it might be tempting to try to interpret the observed pattern as if it were first order, a triplet at 7.25 ppm (*meta*, 2 H) and an overlapping triplet (*para*, 1 H) with a doublet (*ortho*, 2 H) at about 6.9 ppm.

Anisotropy—Electron-Withdrawing Groups. A carbonyl or a nitro group would be expected to show (aside from anisotropy effects) a reverse effect, because these groups are electron withdrawing. It would be expected that the group would act to decrease the electron density around the *ortho* and *para* positions, thus deshielding the *ortho* and *para* hydrogens and providing a pattern exactly the reverse of the one shown for anisole (3:2 ratio, downfield:upfield). Convince yourself of this by drawing resonance structures. Nevertheless, the actual NMR spectra of nitrobenzene and benzaldehyde do not have the appearances that would be predicted on the basis of resonance structures. Instead, the *ortho* protons are much more deshielded than the *meta* and *para* protons, due to the magnetic anisotropy of the π bonds in these groups.

Anisotropy is observed when a substituent group bonds a carbonyl group directly to the benzene ring (see Figure 26.19). Once again, the ring protons fall into two groups, with the *ortho* protons downfield from the *meta/para* protons. Benzaldehyde (see Figure 26.20) and acetophenone both show this effect in their NMR spectra. A similar effect is sometimes observed when a carbon–carbon double bond is attached to the ring. The 300-MHz spectrum of benzaldehyde (see Figure 26.20B) is a nearly first-order spectrum and shows a doublet (H_C, 2 H), a triplet (H_B, 1 H), and a triplet (H_A, 2 H). It can be analyzed by the $n + 1$ rule.

B. *para*-Disubstituted Rings

Of the possible substitution patterns of a benzene ring, some are easily recognized. One of these is the *para*-disubstituted benzene ring. Examine anethole (see Figure 26.21) as a first example.

On one side of the anethole ring shown in Figure 26.21, proton H_a is coupled to H_b, $^3J = 8$ Hz, resulting in a doublet at about 6.80 ppm in the spectrum. Proton H_a appears upfield (smaller ppm value) relative to H_b because of shielding by the electron-releasing effect of the methoxy group. Likewise, H_b is coupled to H_a, $^3J = 8$ Hz, producing another doublet at 7.25 ppm for this proton. Because of the plane of symmetry, both halves of the ring are equivalent. Thus, H_a and H_b on the other side of the ring also appear at 6.80 ppm and 7.25 ppm, respectively. Each doublet, therefore, integrates for two protons each. A *para*-disubstituted ring, with two different

Figure 26.20
The aromatic ring portions of the ¹H NMR spectra of benzaldehyde at
(A) 60 MHz and (B) 300 MHz.

Figure 26.21
The aromatic ring protons of the 300-MHz ¹H NMR spectrum of anethole
showing a *para*-disubstituted pattern.

Figure 26.22
The aromatic ring protons of the 300-MHz ^{1}H NMR spectrum of
4-allyloxyanisole.

substituents attached, is easily recognized by the appearance of two doublets, each integrating for two protons each.

As the chemical shifts of H_a and H_b approach each other in value, the *para*-disubstituted pattern becomes similar to that of 4-allyloxyanisole (see Figure 26.22). The inner peaks move closer together, and the outer ones become smaller or even disappear. Ultimately, when H_a and H_b approach each other closely enough in chemical shift, the outer peaks disappear, and the two inner peaks merge into a *singlet;* 1,4-dimethylbenzene (*para*-xylene), for instance, gives a singlet at 7.05 ppm. Hence, a single aromatic resonance integrating for four protons could easily represent a *para*-disubstituted ring, but the substituents would obviously be either identical or very similar.

C. Other Substitution

Figure 26.23 shows the 300-MHz ^{1}H spectra of the aromatic ring portions of 2-, 3-, and 4-nitroaniline (the *ortho, meta,* and *para* isomers). The characteristic pattern of a *para*-disubstituted ring, with its pair of doublets, makes it easy to recognize 4-nitroaniline. The splitting patterns for 2- and 3-nitroaniline are first order, and they can be analyzed by the *n + 1* rule. As an exercise, see if you can analyze these patterns, assigning the multiplets to specific protons on the ring. Use the indicated multiplicities (s, d, t) and expected chemical shifts to help your assignments. Remember that the amino group releases electrons by resonance, and the nitro group shows a significant anisotropy toward *ortho* protons. You may ignore any *meta* and *para* couplings, remembering that these long-range couplings will be too small in magnitude to be observed on the scale on which these figures are presented. If the spectra were expanded, you would be able to observe ^4J couplings.

The spectrum shown in Figure 26.24 is of 2-nitrophenol. It is helpful to look also at the coupling constants for the benzene ring found in Table 26.4. Because the spectrum is expanded, it is now possible to see ^3J couplings (about 8 Hz), as well as ^4J couplings (about 1.5 Hz). ^5J couplings are not observed ($^5J = 0$). Each of the protons on this compound is assigned on the spectrum. Proton H_d appears downfield at 8.11 ppm as a doublet of doublets ($^3J_{ad} = 8$ Hz and $^4J_{cd} = 1.5$ Hz); H_c appears at 7.6 ppm as a triplet of doublets ($^3J_{ac} = {}^3J_{bc} = 8$ Hz and $^4J_{cd} = 1.5$ Hz); H_b appears at 7.17 ppm as a doublet of doublets ($^3J_{bc} = 8$ Hz and $^4J_{ab} = 1.5$ Hz); and H_a

Figure 26.23
The 300-MHz ^{1}H NMR spectra of the aromatic ring portions of 2-, 3-, and 4-nitroaniline (s, singlet; d, doublet; t, triplet). The NH$_2$ group is not shown.

appears at 7.0 ppm as a triplet of doublets ($^3J_{ac} = {}^3J_{ad} = 8$ Hz and $^4J_{ab} = 1.5$ Hz). H$_d$ appears the furthest downfield because of the anisotropy of the nitro group. H$_a$ and H$_b$ are relatively shielded because of the resonance-releasing effect of the hydroxyl group, which shields these two protons. H$_c$ is assigned by a process of elimination in the absence of these two effects.

26.14 Protons Attached to Atoms Other Than Carbon

Protons attached to atoms other than carbon often have a widely variable range of absorptions. Several of these groups are tabulated in Table 26.6. In addition, under the usual conditions of determining an NMR spectrum, protons on heteroelements normally do not couple with protons on adjacent carbon atoms to give spin–spin splitting. The primary reason is that such protons often exchange rapidly with those of the solvent medium. The absorption position is variable because these groups also undergo various degrees of hydrogen bonding in solutions of different

Figure 26.24

Expansions of the aromatic ring proton multiplets from the 300-MHz ^{1}H spectrum of 2-nitrophenol. The accompanying hydroxyl absorption (OH) is not shown. Coupling constants are indicated on some of the peaks of the spectrum to give an idea of scale.

Table 26.6 Typical Ranges for Groups With Variable Chemical Shift

Acids	RCOOH	10.5–12.0 ppm
Phenols	ArOH	4.0–7.0
Alcohols	ROH	0.5–5.0
Amines	RNH$_2$	0.5–5.0
Amides	RCONH$_2$	5.0–8.0
Enols	CH=CH—OH	≥ 15

concentrations. The amount of hydrogen bonding that occurs with a proton radically affects the valence electron density around that proton and produces correspondingly large changes in the chemical shift. The absorption peaks for protons that have hydrogen bonding or are undergoing exchange are frequently broad relative to other singlets and can often be recognized on that basis. For a different reason, called **quadrupole broadening**, protons attached to nitrogen atoms often show an extremely broad resonance peak, often almost indistinguishable from the baseline.

26.15 Chemical Shift Reagents

Researchers have known for some time that interactions between molecules and solvents, such as those due to hydrogen bonding, can cause large changes in the resonance positions of certain types of protons (for example, hydroxyl and amino). They have also known that the resonance positions of some groups of protons can be greatly affected by changing from the usual NMR solvents such as CCl_4 and $CDCl_3$ to solvents such as benzene, which impose local anisotropic effects on surrounding molecules. In many cases, it is possible to resolve partially overlapping multiplets by such a solvent change. The use of **chemical shift reagents** for this purpose dates from about 1969. Most of these chemical shift reagents are organic complexes of paramagnetic rare earth metals from the lanthanide series of elements. When these metal complexes are added to the compound whose spectrum is being determined, profound shifts in the resonance positions of the various groups of protons are observed. The direction of the shift (upfield or downfield) depends primarily on which metal is being used. Complexes of europium, erbium, thulium, and ytterbium shift resonances to lower field; complexes of cerium, praseodymium, neodymium, samarium, terbium, and holmium generally shift resonances to higher field. The advantage of using such reagents is that shifts similar to those observed at higher field can be induced without the purchase of an expensive higher-field instrument.

Of the lanthanides, europium is probably the most commonly used metal. Two of its widely used complexes are *tris*-(dipivalomethanato)europium and *tris*-(6,6,7,7,8,8,8-heptafluoro-2,2-dimethyl-3,5-octanedionato)europium. These are frequently abbreviated $Eu(dpm)_3$ and $Eu(fod)_3$, respectively.

These lanthanide complexes produce spectral simplifications in the NMR spectrum of any compound that has a relatively basic pair of electrons (unshared pair) that can coordinate with Eu^{3+}. Typically, aldehydes, ketones, alcohols, thiols, ethers, and amines will all interact:

The amount of shift that a given group of protons will experience depends (1) on the distance separating the metal (Eu3+) and that group of protons, and (2) on the concentration of the shift reagent in the solution. Because of the latter dependence, it is necessary when reporting a lanthanide-shifted spectrum to report the number of mole equivalents of shift reagent used or its molar concentration.

The distance factor is illustrated in the spectra of hexanol, which are given in Figures 26.25 and 26.26. In the absence of shift reagent, the normal spectrum is obtained (see Figure 26.25). Only the triplet of the terminal methyl group and the triplet of the methylene group next to the hydroxyl are resolved in the spectrum. The other protons (aside from OH) are found together in a broad unresolved group.

Figure 26.25
90-MHz ¹H NMR spectrum of hexanol determined without
Eu(dpm)₃ © National Institute of Advanced Industrial Science and
Technology.

Figure 26.26
The 100-MHz ¹HNMR spectrum of hexanol with 0.29 mole equivalents
of Eu(dpm)₃ added. From J. K. M. Sanders and D. H. Williams, Chemical
Communications, (1970): 422. Reproduced with permission of the Royal
Society of Chemistry.

With shift reagent added (see Figure 26.26), each of the methylene groups is clearly
separated and resolved into the proper multiplet structure. The spectrum is first-
order and simplified; all the splittings are explained by the $n + 1$ rule.

One final consequence of using a shift reagent should be noted. Notice in Figure 26.26 that the multiplets are not as nicely resolved into sharp peaks as you
might expect. This is due to the fact that shift reagents cause a small amount of
peak broadening. At high-shift reagent concentrations, this problem becomes serious, but at most useful concentrations the amount of broadening experienced is
tolerable.

Section 26.16
Diastereopic protons

Coupling constants were discussed in Section 26.9 and 26.10 with Table 26.4 showing typical values for coupling constants in organic compounds. A simple organic compound is shown in Figure 26.27, where it is easy to predict the splitting patterns using the $n + 1$ rule. The protons H_c and H_d are equivalent, and as a group they are split by the proton H_e into a doublet, integrating for 2 H. Notice that the protons H_c and H_d are in the same electronic environment, adjacent to the two chlorine atoms, and will not split each other. *Only non-equivalent protons will split each other!* Proton H_e is split by two neighboring protons H_c and H_d into a triplet, integrating for 1 H. All of these couplings involve protons that are 3 bonds away from each other, and are referred to as ^3J couplings. Similarly, the methyl group H_a appears as a triplet, integrating for 3 H, while its neighboring methylene group H_b appears as a quartet, integrating for 2 H. Many organic compounds show these simple splitting patterns. These common organic compounds show couplings between protons that are 3 bonds away from each other (^3J) making the application of the $n + 1$ rule possible (see Section 26.9).

Figure 26.28 shows the structure of the product from the chiral reduction of ethyl acetoacetate (Experiment 28) the 300 MHz NMR spectrum is shown in Experiment 28. This high field NMR spectrum makes it possible to do a detailed analysis of the compound.[3] The protons H_c and H_d are in different environments; H_c is opposite the OH group while H_d is further away from the OH group. The carbons atom labeled with an asterisk has a stereocenter. Often the presence of a stereocenter will make the protons on a methylene group non-equivalent. These non-equivalent protons are referred to as diastereotopic protons. The diasterotopic protons in compounds attached to an sp^3 hybridized carbon atom possess large coupling constants, with ^2J values of 11 to 15 Hz.[4] In fact, these values are typically larger then ^3J coupling constants in compounds with sp^3 hybridization. Referring to the 300 MHz NMR spectrum of the racemic product in Experiment 28, H_c is split into a doublet by H_d and each leg of the doublet is split again into doublets by the neighboring proton, H_f. The second coupling is a three bond coupling, $^3J_{cf}$. The observed pattern is referred to as a doublet of doublets, shown in the analysis in Figure 26.28. Likewise, H_d also becomes a doublet of doublets. Both H_c and H_d appear at different places in the spectrum (See Figure 1 and Figure 2 in Experiment 28). One may notice in Figure 26.28 that the spacing of the doublets, $^3J_{cf}$, differs from the spacing, $^3J_{df}$. The reason for these differences is that the dihedral angle for H_c to H_f is 180 degrees, while the dihedral angle for H_d to H_f is 60 degrees. The dihedral angles often influence the value of the ^3J coupling constants.

Another example of a compound with diastereotopic methylene protons is shown in Figure 26.29. Notice that the hydrogen atoms on the methylene

Figure 26.27

Analysis of the NMR pattern for ethyl 3,3-dichloropropanoate. Proton H_c and H_d are equivalent and do not split each other. *These methylene protons are not diastereotopic.*

---

[3] Often lower field NMR spectra determined at 60 MHz are more difficult to analyze because of more closely spaced peaks.

[4] The geminal protons (^2J) attached to the terminal carbon atom of an alkene are non-equivalent and will split each other. These ^2J protons attached to an sp^2 carbon atom have much smaller coupling constants, often less than 5 Hz, compared to ^2J protons with sp^3 hybridized carbon atoms. (See Section 26.10 and 26.11.)

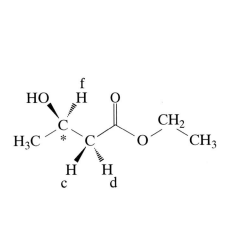

Figure 26.28

The structure of ethyl 3-hydroxybutanoate obtained from the reduction of ethyl 3-hydroxybutanoate (Experiment 28). This compound possesses diastereotopic methylene protons, H_c and H_d. An analysis of the diastereotopic protons is also shown in this figure.

Figure 26.29

The Diels–Alder reaction with anthracene-9–methanol from Experiment 48. This compound possesses diastereotopic methylene protons, H_f and H_g.

group are in a different environment. Proton H_f is on the same side as the nitrogen-containing ring, while H_g is on the opposite side of the nitrogen-containing ring. One observes that the molecule is not symmetrical, leading to the methylene group having diastereotopic protons. If the nitrogen-containing ring were not present, the molecule would have been symmetrical, and the methylene protons would have been equivalent and thus not diasterotopic.

This compound is produced in Experiment 48. The 500 MHz NMR spectrum of this product is shown in Figure 26.30, with insets showing expansions of the regions from 3.25 to 3.40 ppm and 4.7 to 5.2 ppm. The Hz values that appear above the peaks in the expansions may be used to calculate the coupling constants. The diastereotopic protons H_f and H_g appear at 4.96 ppm and 5.13 ppm (we don't know the assignments precisely). Assuming the correct assignment, proton H_g appears at 4.96 ppm as a doublet ($^2J_{fg}$ = 2490.12 – 2478.40 Hz =about 11.7 Hz). However, each leg of the doublet is split again into doublets, ($^3J_{bg}$ = 2490.12 - 2485.36 Hz = about 4.8 Hz. The 4.8 Hz coupling constant is for the ^3J coupling of H_g to the proton on the OH group, H_b. The resulting pattern at 4.96 ppm is a doublet of doublets. Another doublet of doublets appears at 5.13 ppm for the non-equivalent diastereotopic proton H_f.

Figure 26.30
The 500 MHz NMR spectrum of the the Diels-Alder reaction with anthracene-9-methanol from Experiment 48. The inserts show expansions of the regions from 3.25 to 3.40 ppm and 4.7 to 5.2 ppm. *The eight aromatic ring protons are not shown.*

The other coupling constants may be extracted from the pattern at 3.27 ppm, a doublet of doublets, $^3J_{cd}$ =8.8 Hz and $^3J_{ce}$ =3.3 Hz. Proton H_d appears at 3.36 ppm as doublet J_{cd} =8.8 Hz. Finally, H_e appears as a doublet at 4.75 ppm with $^3J_{ce}$ =3.3 Hz. The coupling constants may be summarized as follows:

$^2J_{fg}$ = 11.7 Hz (diasterotopic protons at 4.96 ppm and 5.13 ppm)

$^3J_{bf}$ = $^3J_{bg}$ =4.8 Hz (coupling of OH to each of the diasterotopic protons)

$$^{3}J_{ce} = 3.3 \text{ Hz (coupling of H}_c \text{ to H}_e)$$

$$^{3}J_{cd} = 8.8 \text{ Hz (coupling of H}_e \text{ to H}_d)$$

REFERENCES

Textbooks

Friebolin, H. *Basic One- and Two-Dimensional NMR Spectroscopy,* 5th ed. VCH Publishers: New York, **2010**.

Gunther, H. *NMR Spectroscopy,* 2nd ed. John Wiley & Sons: New York, **1995**.

Jackman, L. M.; Sternhell, S. *Nuclear Magnetic Resonance Spectroscopy in Organic Chemistry,* 2nd ed. Pergamon Press: New York, **1969**.

Macomber, R. S. *A Complete Introduction to Modern NMR Spectroscopy.* John Wiley & Sons: New York, **2008**.

Mocomber, R. S. *NMR Spectroscopy: Essential Theory and Practice.* College Outline Series, Harcourt Brace Jovanovich: New York, **1998**.

Pavia, D. L.; Lampman, G. M.; Kriz, G. S.; Vyvyan, J. R. *Introduction to Spectroscopy,* 4th ed. Brooks Cole: Belmont, CA, 2008.

Sanders, J. K.; Hunter, B. K. *Modern NMR Spectroscopy—A Guide for Chemists,* 2nd ed. Oxford University Press: Oxford, **1993**.

Silverstein, R. M.; Webster, F. X.; Kiemle, D. *Spectrometric Identification of Organic Compounds,* 7th ed. John Wiley & Sons: New York, **2005**.

Compilations of Spectra

Pouchert, C. J. *The Aldrich Library of NMR Spectra,* 60 MHz, 2nd ed. Aldrich Chemical Company: Milwaukee, WI, **1983**.

Pouchert, C.J.; Behnke, J. *The Aldrich Library of ^{13}C and ^{1}H FT-NMR Spectra, 300 MHz.* Aldrich Chemical Company: Milwaukee, WI, **1993**.

Pretsch E.; Clerc, T.; Seibl, J.; Simon, W. *Tables of Spectra Data for Structure Determination of Organic Compounds,* 2nd ed. Springer-Verlag: Berlin and New York, **1989**.

Translated from the German by K. Biemann.

Web Sites

http://www.aist.go.jp/RIODB/SDBS/menu-e.html
Integrated Spectral DataBase System for Organic Compounds, National Institute of Materials and Chemical Research, Tsukuba, Ibaraki 305-8565, Japan. This database includes infrared, mass spectra, and NMR data (proton and carbon-13) for a large number of compounds.

http://www.chem.ucla.edu/~webspectra/
UCLA Department of Chemistry and Biochemistry in connection with Cambridge University Isotope Laboratories maintains a Web site, WebSpectra, that provides NMR and IR spectroscopy problems for students to interpret. They provide links to other sites with problems for students to solve.

PROBLEMS

1. Describe the method that you should use to determine the proton NMR spectrum of a carboxylic acid, which is insoluble in all the common organic solvents that your instructor is likely to make available.

2. To save money, a student uses chloroform instead of deuterated chloroform to run a proton NMR spectrum. Is this a good idea?

3. Look up the solubilities for the following compounds and decide whether you would select deuterated chloroform or deuterated water to dissolve the substances for NMR spectroscopy.

    a. Glycerol (1,2,3-propanetriol)

    b. 1,4-Diethoxybenzene

    c. Propyl pentanoate (propyl ester of pentanoic acid)

4. Assign each of the proton patterns in the spectra of 2-, 3-, and 4-nitroaniline as shown in Figure 26.23.

5. The following two compounds are isomeric esters derived from acetic acid, each with formula $C_5H_{10}O_2$. These expanded spectra clearly show the splitting patterns: singlet, doublet, triplet, quartet, etc. Integral curves are drawn on the spectra, along with relative integration values provided just above the scale and under each set of peaks. These numbers indicate the number of protons assigned to each pattern. Remember that these integral values are approximate. You will need to round the values off to the nearest whole number. Draw the structure of each compound.

$C_5H_{10}O_2$

2.00   2.98   2.04   2.94

4.0   3.5   3.0   2.5   2.0   1.5   1.0

    b. The set of peaks centering on 5 ppm is expanded in both the *x* and *y* directions in order to show the pattern more clearly. This expanded pattern is shown as an inset on the full spectrum.

C₅H₁₀O₂

6. The compound that gives the following NMR spectrum has the formula C₃H₆Br₂. Draw the structure.

C₃H₆Br₂

7. Draw the structure of an ether with formula $C_5H_{12}O_2$ that fits the following NMR spectrum.

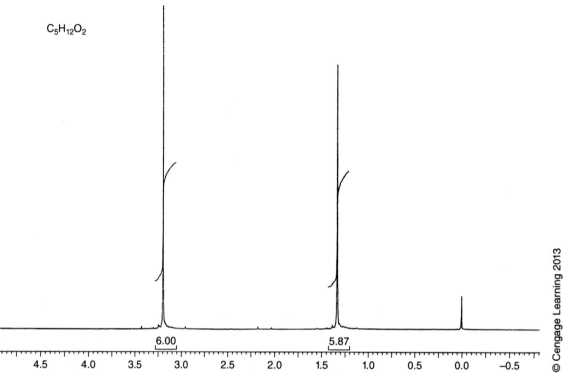

8. Following are the NMR spectra of three isomeric esters with the formula $C_7H_{14}O_2$, all derived from propanoic acid. Provide a structure for each.

   a. The set of peaks centering on about 1.9 ppm is expanded in both the x and y directions in order to show the pattern more clearly. This expanded pattern is shown as an inset on the full spectrum.

b.

$C_7H_{14}O_2$

2.00   8.58   2.83

2.6   2.5   2.4   2.3   2.2   2.1   2.0   1.9   1.8   1.7   1.6   1.5   1.4   1.3   1.2   1.1   1.0   0.9

© Cengage Learning 2013

c.

$C_7H_{14}O_2$

2.08   2.02   2.13   2.14   2.94   3.00

4.0   3.5   3.0   2.5   2.0   1.5   1.0

© Cengage Learning 2013

9. The two isomeric carboxylic acids that give the following NMR spectra both have the formula $C_3H_5ClO_2$. Draw their structures.

a. The broad singlet integrating for one proton that is shown as an inset on the spectrum appears downfield at 11.5 ppm.

b. The singlet integrating for one proton that is shown as an inset on the spectrum appears downfield at 12.0 ppm.

10. The following compounds are isomers with formula $C_{10}H_{12}O$. Their infrared spectra show strong bands near 1715 cm^{-1} and in the range from 1600 cm^{-1} to 1450 cm^{-1}. Draw their structures.

a.

b.

Carbon-13 Nuclear Magnetic Resonance Spectroscopy

Carbon-12, the most abundant isotope of carbon, does not possess spin ($I = 0$); it has both an even atomic number and an even atomic weight. The second principal isotope of carbon, ^{13}C, however, does have the nuclear spin property ($I = \frac{1}{2}$). ^{13}C atom resonances are not easy to observe, due to a combination of two factors. First, the natural abundance of ^{13}C is low; only 1.08% of all carbon atoms are ^{13}C. Second, the magnetic moment μ of ^{13}C is low. For these two reasons, the resonances of ^{13}C are about 6000 times weaker than those of hydrogen. With special Fourier transform (FT) instrumental techniques, which are not discussed here, it is possible to observe ^{13}C nuclear magnetic resonance (carbon-13) spectra on samples that contain only the natural abundance of ^{13}C.

The most useful parameter derived from carbon-13 spectra is the chemical shift. Integrals are unreliable and are not necessarily related to the relative numbers of ^{13}C atoms present in the sample. Hydrogens that are attached to ^{13}C atoms cause spin–spin splitting, but spin–spin interaction between adjacent carbon atoms is rare. With the low natural abundance of carbon-13 (0.0108), the probability of finding two ^{13}C atoms adjacent to one another is extremely low.

Carbon spectra can be used to determine the number of non-equivalent carbons and to identify the types of carbon atoms (methyl, methylene, aromatic, carbonyl, and so on) that may be present in a compound. Thus, carbon NMR provides direct information about the carbon skeleton of a molecule. Because of the low natural abundance of carbon-13 in a sample, it is often necessary to acquire multiple scans over what is needed for proton NMR.

For a given magnetic field strength, the resonance frequency of a ^{13}C nucleus is about one-fourth the frequency required to observe proton resonances. For example, in a 7.05-tesla applied magnetic field, protons are observed at 300 MHz, and ^{13}C nuclei are observed at about 75 MHz.

27.1 Preparing a Sample for Carbon-13 NMR

Technique 26, Section 26.1, describes the technique for preparing samples for proton NMR. Much of what is described there also applies to carbon NMR. There are some differences, however, in determining a carbon spectrum. Fourier transform instruments require a deuterium signal to stabilize (lock) the field. Therefore, the solvents must contain deuterium. Deuterated chloroform, $CDCl_3$, is used most commonly for this purpose because of its relatively low cost. Other deuterated solvents may also be used.

Modern FT–NMR spectrometers allow chemists to obtain both the proton and carbon NMR spectra of the same sample in the same NMR tube. After changing several parameters in the program operating the spectrometer, you can obtain both spectra without removing the sample from the probe. The only real difference is that a proton spectrum may be obtained after a few scans, whereas the carbon spectrum may require 10–100 times more scans.

Tetramethylsilane (TMS) may be added as an internal reference standard, where the chemical shift of the methyl carbon is defined as 0.00 ppm. Alternatively, you may use the center peak of the $CDCl_3$ pattern, which is found at 77.0 ppm. This pattern can be observed as a small "triplet" near 77.0 ppm in a number of the spectra given in this chapter.

27.2 Carbon-13 Chemical Shifts

An important parameter derived from carbon-13 spectra is the chemical shift. The correlation chart in Figure 27.1 shows typical ^{13}C chemical shifts, listed in parts per million (ppm) from TMS, where the carbons of the methyl groups of TMS (not the hydrogens) are used for reference. Notice that the chemical shifts appear over a range (0–220 ppm) much larger than that observed for protons (0–12 ppm). Because of the very large range of values, nearly every non-equivalent carbon atom in an organic molecule gives rise to a peak with a different chemical shift. Peaks rarely overlap as they often do in proton NMR.

The correlation chart is divided into four sections. Saturated carbon atoms appear at the highest field, nearest to TMS (8–60 ppm). The next section of the chart demonstrates the effect of electronegative atoms (40–80 ppm). The third section includes alkene and aromatic-ring carbon atoms (100–175 ppm). Finally, the fourth section contains carbonyl carbons, which appear at the lowest field values (155–220 ppm).

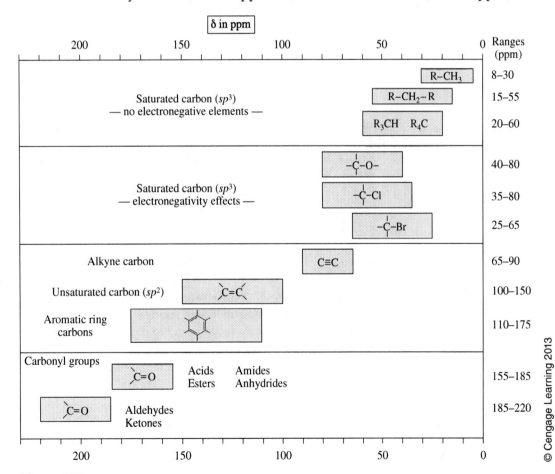

Figure 27.1
A correlation chart for ^{13}C chemical shifts (chemical shifts are listed in parts per million from tetramethylsilane).

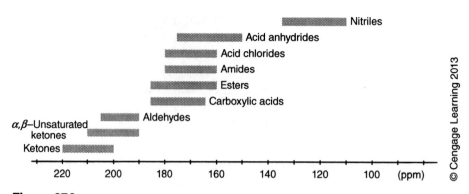

Figure 27.2

A ^{13}C correlation chart for carbonyl and nitrile functional groups.

Electronegativity, hybridization, and anisotropy all affect ^{13}C chemical shifts in nearly the same fashion as they affect ^{1}H chemical shifts; however ^{13}C chemical shifts are about 20 times larger. Electronegativity (see Section 26.7) produces the same deshielding effect in carbon NMR as in proton NMR—the electronegative element produces a large downfield shift. The shift is greater for a ^{13}C atom than for a proton because the electronegative atom is directly attached to the ^{13}C atom and the effect occurs through only a single bond, C—X. With protons, the electronegative atoms are attached to carbon, not hydrogen; the effect occurs through two bonds, H—C—X, rather than one.

Analogous with ^{1}H shifts, changes in hybridization also produce larger shifts for the carbon-13 that is *directly involved* (no bonds) than they do for the hydrogens attached to that carbon (one bond). In ^{13}C NMR, the carbons of carbonyl groups have the largest chemical shifts, due both to sp^2 hybridization and to the fact that an electronegative oxygen is directly attached to the carbonyl carbon, deshielding it even further. Anisotropy (see Section 26.8) is responsible for the large chemical shifts of the carbons in aromatic rings and alkenes.

Notice that the range of chemical shifts is larger for carbon atoms than for hydrogen atoms. Because the factors affecting carbon shifts operate either through one bond or directly on carbon, they are greater than those for hydrogen, which operate through more bonds. As a result, the entire range of chemical shifts becomes larger for ^{13}C (0–220 ppm) than for ^{1}H (0–12 ppm).

Many of the important functional groups of organic chemistry contain a carbonyl group. In determining the structure of a compound containing a carbonyl group, it is frequently helpful to have some idea of the type of carbonyl group in the unknown. Figure 27.2 illustrates the typical ranges of ^{13}C chemical shifts for some carbonyl-containing functional groups. Although there is some overlap in the ranges, ketones and aldehydes are easy to distinguish from the other types. Chemical shift data for carbonyl carbons are particularly powerful when combined with data from an infrared spectrum.

27.3 Proton-Coupled ^{13}C Spectra—Spin–Spin Splitting of Carbon-13 Signals

Unless a molecule is artificially enriched by synthesis, the probability of finding two ^{13}C atoms in the same molecule is low. The probability of finding two ^{13}C atoms adjacent to each other in the same molecule is even lower. Therefore, we rarely observe homonuclear (carbon–carbon) spin–spin splitting patterns where the interaction occurs between two ^{13}C atoms. However, the spins of protons attached directly to ^{13}C atoms do interact with the spin of carbon and cause the carbon signal to be split according to the $n + 1$ rule. This is **heteronuclear** (carbon–hydrogen) coupling involving two different types of atoms. With ^{13}C NMR, we generally examine splitting

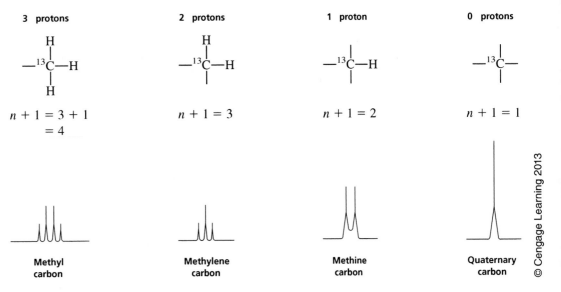

Figure 27.3
The effect of attached protons on ^{13}C resonances.

that arises from the protons *directly attached* to the carbon atom being studied. This is a one-bond coupling. In proton NMR, the most common splittings are *homonuclear* (hydrogen–hydrogen), which occur between protons attached to *adjacent* carbon atoms. In these cases, the interaction is a three-bond coupling, H—C—C—H.

Figure 27.3 illustrates the effect of protons directly attached to a ^{13}C atom. The *n + 1* rule predicts the degree of splitting in each case. The resonance of a ^{13}C atom with three attached protons, for instance, is split into a quartet ($n + 1 = 3 + 1 = 4$). Because the hydrogens are directly attached to the carbon-13 (one-bond couplings), the coupling constants for this interaction are quite large, with J values of about 100 Hz to 250 Hz. Compare the typical three-bond H—C—C—H couplings that are common in NMR spectra, which have J values of about 4 Hz to 18 Hz.

It is important to note while examining Figure 27.3 that you are not "seeing" protons directly when looking at a ^{13}C spectrum (proton resonances occur at frequencies outside the range used to obtain ^{13}C spectra); you are observing only the effect of the protons on ^{13}C atoms. Also remember that we cannot observe ^{12}C, because it is NMR inactive.

Spectra that show the spin–spin splitting, or coupling, between carbon-13 and the protons directly attached to it are called **proton-coupled spectra.** Figure 27.4 A is the proton-coupled ^{13}C NMR spectrum of ethyl phenylacetate. In this spectrum, the first quartet downfield from TMS (14.2 ppm) corresponds to the carbon of the methyl group. It is split into a quartet ($J = 127$ Hz) by the three attached hydrogen atoms (^{13}C—H, one-bond couplings). In addition, although it cannot be seen on the scale of this spectrum (an expansion must be used), each of the quartet lines is split into a closely spaced triplet (J = ca. 1 Hz). This additional fine splitting is caused by the two protons on the adjacent —CH_2— group. These are two-bond couplings (H—C—^{13}C) of a type that occurs commonly in ^{13}C spectra, with coupling constants that are generally quite small (J = 0–2 Hz) for systems with carbon atoms in an aliphatic chain. Because of their small size, these couplings are frequently ignored in the routine analysis of spectra, with greater attention being given to the larger one-bond splittings seen in the quartet itself.

There are two —CH_2— groups in ethyl phenylacetate. The one corresponding to the ethyl —CH_2—group is found farther downfield (60.6 ppm), as this carbon is deshielded by the attached oxygen. It is a triplet because of the two attached

Figure 27.4
Ethyl phenylacetate. (A) The proton-coupled ^{13}C NMR spectrum (20 MHz).
(B) The proton-decoupled ^{13}C spectrum (20 MHz). (From Moore, J. A., Dalrymple,
D. L., and Rodig, O. R. *Experimental Methods in Organic Chemistry*, 3rd ed.
[W. B. Saunders: Philadelphia, 1982])

hydrogens (one-bond couplings). Again, although it is not seen in this unexpanded
spectrum, the three hydrogens on the adjacent methyl group finely split each of the
triplet peaks into a quartet. The benzyl —CH_2— carbon is the intermediate triplet
(41.4 ppm). Farthest downfield is the carbonyl-group carbon (171.1 ppm). On the
scale of this presentation, it is a singlet (no directly attached hydrogens), but because of the adjacent benzyl —CH_2— group, it is actually split finely into a triplet.
The aromatic ring carbons also appear in the spectrum, and they have resonances
in the range from 127 ppm to 136 ppm. Section 27.7 will discuss aromatic ring ^{13}C
resonances.

Proton-coupled spectra for large molecules are often difficult to interpret. The
multiplets from different carbons commonly overlap because the ^{13}C—H coupling
constants are frequently larger than the chemical shift differences of the carbons in
the spectrum. Sometimes, even simple molecules such as ethyl phenylacetate (Figure 27.4A) are difficult to interpret. Proton decoupling, which is discussed in the
next section, avoids this problem.

**27.4 Proton-
Decoupled
^{13}C Spectra**

By far, the great majority of ^{13}C NMR spectra are obtained as proton-decoupled
spectra. The decoupling technique obliterates all interactions between protons
and ^{13}C nuclei; therefore, only singlets are observed in a decoupled ^{13}C NMR spectrum. Although this technique simplifies the spectrum and avoids overlapping
multiplets, it has the disadvantage that the information on attached hydrogens
is lost.

Proton **decoupling** is accomplished in the process of determining a ^{13}C NMR
spectrum by simultaneously irradiating all of the protons in the molecule with
a broad spectrum of frequencies in the proper range for protons. Modern NMR

spectrometers provide a second, tunable radio-frequency generator, the decoupler, for this purpose. Irradiation causes the protons to become saturated, and they undergo rapid upward and downward transitions, among all their possible spin states. These rapid transitions decouple any spin–spin interactions between the hydrogens and the ^{13}C nuclei being observed. In effect, all spin interactions are averaged to zero by the rapid changes. The carbon nucleus "senses" only one average spin state for the attached hydrogens rather than two or more distinct spin states.

Figure 27.4B is a proton-decoupled spectrum of ethyl phenylacetate. The proton-coupled spectrum (see Figure 27.4A) was discussed in Section 27.3. It is interesting to compare the two spectra to see how the proton-decoupling technique simplifies the spectrum. Every chemically and magnetically distinct carbon gives only a single peak. Notice, however, that the two *ortho* ring carbons (carbons 2 and 6) and the two *meta* ring carbons (carbons 3 and 5) are equivalent by symmetry and that each pair gives only a single peak.

Figure 27.5 is a second example of a proton-decoupled spectrum. Notice that the spectrum shows three peaks corresponding to the exact number of carbon atoms in 1-propanol. If there are no equivalent carbon atoms in a molecule, a ^{13}C peak will be observed for *each* carbon. Notice also that the assignments given in Figure 27.5 are consistent with the values in the chemical shift chart (see Figure 27.1). The carbon atom closest to the electronegative oxygen is farthest downfield, and the methyl carbon is at highest field.

The three-peak pattern centered at $\delta = 77$ ppm is due to the solvent $CDCl_3$. This pattern results from the coupling of a deuterium (^2H) nucleus to the ^{13}C nucleus. Often, the $CDCl_3$ pattern is used as an internal reference in place of TMS.

Figure 27.5
The proton-decoupled ^{13}C NMR spectrum of 1-propanol (22.5 MHz).

27.5 Some Sample Spectra—Equivalent Carbons

Equivalent ^{13}C atoms appear at the same chemical shift value. Figure 27.6 shows the proton-decoupled carbon spectrum for 2,2-dimethylbutane. The three methyl groups at the left side of the molecule are equivalent by symmetry.

$$CH_3-\underset{\underset{CH_3}{|}}{\overset{\overset{CH_3}{|}}{C}}-CH_2-CH_3$$

Although this compound has a total of six carbons, there are only four peaks in the ^{13}C NMR spectrum. The ^{13}C atoms that are equivalent appear at the same chemical shift. The single methyl carbon, a, appears at highest field (9 ppm), and the three equivalent methyl carbons, b, appear at 29 ppm. The quaternary carbon, c, gives rise to the small peak at 30 ppm, and the methylene carbon, d, appears at 37 ppm. The relative sizes of the peaks are related, in part, to the number of each type of carbon atom present in the molecule. For example, notice in Figure 27.6 that the peak at 29 ppm (b) is much larger than the others. This peak is generated by three carbons. The quaternary carbon at 30 ppm (c) is very weak. Because no hydrogens are attached to this carbon, there is very little nuclear Overhauser enhancement (NOE) (see Section 27.6). Without attached hydrogen atoms, relaxation times are also longer than for other carbon atoms. Quaternary carbons, those with no hydrogens attached, frequently appear as weak peaks in proton-decoupled ^{13}C NMR spectra (see Section 27.6).

Figure 27.7 is a proton-decoupled ^{13}C spectrum of cyclohexanol. This compound has a plane of symmetry passing through its hydroxyl group, and it shows only four carbon resonances. Carbons a and c are doubled due to symmetry and give rise to larger peaks than carbons b and d. Carbon d, bearing the hydroxyl group, is deshielded by oxygen and has its peak at 70.0 ppm. Notice that this peak has the lowest intensity of all of the peaks. Its intensity is lower than that of carbon b in part because the carbon d peak receives the least amount of NOE; there is only one hydrogen attached to the hydroxyl carbon, whereas each of the other carbons has two hydrogens.

A carbon attached to a double bond is deshielded due to its sp^2 hybridization and some diamagnetic anisotropy. This effect can be seen in the ^{13}C NMR spectrum of cyclohexene (Figure 27.8). Cyclohexene has a plane of symmetry that runs

Figure 27.6

The proton-decoupled ^{13}C NMR spectrum of 2,2-dimethylbutane.

Figure 27.7
The proton-decoupled ^{13}C NMR spectrum of cyclohexanol.

Figure 27.8
The proton-decoupled ^{13}C NMR spectrum of cyclohexene. (The peaks marked with an x results from impurities.)

perpendicular to the double bond. As a result, we observe only three absorption peaks. There are two of each type of sp^3 carbon. Each of the double-bond carbons c has only one hydrogen, whereas each of the remaining carbons has two. As a result of a reduced NOE, the double-bond carbons (127 ppm) have a lower-intensity peak in the spectrum.

In Figure 27.9, the spectrum of cyclohexanone, the carbonyl carbon has the lowest intensity. This is due not only to reduced NOE (no hydrogen attached) but also to the long relaxation time of the carbonyl carbon (see Section 27.6). Notice also that Figure 27.2 predicts the large chemical shift for this carbonyl carbon (211 ppm).

27.6 Nuclear Overhauser Enhancement (NOE)

When we obtain a proton-decoupled ^{13}C spectrum, the intensities of many of the carbon resonances increase significantly above those observed in a proton-coupled experiment. Carbon atoms with hydrogen atoms directly attached are enhanced the most, and the enhancement increases (but not always linearly) as more hydrogens

© Cengage Learning 2013

Figure 27.9

The proton-decoupled ^{13}C NMR spectrum of cyclohexanone. (The peak marked with an x is an impurity.)

are attached. This effect is known as the nuclear Overhauser effect, and the degree of increase in the signal is called the **nuclear Overhauser enhancement (NOE).** Thus, we expect that the intensity of the carbon peaks should increase in the following order in a typical carbon-13 NMR spectrum:

$$CH_3 > CH_2 > CH > C$$

Carbon atom relaxation times influence the intensity of peaks in a spectrum. When more protons are attached to a carbon atom, relaxation times become shorter, resulting in more intense peaks. We expect methyl and methylene groups to be relatively more intense than the intensity observed for quaternary carbon atoms where there are no attached protons. Thus, a weak-intensity peak is observed for the quaternary carbon atom at 30 ppm in 2,2-dimethylbutane (see Figure 27.6).

In addition, weak carbonyl carbon peaks are observed at 171 ppm in ethyl phenylacetate (see Figure 27.4) and at 211 ppm in cyclohexanone (see Figure 27.9).

27.7 Compounds with Aromatic Rings

Compounds with carbon–carbon double bonds or aromatic rings give rise to chemical shifts from 100 ppm to 175 ppm. Because relatively few other peaks appear in this range, a great deal of useful information is available when peaks appear here.

A **monosubstituted** benzene ring shows *four* peaks in the aromatic carbon area of a proton-decoupled ^{13}C spectrum, because the *ortho* and *meta* carbons are doubled by symmetry. Often the carbon with no protons attached, the *ipso* carbon, has a very weak peak due to a long relaxation time and a weak NOE. In addition, there are two larger peaks for the doubled *ortho* and *meta* carbons and a medium-sized peak for the *para* carbon. In many cases, it is not important to be able to assign all of the peaks precisely. In the example of toluene, shown in Figure 27.10, notice that carbons c and d are not easy to assign by inspection of the spectrum.

Toluene   c,d   c,d   Difficult to assign

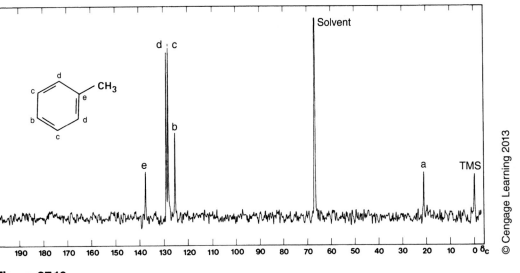

Figure 27.10

The proton-decoupled ^{13}C NMR spectrum of toluene.

In a proton-coupled 13C spectrum, a monosubstituted benzene ring shows three doublets and one singlet. The singlet arises from the *ipso* carbon, which has no attached hydrogen. Each of the other carbons in the ring (*ortho, meta,* and *para*) has one attached hydrogen and yields a doublet.

Figure 27.4B is the proton-decoupled spectrum of ethyl phenylacetate, with the assignments noted next to the peaks. Notice that the aromatic ring region shows four peaks between 125 ppm and 135 ppm, consistent with a monosubstituted ring. There is one peak for the methyl carbon (13 ppm) and there are two peaks for the methylene carbons. One of the methylene carbons is directly attached to an electronegative oxygen atom and appears at 61 ppm, and the other is more shielded (41 ppm). The carbonyl carbon (an ester) has resonance at 171 ppm. All of the carbon chemical shifts agree with the values in the correlation chart (Figure 27.1).

Depending on the mode of substitution, a symmetrically **disubstituted** benzene ring can show two, three, or four peaks in the proton-decoupled ^{13}C spectrum. The following drawings illustrate this for the isomers of dichlorobenzene.

Figure 27.11 shows the spectra of all three dichlorobenzenes, each of which has the number of peaks consistent with the analysis just given. You can see that ^{13}C NMR spectroscopy is very useful in the identification of isomers.

Most other polysubstitution patterns on a benzene ring yield six peaks in the proton-decoupled ^{13}C NMR spectrum, one for each carbon. However, when identical substituents are present, watch carefully for planes of symmetry that may reduce the number of peaks.

Figure 27.11
The proton-decoupled ^{13}C NMR spectra of the three isomers of dichlorobenzene (25 MHz).

REFERENCES

Textbooks

Friebolin, H. *Basic One- and Two-Dimensional NMR Spectroscopy*, 5th ed. VCH Publishers: New York, **2010**.

Gunther, H. *NMR Spectroscopy*, 2nd ed. John Wiley & Sons: New York, **1995**.

Levy, G. C. *Topics in Carbon-13 Spectroscopy*. John Wiley & Sons: New York, **1984**.

Levy, G. C.; Lichter, R. L.; Nelson, G. L. *Carbon-13 Nuclear Magnetic Resonance Spectroscopy*, 2nd ed. John Wiley & Sons: New York, **1980**.

Macomber, R. S. *A Complete Introduction to Modern NMR Spectroscopy*. John Wiley & Sons: New York, **2008**.

Macomber, R. S. *NMR Spectroscopy—Essential Theory and Practice*. College Outline Series, Harcourt Brace Jovanovich: New York, **1988**.

Pavia, D. L.; Lampman, G. M.; Kriz, G. S.; and Vyvyan, J. R. *Introduction to Spectroscopy*, 4th ed. Brooks/Cole: Belmont, CA, **2008**.

Sanders, J. K. M.; Hunter, B. K. *Modern NMR Spectroscopy—A Guide for Chemists*, 2d ed. Oxford University Press: Oxford, England, **1993**.

Silverstein, R. M.; Webster, F. X.; Kiemle, D. *Spectrometric Identification of Organic Compounds*, 7th ed. John Wiley & Sons: New York, **2005**.

Compilations of Spectra

Johnson, L. F.; Jankowski, W. C. *Carbon-13 NMR Spectra: A Collection of Assigned, Coded, and Indexed Spectra, 25 MHz*. Wiley-Interscience: New York, **1972**.

Pouchert, C. J.; Behnke, J. *The Aldrich Library of ^{13}C and ^{1}H FT–NMR Spectra, 75 and 300 MHz.* Aldrich Chemical Company: Milwaukee, WI, **1993**.

Pretsch, E.; Clerc, T.; Seibl, J.; Simon, W. *Tables of Spectral Data for Structure Determination of Organic Compounds,* 2nd ed. Springer-Verlag: Berlin and New York, **1989**. Translated from the German by K. Biemann.

Web Sites

http://www.aist.go.jp/RIODB/SDBS/menu-e.html
Integrated Spectral DataBase System for Organic Compounds, National Institute of Materials and Chemical Research, Tsukuba, Ibaraki 305-8565, Japan. This database includes infrared, mass spectra, and NMR data (proton and carbon-13) for a number of compounds.

http://www.chem.ucla.edu/~webspectra
UCLA Department of Chemistry and Biochemistry in connection with Cambridge University Isotope Laboratories maintains a Web site, WebSpectra, that provides NMR and IR spectroscopy problems for students to interpret. They provide links to other sites with problems for students to solve.

PROBLEMS

1. Predict the number of peaks that you would expect in the proton-decoupled ^{13}C spectrum of each of the following compounds. Problems 1a and 1b are provided as examples. Dots are used to show the non-equivalent carbon atoms in these two examples.

a. CH_3—$\overset{\overset{\text{O}}{\|}}{C}$—O—$CH_2$—$CH_3$ **Four peaks**

b.   **Five peaks**

c.

d.

e. Br—CH_2—CH=CH—$\overset{\overset{\text{O}}{\|}}{C}$—O—$CH_3$

f.

g.

h.

i.

j.

k.

2. Following are the ¹H and ¹³C spectra for two isomeric bromoalkanes (A and B) with formula C_4H_9Br. Integral curves are drawn on the spectra, along with relative integral values provided just above the scale and under each set of peaks. These numbers indicate the relative number of protons assigned to each pattern. Remember that these integral values are approximate. You will need to round the values off to the nearest whole number. Also, in some cases, the lowest whole-number ratios are given. In that case, the values provided may need to be multiplied by two or three in order to obtain the actual number of protons in each pattern.

¹H
A

¹³C
A

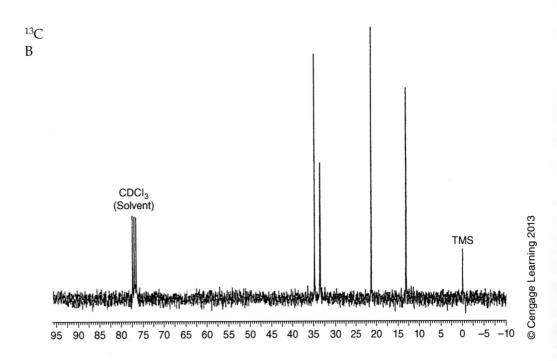

3. Following are the ^1H and ^{13}C spectra for each of three isomeric ketones (**A, B,** and **C**) with formula $C_7H_{14}O$. Integral curves are drawn on the spectra, along with relative integral values provided just above the scale and under each set of peaks. These numbers indicate the relative number of protons assigned to each pattern. Remember that these integral values are approximate. You will need to round the values off to the nearest whole number. Also, in some cases, the lowest whole-number ratios are given. In that case, the values provided may need to be multiplied by two or three in order to obtain the actual number of protons in each pattern.

¹H
A

¹³C
A

¹H
B

¹³C
B

¹H
C

²³C
C

Mass Spectrometry

In its simplest form, the mass spectrometer performs three essential functions. First, molecules are bombarded by a stream of high-energy electrons, converting some of the molecules to positive ions. Because of their high energy, some of these ions **fragment,** or break apart into smaller ions. All of these ions are accelerated in an electric field. Second, the accelerated ions are separated according to their mass-to-charge ratio in a magnetic or electric field. Finally, the ions with a particular mass-to-charge ratio are detected by a device that is able to count the number of ions that strike it. The output of the detector is amplified and fed to a recorder. The trace from the recorder is a **mass spectrum**—a graph of the number of particles detected as a function of mass-to-charge ratio.

Ions are formed in an **ionization chamber.** The sample is introduced into the ionization chamber using a sample inlet system. In the ionization chamber, a heated **filament** emits a beam of high-energy electrons. The filament is heated to several thousand degrees Celsius. In normal operation, the electrons have an energy of about 70 electron-volts. These high-energy electrons strike a stream of molecules that has been admitted from the sample system and ionize the molecules in the sample stream by removing electrons from them. The molecules are thus converted into **radical-cations.**

$$e^- + M \longrightarrow 2e^- + M^+$$

The energy required to remove an electron from an atom or molecule is its **ionization potential.** The ionized molecules are accelerated and focused into a beam of rapidly moving ions by means of charged plates.

From the ionization chamber, the beam of ions passes through a short field-free region. From there, the beam enters the **mass analyzer,** where the ions are separated according to their mass-to-charge ratio.

The detector of most instruments consists of a counter that produces a current proportional to the number of ions that strike it. Electron multiplier circuits allow accurate measurement of the current from even a single ion striking the detector. The signal from the detector is fed to a **recorder,** which produces the actual mass spectrum.

28.1 The Mass Spectrum

The **mass spectrum** is a plot of ion abundance versus mass-to-charge (m/e) ratio. A typical mass spectrum is shown in Figure 28.1. The spectrum shown is that of dopamine, a substance that acts as a neurotransmitter in the central nervous system. The spectrum is displayed as a bar graph of percentage ion abundance (relative abundance) plotted against m/e.

Dopamine

© Cengage Learning 2013

Figure 28.1

The mass spectrum of dopamine.

The most abundant ion formed in the ionization chamber gives rise to the tallest peak in the mass spectrum, called the **base peak.** For dopamine, the base peak appears at $m/e = 124$. The relative abundances of all the other peaks in the spectrum are reported as percentages of the abundance of the base peak.

The beam of electrons in the ionization chamber converts some of the sample molecules into positive ions. Removal of a single electron from a molecule yields an ion whose weight is the actual molecular weight of the original molecule. This ion is the **molecular ion,** frequently symbolized as M+.

The value of m/e at which the molecular ion appears on the mass spectrum, assuming that the ion has only one electron removed, gives the molecular weight of the original molecule. In the mass spectrum of dopamine, the molecular ion appears at $m/e = 153$, the molecular weight of dopamine. If you can identify the molecular ion peak in the mass spectrum, you can use the spectrum to determine the molecular weight of an unknown substance. If the presence of heavy isotopes is ignored for the moment, the molecular ion peak corresponds to the heaviest particle observed in the mass spectrum.

Molecules do not occur in nature as isotopically pure species. Virtually all atoms have heavier isotopes that occur in varying natural abundances. Hydrogen occurs largely as ^1H, but a few percent of hydrogen atoms occur as the isotope ^2H. Further, carbon normally occurs as ^{12}C, but a few percent of carbon atoms are the heavier isotope, ^{13}C. With the exception of fluorine, most other elements have a certain percentage of heavier isotopes that occur naturally. Peaks caused by ions bearing these heavier isotopes are also found in the mass spectrum. The relative abundances of these isotopic peaks are proportional to the abundances of the isotopes in nature. Most often, the isotopes occur at one or two mass units above the mass of the "normal" atom. Therefore, besides looking for the molecular ion (M+) peak, you should also attempt to locate the M+1 and M+2 peaks. As will be demonstrated later, you can use the relative abundances of these M+1 and M+2 peaks to determine the molecular formula of the substance being studied.

The beam of electrons in the ionization chamber can produce the molecular ion. This beam also has sufficient energy to break some of the bonds in the molecule, producing a series of molecular fragments. Fragments that are positively charged are also accelerated in the ionization chamber, sent through the analyzer, detected, and recorded on the mass spectrum. These **fragment ion peaks** appear at m/e values corresponding to their individual masses. Very often, a fragment ion rather than the molecular ion will be the most abundant ion produced in the mass spectrum (the base peak).

A second means of producing fragment ions occurs with the molecular ion, which, once it is formed, is so unstable that it disintegrates before it can pass into the accelerating region of the ionization chamber. Lifetimes shorter than 10^{-5} seconds are typical in this type of fragmentation. Those fragments that are charged then appear as fragment ions in the mass spectrum. As a result of these fragmentation processes, the typical mass spectrum can be quite complex, containing many more peaks than the molecular ion and M+1 and M+2 peaks. Structural information about a substance can be determined by examining the fragmentation pattern in the mass spectrum. Fragmentation patterns are discussed further in Section 28.3.

28.2 Molecular Formula Determination

Mass spectrometry can be used to determine the molecular formulas of molecules that provide reasonably abundant molecular ions. Although there are at least two principal techniques for determining a molecular formula, only one will be described here.

The molecular formula of a substance can be determined through the use of **precise atomic masses.** High-resolution mass spectrometers are required for this method. Atoms are normally thought of as having integral atomic masses; for example, $H = 1$, $C = 12$, and $O = 16$. If you can determine atomic masses with sufficient precision, however, you find that the masses do not have values that are exactly integral. The mass of each atom actually differs from a whole mass number by a small fraction of a mass unit. The actual masses of some atoms are given in Table 28.1.

Depending on the atoms that are contained within a molecule, it is possible for particles of the same nominal mass to have slightly different measured masses when precise mass determinations are possible. To illustrate, a molecule whose molecular weight is 60 could be C_3H_8O, $C_2H_8N_2$, $C_2H_4O_2$, or CH_4N_2O. The species have the following precise masses:

C_3H_8O	60.05754
$C_2H_8N_2$	60.06884
$C_2H_4O_2$	60.02112
CH_4N_2O	60.03242

Table 28.1 Precise masses of some common elements

Element	Atomic Weight	Nuclide	Precise Mass
Hydrogen	1.00797	^{1}H	1.00783
		^{2}H	2.01410
Carbon	12.01115	^{12}C	12.0000
		^{13}C	13.00336
Nitrogen	14.0067	^{14}N	14.0031
		^{15}N	15.0001
Oxygen	15.9994	^{16}O	15.9949
		^{17}O	16.9991
		^{18}O	17.9992
Fluorine	18.9984	^{19}F	18.9984
Silicon	28.086	^{28}Si	27.9769
		^{29}Si	28.9765
		^{30}Si	29.9738
Phosphorus	30.974	^{31}P	30.9738
Sulfur	32.064	^{32}S	31.9721
		^{33}S	32.9715
		^{34}S	33.9679
Chlorine	35.453	^{35}Cl	34.9689
		^{37}Cl	36.9659
Bromine	79.909	^{79}Br	78.9183
		^{81}Br	80.9163
Iodine	126.904	^{127}I	126.9045

Observing a molecular ion with a mass of 60.058 would establish that the unknown molecule was C_3H_8O. Distinguishing among these possibilities is well within the capability of a modern high-resolution instrument.

In another method, these four compounds may also be distinguished by differences in the relative intensities of their M, M+1, and M+2 peaks. The predicted intensities are either calculated by formula or looked up in tables. Details of this method may be found in the References at the end of this chapter.

28.3 Detecting Halogens

When chlorine or bromine is present in a molecule, the isotope peak that is two mass units heavier than the molecular ion (the M+2 peak) becomes very significant. The heavy isotope of each of these elements is two mass units heavier than the lighter isotope. The natural abundance of ^{37}Cl is 32.5% that of ^{35}Cl; the natural abundance of ^{81}Br is 98.0% that of ^{79}Br. When these elements are present, the M+2 peak becomes intense, and the pattern is characteristic of the particular halogen present. If a compound contains two chlorine or bromine atoms, a distinct M+4 peak should be observed, as well as an intense M+2 peak. In these cases, you should exercise caution in identifying the molecular ion peak in a mass spectrum, but the pattern of peaks is characteristic of the nature of the halogen substitution in the molecule. Table 28.2 gives the relative intensities of isotope peaks for various combinations of bromine and chlorine atoms. The patterns of molecular ion and isotopic peaks observed with halogen substitution are shown in Figure 28.2. Examples of these patterns can be seen in the mass spectra of chloroethane (Figure 28.3) and bromoethane (Figure 28.4).

28.4 Fragmentation Patterns

When the molecule has been bombarded by high-energy electrons in the ionization chamber of a mass spectrometer, besides losing one electron to form an ion, the molecule also absorbs some of the energy transferred in the collision between the molecule and the incident electrons. This extra energy puts the molecular ion in an excited vibrational state. The vibrationally excited molecular ion is often unstable and may lose some of this extra energy by breaking apart into fragments. If the lifetime of an individual molecular ion is longer than 10^{-5} seconds, a peak corresponding to the molecular ion will be observed in the mass spectrum. Those molecular ions with lifetimes shorter than 10^{-5} seconds will break apart into fragments before they are accelerated within the ionization chamber. In such cases, peaks

Table 28.2 Relative intensities of isotope peaks for various combinations of bromine and chlorine

Halogen	M	M+2	M+4	M+6
Br	100	97.7	—	—
Br_2	100	195.0	95.4	—
Br_3	100	293.0	286.0	93.4
Cl	100	32.6	—	—
Cl_2	100	65.3	10.6	—
Cl_3	100	97.8	31.9	3.47
BrCl	100	130.0	31.9	—
Br_2Cl	100	228.0	159.0	31.2
$BrCl_2$	100	163.0	74.4	10.4

© Cengage Learning 2013

Figure 28.2
Mass spectra expected for various combinations of bromine and chlorine.

Figure 28.3
The mass spectrum of chloroethane.

Figure 28.4
The mass spectrum of bromoethane.

corresponding to the mass-to-charge ratios for these fragments will also appear in the mass spectrum. For a given compound, not all the molecular ions formed by ionization have precisely the same lifetime. The ions have a range of lifetimes; some individual ions may have shorter lifetimes than others. As a result, peaks are usually observed arising from both the molecular ion and the fragment ions in a typical mass spectrum.

For most classes of compounds, the mode of fragmentation is somewhat characteristic. In many cases, it is possible to predict how a molecule will fragment. Remember that the ionization of the sample molecule forms a molecular ion that not only carries a positive charge but also has an unpaired electron. The molecular ion, then, is actually a **radical–cation,** and it contains an odd number of electrons. In the structural formulas that follow, the radical–cation is indicated by enclosing the structure in square brackets. The positive charge and the unshared electron are shown as superscripts.

$$[\mathbf{R - CH_3}]^{\ddagger}$$

When fragment ions form in the mass spectrometer, they almost always form by means of unimolecular processes. The pressure of the sample in the ionization chamber is too low to permit a significant number of bimolecular collisions. Those unimolecular processes that require the least energy will give rise to the most abundant fragment ions.

Fragment ions are cations. Much of the chemistry of these fragment ions can be explained in terms of what is known about carbocations in solution. For example, alkyl substitution stabilizes fragment ions (and promotes their formation) in much the same way that it stabilizes carbocations. Those fragmentation processes that lead to more stable ions will be favored over processes that lead to the formation of less stable ions.

Fragmentation often involves the loss of an electrically neutral fragment. The neutral fragment does not appear in the mass spectrum, but you can deduce its existence by noting the difference in masses of the fragment ion and the original molecular ion. Again, processes that lead to the formation of a more stable neutral fragment will be favored over those that lead to the formation of a less stable neutral fragment. The loss of a stable neutral molecule, such as water, is commonly observed in the mass spectrometer.

A. Cleavage of One Bond

The most common mode of fragmentation involves the cleavage of one bond. In this process, the odd-electron molecular ion yields an odd-electron neutral fragment and an even-electron fragment ion. The neutral fragment that is lost is a **free radical,** whereas the ionic fragment is of the carbocation type. Cleavages that lead to the formation of more stable carbocations will be favored. Thus, the ease of fragmentation to form ions increases in the following order:

$$CH_3^+ < RCH_2^+ < R_2CH^+ < R_3C^+ < CH_2{=}CH{-}CH_2^+ < C_6H_5{-}CH_2^+$$

Increasing ease of formation →

The following reactions show examples of fragmentation that take place with the cleavage of one bond:

$$\left[R{-}CH_3 \right]^{+\cdot} \longrightarrow R^+ + \cdot CH_3$$

$$\left[R{-}\overset{\overset{\displaystyle O}{\|}}{C}{-}R'' \right]^{+\cdot} \longrightarrow {+}\overset{\overset{\displaystyle O}{\|}}{C}{-}R' + \cdot R$$

$$\left[R{-}X \right]^{+\cdot} \longrightarrow R^+ + \cdot X$$

**where X = halogen, OR,
SR, or NR₂, and where
R = H, alkyl, or aryl**

© Cengage Learning 2013

B. Cleavage of Two Bonds

The next most important type of fragmentation involves the cleavage of two bonds. In this type of process, the odd-electron molecular ion yields an odd-electron fragment ion and an even-electron neutral fragment, usually a small, stable molecule. Examples of this type of cleavage are shown next:

$$\left[\begin{array}{cc} H & OH \\ RCH & \!\!\!{-}\!\!\! & CHR' \end{array} \right]^{+\cdot} \longrightarrow \left[RCH{=}CHR' \right]^{+\cdot} + H_2O$$

$$\left[\begin{array}{cc} CH_2 & \!\!\!{-}\!\!\! & CH_2 \\ RCH & \!\!\!{-}\!\!\! & CH_2 \end{array} \right]^{+} \longrightarrow \left[RCH{=}CH_2 \right]^{+\cdot} + CH_2{=}CH_2$$

$$\left[\begin{array}{c} RCH{-}CH_2{-}O{-}\overset{\overset{\displaystyle O}{\|}}{C}{-}CH_3 \\ H \end{array} \right]^{+\cdot} \longrightarrow \left[RCH{=}CH_2 \right]^{+} + HO{-}\overset{\overset{\displaystyle O}{\|}}{C}{-}CH_3$$

© Cengage Learning 2013

C. Other Cleavage Processes

In addition to the processes just mentioned, fragmentation reactions involving rearrangements, migrations of groups, and secondary fragmentations of fragment ions are also possible. These processes occur less often than the types of processes just described. Nevertheless, the pattern of molecular ion and fragment ion peaks observed in the typical mass spectrum is quite complex and unique for each particular molecule. As a result, the mass spectral pattern observed for a given substance can be compared with the mass spectra of known compounds as a means of identification. The mass spectrum is like a fingerprint. For a treatment of the specific modes of fragmentation characteristic of particular classes of compounds, refer to more advanced textbooks (see References at the end of this chapter). The unique appearance of the mass spectrum for a given compound is the basis for identifying the components of a mixture in the **gas chromatography–mass spectrometry (GC–MS)** technique (see Technique 22, Section 22.14). The mass spectrum of every component in a mixture is compared with standard spectra stored in the computer memory of the instrument. The printed output produced by a GC–MS instrument includes an identification based on the results of the computer matching of mass spectra.

28.5 Interpreted Mass Spectra

In this section, the mass spectra of some representative organic compounds are presented. The important fragment ion peaks in each mass spectrum are identified. In some of the examples, identification of the fragments is presented without explanation, although some interpretation is provided where an unusual or interesting process takes place. In the first example, that of butane, a more complete explanation of the symbolism used is offered.

Butane; C_4H_{10}, MW = 58 (Figure 28.5)

$$CH_3 + CH_2 + CH_2 + CH_3$$
$$15 \qquad 29 \qquad 43$$

In the structural formula of butane, the dashed lines represent the location of bond-breaking processes that occur during fragmentation. In each case, the

Figure 28.5
The mass spectrum of butane.

fragmentation process involves the breaking of one bond to yield a neutral radical and a cation. The arrows point toward the fragment that bears the positive charge. This positive fragment is the ion that appears in the mass spectrum. The mass of the fragment ion is indicated beneath the arrow.

The mass spectrum shows the molecular ion at $m/e = 58$. Breaking of the C1—C2 bond yields a three-carbon fragment with a mass of 43.

$$CH_3-CH_2-CH_2 | CH_3 \longrightarrow CH_3-CH_2-CH_2^+ + \cdot CH_3$$
$$m/e = 43$$

Cleavage of the central bond yields an ethyl cation, with a mass of 29.

$$CH_3-CH_2 | CH_2-CH_3 \longrightarrow CH_3-CH_2^+ + \cdot CH_2-CH_3$$
$$m/e = 29$$

The terminal bond can also break to yield a methyl cation, which has a mass of 15.

$$CH_3 | CH_2-CH_2-CH_3 \longrightarrow CH_3^+ + \cdot CH_2-CH_2-CH_3$$
$$m/e = 15$$

Each of these fragments appears in the mass spectrum of butane and has been identified.

2,2,4-Trimethylpentane; C_8H_{18}, MW $=114$ (Figure 28.6)

Figure 28.6

The mass spectrum of 2,2,4-trimethylpentane ("isooctane").

Notice that in the case of 2,2,4-trimethylpentane, by far the most abundant fragment is the *tert*-butyl cation ($m/e = 57$). This result is not surprising when one considers that the *tert*-butyl cation is a particularly stable carbocation.

Cyclopentane; C_5H_{10}, MW $=70$ (Figure 28.7)

$$\begin{array}{c} CH_2 \\ CH_2 \qquad CH_2 \quad \uparrow 42 \\ CH_2 - CH_2 \end{array}$$

In the case of cyclopentane, the most abundant fragment results from the simultaneous cleavage of two bonds. This mode of fragmentation eliminates a neutral molecule of ethene (MW $= 28$) and results in the formation of a cation at $m/e = 42$.

1-Butene; C_4H_8, MW $= 56$ (Figure 28.8)

$$CH_2 {=} CH - CH_2 {+} CH_3$$
$$41$$

An important fragment in the mass spectra of alkenes is the allyl cation ($m/e = 41$). This cation is particularly stable due to resonance.

$$[\,^+CH_2{-}CH{=}CH_2 \longleftrightarrow CH_2{=}CH{-}CH_2^+\,]$$

Toluene; C_7H_8, MW $= 92$ (Figure 28.9)

$$\bigcirc\!\!\!-CH_2{+}H$$
$$91$$

When an alkyl group is attached to a benzene ring, preferential fragmentation occurs at a benzylic position to form a fragment ion of the formula $C_7H_7^+$ ($m/e = 91$). In the mass spectrum of toluene, loss of hydrogen from the molecular ion gives a strong peak at $m/e = 91$. Although it may be expected that this fragment ion peak is due to the benzyl carbocation, evidence suggests the benzyl carbocation

Figure 28.7
The mass spectrum of cyclopentane.

Figure 28.8
The mass spectrum of 1-butene.

Figure 28.9
The mass spectrum of toluene.

actually rearranges to form the **tropylium ion.** Isotope-labeling experiments tend to confirm the formation of the tropylium ion. The tropylium ion is a seven-carbon ring system that contains six electrons in π-molecular orbitals and hence is resonance stabilized in a manner similar to that observed in benzene.

Figure 28.10
The mass spectrum of 1-butanol.

1-Butanol; $C_4H_{10}O$, MW = 74 (Figure 28.10)

$$CH_3 - CH_2 - CH_2 \dashv CH_2 - OH$$
$$31$$

The most important fragmentation reaction for alcohols is loss of an alkyl group:

$$\left[\begin{array}{c} R' \\ | \\ R - C - OH \\ | \\ R'' \end{array} \right]^{\overset{+}{\cdot}} \longrightarrow R\cdot + \begin{array}{c} R' \\ \diagdown \\ \diagup \\ R'' \end{array} C = OH^+$$

The largest alkyl group is the one that is lost most readily. In the spectrum of 1-butanol, the intense peak at $m/e = 31$ is due to the loss of a propyl group to form

$$\begin{array}{c} H \\ \diagdown \\ \diagup \\ H \end{array} C = OH^+$$

A second common mode of fragmentation involves dehydration. Loss of a molecule of water from 1-butanol leaves a cation of mass 56.

$$CH_3 - CH_2 - CH - CH_2 \overset{56}{\text{\textbrokenbar}}$$
$$\qquad\qquad\quad H \qquad OH$$

Benzaldehyde; C_7H_6O, MW = 106 (Figure 28.11)

$$77 \qquad 105$$

Figure 28.11
The mass spectrum of benzaldehyde.

The loss of a hydrogen atom from an aldehyde is a favorable process. The resulting fragment ion is a benzoyl cation, a particularly stable type of carbocation.

$$m/e = 105$$

Loss of the entire aldehyde functional group leaves a phenyl cation. This ion can be seen in the spectrum of an *m/e* value of 77.

2-Butanone; C_4H_8O, MW = 72 (Figure 28.12)

$$CH_3-CH_2 \overset{\overset{\displaystyle O}{\overset{\|}{C}}}{|} CH_3$$

57

43

If the methyl group is lost as a neutral fragment, the resulting cation, an **acylium ion,** has an *m/e* value of 57. If the ethyl group is lost, the resulting acylium ion appears at an *m/e* value of 43.

$$CH_3-CH_2-\overset{\overset{\displaystyle O}{\|}}{C}+CH_3 \longrightarrow CH_3-CH_2-\overset{\overset{\displaystyle O}{\|}}{C}+ + \cdot CH_3$$
m/e = 57

$$CH_3-CH_2+\overset{\overset{\displaystyle O}{\|}}{C}-CH_3 \longrightarrow CH_3-\overset{\overset{\displaystyle O}{\|}}{C}+ + \cdot CH_2CH_3$$
m/e = 43

Figure 28.12
The mass spectrum of 2-butanone.

Figure 28.13
The mass spectrum of acetophenone.

Acetophenone; C_8H_8O, MW = 120 (Figure 28.13)

Aromatic ketones undergo α-cleavage to lose the alkyl group and form the benzoyl cation ($m/e = 105$). This ion subsequently loses carbon monoxide to form the phenyl cation ($m/e = 77$). Aromatic ketones also undergo α-cleavage on the other side of the carbonyl group, forming an alkyl acylium ion. In the case of acetophenone, this ion appears at an m/e value of 43.

Propanoic acid; $C_3H_6O_2$, MW = 74 (Figure 28.14)

With short-chain carboxylic acids, the loss of OH and COOH through α-cleavage on either side of the C＝O group may be observed. In the mass spectrum of propanoic acid, loss of OH gives rise to a peak at m/e = 57. Loss of COOH gives rise to a peak at m/e = 29. Loss of the alkyl group as a free radical, leaving the $COOH^+$ ion (m/e = 45), also occurs. The intense peak at m/e = 28 is due to additional fragmentation of the ethyl portion of the acid molecule.

Figure 28.14
The mass spectrum of propanoic acid.

© Cengage Learning 2013

Figure 28.15
The mass spectrum of methyl butanoate.

Methyl butanoate; $C_5H_{10}O_2$, MW = 102 (Figure 28.15)

$$CH_3-CH_2-CH_2 \overset{|}{\underset{|}{\cancel{\vdash}}} \overset{O}{\underset{\|}{C}} \overset{|}{\underset{|}{\cancel{\vdash}}} O-CH_3$$

43 ◄-- 59
71

© Cengage Learning 2013

The most important of the α-cleavage reactions involves the loss of the alkoxy group from the ester to form the corresponding acylium ion, RCO^+. The acylium ion peak appears at $m/e = 71$ in the mass spectrum of methyl butanoate. A second important peak results from the loss of the alkyl group from the acyl portion of the ester molecule, leaving a fragment $CH_3-O-C{=}O^+$ that appears at $m/e = 59$. Loss of the carboxylate function group to leave the alkyl group as a cation gives rise to a peak at $m/e = 43$. The intense peak at $m/e = 74$ results from a rearrangement process (see Section 28.6).

1-Bromohexane; $C_6H_{13}Br$, MW = 165 (Figure 28.16)

$$CH_3-CH_2 \overset{|}{\underset{|}{\cancel{\vdash}}} CH_2 \overset{|}{\underset{|}{\cancel{\vdash}}} CH_2-CH_2-CH_2 \overset{|}{\underset{|}{\cancel{\vdash}}} Br$$

◄--- 43   ◄--- 85
--► 135/137

© Cengage Learning 2013

The most interesting characteristic of the mass spectrum of 1-bromohexane is the presence of the doublet in the molecular ion. These two peaks, of equal height, separated by two mass units, are strong evidence that bromine is present in the substance. Notice also that loss of the terminal ethyl group yields a fragment ion that still contains bromine ($m/e = 135$ and 137). The presence of the doublet demonstrates that this fragment contains bromine.

Figure 28.16
The mass spectrum of 1-bromohexane.

28.6 Rearrangement Reactions

Because the fragment ions that are detected in a mass spectrum are cations, we can expect that these ions will exhibit behavior we are accustomed to associate with carbocations. It is well known that carbocations are prone to rearrangement reactions, converting a less stable carbocation into a more stable one. These types of rearrangements are also observed in the mass spectrum. If the abundance of a cation is especially high, it is assumed that a rearrangement to yield a longer-lived cation must have occurred.

Other types of rearrangements are also known. An example of a rearrangement that is not normally observed in solution chemistry is the rearrangement of a benzyl cation to a tropylium ion. This rearrangement is seen in the mass spectrum of toluene (Figure 28.9).

A particular type of rearrangement process that is unique to mass spectrometry is the **McLafferty rearrangement.** This type of rearrangement occurs when an alkyl chain of at least three carbons in length is attached to an energy-absorbing structure such as a phenyl or carbonyl group that can accept the transfer of a hydrogen ion. The mass spectrum of methyl butanoate (Figure 28.15) contains a prominent peak at $m/e = 74$. This peak arises from a McLafferty rearrangement of the molecular ion.

REFERENCES

Beynon, J. H. *Mass Spectrometry and Its Applications to Organic Chemistry.* Elsevier: Amsterdam, **1960**.

Biemann, K. *Mass Spectrometry: Organic Chemical Applications.* McGraw-Hill: New York, **1962**.

Budzikiewicz, H.; Djerassi, C.; Williams, D. H. *Mass Spectrometry of Organic Compounds.* Holden-Day: San Francisco, **1967**.

McLafferty, F. W.; Tureček, F. *Interpretation of Mass Spectra,* 4th ed. University Science Books: Mill Valley, CA, **1993**.

Pavia, D.L.; Lampman, G. M.; Kriz, G.S.; and Vyvyan, J.R. *Introduction to Spectroscopy,* 4th ed., Brooks/Cole: Belmont, CA, **2008**.

Silverstein, R.M.; Webster, F.X.; and Kiemle, D. *Spectrometric Identification of Organic Compounds,* 7th ed., John Wiley: New York, **2005**.

Guide to the Chemical Literature

Often, you may need to go beyond the information contained in the typical organic chemistry textbook and use reference material in the library. At first glance, using library materials may seem formidable because of the numerous sources the library contains. If, however, you adopt a systematic approach, the task can prove rather useful. This description of various popular sources and an outline of logical steps to follow in the typical literature search should be helpful.

29.1 Locating Physical Constants: Handbooks

To find information on routine physical constants, such as melting points, boiling points, indices of refraction, and densities, you should first consider a handbook. Examples of suitable handbooks are

Aldrich Handbook of Fine Chemicals. Sigma-Aldrich: Milwaukee, WI, **2012–2013**.

Haynes, W. M., ed. *CRC Handbook of Chemistry and Physics,* 91st ed. CRC Press: Boca Raton, FL, **2010**.

O'Neil, M. S, ed. *The Merck Index,* 14th ed. Merck: Whitehouse Station, NJ, **2006**.

Speight, J., ed. *Lange's Handbook of Chemistry,* 16th ed. McGraw-Hill: New York, **2004**.

Each of these references is discussed in detail in Technique 4. The *CRC Handbook* is the reference consulted most often because the book is so widely available. There are, however, distinct advantages to using the other handbooks. The *CRC Handbook* uses the *Chemical Abstracts* system of nomenclature that requires you to identify the parent name; 3-methyl-1-butanol is listed as 1-butanol, 3-methyl.

The *Merck Index* lists fewer compounds, but there is far more information provided for the ones listed. If the compound is a medicinal or natural product, this is the reference of choice. This handbook contains literature references for the isolation and synthesis of a compound, along with certain properties of medicinal interest, such as toxicity. *Lange's Handbook* and the *Aldrich Handbook* list compounds in alphabetical order; 3- methyl-1-butanol is listed as 3-methyl-1-butanol.

A more complete handbook that is usually housed in the library is

Buckingham, J., ed. *Dictionary of Organic Compounds.* Chapman & Hall/Methuen: New York, **1982–1992**.

This is a revised version of an earlier four-volume handbook edited by I. M. Heilbron and H. M. Bunbury. In its present form, it consists of seven volumes with 10 supplements.

29.2 General Synthetic Methods

Many standard introductory textbooks in organic chemistry provide tables that summarize most of the common reactions, including side reactions, for a given class of compounds. These books also describe alternative methods of preparing compounds.

Brown, W. H.; Foote, C. S.; Iverson, B. L.; Anslyn, E. *Organic Chemistry,* 6th ed. Brooks/Cole: Pacific Grove, CA, **2012**.

Bruice, P. Y. *Organic Chemistry,* 6th ed. Prentice-Hall: New York, **2011**.

Carey, F. A.; Giuliano, R. M. *Organic Chemistry*, 8th ed. McGraw-Hill: New York, **2011**.

Ege, S. *Organic Chemistry*, 5th ed. Houghton-Mifflin: Boston, **2004**.

Fessenden, R. J.; Fessenden, J. S. *Organic Chemistry*, 6th ed. Brooks/Cole: Pacific Grove, CA, **1998**.

Fox, M. A.; Whitesell, J. K. *Organic Chemistry*, 3rd ed. Jones & Bartlett: Boston, **2004**.

Hornback, J. *Organic Chemistry.* 2nd ed. Brooks/Cole: Pacific Grove, CA, **2006**.

Jones, M., Jr. *Organic Chemistry*, 3rd ed. W. W. Norton: New York, **2003**.

Loudon, G. M. *Organic Chemistry*, 8th ed. Benjamin/Cummings: Menlo Park, CA, **2012**.

McMurry, J. *Organic Chemistry*, 7th ed. Brooks/Cole: Pacific Grove, CA, **2008**.

Morrison, R. T.; Boyd, R. N. *Organic Chemistry*, 8th ed. Prentice-Hall: Englewood Cliffs, NJ, **2012**.

Smith, M. B.; and March, J. *Advanced Organic Chemistry*, 6th ed. John Wiley & Sons: New York, **2007**.

Solomons, T. W. G.; Fryhle, C. *Organic Chemistry*, 10th ed. John Wiley & Sons: New York, **2011**.

Streitwieser, A.; Heathcock, C. H.; Kosower, E. M. *Introduction to Organic Chemistry*, 4th ed. Prentice-Hall: New York, **1992**.

Vollhardt, K. P. C.; Schore, N. E. *Organic Chemistry*, 6th ed. W. H. Freeman: New York, **2011**.

Wade, L. G., Jr. *Organic Chemistry*, 7th ed. Prentice-Hall: Englewood Cliffs, NJ, **2010**.

29.3 Searching the Chemical Literature

If the information you are seeking is not available in any of the handbooks mentioned in Section 29.1 or if you are searching for more detailed information than they can provide, then a proper literature search is in order. Although an examination of standard textbooks can provide some help, you often must use all the resources of the library, including journals, reference collections, and abstracts. The following sections outline how the various types of sources should be used and what sort of information can be obtained from them.

The methods discussed for searching the literature use mainly printed materials. Modern search methods also make use of computerized databases and are discussed in Section 29.11. These are vast collections of data and bibliographic materials that can be scanned rapidly from remote computer terminals. Although computerized searching is widely available, it may not be readily accessible to undergraduate students. The following references provide excellent introductions to the literature of organic chemistry:

Carr, C. Teaching and Using Chemical Information. *Journal of Chemical Education*, **1993**, 719.

Maizell, R. E. *How to Find Chemical Information*, 3rd ed. John Wiley & Sons: *New York*, **1998**.

Smith, M. B.; March, J. *Advanced Organic Chemistry*, 6th ed. John Wiley & Sons: New York, **2007**.

Somerville, A. N. Information Sources for Organic Chemistry, 1: Searching by Name Reaction and Reaction Type. *Journal of Chemical Education*, **1991**, 553.

Somerville, A. N. Information Sources for Organic Chemistry, 2: Searching by Functional Group. *Journal of Chemical Education*, **1991**, 842.

Somerville, A. N. Information Sources for Organic Chemistry, 3: Searching by Reagent. *Journal of Chemical Education*, **1992**, 379.

Wiggins, G. *Chemical Information Sources*. McGraw-Hill: New York, 1991. Integrates printed materials and computer sources of information.

29.4 Collections of Spectra

Collections of infrared, nuclear magnetic resonance, and mass spectra can be found in the following catalog of spectra:

Cornu, A.; and Massot, R. *Compilation of Mass Spectral Data*, 2nd ed. Heyden and Sons: London, **1975**.

High-Resolution NMR Spectra Catalog. Varian Associates: Palo Alto, CA, Vol.1, 1962; Vol. 2, **1963**.

Johnson, L. F.; Jankowski, W. C. *Carbon-13 NMR Spectra*. John Wiley & Sons: New York, **1972**.

Pouchert, C. J. *Aldrich Library of Infrared Spectra,* 3rd ed. Aldrich Chemical Co.: Milwaukee, **1981**.

Pouchert, C. J. *Aldrich Library of FT-IR Spectra,* 2nd ed. Aldrich Chemical Co.: Milwaukee, **1997**.

Pouchert, C. J. *Aldrich Library of NMR Spectra,* 2nd ed. Aldrich Chemical Co.: Milwaukee, **1983**.

Pouchert, C. J.; Behnke, J. *Aldrich Library of ^{13}C and ^1H FT NMR Spectra.* Aldrich Chemical Co.: Milwaukee, **1993**.

Sadtler Standard Spectra. Sadtler Research Laboratories: Philadelphia Continuing collection.

Stenhagen, E.; Abrahamsson, S.; McLafferty, F. W. *Registry of Mass Spectral Data,* 4 vols. Wiley-Interscience: New York, **1974**.

The American Petroleum Institute has also published collections of infrared, nuclear magnetic resonance, and mass spectra.

29.5 Advanced Textbooks

Much information about synthetic methods, reaction mechanisms, and reactions of organic compounds is available in any of the many current advanced textbooks in organic chemistry. Examples of such books are

Carey, F. A.; Sundberg, R. J. *Advanced Organic Chemistry. Part A. Structure and Mechanisms; Part B. Reactions and Synthesis,* 5th ed. Kluwer Academic: New York, **2007**.

Carruthers, W. *Some Modern Methods of Organic Synthesis,* 4th ed. Cambridge University Press: Cambridge, UK, **2004**.

Corey, E. J., and Cheng, X-M. *The Logic of Chemical Synthesis.* John Wiley & Sons: New York, **1995**.

Fieser, L. F.; Fieser, M. *Advanced Organic Chemistry.* Reinhold: New York, **1961**.

Finar, I. L. *Organic Chemistry,* 6th ed. Longman Group: London, **1986**.

House, H. O. *Modern Synthetic Reactions,* 2nd ed. W. H. Benjamin: Menlo Park, CA, **1972**.

Noller, C. R. *Chemistry of Organic Compounds,* 3rd ed. W. B. Saunders: Philadelphia, **1965**.

Smith, M. B. *Organic Synthesis,* 2nd ed. McGraw-Hill: New York, **2002**.

Smith, M. B.; March, J. *Advanced Organic Chemistry,* 6th ed. John Wiley & Sons: New York, **2007**.

Stowell, J. C. *Intermediate Organic Chemistry,* 2nd ed. John Wiley & Sons: New York, **1993**.

Warren, S.; Wyatt, P. *Organic Synthesis: The Disconnection Approach.* 2nd ed. John Wiley & Sons: New York, **2009**.

Zweifel, G. S.; Nantz, M. H. *Modern Organic Synthesis.* W. H. Freeman and Company: New York, **2007**.

These books often contain references to original papers in the literature for students wanting to follow the subject further. Consequently, you obtain not only a review of the subject from such a textbook but also a key reference that is helpful toward a more extensive literature search. The textbook by Smith and March is particularly useful for this purpose.

29.6 Specific Synthetic Methods

Anyone interested in locating information about a particular method of synthesizing a compound should first consult one of the many general textbooks on the subject. Useful ones are:

Anand, N., Bindra, J. S., Ranganathan, S. *Art in Organic Synthesis,* 2nd ed. John Wiley & Sons: New York, **1988**.

Barton, D., Ollis, W. D., eds. *Comprehensive Organic Chemistry,* 6 vols. Pergamon Press: Oxford, **1979**.

Buehler, C. A., Pearson, D. E. *Survey of Organic Synthesis.* Wiley-Interscience: New York, 1970, 2 vols., **1977**.

Carey, F. A.; Sundberg, R. J. *Advanced Organic Chemistry. Part B. Reactions and Synthesis,* 4th ed. Kluwer: New York, **2000**.

Compendium of Organic Synthetic Methods. Wiley-Interscience: New York, **1971–2002**. This is a continuing series, now in 10 volumes.

Fieser, L. F.; Fieser, M. *Reagents for Organic Synthesis.* Wiley-Interscience: New York, **1967–2008**. This is a continuing series, now in 24 volumes.

Greene, T. W.; Wuts, P. G. M. *Protective Groups in Organic Synthesis,* 4th ed. John Wiley & Sons: New York, **2007**.

House, H. O. *Modern Synthetic Reactions,* 2nd ed. W. H. Benjamin: Menlo Park, CA, **1972**.

Larock, R. C. *Comprehensive Organic Transformations,* 2nd ed. Wiley-VCH: New York, **1999**.

Mundy, B. P.; Ellerd, M. G. *Name Reactions and Reagents in Organic Synthesis.* 2nd ed. John Wiley & Sons: New York, **2005**.

Patai, S., ed. *The Chemistry of the Functional Groups.* Interscience, 1964–present: London, **2005**. This series consists of many volumes, each one specializing in a particular functional group.

Smith, M. B.; March, J. *Advanced Organic Chemistry,* 6th ed. John Wiley & Sons: New York, **2007**.

Trost, B. M.; Fleming, I. *Comprehensive Organic Synthesis.* Pergamon/Elsevier Science: Amsterdam, 1992. This series consists of 9 volumes plus supplements.

Vogel, A. I. *Vogel's Textbook of Practical Organic Chemistry, Including Qualitative Organic Analysis,* 5th ed. Longman Group: London, 1989. Revised by members of the School of Chemistry, Thames Polytechnic.

Wagner, R. B.; Zook, H. D. *Synthetic Organic Chemistry.* John Wiley & Sons: New York, **1956**.

Wang, Z. Comprehensive Organic Name Reactions and Reagents. John Wiley: New York, **2009**.

More specific information, including actual reaction conditions, exists in collections specializing in organic synthetic methods. The most important of these are:

Organic Syntheses. John Wiley & Sons: New York, **1921**–present. Published annually.
Organic Syntheses, Collective Volumes. John Wiley & Sons: New York, **1941–2004**.
Vol. 1, 1941, Annual Volumes 1–9
Vol. 2, 1943, Annual Volumes 10–19
Vol. 3, 1955, Annual Volumes 20–29
Vol. 4, 1963, Annual Volumes 30–39
Vol. 5, 1973, Annual Volumes 40–49
Vol. 6, 1988, Annual Volumes 50–59
Vol. 7, 1990, Annual Volumes 60–64
Vol. 8, 1993, Annual Volumes 65–69
Vol. 9, 1998, Annual Volumes 70–74
Vol. 10, 2004, Annual Volumes 75–79

It is much more convenient to use the collective volumes where the earlier annual volumes of *Organic Syntheses* are combined in groups of 9 or 10 in the first six collective volumes (Volumes 1–6), and then in groups of 5 for the next four volumes (Volumes 7, 8, 9, and 10). Useful indices are included at the end of each of the collective volumes that classify methods according to the type of reaction, type of compound prepared, formula of compound prepared, preparation or purification of solvents and reagents, and use of various types of specialized apparatus.

The main advantage of using one of the *Organic Syntheses* procedures is that they have been tested to make sure that they work as written. Often, an organic chemist will adapt one of these tested procedures to the preparation of another compound. One of the features of the advanced organic textbook by Smith and March is that it includes references to specific preparative methods contained in *Organic Syntheses.*

More advanced material on organic chemical reactions and synthetic methods may be found in any one of a number of annual publications that review the original literature and summarize it. Examples include

Advances in Organic Chemistry: Methods and Results. John Wiley & Sons: New York, **1960**–present.

Annual Reports in Organic Synthesis. Academic Press: Orlando, FL, **1985–1995**.

Annual Reports of the Chemical Society, Section B. Chemical Society: London, **1905**–present. Specifically, the section Synthetic Methods.

Organic Reactions. John Wiley & Sons: New York, **1942**–present.

Progress in Organic Chemistry. John Wiley & Sons: New York, **1952–1973**.

Each of these publications contains a great many citations to the appropriate articles in the original literature.

29.7 Advanced Laboratory Techniques

The student who is interested in reading about techniques more advanced than those described in this textbook, or in more complete descriptions of techniques, should consult one of the advanced textbooks specializing in organic laboratory techniques. Besides focusing on apparatus construction and the performance of complex reactions, these books provide advice on purifying reagents and solvents. Useful sources of information on organic laboratory techniques include:

Bates, R. B.; Schaefer, J. P. *Research Techniques in Organic Chemistry*. Prentice-Hall: Englewood Cliffs, NJ, **1971**.

Krubsack, A. J. *Experimental Organic Chemistry*. Allyn & Bacon: Boston, **1973**.

Leonard, J.; Lygo, B.; Procter, G. *Advanced Practical Organic Chemistry*, 2nd ed. Chapman & Hall: London, **1995**.

Monson, R. S. *Advanced Organic Synthesis: Methods and Techniques*. Academic Press: New York, **1971**.

Pirrung, M. C. *The Synthetic Organic Chemist's Companion*. John Wiley: New York, **2009**.

Techniques of Chemistry. John Wiley & Sons: New York, 1970–present. Currently 23 volumes. The successor to *Technique of Organic Chemistry*, this series covers experimental methods of chemistry, such as purification of solvents, spectral methods, and kinetic methods.

Weissberger, A., et al., eds. *Technique of Organic Chemistry*, 3rd ed., 14 vols. Wiley-Interscience: New York, **1959–1969**.

Wiberg, K. B. *Laboratory Technique in Organic Chemistry*. McGraw-Hill: New York, **1960**.

Numerous works and some general textbooks specialize in particular techniques. The preceding list is representative only of the most common books in this category. The following books deal specifically with microscale and semimicroscale techniques.

Cheronis, N. D.; Micro and Semimicro Methods. In A. Weissberger, ed., *Technique of Organic Chemistry*, Vol. 6. Wiley-Interscience: New York, **1954**.

Cheronis, N. D.; Ma, T. S. *Organic Functional Group Analysis by Micro and Semimicro Methods*. Wiley-Interscience: New York, **1964**.

Ma, T. S.; Horak, V. *Microscale Manipulations in Chemistry*. Wiley-Interscience: New York, **1976**.

29.8 Reaction Mechanisms

As with the case of locating information on synthetic methods, you can obtain a great deal of information about reaction mechanisms by consulting one of the common textbooks on physical organic chemistry. The textbooks listed here provide a general description of mechanisms, but they do not contain specific literature citations. Very general textbooks include:

Bruckner, R. *Advanced Organic Chemistry: Reaction Mechanisms*. Academic Press: New York, **2001**.

Miller, A.; Solomon, P. *Writing Reaction Mechanisms in Organic Chemistry*, 2nd ed. Academic Press: San Diego, CA, **1999**.

Sykes, P. *A Primer to Mechanisms in Organic Chemistry*. Benjamin/Cummings: Menlo Park, CA, **1995**.

More advanced textbooks include

Carey, F. A.; Sundberg, R. J. *Advanced Organic Chemistry. Part A. Structure and Mechanisms*, 4th ed. Kluwer: New York, **2000**.

Hammett, L. P. *Physical Organic Chemistry: Reaction Rates, Equilibria, and Mechanisms*, 2nd ed. McGraw-Hill: New York, **1970**.

Hine, J. *Physical Organic Chemistry*, 2nd ed. McGraw-Hill: New York, **1962**.

Ingold, C. K. *Structure and Mechanism in Organic Chemistry*, 2nd ed. Cornell University Press: Ithaca, NY, **1969**.

Isaacs, N. S. *Physical Organic Chemistry*, 2nd ed. John Wiley & Sons: New York, **1995**.

Jones, R. A. Y. *Physical and Mechanistic Organic Chemistry*, 2nd ed. Cambridge University Press: Cambridge, **1984**.

Lowry, T. H.; Richardson, K. S. *Mechanism and Theory in Organic Chemistry*, 3rd ed. Harper & Row: New York, **1987**.

Moore, J. W.; Pearson, R. G. *Kinetics and Mechanism*, 3rd ed. John Wiley & Sons: New York, **1981**.

Smith, M. B.; March, J. *Advanced Organic Chemistry*, 6th ed. John Wiley & Sons: New York, **2007**.

These books include extensive bibliographies that permit the reader to delve more deeply into the subject.

Most libraries also subscribe to annual series of publications that specialize in articles dealing with reaction mechanisms. Among these are

Advances in Physical Organic Chemistry. Academic Press: London, **1963**–present.

Annual Reports of the Chemical Society. Section B. Chemical Society: London, 1905–present. Specifically, the section Reaction Mechanisms.

Organic Reaction Mechanisms. John Wiley & Sons: Chichester, **1965**–present.

Progress in Physical Organic Chemistry. Interscience: New York, **1963**–present.

These publications provide the reader with citations from the original literature that can be very useful in an extensive literature search.

29.9 Organic Qualitative Analysis

Many laboratory manuals provide basic procedures for identifying organic compounds through a series of chemical tests and reactions. Occasionally, you might require a more complete description of analytical methods or a more complete set of tables of derivatives. Textbooks specializing in organic qualitative analysis should fill this need. Examples of sources for such information include

Cheronis, N. D.; Entriken, J. B. *Identification of Organic Compounds: A Student's Text Using Semimicro Techniques*. Interscience: New York, **1963**.

Pasto, D. J.; Johnson, C. R. *Laboratory Text for Organic Chemistry: A Source Book of Chemical and Physical Techniques*. Prentice-Hall: Englewood Cliffs, NJ, **1979**.

Rappoport, Z. ed. *Handbook of Tables for Organic Compound Identification*, 3rd ed. CRC Press: Boca Raton, FL, **1967**.

Shriner, R. L.; Hermann, C. K. F.; Merrill, T. C.; Curtin, D. Y.; Fuson, R. C. *The Systematic Identification of Organic Compounds*, 7th ed. John Wiley & Sons: New York, **1998**.

Vogel, A. I. *Elementary Practical Organic Chemistry. Part 2. Qualitative Organic Analysis*, 2nd ed. John Wiley & Sons: New York, **1966**.

Vogel, A. I. *Vogel's Textbook of Practical Organic Chemistry, Including Qualitative Organic Analysis*, 5th ed. Longman Group: London, **1989**. Revised by members of the School of Chemistry, Thames Polytechnic.

29.10 Beilstein and Chemical Abstracts

One of the most useful sources of information about the physical properties, synthesis, and reactions of organic compounds is *Beilsteins Handbuch der Organischen Chemie*. This is a monumental work, initially edited by Friedrich Konrad Beilstein and updated through several revisions by the Beilstein Institute in Frankfurt am Main, Germany. The original edition (the *Hauptwerk*, abbreviated H) was published in 1918 and covers completely the literature to 1909. Five supplementary series (*Ergänzungswerken*) have been published since that time. The first supplement (*Erstes Ergänzungswerk*, abbreviated E I) covers the literature from 1910 to 1919; the second supplement (*Zweites Ergänzungswerk*, E II) covers 1920–1929; the third supplement (*Drittes Ergänzungswerk,* E III) covers 1930–1949; the fourth supplement (*Viertes Ergänzungswerk,* E IV) covers 1950–1959; and the fifth supplement (in English) covers 1960–1979. Volumes 17–27 of supplementary series III and IV, covering heterocyclic compounds, are combined in a joint issue, E III/IV. Supplementary series III, IV, and V are not complete, so the coverage of *Handbuch der Organischen Chemie* can be considered complete to 1929, with partial coverage to 1979.

Beilsteins Handbuch der Organischen Chemie, usually referred to simply as *Beilstein,* also contains two types of cumulative indices. The first of these is a name index (*Sachregister*), and the second is a formula index (*Formelregister*). These indices are particularly useful for a person wishing to locate a compound in *Beilstein.*

The principal difficulty in using *Beilstein* is that it is written in German through the fourth supplement. The fifth supplement is in English. Although some reading knowledge of German is useful, you can obtain information from the work by learning a few key phrases. For example, *Bildung* is "formation" or "structure." *Darst* or *Darstellung* is "preparation," *Kp* or *Siedepunkt* is "boiling point," and *F* or *Schmelzpunkt* is "melting point." Furthermore, the names of some compounds in German are not cognates of the English names. Some examples are *Apfelsäure* for "malic acid" (*säure* means "acid"), *Harnstoff* for "urea," *Jod* for "iodine," and *Zimtsäure* for "cinnamic acid." If you have access to a German–English dictionary for chemists, many of these difficulties can be overcome. The best such dictionary is

Patterson, A. M. *German–English Dictionary for Chemists,* 4th ed. John Wiley & Sons: New York, **1991**.

Beilstein is organized according to a very sophisticated and complicated system. However, most students do not wish to become experts on *Beilstein* to this extent. A simpler, though slightly less reliable, method is to look for the compound in the formula index that accompanies the second supplement. By looking under the molecular formula, you will find the names of compounds that have that formula. After that name will be a series of numbers that indicate the pages and volume in which that compound is listed. Suppose, as an example, that you are searching for information on *p*-nitroaniline. This compound has the molecular formula $C_6H_6N_2O_2$. Searching for this formula in the formula index to the second supplement, you find

4-Nitro-anilin **12** 711, **I** 349, **II** 383

This information tells you that *p*-nitroaniline is listed in the main edition, *Hauptwerk,* in Volume 12, page 711. Locate this particular volume, which is devoted to isocyclic monoamines and turn to page 711 to find the beginning of the section on *p*-nitroaniline. At the left side of the top of this page is "Syst. No. 1671." This is the system number given to compounds in this part of Volume 12. The system number is useful, as it can help you find entries for this compound in subsequent supplements. The organization of *Beilstein* is such that all entries on *p*-nitroaniline in each of the supplements will be found in Volume 12. The entry in the formula index also indicates that material on this compound may be found in the first supplement on page 349 and in the second supplement on page 383. On page 349 of Volume 12 of the first supplement, there is a heading, "XII, 710–712," and on the left is "Syst. No. 1671." Material on *p*-nitroaniline is found in each supplement on a page that is headed with the volume and page of the *Hauptwerk* in which the same compound is found. On page 383 of Volume 12 of the second supplement, the heading in the center of the top of the page is "H12, 710–712." On the left, you find "Syst. No. 1671." Again, because *p*-nitroaniline appeared in Volume 12, page 711, of the main edition, you can locate it by searching through Volume 12 of any supplement until you find a page with the heading corresponding to Volume 12, page 711.

Because the third and fourth supplements are not complete, there is no comprehensive formula index for these supplements. However, you can still find material on *p*-nitroaniline by using the system number and the volume and page in the main work. In the third supplement, because the amount of information available has grown so much since the early days of Beilstein's work, Volume 12 has now expanded so that it is found in several bound parts. However, you select the part that includes system number 1671. In this part of Volume 12, you look through the pages until you find a page headed "Syst. No. 1671/H711." The information on *p*-nitroaniline is found on this page (page 1580). If Volume 12 of the fourth supplement were available, you would go on in the same way to locate more recent data on *p*-nitroaniline. This example is meant to illustrate how you can locate information on particular compounds without having to learn the *Beilstein* system of classification. You might do well to test your ability at finding compounds in *Beilstein* as we have described here.

Guidebooks to using *Beilstein*, which include a description of the *Beilstein* system, are recommended for anyone who wants to work extensively with *Beilstein*. Among such sources are:

Heller, S. R. *The Beilstein System: Strategies for Effective Searching.* Oxford University Press: New York, **1997**.

How to Use Beilstein. Beilstein Institute, Frankfurt am Main. Springer-Verlag: Berlin, **1977**.

Huntress, E. H. *A Brief Introduction to the Use of* Beilsteins Handbuch der Organischen Chemie, 2nd ed. John Wiley & Sons: New York, **1938**.

Weissbach, O. *The Beilstein Guide: A Manual for the Use of* Beilsteins Handbuch der Organischen Chemie. Springer-Verlag: New York, **1976**.

Beilstein reference numbers are listed in such handbooks as *CRC Handbook of Chemistry and Physics* and *Lange's Handbook of Chemistry.* Additionally, *Beilstein* numbers are included in the *Aldrich Handbook of Fine Chemicals*, issued by the Aldrich Chemical Company. If the compound you are seeking is listed in one of these handbooks, you will find that using *Beilstein* is simplified.

Another very useful publication for finding references for research on a particular topic is *Chemical Abstracts*, published by the Chemical Abstracts Service of the American Chemical Society. *Chemical Abstracts* contains abstracts of articles appearing in more than 10,000 journals from virtually every country conducting scientific research. These abstracts list the authors, the journal in which the article appeared, the title of the article, and a short summary of the contents of the article. Abstracts of articles that appeared originally in a foreign language are provided in English, with a notation indicating the original language.

To use *Chemical Abstracts*, you must know how to use the various indices that accompany it. At the end of each volume, there appears a set of indices, including a formula index, a general subject index, a chemical substances index, an author index, and a patent index. The listings in each index refer the reader to the appropriate abstract according to the number assigned to it. There are also collective indices that combine all the indexed material appearing in a 5-year period (10-year period before 1956). In the collective indices, the listings include the volume number as well as the abstract number.

For material after 1929, *Chemical Abstracts* provides the most complete coverage of the literature. For material before 1929, use *Beilstein* before consulting *Chemical Abstracts*. *Chemical Abstracts* has the advantage that it is written entirely in English. Nevertheless, most students perform a literature search to find a relatively simple compound. Finding the desired entry for a simple compound is much easier in *Beilstein* than in *Chemical Abstracts*. For simple compounds, the indices in *Chemical*

Abstracts are likely to contain very many entries. To locate the desired information, you must comb through this multitude of listings–potentially a very time-consuming task.

The opening pages of each index in *Chemical Abstracts* contain a brief set of instructions on using that index. If you want a more complete guide to *Chemical Abstracts*, consult a textbook designed to familiarize you with these abstracts and indices. Two such books are:

CAS Printed Access Tools: A Workbook. Chemical Abstracts Service, American Chemical Society: Washington, DC, **1977**.

How to Search Printed CA. Chemical Abstracts Service, American Chemical Society: Washington, DC, **1989**.

Chemical Abstracts Service maintains a computerized database that permits users to search through *Chemical Abstracts* rapidly and thoroughly. This service, which is called *CA Online*, is described in Section 29.11. *Beilstein* is also available for online searching by computer.

29.11 Computer Online Searching

You can search a number of chemistry databases online by using a computer and modem or a direct Internet connection. Many academic and industrial libraries can access these databases through their computers. One organization that maintains a large number of databases is the Scientific and Technical Information Network (STN International). The fee charged to the library for this service depends on the total time used in making the search, the type of information being asked for, the time of day when the search is being conducted, and the type of database being searched.

The Chemical Abstracts Service database (*CA Online*) is one of many databases available on STN. It is particularly useful to chemists. Unfortunately, this database extends back only to about 1967, although some earlier references are available. Searches for references earlier than 1967 must be made with printed abstracts (see Section 29.10). Searching online is much faster than searching in the printed abstracts. In addition, you can tailor the search in a number of ways by using keywords and the Chemical Abstracts Service Registry Number (CAS Number) as part of the search routine. The CAS Number is a specific number assigned to every compound listed in the *Chemical Abstracts* database. The CAS Number is used as a key in an online search to locate information about the compound. For the more common organic compounds, you can easily obtain CAS Numbers from the catalogs of most of the companies that supply chemicals. Another advantage of performing an online search is that the *Chemical Abstracts* files are updated much more quickly than the printed versions of abstracts. This means that your search is more likely to reveal the most current information available.

Other useful databases available from STN include *Beilstein* and *CASREACTS*. As described in Section 29.10, *Beilstein* is very useful to organic chemists. Currently, there are more than 3.5 million compounds listed in the database. You can use the CAS Numbers to help in a search that has the potential of going back to 1830. *CASREACTS* is a chemical reactions database derived from over 100 journals covered by *Chemical Abstracts*, starting in 1985. With this database, you can specify a starting material and a product using the CAS Numbers. Further information on *CA Online, Beilstein, CASREACTS*, and other databases can be obtained from the following references:

Heller, S. R., ed. *The Beilstein Online Database: Implementation, Content and Retrieval*. American Chemical Society: Washington, DC, **1990**.

Smith, M. B.; March, J. *Advanced Organic Chemistry*, 5th ed. John Wiley & Sons: New York, **2001**.

Somerville, A. N. Information Sources for Organic Chemistry, 2: Searching by Functional Group. *Journal of Chemical Education,* **1991,** 842.

Somerville, A. N. Subject Searching of Chemical Abstracts Online. *Journal of Chemical Education,* **1993,** 200.

Wiggins, G. *Chemical Information Sources.* McGraw-Hill: New York, **1990.** Integrates printed materials and computer sources of information.

SciFinder and SciFinder Scholar

The newest tools for online searching are SciFinder and SciFinder Scholar, the latter being the academic version of the software. This online service requires a yearly subscription and is available for use at many colleges and universities. SciFinder allows you to search several multidisciplinary CAS databases that contain information from as far back as 1907 to the present. The database may be searched in a variety of ways: by name, chemical substance, reaction, research topic, CAS number, or author. The program has drawing tools similar to ChemDraw, and what makes the program extremely useful is the ability to draw a structure on the screen and search for it. This avoids the need to name the structure first. In addition, substructure searching is allowed, which means that you may enter a partial structure and the program will find all references having compounds with the features you have indicated. Once you retrieve literature references, hyperlinks allow you view abstracts of the papers or retrieve physical property information. SciFinder is easy to use and requires minimal training. A recent book explains the program thoroughly:

Ridley, D. D. *Information Retrieval: SciFinder and SciFinder Scholar.* Wiley: New York, **2002.**

For these who are at a university that subscribes to the service, there is an online tutorial at www.cas.org/SCIFINDER/SCHOLAR.

29.12 Scientific Journals

Ultimately, someone wanting information about a particular area of research will be required to read articles from the scientific journals. These journals are of two basic types: review journals and primary scientific journals. Journals that specialize in review articles summarize all of the work that bears on the particular topic. These articles may focus on the contributions of one particular researcher, but often consider the contributions of many researchers to the subject. These articles also contain extensive bibliographies, which refer you to the original research articles. Among the important journals devoted, at least partly, to review articles are

> *Accounts of Chemical Research*
> *Angewandte Chemie* (International Edition, in English)
> *Chemical Reviews*
> *Chemical Society Reviews* (formerly known as *Quarterly Reviews*)
> *Nature*
> *Science*

The details of the research of interest appear in the primary scientific journals. Although there are thousands of journals published in the world, a few important journals specializing in articles dealing with organic chemistry include

> *Canadian Journal of Chemistry*
> *European Journal of Organic Chemistry* (formerly known as *Chemische Berichte*)
> *Journal of Organic Chemistry*
> *Journal of the American Chemical Society*
> *Journal of the Chemical Society, Chemical Communications*
> *Journal of the Chemical Society, Perkin Transactions* (Parts I and II)

Journal of Organometallic Chemistry
Organic Letters
Organometallics
Synlett
Synthesis
Tetrahedron
Tetrahedron Letters

29.13 Topics of Current Interest

The following journals and magazines are good sources for topics of educational and current interest. They specialize in news articles and focus on current events in chemistry or in science in general. Articles in these journals (magazines) can be useful in keeping you abreast of developments in science that are not part of your normal specialized scientific reading.

American Scientist
Chemical and Engineering News
Chemistry and Industry
Chemistry in Britain
Chemtech
Discover
Journal of Chemical Education
Nature
Omni
Science
Scientific American

Other sources for topics of current interest include the following:

Encyclopedia of Chemical Technology, 4th ed., 25 vols. plus index and supplements, **1992**.
 Also called *Kirk-Othmer Encyclopedia of Chemical Technology*.

McGraw-Hill Encyclopedia of Science and Technology, 20 volumes and supplements, **1997**.

29.14 How to Conduct a Literature Search

The easiest method to follow in searching the literature is to begin with secondary sources and then go to the primary sources. In other words, you would try to locate material in a textbook, *Beilstein*, or *Chemical Abstracts*. From the results of that search, you would then consult one of the primary scientific journals.

A literature search that ultimately requires you to read one or more papers in the scientific journals is best conducted if you can identify a particular paper central to the study. Often, you can obtain this reference from a textbook or a review article on the subject. If this is not available, a search through *Beilstein* is required. A search through one of the handbooks that provides *Beilstein* reference numbers (see Section 29.10) may be helpful. Searching through *Chemical Abstracts* would be considered the next logical step. From these sources, you should be able to identify citations from the original literature on the subject.

Additional citations may be found in the references cited in the journal article. In this way, the background leading to the research can be examined. It is also possible to conduct a search forward in time from the date of the journal article through the *Science Citation Index*. This publication provides the service of listing articles and the papers in which these articles were cited. Although the *Science Citation Index* consists of several types of indices, the *Citation Index* is most useful for the purposes described here. A person who knows of a particular key reference on a subject can examine the *Science Citation Index* to obtain a list of papers that have used that seminal reference in support of the work described. The *Citation Index* lists papers by their senior author, journal, volume, page, and date, followed by citations of papers that have referred to that article, author, journal, volume, page, and date of each. The *Citation Index* is published in annual volumes, with quarterly supplements issued during the current year. Each volume contains a complete list of the citations of the key articles made during that year. A disadvantage is that *Science Citation Index* has been available only since 1961. An additional disadvantage is that you may miss journal articles on the subject of interest if *Citation Index* failed to cite that particular key reference in its bibliographies—a reasonably likely possibility.

You can, of course, conduct a literature search by a "brute force" method, by beginning the search with *Beilstein* or even with the indices in *Chemical Abstracts*. However, the task can be made much easier by performing a computer search (see Section 29.11) or by starting with a book or an article of general and broad coverage, which can provide a few citations for starting points in the search.

The following guides to using the chemical literature are provided for the reader who is interested in going farther into this subject.

Bottle, R. T.; and Rowland, J. F. B., eds. *Information Sources in Chemistry*, 4th ed. Bowker-Saur: New York, **1992**.

Maizell, R. E. *How to Find Chemical Information: A Guide for Practicing Chemists, Educators, and Students*, 3rd ed. John Wiley & Sons: New York, **1998**.

Mellon, M. G. *Chemical Publications*, 5th ed. McGraw-Hill: New York, **1982**.

Wiggins, G. *Chemical Information Sources*. McGraw-Hill: New York, **1991**. Integrates printed materials and computer sources of information.

PROBLEMS

1. Find the following compounds in the formula index for the *Second Supplement of Beilstein* (see Section 29.10). (1) List the page numbers from the main work and the supplements (first and second). (2) Using these page numbers, look up the system number (Syst. No.) and the main work number (*Hauptwerk* number, H) for each compound in the main work and the first and second supplements. In some cases, a compound may not be found in all three places. (3) Now use the system number and main work number to find each of these compounds in the third and fourth supplements. List the page numbers where these compounds are found.

   a. 2,5-hexanedione (acetonylacetone)

   b. 3-nitroacetophenone

   c. 4-*tert*-butylcyclohexanone

   d. 4-phenylbutanoic acid (4-phenylbutyric acid, γ-phenylbuttersäure)

2. Using the *Science Citation Index* (see Section 29.14), list five research papers by complete title and journal citation for each of the following chemists who have been awarded the Nobel Prize. Use the *Five-Year Cumulative Source Index* for the years 1980–1984 as your source.

   a. H. C. Brown

   b. R. B. Woodward

   c. D. J. Cram

   d. G. Olah

3. The reference book by Smith and March is listed in Section 29.2. Using Appendix 2 in this book, give two methods for preparing the following functional groups. You will need to provide equations.

   a. carboxylic acids

   b. aldehydes

   c. esters (carboxylic esters)

4. *Organic Syntheses* is described in Section 29.6. There are currently nine collective volumes in the series, each with its own index. Find the compounds listed below and provide the equations for preparing each compound.

   a. 2-methylcyclopentane-1,3-dione

   b. *cis*-Δ^4-tetrahydrophthalic anhydride (listed as tetrahydrophthalic anhydride)

5. Provide four methods that may be used to oxidize an alcohol to an aldehyde. Give complete literature references for each method, as well as equations. Use the *Compendium of Organic Synthetic Methods* or *Survey of Organic Syntheses* by Buehler and Pearson (see Section 29.6).

Appendices

Tables of Unknowns and Derivatives

More extensive tables of unknowns may be found in Z. Rappoport, ed. *Handbook of Tables for Organic Compound Identification*, 3rd ed. CRC Press: Boca Raton FL, 1967.

ALDEHYDES

Compound	BP	MP	Semi-carbazone*	2,4-Dinitro-phenyl-hydrazone*
Ethanal (acetaldehyde)	21	—	162	168
Propanal (propionaldehyde)	48	—	89	148
Propenal (acrolein)	52	—	171	165
2-Methylpropanal (isobutyraldehyde)	64	—	125	187
Butanal (butyraldehyde)	75	—	95	123
3-Methylbutanal (isovaleraldehyde)	92	—	107	123
Pentanal (valeraldehyde)	102	—	—	106
2-Butenal (crotonaldehyde)	104	—	199	190
2-Ethylbutanal (diethylacetaldehyde)	117	—	99	95
Hexanal (caproaldehyde)	130	—	106	104
Heptanal (heptaldehyde)	153	—	109	108
2-Furaldehyde (furfural)	162	—	202	212
2-Ethylhexanal	163	—	254	114
Octanal (caprylaldehyde)	171	—	101	106
Benzaldehyde	179	—	222	237
Nonanal (nonyl aldehyde)	185	—	100	100
Phenylethanal (phenylacetaldehyde)	195	33	153	121
2-Hydroxybenzaldehyde (salicylaldehyde)	197	—	231	248
4-Methylbenzaldehyde (*p*-tolualdehyde)	204	—	234	234
3,7-Dimethyl-6-octenal (citronellal)	207	—	82	77
Decanal (decyl aldehyde)	207	—	102	104
2-Chlorobenzaldehyde	213	11	229	213
3-Chlorobenzaldehyde	214	18	228	248
3-Methoxybenzaldehyde (*m*-anisaldehyde)	230	—	233 d.	—
3-Bromobenzaldehyde	235	—	205	—
4-Methoxybenzaldehyde (*p*-anisaldehyde)	248	2.5	210	253
trans-Cinnamaldehyde	250 d.	—	215	255

ALDEHYDES *(Cont.)*

Compound	BP	MP	Semi-carbazone*	2,4-Dinitro-phenyl-hydrazone*
3,4-Methylenedioxybenzaldehyde (piperonal)	263	37	230	266 d.
2-Methoxybenzaldehyde (*o*-anisaldehyde)	245	38	215 d.	254
3,4-Dimethoxybenzaldehyde	—	44	177	261
2-Nitrobenzaldehyde	—	44	256	265
4-Chlorobenzaldehyde	—	48	230	254
4-Bromobenzaldehyde	—	57	228	257
3-Nitrobenzaldehyde	—	58	246	293
2,4-Dimethoxybenzaldehyde	—	71	—	—
2,4-Dichlorobenzaldehyde	—	72	—	—
4-Dimethylaminobenzaldehyde	—	74	222	325
4-Hydroxy-3-methoxybenzaldehyde (vanillin)	—	82	230	271
3-Hydroxybenzaldehyde	—	104	198	259
5-Bromo-2-hydroxybenzaldehyde (5-bromosalicylaldehyde)	—	106	297 d.	—
4-Nitrobenzaldehyde	—	106	221	320 d.
4-Hydroxybenzaldehyde	—	116	224	280 d.
(±)-Glyceraldehyde	—	142	160 d.	167

Note: "d" indicates "decomposition."
*See Appendix 2, "Procedures for Preparing Derivatives."

KETONES

Compound	BP	MP	Semi-carbazone*	2,4-Dinitro-phenyl-hydrazone*
2-Propanone (acetone)	56	—	187	126
2-Butanone (methyl ethyl ketone)	80	—	146	117
3-Buten-2-one (methyl vinyl ketone)	81	—	140	—
3-Methyl-2-butanone (isopropyl methyl ketone)	94	—	112	120
2-Pentanone (methyl propyl ketone)	102	—	112	143
3-Pentanone (diethyl ketone)	102	—	138	156
3,3-Dimethyl-2-butanone (pinacolone)	106	—	157	125
4-Methyl-2-pentanone (isobutyl methyl ketone)	117	—	132	95
2,4-Dimethyl-3-pentanone (diisopropyl ketone)	124	—	160	86
3-Hexanone	125	—	113	130
2-Hexanone (methyl butyl ketone)	128	—	121	106
4-Methyl-3-penten-2-one (mesityl oxide)	130	—	164	200
Cyclopentanone	131	—	210	146

KETONES *(Cont.)*

Compound	BP	MP	Semi-carbazone*	2,4-Dinitro-phenyl-hydrazone*
5-Hexen-2-one	131	—	102	108
2,3-Pentanedione	134	—	122 (mono) 209 (di)	209
5-Methyl-3-hexanone	136	—	—	—
2,4-Pentanedione (acetylacetone)	139	—	122 (mono) 209 (di)	209
4-Heptanone (dipropyl ketone)	144	—	132	75
5-Methyl-2-hexanone	145	—	—	—
1-Hydroxy-2-propanone (hydroxyacetone, acetol)	146	—	196	129
3-Heptanone	148	—	101	—
2-Heptanone (methyl amyl ketone)	151	—	123	89
Cyclohexanone	156	—	166	162
2-Methylcyclohexanone	165	—	191	136
3-Octanone	167	—	—	—
2,6-Dimethyl-4-heptanone (diisobutyl ketone)	168	—	122	66
2-Octanone	173	—	122	92
Cycloheptanone	181	—	163	148
Ethyl acetoacetate	181	—	129 d.	93
5-Nonanone	186	—	90	—
3-Nonanone	187	—	112	—
2,5-Hexanedione (acetonylacetone)	191	−9	185 (mono) 244 (di)	257 (di)
2-Nonanone	195	−8	118	—
Acetophenone (methyl phenyl ketone)	202	20	198	238
2-Hydroxyacetophenone	215	28	210	212
l-Phenyl-2-propanone (phenylacetone)	216	27	198	156
Propiophenone (1-phenyl-1-propanone)	218	21	173	191
Isobutyrophenone (2-methyl-1-phenyl-1-propanone)	222	—	181	163
1-Phenyl-2-butanone	226	—	135	—
4-Methylacetophenone	226	28	205	258
3-Chloroacetophenone	228	—	232	—
2-Chloroacetophenone	229	—	160	—
Butyrophenone (1-phenyl-1-butanone)	230	12	187	190
2-Undecanone	231	12	122	63
4-Chloroacetophenone	232	12	204	231
4-Phenyl-2-butanone (benzylacetone)	235	—	142	127
2-Methoxyacetophenone	239	—	183	—
3-Methoxyacetophenone	240	—	196	—
Valerophenone (1-phenyl-1-pentanone)	248	—	160	166

KETONES *(Cont.)*

Compound	BP	MP	Semi-carbazone*	2,4-Dinitro-phenyl-hydrazone*
4-Chloropropiophenone	—	36	176	—
4-Phenyl-3-buten-2-one (benzalacetone)	—	37	187	227
4-Methoxyacetophenone	—	38	198	220
3-Bromopropiophenone	—	40	183	—
1-Indanone	—	41	233	258
Benzophenone	—	48	164	238
4-Bromoacetophenone	—	51	208	230
3,4-Dimethoxyacetophenone	—	51	218	207
2-Acetonaphthone (methyl 2-naphthyl ketone)	—	53	234	262 d.
Desoxybenzoin (benzyl phenyl ketone)	—	60	148	204
1,1-Diphenylacetone	—	61	170	—
4-Chlorobenzophenone	—	76	—	185
3-Nitroacetophenone	—	80	257	228
4-Nitroacetophenone	—	80	—	—
4-Bromobenzophenone	—	82	350	230
Fluorenone	—	83	—	283
4-Hydroxyacetophenone	—	109	199	210
Benzoin	—	136	206	245
4-Hydroxypropiophenone	—	148	—	229
(±)-Camphor	—	179	237	164

Note: "d" indicates "decomposition."

*See Appendix 2, "Procedures for Preparing Derivatives."

CARBOXYLIC ACIDS

Compound	BP	MP	*p*-Toluidide*	Anilide*	Amide*
Methanoic acid (formic acid)	101	8	53	47	43
Ethanoic acid (acetic acid)	118	17	148	114	82
Propenoic acid (acrylic acid)	139	13	141	104	85
Propanoic acid (propionic acid)	141	—	124	103	81
2-Methylpropanoic acid (isobutyric acid)	154	—	104	105	128
Butanoic acid (butyric acid)	162	—	72	95	115
3-Butenoic acid (vinylacetic acid)	163	—	—	58	73
2-Methylpropenoic acid (methacrylic acid)	163	16	—	87	102
Pyruvic acid	165 d.	14	109	104	124

CARBOXYLIC ACIDS *(Cont.)*

Compound	BP	MP	*p*-Toluidide*	Anilide*	Amide*
3-Methylbutanoic acid (isovaleric acid)	176	—	106	109	135
3,3-Dimethylbutanoic acid	185	—	134	132	132
Pentanoic acid (valeric acid)	186	—	74	63	106
2-Chloropropanoic acid	186	—	124	92	80
Dichloroacetic acid	194	6	153	118	98
2-Methylpentanoic acid	195	—	80	95	79
Hexanoic acid (caproic acid)	205	—	75	95	101
2-Bromopropanoic acid	205 d.	24	125	99	123
Heptanoic acid	223	—	81	70	96
2-Ethylhexanoic acid	228	—	—	—	102
Cyclohexanecarboxylic acid	233	31	—	146	186
Octanoic acid (caprylic acid)	237	16	70	57	107
Nonanoic acid	254	12	84	57	99
Decanoic acid (capric acid)	—	32	78	70	108
4-Oxopentanoic acid (levulinic acid)	—	33	108	102	108 d.
Trimethylacetic acid (pivalic acid)	—	35	120	130	155
3-Chloropropanoic acid	—	40	—	—	101
Dodecanoic acid (lauric acid)	—	43	87	78	100
3-Phenylpropanoic acid (hydrocinnamic acid)	—	48	135	98	105
Bromoacetic acid	—	50	—	131	91
4-Phenylbutanoic acid	—	52	—	—	84
Tetradecanoic acid (myristic acid)	—	54	93	84	103
Trichloroacetic acid	—	57	113	97	141
3-Bromopropanoic acid	—	61	—	—	111
Hexadecanoic acid (palmitic acid)	—	62	98	90	106
Chloroacetic acid	—	63	162	137	121
Cyanoacetic acid	—	66	—	198	120
Octadecanoic acid (stearic acid)	—	69	102	95	109
trans-2-Butenoic acid (crotonic acid)	—	72	132	118	158
Phenylacetic acid	—	77	136	118	156
α-Methyl-*trans*-cinnamic acid	—	81	—	—	128
4-Methoxyphenylacetic acid	—	87	—	—	189
3,4-Dimethoxyphenyl acetic acid	—	97	—	—	147
Pentanedioic acid (glutaric acid)	—	98	218 (di)	224 (di)	176 (di)
Phenoxyacetic acid	—	99	—	99	102
2-Methoxybenzoic acid (*o*-anisic acid)	—	100	—	131	129
2-Methylbenzoic acid (*o*-toluic acid)	—	104	144	125	142
Nonanedioic acid (azelaic acid)	—	106	201 (di)	107 (mono) 186 (di)	93 (mono) 175 (di)

CARBOXYLIC ACIDS *(Cont.)*

Compound	BP	MP	*p*-Toluidide*	Anilide*	Amide*
3-Methoxybenzoic acid (*m*-anisic acid)	—	107	—	—	136
3-Methylbenzoic acid (*m*-toluic acid)	—	111	118	126	94
4-Bromophenylacetic acid	—	117	—	—	194
(±)-Phenylhydroxyacetic acid (mandelic acid)	—	118	172	151	133
Benzoic acid	—	122	158	163	130
2,4-Dimethylbenzoic acid	—	126	—	141	180
2-Benzoylbenzoic acid	—	127	—	195	165
Maleic acid	—	130	142 (di)	198 (mono) 187 (di)	172 (mono) 260 (di)
Decanedioic acid (sebacic acid)	—	133	201 (di)	122 (mono) 200 (di)	170 (mono) 210 (di)
3-Chlorocinnamic acid	—	133	142	135	76
2-Furoic acid	—	133	170	124	143
trans-Cinnamic acid	—	133	168	153	147
2-Acetylsalicylic acid (aspirin)	—	138	—	136	138
5-Chloro-2-nitrobenzoic acid	—	139	—	164	154
2-Chlorobenzoic acid	—	140	131	118	139
3-Nitrobenzoic acid	—	140	162	155	143
4-Chloro-2-nitrobenzoic acid	—	142	—	—	172
2-Nitrobenzoic acid	—	146	—	155	176
2-Aminobenzoic acid (anthranilic acid)	—	146	151	131	109
Diphenylacetic acid	—	148	172	180	167
2-Bromobenzoic acid	—	150	—	141	155
Benzilic acid	—	150	190	175	154
Hexanedioic acid (adipic acid)	—	152	239	151 (mono) 241 (di)	125 (mono) 220 (di)
Citric acid	—	153	189 (tri)	198 (tri)	210 (tri)
4-Nitrophenylacetic acid	—	153	—	198	198
2,5-Dichlorobenzoic acid	—	153	—	—	155
3-Chlorobenzoic acid	—	156	—	123	134
2,4-Dichlorobenzoic acid	—	158	—	—	194
4-Chlorophenoxyacetic acid	—	158	—	125	133
2-Hydroxybenzoic acid (salicylic acid)	—	158	156	136	142
5-Bromo-2-hydroxybenzoic acid (5-bromosalicylic acid)	—	165	—	222	232
3,4-Dimethylbenzoic acid	—	165	—	104	130
2-Chloro-5-nitrobenzoic acid	—	166	—	—	178
Methylenesuccinic acid (itaconic acid)	—	166 d.	—	152 (mono)	191 (di)
(+)-Tartaric acid	—	169	—	180 (mono) 264 (di)	171 (mono) 196 (di)

CARBOXYLIC ACIDS *(Cont.)*

Compound	BP	MP	*p*-Toluidide*	Anilide*	Amide*
5-Chlorosalicylic acid	—	172	—	—	227
4-Methylbenzoic acid (*p*-toluic acid)	—	180	160	145	160
4-Chloro-3-nitrobenzoic acid	—	182	—	131	156
4-Methoxybenzoic acid (*p*-anisic acid)	—	184	186	169	167
Butanedioic acid (succinic acid)	—	188	180 (mono) 255 (di)	143 (mono) 230 (di)	157 (mono) 260 (di)
4-Ethoxybenzoic acid	—	198	—	170	202
Fumaric acid	—	200 s.	—	233 (mono) 314 (di)	270 (mono) 266 (di)
3-Hydroxybenzoic acid	—	201 s.	163	157	170
3,5-Dinitrobenzoic acid	—	202	—	234	183
3,4-Dichlorobenzoic acid	—	209	—	—	133
Phthalic acid	—	210 d.	150 (mono) 201 (di)	169 (mono) 253 (di)	144 (mono) 220 (di)
4-Hydroxybenzoic acid	—	214	204	197	162
3-Nitrophthalic acid	—	215	226 (di)	234 (di)	201 (di)
Pyridine-3-carboxylic acid (nicotinic acid)	—	236	150	132	128
4-Nitrobenzoic acid	—	240	204	211	201
4-Chlorobenzoic acid	—	242	—	194	179
4-Bromobenzoic acid	—	251	—	197	190

Note: "d" indicates "decomposition"; "s" indicates "sublimation."
*See Appendix 2, "Procedures for Preparing Derivatives."

PHENOLS†

Compound	BP	MP	α-Naphthyl-urethane*	Bromo Derivative*			
				Mono	Di	Tri	Tetra
2-Chlorophenol	176	7	120	48	76	—	—
3-Methylphenol (*m*-cresol)	203	12	128	—	—	84	—
2-Ethylphenol	207	—	—	—	—	—	—
2,4-Dimethylphenol	212	23	135	—	—	—	—
2-Methylphenol (*o*-cresol)	191	32	142	—	56	—	—
2-Methoxyphenol (guaiacol)	204	32	118	—	—	116	—
4-Methylphenol (*p*-cresol)	202	35	146	—	49	—	198
3-Chlorophenol	214	35	158	—	—	—	—
4-Methyl-2-nitrophenol	—	35	—	—	—	—	—
2,4-Dibromophenol	238	40	—	95	—	—	—
Phenol	181	42	133	—	—	95	—
4-Chlorophenol	217	43	166	33	90	—	—

PHENOLS† *(Cont.)*

Compound	BP	MP	α-Naphthyl-urethane*	Bromo Derivative*			
				Mono	Di	Tri	Tetra
4-Ethylphenol	219	45	128	—	—	—	—
2-Nitrophenol	216	45	113	—	117	—	—
2-Isopropyl-5-methylphenol (thymol)	234	51	160	55	—	—	—
4-Methoxyphenol	243	56	—	—	—	—	—
3,4-Dimethylphenol	225	64	141	—	—	171	—
4-Bromophenol	238	64	169	—	—	—	—
4-Chloro-3-methylphenol	235	66	153	—	—	—	—
3,5-Dimethylphenol	220	68	—	—	—	166	—
2,6-Di-*tert*-butyl-4-methylphenol	—	70	—	—	—	—	—
2,4,6-Trimethylphenol	232	72	—	—	—	—	—
2,5-Dimethylphenol	212	75	173	—	—	178	—
1-Naphthol (α-naphthol)	278	94	152	—	105	—	—
2-Methyl-4-nitrophenol	186	96	—	—	—	—	—
2-Hydroxyphenol (catechol)	245	104	175	—	—	—	192
2-Chloro-4-nitrophenol	—	106	—	—	—	—	—
3-Hydroxyphenol (resorcinol)	—	109	—	—	—	112	—
4-Nitrophenol	—	112	150	—	142	—	—
2-Naphthol (β-naphthol)	—	123	157	84	—	—	—
3-Methyl-4-nitrophenol	—	129	—	—	—	—	—
1,2,3-Trihydroxybenzene (pyrogallol)	—	133	—	—	158	—	—
4-Phenylphenol	—	164	—	—	—	—	—

*See Appendix 2, "Procedures for Preparing Derivatives."

†Also check:

Salicylic acid (2-hydroxybenzoic acid)

Esters of salicylic acid (salicylates)

Salicylaldehyde (2-hydroxybenzaldehyde)

4-Hydroxybenzaldehyde

4-Hydroxypropiophenone

3-Hydroxybenzoic acid

4-Hydroxybenzoic acid

4-Hydroxybenzophenone

PRIMARY AMINES†

Compound	BP	MP	Benzamide*	Acetamide*
t-Butylamine	46	—	134	101
Propylamine	48	—	84	—
Allylamine	56	—	—	—
sec-Butylamine	63	—	76	—

PRIMARY AMINES† *(Cont.)*

Compound	BP	MP	Benzamide*	Acetamide*
Isobutylamine	69	—	57	—
Butylamine	78	—	42	—
Isopentylamine (ioamylamine)	96	—	—	—
Pentylamine (amylamine)	104	—	—	—
Enthylenediamine	118	—	244 (di)	172 (di)
Hexylamine	132	—	40	—
Cyclohexylamine	135	—	149	101
1,3-Diaminopropane	140	—	148 (di)	126 (di)
Furfurylamine	145	—	—	—
Heptylamine	156	—	—	—
Octylamine	180	—	—	—
Benzylamine	184	—	105	65
Aniline	184	—	163	114
2-Methylaniline (*o*-toluidine)	200	—	144	110
3-Methylaniline (*m*-toluidine)	203	—	125	65
2-Chloroaniline	208	—	99	87
2,6-Dimethylaniline	216	11	168	177
2,5-Dimethylaniline	216	14	140	139
3,5-Dimethylaniline	220	—	144	—
4-Isopropylaniline	225	—	162	102
2-Methoxyaniline (*o*-anisidine)	225	6	60	85
3-Chloroaniline	230	—	120	74
2-Ethoxyaniline (*o*-phenetidine)	231	—	104	79
4-Chloro-2-methylaniline	241	29	142	140
4-Ethoxyaniline (*p*-phenetidine)	250	2	173	137
3-Bromoaniline	251	18	120	87
2-Bromoaniline	250	31	116	99
2,6-Dichloroaniline	—	39	—	—
4-Methylaniline (*p*-toluidine)	200	43	158	147
2-Ethylaniline	210	47	147	111
2,5-Dichloroaniline	251	50	120	132
4-Methoxyaniline (*p*-anisidine)	—	58	154	130
2,4-Dichloroaniline	245	62	117	145
4-Bromoaniline	245	64	204	168
4-Chloroaniline	—	72	192	179
2-Nitroaniline	—	72	110	92
2,4,6-Trichloroaniline	262	75	174	204
Ethyl *p*-aminobenzoate	—	89	148	110
o-Phenylenediamine	258	102	301 (di)	185 (di)
2-Methyl-5-nitroaniline	—	106	186	151
4-Aminoacetophenone	—	106	205	167

PRIMARY AMINES† *(Cont.)*

Compound	BP	MP	Benzamide*	Acetamide*
2-Chloro-4-nitroaniline	—	108	161	139
3-Nitroaniline	—	114	157	155
4-Methyl-2-nitroaniline	—	116	148	99
4-Chloro-2-nitroaniline	—	118	133	104
2,4,6-Tribromoaniline	—	120	200	232
2-Methyl-4-nitroaniline	—	130	—	202
2-Methoxy-4-nitroaniline	—	138	149	153
p-Phenylenediamine	—	140	128 (mono) 300 (di)	162 (mono) 304 (di)
4-Nitroaniline	—	148	199	215
4-Aminoacetanilide	—	162	—	304
2,4-Dinitroaniline	—	180	202	120

*See Appendix 2, "Procedures for Preparing Derivatives."
†Also check 4-aminobenzoic acid and its esters.

SECONDARY AMINES

Compound	BP	MP	Benzamide*	Acetamide*
Diethylamine	56	—	42	—
Diisopropylamine	84	—	—	—
Pyrrolidine	88	—	Oil	—
Piperidine	106	—	48	—
Dipropylamine	110	—	—	—
Morpholine	129	—	75	—
Diisobutylamine	139	—	—	86
N-Methylcyclohexylamine	148	—	85	—
Dibutylamine	159	—	—	—
Benzylmethylamine	184	—	—	—
N-Methylaniline	196	—	63	102
N-Ethylaniline	205	—	60	54
N-Ethyl-*m*-toluidine	221	—	72	—
Dicyclohexylamine	256	—	153	103
N-Benzylaniline	298	37	107	58
Indole	254	52	68	157
Diphenylamine	302	52	180	101
N-phenyl-1-naphthylamine	335	62	152	115

*See Appendix 2, "Procedures for Preparing Derivatives."

TERTIARY AMINES†

Compound	BP	MP	Methiodide*
Triethylamine	89	—	280
Pyridine	115	—	117
2-Methylpyridine (α-picoline)	129	—	230
2,6-Dimethylpyridine (2,6-lutidine)	143	—	233
4-Methylpyridine (4-picoline)	143	—	—
3-Methylpyridine (β-picoline)	144	—	92
Tripropylamine	157	—	207
N,N-Dimethylbenzylamine	183	—	179
N,N-Dimethylaniline	193	—	228 d.
Tributylamine	216	—	186
N,N-Diethylaniline	217	—	102
Quinoline	237	—	72/133

Note: "d" indicates "decomposition."

*See Appendix 2, "Procedures for Preparing Derivatives."

† Also check nicotinic acid and its esters.

ALCOHOLS

Compound	BP	MP	3,5-Di-nitrobenzoate*	Phenyl-urethane*
Methanol	65	—	108	47
Ethanol	78	—	93	52
2-Propanol (isopropyl alcohol)	82	—	123	88
2-Methyl-2-propanol (t-butyl alcohol)	83	26	142	136
3-Buten-2-ol	96	—	54	—
2-Propen-1-ol (allyl alcohol)	97	—	49	70
1-Propanol	97	—	74	57
2-Butanol (sec-butyl alcohol)	99	—	76	65
2-Methyl-2-butanol (t-pentyl alcohol)	102	−8.5	116	42
2-Methyl-3-butyn-2-ol	104	—	112	—
2-Methyl-1-propanol (isobutyl alcohol)	108	—	87	86
3-Buten-1-ol	113	—	59	25
3-Methyl-2-butanol	114	—	76	68
2-Propyn-1-ol (propargyl alcohol)	114	—	—	—
3-Pentanol	115	—	101	48
1-Butanol	118	—	64	61
2-Pentanol	119	—	62	—
3,3-Dimethyl-2-butanol	120	—	107	77
2,3-Dimethyl-2-butanol	121	—	111	65
2-Methyl-2-pentanol	123	—	72	—

ALCOHOLS *(Cont.)*

Compound	BP	MP	3,5-Di-nitrobenzoate*	Phenyl-urethane*
3-Methyl-3-pentanol	123	—	96	43
2-Methoxyethanol	124	—	—	(113)†
2-Methyl-3-pentanol	128	—	85	50
2-Chloroethanol	129	—	95	51
3-Methyl-1-butanol (isoamyl alcohol)	132	—	61	56
4-Methyl-2-pentanol	132	—	65	143
2-Ethoxyethanol	135	—	75	(67)†
3-Hexanol	136	—	97	—
1-Pentanol	138	—	46	46
2-Hexanol	139	—	39	(61)†
2,4-Dimethyl-3-pentanol	140	—	—	95
Cyclopentanol	140	—	115	132
2-Ethyl-1-butanol	146	—	51	—
2,2,2-Trichloroethanol	151	—	142	87
1-Hexanol	157	—	58	42
2-Heptanol	159	—	49	(54)†
Cyclohexanol	160	—	113	82
3-Chloro-1-propanol	161	—	77	38
(2-Furyl)-methanol (furfuryl alcohol)	170	—	80	45
1-Heptanol	176	—	47	60
2-Octanol	179	—	32	114
2-Ethyl-1-hexanol	185	—	—	(61)†
1-Octanol	195	—	61	74
3,7-Dimethyl-1,6-octadien-3-ol (linalool)	196	—	—	66
2-Nonanol	198	—	43	(56)†
Benzyl alcohol	204	—	113	77
1-Phenylethanol	204	20	92	95
1-Nonanol	214	—	52	62
1,3-Propanediol	215	—	178 (di)	137 (di)
2-Phenylethanol	219	—	108	78
1-Decanol	231	7	57	59
3-Phenylpropanol	236	—	45	92
1-Dodecanol (lauryl alcohol)	—	24	60	74
3-Phenyl-2-propen-1-ol (cinnamyl alcohol)	250	34	121	90
α-Terpineol	221	36	78	112
1-Tetradecanol (myristyl alcohol)	—	39	67	74
(–)-Menthol	212	41	158	111
1-Hexadecanol (cetyl alcohol)	—	49	66	73
2,2-Dimethyl-1-propanol (neopentyl alcohol)	113	56	—	144
4-Methylbenzyl alcohol	217	59	117	79

ALCOHOLS *(Cont.)*

Compound	BP	MP	3,5-Di-nitrobenzoate*	Phenyl-urethane*
1-Octadecanol (stearyl alcohol)	—	59	77	79
Diphenylmethanol (benzhydrol)	—	68	141	139
4-Nitrobenzyl alcohol	—	93	157	—
Benzoin	—	136	—	165
Cholesterol	—	147	—	168
Triphenylmethanol	—	161	—	—
(+)-Bomeol	—	208	154	138

*See Appendix 2, "Procedures for Preparing Derivatives."

† α-Naphthylurethane.

ESTERS

Compound	BP	MP	Compound	BP	MP
Methyl formate	32	—	(ethyl 2-methylpropanoate)	110	—
Ethyl formate	54	—	Isopropyl propionate		
Methyl acetate	57	—	(isopropyl propanoate)	110	—
Isopropyl formate	71	—	2-Butyl acetate (*sec*-butyl acetate)	111	—
Vinyl acetate	72	—	Methyl isovalerate	117	—
Ethyl acetate	77	—	(methyl 3-methylbutanoate)		
Methyl propionate			Isobutyl acetate		
(methyl propanoate)	80	—	(2-methylpropyl acetate)	117	—
Methyl acrylate	80	—	Ethyl pivalate		
Propyl formate	81	—	(ethyl 2,2-dimethylpropanoate)	118	—
Isopropyl acetate	89	—	Methyl crotonate (methyl 2-butenoate)	119	—
Ethyl chloroformate	93	—	Ethyl butyrate (ethyl butanoate)	121	—
Methyl isobutyrate	93	—	Propyl propionate (propyl propanoate)	123	—
(methyl 2-methylpropanoate)			Butyl acetate	126	—
2-Propenyl acetate (isopropenyl acetate)	94	—	Methyl valerate (methyl pentanoate)	128	—
tert-Butyl acetate			Methyl methoxyacetate	130	—
(1,1-dimethylethyl acetate)	98	—	Methyl chloroacetate	130	—
Ethyl propionate (ethyl propanoate)	99	—	Ethyl isovalerate		
Methyl methacrylate			(ethyl 3-methylbutanoate)	134	—
(methyl 2-methylpropenoate)	100	—	Ethyl crotonate (ethyl 2-butenoate)	138	—
Methyl pivalate			Isopentyl acetate		
(methyl trimethyl acetate)	101	—	(3-methylbutyl acetate)	142	—
Ethyl acrylate (ethyl propenoate)	101	—	2-Methoxyethyl acetate	145	—
Propyl acetate	102	—	Ethyl chloroacetate	145	—
Methyl butyrate (methyl butanoate)	102	—	Ethyl valerate (ethyl pentanoate)	146	—
Ethyl isobutyrate			Ethyl α-chloropropanoate	146	—

ESTERS *(Cont.)*

Compound	BP	MP	Compound	BP	MP
Pentyl acetate	147	—	Methyl salicylate	224	—
Methyl hexanoate	151	—	Diethyl maleate	224	—
Ethyl lactate	154	—	Ethyl phenylacetate	228	—
Butyl butyrate	167	—	Propyl benzoate	231	—
Ethyl hexanoate	168	—	Ethyl salicylate	234	—
Hexyl acetate	169	—	Dimethyl suberate	268	—
Methyl acetoacetate	170	—	Ethyl cinnamate	271	—
Methyl heptanoate (methyl enanthlate)	172	—	Dimethyl phthalate	284	—
Furfuryl acetate	176	—	Diethyl phthalate	298	—
Methyl 2-furoate	181	—	Methyl cinnamate	—	36
Dimethyl malonate	181	—	Ethyl 2-furoate	—	36
Ethyl acetoacetate	181	—	Methyl stearate	—	39
Diethyl oxalate	185	—	Dimethyl itaconate	—	39
Ethyl heptanoate	187	—	Phenyl salicylate	—	42
Heptyl acetate	192	—	Diethyl terephthalate	—	44
Dimethyl succinate	196	—	Methyl 4-chlorobenzoate	—	44
Phenyl acetate	197	—	Ethyl 3-nitrobenzoate	—	47
Diethyl malonate	199	—	Methyl mandelate	—	53
Methyl benzoate	199	—	Ethyl 4-nitrobenzoate	—	56
Dimethyl maleate	204	—	Dimethyl isophthalate	—	68
Ethyl levulinate	206	—	Phenyl benzoate	—	69
Ethyl octanoate	208	—	Methyl 3-nitrobenzoate	—	78
Ethyl cyanoacetate	208	—	Methyl 4-bromobenzoate	—	81
Ethyl benzoate	212	—	Ethyl 4-aminobenzoate	—	89
Benzyl acetate	217	—	Methyl 4-nitrobenzoate	—	96
Diethyl succinate	217	—	Dimethyl fumarate	—	102
Diethyl fumarate	219	—	Cholesterol acetate	—	114
Methyl phenylacetate	220	—	Ethyl 4-hydroxybenzoate	—	116

Procedures for Preparing Derivatives

CAUTION

Some of the chemicals used in preparing derivatives are suspected carcinogens. Before beginning any of these procedures, consult the list of suspected carcinogens in Technique 1, Section 1.4 Exercise care in handling these substances.

ALDEHYDES AND KETONES

Semicarbazones

Place 0.5 mL of a 2M stock solution of semicarbazide hydrochloride (or 0.5 mL of a solution prepared by dissolving 1.11 g of semicarbazide hydrochloride [MW =111.5] in 5 mL of water) in a small test tube. Add 0.15 g of the unknown compound to the test tube. If the unknown does not dissolve in the solution or if the solution becomes cloudy, add enough methanol (maximum of 2 mL) to dissolve the solid and produce a clear solution. If a solid or cloudiness remains after adding 2 mL of methanol, do not add any more methanol and continue this procedure with the solid present. Using a Pasteur pipette, add 10 drops of pyridine and heat the mixture in a hot water bath (about 60°C) for about 10–15 minutes. By that time, the product should have begun to crystallize. If the product does not crystallize, evaporate ½ the volume of methanol. Collect the product by vacuum filtration. The product can be recrystallized from ethanol if necessary.

Semicarbazones (Alternative Method)

Dissolve 0.25 g of semicarbazide hydrochloride and 0.38 g of sodium acetate in 1.3 mL of water. Then dissolve 0.25 g of the unknown in 2.5 mL of ethanol. Mix the two solutions together in a 25-mL Erlenmeyer flask and heat the mixture to boiling for about 5 minutes. After heating the mixture, place the reaction flask in a beaker of ice and scratch the sides of the flask with a glass rod to induce crystallization of the derivative. Collect the derivative by vacuum filtration and recrystallize it from ethanol.

2,4-Dinitrophenylhy-drazones

Place 2 mL of a solution of 2,4-dinitrophenylhydrazine (prepared as described for the classification test in Experiment 52D) in a test tube and add 0.15 g of the unknown compound. If the unknown is a solid, it should be dissolved in the minimum amount of 95% ethanol or 1,2-dimethoxyethane before it is added. If crystallization is not immediate, gently warm the solution for a minute in a hot water bath (90°C) and then set it aside to crystallize. Collect the product by vacuum filtration.

It is a good idea to make sure the derivative is dry. To dry a "wet" derivative, rinse the solid on the filter sequentially with a few drops of ethanol, followed by a few drops of ether and finally with a few drops of hexane. You should avoid using too much of these solvents to avoid dissolving the derivative.

CARBOXYLIC ACIDS

Working in a hood, place 0.50 g of the acid and 2 mL of thionyl chloride into a small round-bottom flask. Add a magnetic stir bar, and attach a water-jacketed condenser and a drying tube packed with calcium chloride to the flask. While stirring, heat the reaction mixture to boiling for 30 minutes on a hot plate. Allow the mixture to cool to room temperature. Use this mixture to prepare the amide, anilide, or *p*-toluidide derivatives by one of the following three procedures.

Amides

Working in a hood, add the thionyl chloride/carboxylic acid mixture dropwise from a Pasteur pipette into a beaker containing 5 mL of ice-cold concentrated ammonium hydroxide. The reaction is very exothermic. Stir the mixture vigorously after the addition for about 5 minutes. When the reaction is complete, collect the product by vacuum filtration and recrystallize it from water or from water-ethanol, using the mixed-solvents method (see Technique 11, Section 11.10).

Anilides

Dissolve 0.5 g of aniline in 10 mL of methylene chloride in a 50-mL Erlenmeyer flask Using a Pasteur pipette, carefully add the mixture of thionyl chloride/carboxylic acid to this solution. Warm the mixture for an additional 5 minutes on a hot plate, add a magnetic stir bar, and stir the mixture for 20 minutes at room temperature. Then transfer the methylene chloride solution to a small separatory funnel and wash it sequentially with 2.5 mL of water, 2.5 mL of 5% hydrochloric acid, 2.5 mL of 5% sodium hydroxide, and a second 2.5-mL portion of water (the methylene chloride solution should be the bottom layer). Dry the methylene chloride layer over a small amount of anhydrous sodium sulfate. Decant the methylene chloride layer away from the drying agent into a small flask and evaporate the methylene chloride on a warm hot plate in the hood. Use a stream of air or nitrogen to speed up the evaporation. Recrystallize the product from water or from ethanol–water, using the mixed-solvents method (see Technique 11, Section 11.10).

p-Toluidides

Use the same procedure as that described in preparing anilides, but substitute *p*-toluidine for aniline.

PHENOLS

α-Naphthyl-urethanes

Follow the procedure given later for preparing phenylurethanes from alcohols, but substitute α-naphthylisocyanate for phenylisocyanate.

Bromo Derivatives

First, if a stock brominating solution is not available, prepare one by dissolving 0.75 g of potassium bromide in 5 mL of water and adding 0.5 g of bromine. Dissolve 0.1 g of the phenol in 1 mL of methanol or 1,2-dimethoxyethane; then add 1 mL of water. Add 1 mL of the brominating mixture to the phenol solution and swirl the mixture vigorously. Then continue adding the brominating solution dropwise while swirling, until the color of the bromine reagent persists. Finally, add 3–5 mL of water and shake the mixture vigorously. Collect the precipitated product by vacuum filtration and wash it well with water. Recrystallize the derivative from methanol–water, using the mixed–solvents method (see Technique 11, Section 11.10).

AMINES

Acetamides

Place 0.15 g of the amine and 0.5 mL of acetic anhydride in a small Erlenmeyer flask. Heat the mixture for about 5 minutes; then add 5 mL of water and stir the solution vigorously to precipitate the product and hydrolyze the excess acetic anhydride. If the product does not crystallize, it may be necessary to scratch the walls of the flask with a glass rod. Collect the crystals by vacuum filtration and wash them with several portions of cold 5% hydrochloric acid. Recrystallize the derivative from methanol–water, using the mixed-solvents method (see Technique 11, Section 11.10).

Aromatic amines, or those amines that are not very basic, may require pyridine (2 mL) as a solvent and a catalyst for the reaction. If pyridine is used, a longer period of heating is required (up to 1 hour), and the reaction should be carried out in an apparatus equipped with a reflux condenser. After reflux, the reaction mixture must be extracted with 5–10 mL of 5% sulfuric acid to remove the pyridine.

Benzamides

Using a centrifuge tube, suspend 0.15 g of the amine in 1 mL of 10% sodium hydroxide solution and add 0.5 g of benzoyl chloride. Cap the tube and shake the mixture vigorously for about 10 minutes. After shaking the mixture, add enough dilute hydrochloric acid to bring the pH of the solution to pH 7 or 8. Collect the precipitate by vacuum filtration, wash it thoroughly with cold water, and recrystallize it from ethanol–water, using the mixed-solvents method (see Technique 11, Section 11.10).

Benzamides (Alternative Method)

In a small round-bottom flask, dissolve 0.25 g of the amine in a solution of 1.2 mL of pyridine and 2.5 mL of toluene. Add 0.25 mL of benzoyl chloride to the solution, and heat the mixture under reflux for about 30 minutes. Pour the cooled reaction mixture into 25 mL of water, and stir the mixture vigorously to hydrolyze the excess benzoyl chloride. Separate the toluene layer and wash it, first with 1.5 mL of water, and then with 1.5 mL of 5% sodium carbonate. Dry the toluene over granular anhydrous sodium sulfate, decant the toluene into a small Erlenmeyer flask, and remove the toluene by evaporation on a hot plate in the hood. Use a stream of air or nitrogen to speed up the evaporation. Recrystallize the benzamide from ethanol or ethanol-water, using the mixed-solvents method (see Technique 11, Section 11.10).

Methiodides

Mix equal-volume quantities of the amine and methyl iodide in a small round-bottom flask (about 0.25 mL is sufficient) and allow the mixture to stand for several minutes. Then heat the mixture gently under reflux for about 5 minutes. The methiodide should crystallize on cooling. If it does not, you can induce crystallization by scratching the walls of the flask with a glass rod. Collect the product by vacuum filtration and recrystallize it from ethanol or ethyl acetate.

ALCOHOLS

3,5-Dinitrobenzoates

Liquid Alcohols

Dissolve 0.25 g of 3,5-dinitrobenzoyl chloride in 0.25 mL of the alcohol and heat the mixture for about 5 minutes.[1] Allow the mixture to cool and add 1.5 mL of a

---

[1]3,5-Dinitrobenzoyl chloride is an acid chloride and hydrolyzes readily. The purity of this reagent should be checked before its use by determining its melting point (mp 69–71 C). When the carboxylic acid is present, the melting point will be high.

5% sodium carbonate solution and 1 mL of water. Stir the mixture vigorously and crush any solid that forms. Collect the product by vacuum filtration, and wash it with cold water. Recrystallize the derivative from ethanol–water, using the mixed-solvents method (see Technique 11, Section 11.10).

Solid Alcohols

Dissolve 0.25 g of the alcohol in 1.5 mL of dry pyridine and add 0.25 g of 3,5-dinitrobenzoyl chloride. Heat the mixture under reflux for 15 minutes. Pour the cooled reaction mixture into a cold mixture of 2.5 mL of 5% sodium carbonate and 2.5 mL of water. Keep the solution cooled in an ice bath until the product crystallizes, and stir it vigorously during the entire period. Collect the product by vacuum filtration, wash it with cold water, and recrystallize it from ethanol–water, using the mixed-solvents method (see Technique 11, Section 11.10).

Phenylurethanes

Place 0.25 g of the *anhydrous* alcohol in a dry test tube and add 0.25 mL of phenylisocyanate (*α*-naphthylisocyanate for a phenol). If the compound is a phenol, add 1 drop of pyridine to catalyze the reaction. If the reaction is not spontaneous, heat the mixture in a hot water bath (90°C) for 5–10 minutes. Cool the test tube in a beaker of ice, and scratch the tube with a glass rod to induce crystallization. Decant the liquid from the solid product or, if necessary, collect the product by vacuum filtration. Dissolve the product in 2.5–3 mL of hot ligroin or hexane, and filter the mixture by gravity (preheat funnel) to remove any unwanted and insoluble diphenylurea present. Cool the filtrate to induce crystallization of the urethane. Collect the product by vacuum filtration.

E S T E R S

We recommend that esters be characterized by spectroscopic methods whenever possible. A derivative of the alcohol part of an ester can be prepared with the following procedure. For other derivatives, consult a comprehensive textbook. Several are listed in Experiment 55I.

3,5-Dinitrobenzoates

Place 1.0 mL of the ester and 0.75 g of 3,5-dinitrobenzoic acid in a small round-bottom flask. Add 2 drops of concentrated sulfuric acid and a magnetic stir bar to the flask and attach a condenser. If the boiling point of the ester is above 150°C, heat at reflux while stirring for 30–45 minutes. If the boiling point of the ester is above 150°C, heat the mixture at about 150°C for 30–45 minutes. Often the mixture will turn black during the heating process. You should continue the reflux regardless. Cool the mixture, and transfer it to a small separatory funnel. Add 10 mL of ether. Extract the ether layer 2 times with 5 mL of 5% aqueous sodium carbonate (save the ether layer). Wash the organic layer with 5 mL of water, and dry the ether solution over magnesium sulfate. Evaporate the ether in a hot water bath in the hood. Use a stream of air or nitrogen to speed the evaporation. Dissolve the residue, usually an oil, in 2 mL of boiling ethanol and add water dropwise until the mixture becomes cloudy. Cool the solution to induce crystallization of the derivative.

Preparation of a Solid Carboxylic Acid from an Ester

An excellent derivative of an ester can be prepared by a basic hydrolysis of an ester when it yields a solid carboxylic acid. A procedure is provided in Experiment 55I. Melting points for solid carboxylic acids are included in the Carboxylic Acids Table in Appendix 1.

5. What modifications of conditions would be appropriate if the enzyme were to be used?

6. Refer to the essay that precedes this experiment. It gives a structure for thiamine pyrophosphate. Using this structure as a guide, draw a structure for thiamine hydrochloride. The pyrophosphate group is absent in this compound.

7. Draw a mechanism for the cyanide-catalyzed conversion of benzaldehyde to benzoin. The intermediate, shown in brackets, is thought to be involved in the mechanism.

EXPERIMENT 27 ■

Benzil

Oxidation
Catalysis
Crystallization

In this experiment, an α-diketone, benzil, is prepared by the oxidation of an α-hydroxyketone, benzoin (Experiment 26). This oxidation can be done easily with mild oxidizing agents such as Fehling's solution (alkaline cupric tartrate complex) or with nitric acid. In this experiment, the oxidation is performed with copper(II) acetate in the presence of ammonium nitrate.

Copper(II) ion (cupric ion) oxidizes benzoin to benzil forming copper(I) ion (cuprous ion) at the same time by reduction.

$$C_6H_5-\underset{\underset{O}{\|}}{C}-\underset{\underset{OH}{|}}{C}H-C_6H_5 + 2\,Cu^{2+} \longrightarrow C_6H_5-\underset{\underset{O}{\|}}{C}-\underset{\underset{O}{\|}}{C}-C_6H_5 + 2\,Cu^+ + 2\,H^+$$

Copper(I) is then reoxidized by ammonium nitrate back to copper(II). During this process, ammonium nitrate is reduced to ammonium nitrite. Following this, ammonium nitrite decomposes in the presence of acetic acid to yield nitrogen gas and water, Thus, in this experiment, copper(II) acts as a catalyst and is continuously recycled as benzil is formed.

$$2\,Cu^+ + NH_4NO_3 + 2\,H^+ \longrightarrow 2\,Cu^{2+} + NH_4NO_2 + H_2O$$

Ammonium   Ammonium
nitrate   nitrite

$$NH_4NO_2 \xrightarrow{\ H^+\ } N_{2(g)} + 2\,H_2O$$

Required Reading

Review: Technique 3   Sections 3.2 and 3.7
          Technique 5

Special Instructions

This experiment works best when the purity of benzoin is high. The benzoin prepared in Experiment 26 is usually of sufficient purity after it has been crystallized.

Waste Disposal

Dispose of the development solvent in the container for halogenated organic solvents. Dilute the aqueous filtrate from the vacuum filtration of the reaction mixture with water and pour it down the drain. Dispose of the filtrate from the crystallization of benzil in the container for nonhalogenated organic solvents.

Procedure

Reaction Mixture. Place 0.30 g of benzoin (Experiment 26) in a 5-mL conical vial and add 2.0 mL of the copper(II) acetate and ammonium nitrate solution.[1] Add a spin vane and attach an air condenser. Set up the apparatus for heating under reflux as shown in Figure 3.2A (inset), p. 571. Heat the mixture with an aluminum block (or sand bath) at about 135°C. Continue heating with stirring until the solids dissolve completely and the mixture acquires a green color (about 2–3 minutes).[2] At this point, begin to time the reaction. *At the instructor's option,* monitor the reaction by thin-

---

[1] Dissolve 0.20 g of copper(II) acetate and 10.0 g of ammonium nitrate in 14.0 mL of warm water. When the solids have dissolved, add 56.0 mL of glacial acetic acid and mix thoroughly.

[2] With less pure benzoin, the reaction mixture may turn light tan or brown. Normally the color of the mixture will return to green, and the reaction will proceed as intended. If the mixture remains tan or brown for more than 30 minutes, try adding an additional 1.0 mL of the copper (II) acetate-ammonium nitrate solution, then continue heating for 30 minutes more.

layer chromatography (see next paragraph). Continue heating at 135°C for 60 minutes. The mixture should boil gently and nitrogen gas should be evolved.

Thin-Layer Chromatography (Optional). The conversion of benzoin to benzil can be monitored by thin-layer chromatography (Technique 14, Section 14.10, p. 766). Use Whatman Silica Gel Plates No. 4410 222. Prepare a developing chamber from a beaker covered with aluminum foil or a wide-mouth screwcap bottle (see Fig. 14.5, p. 766). Add some methylene chloride to the developing chamber. Prepare 9 micropipets to spot the plates. The preparation of these pipets is described and illustrated in Technique 14, Section 14.4, p. 759. Use a 1% solution of benzoin in methylene chloride and a 1% solution of benzil in methylene chloride as reference standards. Spot each TLC plate with the reference solutions. Use the micropipets to remove samples of the reaction mixture at the following times: 0 minutes, 5 minutes, 10 minutes, 15 minutes, 30 minutes, 45 minutes, and 60 minutes. Use a different micropipet each time and spot a TLC plate with each sample. After developing the plates and allowing them to dry, observe the plates under UV illumination. Record your results.

Isolation of Crude Benzil. Cool the mixture for a few minutes and detach the air condenser. Add 4 mL of cold water to a small beaker. Using a Pasteur pipet transfer the reaction mixture to the beaker. Rinse the conical vial and spin vane with an additional 1.0 mL of water and add this to the beaker. Stir the mixture vigorously with a glass stirring rod to induce crystallization and to break up any solid mass that may form. Vacuum filter the crude benzil on a Hirsch funnel (Technique 4, Section 4.3, and Fig. 4.5, p. 594). Wash it well with cold water (about 5.0 mL). Continue drawing air through the crystals on the Hirsch funnel by suction for about 5 minutes.

Crystallization of Benzil. Weigh the crude benzil and transfer it to a 10-mL Erlenmeyer flask. Add hot 95% ethanol (calculate the volume based on 7 mL of ethanol per gram of benzil) to the flask and heat the mixture while swirling on a hotplate until the solid dissolves. Remove the flask from the heat source and allow the solution to cool slowly. As the solution cools, seed it with solid benzil that forms on a spatula after the spatula is dipped into the solution. The solution will become supersaturated unless this is done, and crystallization will occur too rapidly. Yellow, needle-like crystals are formed. Cool the mixture in an ice bath to complete the crystallization. Vacuum filter the benzil on a Hirsch funnel. Rinse the flask with 1.0 mL of ice cold 95% ethanol and pour this over the crystals on the Hirsch funnel. Wash the crystals with an additional 2 mL of cold 95% ethanol. Continue drawing air through the crystals on the Hirsch funnel by suction for about 5 minutes. Allow the crystals to air-dry.

Yield Calculation and Melting Point Determination. Weigh the benzil and calculate the percentage yield. Determine the melting point. The melting point of pure benzil is 95°C. You should expect that your dry benzil will melt at about 92–94°C. This material is of sufficient purity for conversion to benzilic acid (Experiment 28) or tetraphenylcyclopentadienone (Experiment 29). Submit the benzil to the instructor unless it is to be used to prepare benzilic acid or tetraphenylcyclopentadienone. At the instructor's option, obtain the infrared spectrum of benzil in carbon tetrachloride or chloroform. Compare it with the infrared spectrum of benzil shown in this experiment. Also compare it with the infrared spectrum of benzoin shown in Experiment 26. What differences do you notice?

Infrared spectrum of benzil, CCl$_4$.

REFERENCES

Vogel, A. I. *Vogel's Textbook of Practical Organic Chemistry.* 4th ed., rev. by B. S. Furniss, et al. London and New York: Longman, 1978, p. 807.

EXPERIMENT 28

Benzilic Acid

Anionic rearrangement

In this experiment, benzilic acid will be prepared by causing the rearrangement of the α-diketone benzil. Preparation of benzil is described in Experiment 27. The rearrangement of benzil proceeds in the following way:

EXPERIMENT 25 ■

Triphenylmethanol and Benzoic Acid

Grignard reactions
Extraction
Crystallization

In this experiment, you will prepare a Grignard reagent, or organomagnesium reagent. The reagent is phenylmagnesium bromide.

Bromobenzene   Phenylmagnesium bromide

This reagent will be converted to a tertiary alcohol or a carboxylic acid, depending on the experiment selected.

EXPERIMENT 25A

Benzophenone

Triphenylmethanol

EXPERIMENT 25B

$$\text{Ph—MgBr} + CO_2 \xrightarrow{\text{ether}} \text{Ph—}\underset{\underset{O}{\|}}{C}\text{—O}^-\text{MgBr}^+ \xrightarrow{H_3O^+}$$

$$\text{Ph—}\underset{\underset{O}{\|}}{C}\text{—OH} + \text{MgBr(OH)}$$

Benzoic acid

The alkyl portion of the Grignard reagent behaves as if it had the characteristics of a **carbanion.** We may write the structure of the reagent as a partially ionic compound:

$$\overset{\delta-}{R} \cdots \overset{\delta+}{MgX}.$$

This partially bonded carbanion is a Lewis base. It reacts with strong acids, as you would expect, to give an alkane:

$$\overset{\delta-}{R} \cdots \overset{\delta+}{MgX} + HX \longrightarrow R—H + MgX_2$$

Any compound with a suitably acidic hydrogen will donate a proton to destroy the reagent. Water, alcohols, terminal acetylenes, phenols, and carboxylic acids are all acidic enough to bring about this reaction.

The Grignard reagent also functions as a good nucleophile in nucleophilic addition reactions of the carbonyl group. The carbonyl group has electrophilic character at its carbon atom (due to resonance), and a good nucleophile seeks out this center for addition.

$$\left[\underset{C}{\overset{\overset{\overset{\cdot\cdot}{O}\cdot}{\|}}{\underset{/\quad\backslash}{}}} \longleftrightarrow \underset{\underset{+}{C}}{\overset{\overset{:\overset{\cdot\cdot}{O}:^-}{|}}{\underset{/\quad\backslash}{}}} \right] \qquad \overset{\backslash}{\underset{/}{}}\overset{\delta+}{C}=\overset{\delta-}{\underset{\cdot\cdot}{O}}{\cdot\cdot}$$

The magnesium salts produced form a complex with the addition product, an alkoxide salt. In a second step of the reaction, these must be hydrolyzed (protonated) by addition of dilute aqueous acid:

$$\underset{/\quad\backslash}{\overset{\overset{O}{\|}}{C}} + RMgX \longrightarrow \underset{\underset{R}{|}}{\overset{\overset{O—MgX}{|}}{—C—}} \xrightarrow[H_2O]{HX} \underset{\underset{R}{|}}{\overset{\overset{OH}{|}}{—C—}} + MgX_2$$

Step 1   Step 2

The Grignard reaction is used synthetically to prepare secondary alcohols from aldehydes and tertiary alcohols from ketones. The Grignard reagent will react with esters twice to give tertiary alcohols. Synthetically, it also can be allowed to react with carbon dioxide to give carboxylic acids and with oxygen to give hydroperoxides:

$$RMgX + O{=}C{=}O \longrightarrow R{-}\overset{\overset{\displaystyle O}{\|}}{C}{-}OMgX \xrightarrow[H_2O]{HX} R{-}\overset{\overset{\displaystyle O}{\|}}{C}{-}OH$$

Carboxylic acid

$$RMgX + O_2 \longrightarrow ROOMgX \xrightarrow[H_2O]{HX} ROOH$$

Hydroperoxide

Because the Grignard reagent reacts with water, carbon dioxide, and oxygen, it must be protected from air and moisture when it is used. The apparatus in which the reaction is to be conducted must be scrupulously dry (recall that 18 mL of H_2O is 1 mole), and the solvent must be free of water, or anhydrous. During the reaction, the flask must be protected by a calcium chloride drying tube. Oxygen should also be excluded. In practice this can be done by allowing the solvent ether to reflux. This blanket of solvent vapor keeps air from the surface of the reaction mixture.

In the experiment described here, the principal impurity is **biphenyl,** which is formed by a heat- or light-catalyzed coupling reaction of the Grignard reagent and unreacted bromobenzene. A high reaction temperature favors the formation of this product. Biphenyl is highly soluble in petroleum ether, and it is easily separated from triphenylmethanol. Biphenyl can be separated from benzoic acid by extraction.

Required Reading

Review: Technique 4   Sections 4.3 and 4.7
Technique 5   Section 5.4
Technique 7   Sections 7.5, 7.9, 7.11
Technique 19 Section 19.4

Special Instructions

This experiment must be conducted in one laboratory period either to the point after which benzophenone is added (Experiment 25A) or to the point after which the Grignard reagent is poured over dry ice (Experiment 25B). The Grignard reagent cannot be stored.

This reaction involves the use of diethyl ether, which is extremely flammable. Be certain that no open flames of any sort are in your vicinity when you are using ether.

During this experiment, you will need to use *anhydrous* diethyl ether, which is usually contained in metal cans with a screwcap. You are instructed in the experiment to transfer a small portion of this solvent to a conical vial. Be certain to minimize exposure to atmospheric water. Always recap the container after use. Do not use solvent grade ether because it may contain some water.

All students will prepare the Grignard reagent, phenylmagnesium bromide. At the option of the instructor, you should proceed to either Experiment 25A (triphenylmethanol) or Experiment 25B (benzoic acid).

Waste Disposal

All aqueous solutions may be diluted with additional water and flushed down the sink. Be sure to first decant these solutions away from any magnesium chips. The unreacted magnesium chips should be placed in a solid waste container.

Place all ether solutions in the container for nonhalogenated liquid wastes. Likewise, the mother liquor from the crystallization using isopropyl alcohol (Experiment 25A) should also be placed in the container for nonhalogenated liquid wastes.

Procedure

PREPARATION OF THE GRIGNARD REAGENT: PHENYLMAGNESIUM BROMIDE

Preparation of Glassware. All glassware used in a Grignard reaction must be scrupulously dried. Surprisingly large amounts of water adhere to the walls of glassware, even glassware that is apparently dry. Dry all the pieces of *glassware* shown in the figure in an oven at 110°C for at least 30 minutes. Prepare a drying tube with anhydrous calcium chloride and place it in the oven. In addition, dry the following: two 3-mL and one 5-mL conical vials, which will be needed for solutions and solvents, and a calibrated Pasteur pipet (0.5-mL and 1.0-mL calibration marks) for use in dispensing ether.

Caution: Do not place any plasticware, plastic connectors, plastic syringes, or rubber septa in the oven as they may melt, burn, or soften. If the syringe is glass, you may dry it in the oven. Check with your instructor if in doubt.

If there are visible signs of water in the apparatus, you must first dry the glassware and any plastic connectors by rinsing them with acetone. The glass pieces may then be placed in the oven.

Assemble the apparatus as shown in the figure as soon as the glassware has cooled somewhat. Obtain a 4.5-cm length[1] of magnesium ribbon and scrape both sides of the ribbon with the side of a spatula to remove any oxide coating that may be present. Weigh the strip of magnesium and trim both ends until you have a weight of about 0.037 g (record the actual weight in your notebook). While holding the ribbon with tweezers, cut the strip into about 2-mm sections with sharp scissors, and allow the pieces to fall directly into a *dry* beaker. Remove the 5-mL conical vial from the

---

[1] The length of magnesium ribbon required will vary from one commercial sample of ribbon to another. The instructor should determine the correct length to use.

Apparatus for Experiment 25.

apparatus and transfer the magnesium to the vial. Place a dry magnetic spin vane into the vial and reassemble the apparatus.

Formation of the Grignard Reagent. Transfer about 4 mL of *anhydrous* diethyl ether into a *dry* 5-mL conical vial and cap the vial. Use this vial to store your dry ether during the course of this experiment. During the experiment, remove the ether from this vial with a dry calibrated Pasteur pipet.

Place 0.17 mL of bromobenzene ($MW = 157.0$) into a pre-weighed 3-mL conical vial and determine the weight of the material transferred. Add 1.0 mL of anhydrous ether to the vial. After the bromobenzene dissolves, draw this solution into the syringe and cap the vial that you used for the bromobenzene solution for later use. After inserting the syringe needle through the rubber septum, add 0.2 mL of the bromobenzene solution to the magnesium in the vial. Position the apparatus just above the hotplate and stir the mixture *gently* so as to avoid throwing the magnesium onto the side of the vial. You should begin to notice the evolution of bubbles from the surface of the metal, which signals that the reaction is starting. It will probably be necessary to heat the mixture using your hotplate to start the reaction. The hotplate should be adjusted to its lowest setting. Since ether has a low boiling point (35°C), it may be sufficient to heat the vial by placing it just above the hotplate. Check to see if the bubbling action continues after the apparatus is lifted above the hotplate. The reaction should start, but if you experience difficulty, proceed to the next paragraph.

Optional Steps. You may need to employ one or more of the following procedures if heating fails to start the reaction. If you are experiencing difficulty, remove the syringe and rubber septum. Place a *dry* glass stirring rod into the vial and gently twist the stirring rod so as to crush the magnesium against the glass surface. Reattach the rubber septum and heat the mixture again. Repeat the crushing procedure several times, if necessary, to start the reaction. If the crushing procedure fails to start the reaction, then add one small crystal of iodine to the vial. Again, heat the mixture *gently*. The most drastic action, other than starting the experiment over again, is to prepare a small sample of the Grignard reagent in a test tube. When this reaction starts, add it to the main reaction mixture in the vial.

Completing the Grignard Preparation. When the reaction has started, you should observe the formation of a brownish-gray cloudy solution. Using a syringe, add the remaining solution of bromobenzene slowly over a period of 5 minutes. Be sure to hold the plunger of the syringe so that the entire solution is not added at one time. It may be necessary to heat the mixture occasionally with the hotplate during the addition. If the reaction becomes too vigorous, slow the addition of the bromobenzene solution and raise the apparatus higher above the hotplate. Ideally, the mixture will boil without the application of external heat. *It is important that you heat the mixture if the reflux slows or stops.* As the reaction proceeds, you should observe the gradual disintegration of the magnesium metal. When all the bromobenzene has been added, place 0.50 mL of *anhydrous* ether in the vial that originally contained the bromobenzene solution, draw it into the syringe, and add the ether to the reaction mixture. Remove the syringe after making this addition. You should add additional anhydrous ether to replace any that is lost during the reflux period. You should maintain the level of the reaction solvent so that it is no lower than the 1-mL mark of the conical vial. After a period of about 45 minutes from the beginning of the addition of bromobenzene, most or all of the magnesium metal should have reacted. Cool the mixture to room temperature. As your instructor designates, go on to either Experiment 25A or Experiment 25B.

EXPERIMENT 25A

Procedure

Adduct

Addition of Benzophenone. While the phenylmagnesium bromide solution is being heated and stirred under reflux, make a solution of 0.273 g benzophenone in 0.50 mL of *anhydrous* ether in a 3-mL conical vial. Cap the vial until the reflux period is over. Once the Grignard reagent is cooled to room temperature, draw the benzophenone solution into the syringe. Add this solution as rapidly as possible to the stirred Grignard reagent, but at such a rate that the solution does not reflux too vigorously. Once the addition has been completed, cool the mixture to room temperature. The solution turns red and then gradually solidifies as the adduct is formed. When stirring is no longer effective, remove the syringe and septum and stir the mixture with a spatula. Rinse the vial that contained the benzophenone solution with about 0.2 mL of anhydrous ether and add it to the mixture. Remove the reaction vial from the apparatus and cap it. Occasionally stir the contents of this vial. Recap the vial when it is standing to avoid contact with water vapor. The adduct should be fully formed after about 15 minutes. You may stop here.

Hydrolysis. Add 1.5 mL of 6*M* hydrochloric acid (*dropwise at first*) to neutralize the reaction mixture. The acid converts the adduct to triphenylmethanol and inorganic compounds (MgX$_2$). Eventually, you should obtain two distinct phases: the upper ether layer will contain triphenylmethanol; the lower aqueous hydrochloric acid layer will contain the inorganic compounds. Use a spatula to break up the solid during the addition of hydrochloric acid. You may need to cap the vial and shake it vigorously to dissolve the solid. Since the neutralization procedure evolves heat, some ether will be lost due to evaporation. You should add enough ether to maintain a 3-mL volume in the upper organic phase (use graduations on the vial for measurement). Make sure that you have two distinct liquid phases before separating the layers. More ether or hydrochloric acid may be added, if necessary, to dissolve any remaining solid.[1]

If some material remains undissolved or if there are three layers, transfer all the liquids to your 15-mL screwcapped centrifuge tube. Add more ether and hydrochloric acid to the conical vial, cap it, and shake it; then add the contents to the centrifuge tube. Continue adding small portions of ether and hydrochloric acid to the centrifuge tube and shake it until everything dissolves. At this point, you should have two clear layers.

Separation and Drying. If a small amount of unreacted magnesium metal is present, you will observe bubbles of hydrogen being formed. You may remove the aqueous layer even though the magnesium is still producing hydrogen. Remove the magnetic spin vane with tweezers and rinse it with a little ether. Draw off the lower aqueous phase with a Pasteur pipet and place it in another conical vial. *Remember to save the ether layer* in the first vial because it contains the triphenylmethanol product. Reextract the aqueous phase in the second vial with 0.5 mL of ether. Remove the lower aqueous phase and discard it. Combine the remaining ether phase with the first ether extract. Transfer the combined ether layers to a dry 5-mL conical vial with a dry Pasteur pipet. Dry the ether solution with granular anhydrous sodium sulfate (two microspatulafuls measured in the V-grooved end).

Evaporation. Remove the dried ether solution from the drying agent with a Pasteur pipet, transfer it to a small Erlenmeyer flask, and rinse the drying agent with more diethyl ether. Evaporate the ether solvent in a hood by heating the flask in a warm water bath. Evaporation will occur more quickly if a stream of nitrogen or air is directed into the flask. You should be left with a mixture that varies from a brown oil to a colored solid mixed with an oil. This crude mixture contains the desired triphenylmethanol and the by-product biphenyl. Most of the biphenyl can be removed by adding 1 mL of petroleum ether (bp 30–60°C). Petroleum ether is a mixture of hydrocarbons that easily dissolves the hydrocarbon biphenyl and leaves behind the alcohol triphenylmethanol. Do not confuse this solvent with diethyl ether ("ether"). Heat the mixture slightly, stir it, and then cool the mixture to room temperature. Collect the triphenylmethanol by vacuum filtration on a Hirsch funnel and rinse it with small portions of petroleum ether (Technique 4, Section 4.3, p. 593, and Fig. 4.5, p. 594). Air-dry the solid, weigh it, and calculate the percentage yield of the crude triphenylmethanol (*MW* = 260.3).

Crystallization. Crystallize all your product from hot isopropyl alcohol using a

---

[1] In some cases, it may be necessary to add additional water instead of more hydrochloric acid.

Infrared spectrum of triphenylmethanol KBr.

Craig tube (Technique 5, Section 5.4, p. 609, and Fig. 5.5, p. 611). Step 2 in Figure 5.5 (removal of insoluble impurities) should not be required in this crystallization. Set the crystals aside to air-dry. Report the melting point of the purified triphenylmethanol (literature value, 162°C) and the recovered yield in grams. Submit the sample to the instructor.

Spectroscopy. At the option of the instructor, determine the infrared spectrum of the purified material in a KBr pellet (Technique 19, Section 19.4, p. 807). Your instructor may assign certain tests on the product you prepared. These tests are described in the Instructor's Manual.

EXPERIMENT 49 ◼

Isolation of Casein and Lactose from Milk

Isolation of a protein
Isolation of a sugar

In this experiment, you will isolate several of the chemical substances found in milk. First, you will isolate a phosphorus-containing protein, casein (Experiment 49A). The remaining milk mixture will then be used as a source of a sugar, α-lactose (Experiment 49B). After you isolate the milk sugar, you will make several chemical tests on this material. Fats, which are present in whole milk, are not isolated in this experiment because powdered nonfat milk is used.

Here is the procedure you will follow. First, the casein is precipitated by warming the powdered milk and adding dilute acetic acid. It is important that the heating not be excessive or the acid too strong, because these conditions also hydrolyze lactose into its

Acetal (β linkage)

α-Lactose

Galactose   Glucose   Hemiacetal (OH is α)

Lactose (Aldehyde form)   Free aldehyde

β-Lactose   Hemiacetal (OH is β)

components, glucose and galactose. After the casein has been removed, the excess acetic acid is neutralized with calcium carbonate, and the solution is heated to its boiling point to precipitate the initially soluble protein, albumin. The liquid containing the lactose is poured away from the albumin. Alcohol is added to the solution, and any remaining protein is removed by centrifugation. α-Lactose crystallizes on cooling.

Lactose is an example of a disaccharide. It is made up of two sugar molecules: galactose and glucose. In the following structures, the galactose portion is on the left and glucose is on the right. Galactose is bonded through an acetal linkage to glucose.

Notice that the glucose portion can exist in one of two isomeric hemiacetal structures: α-lactose and β-lactose. Glucose can also exist in a free aldehyde form. This aldehyde form (open form) is an intermediate in the equilibration (interconversion) of α- and β-lactose. Very little of this free aldehyde form exists in the equilibrium mixture. The isomeric α- and β-lactose are diastereomers because they differ in the configuration at one carbon atom, called the anomeric carbon atom.

The sugar α-lactose is easily obtainable by crystallization from a water–ethanol mixture at room temperature. On the other hand, β-lactose must be obtained by a more difficult process, which involves crystallization from a concentrated solution of lactose at temperatures about 93.5°C. In the present experiment, α-lactose is isolated by the simpler experimental procedure indicated above.

α-Lactose undergoes numerous interesting reactions. First, α-lactose interconverts, via the free aldehyde form, to a large extent, to the β-isomer in aqueous solution. This causes a change in the rotation of polarized light from +92.6° to +52.3° with increasing time. The process that causes the change in optical rotation with time is called **mutarotation**. Mutarotation of lactose can be studied in Experiment 50.

A second reaction of lactose is the oxidation of the free aldehyde form by Benedict's reagent. Lactose is referred to as a reducing sugar because it reduces Benedict's reagent (cupric ion to cuprous ion) and produces a red precipitate (Cu_2O). In the process, the aldehyde group is oxidized to a carboxyl group. The reaction that takes place in Benedict's test is

$$R\text{—}CHO + 2\,Cu^{2+} + 4\,OH^- \longrightarrow RCOOH + Cu_2O + 2\,H_2O$$

A third reaction of lactose is the oxidation of the galactose part by the mucic acid test. In this test, the acetal linkage between galactose and glucose units is cleaved by the acidic medium to give free galactose and glucose. Galactose is oxidized with nitric acid to the dicarboxylic acid, galactaric acid (mucic acid). Mucic acid is an insoluble, high-melting solid that precipitates from the reaction mixture. On the other hand, glucose is oxidized to a diacid (glucaric acid), which is more soluble in the oxidizing medium and does not precipitate.

Required Reading

Review: Technique 4

New: Essay   Chemistry of Milk

Special Instructions

Experiments 49A and 49B should both be performed during one laboratory period. The lactose solution must be allowed to stand until the following laboratory period. Casein must dry for 2 or 3 days.

Waste Disposal

Place residues left from the Benedict's test in the container designated for the disposal of copper wastes. Dispose of solid materials obtained from milk in a trash container. Aqueous wastes, including those that contain ethanol, may be diluted with water and poured down the drain.

EXPERIMENT 49A

Isolation of Casein from Milk

Procedure

Precipitation of Casein. Place 4.0 g of powdered milk and 10 mL of water into a 50-mL beaker. Heat the mixture in a water bath to 40°C. Check the temperature of the milk solution with a thermometer. Place 1.0 mL of dilute acetic acid solution[1] in a conical vial for temporary storage. When the mixture has reached 40°C, add the dilute acetic acid dropwise to the warm milk. After every 5 drops, stir the mixture gently using a glass stirring rod with an attached rubber policeman. Using the rubber policeman, push the casein up onto the side of the beaker so that most of the liquid drains from the solid. Then transfer the congealed casein to a 10-mL beaker in portions. If any liquid separates from the casein in the 10-mL beaker, use a Pasteur pipet to transfer the liquid back into the reaction mixture. Continue to add dropwise the remainder of the 1.0 mL of dilute acetic acid to the milk mixture in the 50-mL beaker to precipitate the casein fully. Remove as much of the casein as possible and transfer it to the 10-mL beaker. Avoid adding an excess of acetic acid to the milk solution, as this will cause the lactose in the milk to hydrolyze into glucose and galactose.

When you have removed most of the casein from the milk solution, add 0.2 g of calcium carbonate to the milk in the 50-mL beaker. Stir the mixture for a few minutes and save it for use in Experiment 49B. Use this mixture as soon as possible during the laboratory period. This beaker contains lactose and albumins.

Isolation of Casein. Transfer the casein from the 10-mL beaker to a Hirsch funnel (Technique 4, Section 4.3, p. 593, and Fig. 4.5, p. 594). Draw a vacuum on the casein to remove as much liquid as possible (about 5 minutes). Press the casein with a spatula during this time. Transfer the casein to a piece of filter paper (about 7 cm). Using a spatula, move the solid around on the paper so that the remaining liquid is absorbed into the filter paper. When most of the liquid has been removed, transfer the solid to a watch glass to complete the drying operation. Allow the casein to air-dry completely for 2 to 3 days before weighing the product. You must remove the casein from the filter paper or it will become "glued" to the paper. (You have nearly prepared white glue.) Submit the casein in a labeled vial to the instructor. Calculate the weight percent of the casein isolated from the powdered milk.

E X P E R I M E N T   4 9 B   ■

Isolation of Lactose from Milk

Procedure

Precipitation of Albumins. Heat the mixture directly on a hot plate in the 50-mL beaker that you saved from Experiment 49A to about 75°C for about 5 minutes. This heating operation results in a nearly complete separation of the albumins from the solution. Decant the liquid in the beaker away from the solid into a clean centrifuge tube. You may need to hold the solid with a spatula while transferring the liquid.

[1] The laboratory instructor should prepare a large batch for the class in the ratio of 2 mL glacial acetic acid to 20 mL of water.

Press the albumins with a spatula to remove as much liquid as possible and pour the liquid into the centrifuge tube (save the albumins in the original beaker for the procedure in the next paragraph). You should have about 7 mL of liquid. When the liquid has cooled to about room temperature, centrifuge the contents of the tube for 2–3 minutes. Be sure to place another tube in the centrifuge to balance the unit. Following centrifugation, decant the liquid away from the solid into a 50-mL beaker and save it for use in the next section (Precipitation of Lactose).

Allow the albumins to dry for 2–3 days in the original beaker. Break up the solid and weigh it. Calculate the weight percent of albumins isolated from the powdered milk.

Precipitation of Lactose. Add 15 mL of 95% ethanol to the beaker containing the centrifuged and decanted liquid. Solids will precipitate. Heat this mixture to about 60°C, placing it directly on the hot plate, to dissolve some of the solid. Pour the *hot* liquid into a 40-mL centrifuge tube (or two 15-mL tubes) and centrifuge the hot solution as soon as possible before the solution cools appreciably. Centrifuge the mixture for 2–3 minutes. Be sure to place another tube in the centrifuge to balance the unit. It is important to centrifuge this mixture while it is warm to prevent premature crystallization of the lactose. A considerable quantity of solid forms in the bottom of the centrifuge tube. This solid is not lactose.

Remove the warm supernatant liquid from the tube using a Pasteur pipet and transfer the liquid to a 50-mL Erlenmeyer flask. Discard the solid remaining in the centrifuge tube. Stopper the flask and allow the lactose to crystallize for at least 2 days. Granular crystals will form during this time.

Isolation of Lactose. Collect the lactose by vacuum filtration on a Hirsch funnel. Use about 3 mL of 95% ethanol to aid the transfer and to wash the product. α-Lactose crystallizes with one water of hydration, $C_{12}H_{22}O_{11} \cdot H_2O$. Weigh the product after it is thoroughly dry. Submit the α-lactose in a labeled vial to the instructor unless it is to be used in the following optional tests or in Experiment 50. Calculate the weight percent of the lactose isolated from the powdered milk.

Benedict's Test (Optional). Prepare a hot water bath (above 90°C) for this experiment. Dissolve about 0.01 g of your lactose in 1 mL of water in a test tube. Heat the mixture to dissolve most of the lactose (some cloudiness remains). Place about 1 mL each of 1% solutions of glucose and galactose in separate test tubes. Add to each of the three test tubes 2 mL of Benedict's reagent.[2] Place the test tubes in the hot water bath for 2 minutes. Remove the tubes and note the results. The formation of an orange to brownish-red precipitate indicates a positive test for a reducing sugar. This test is described on pages 525–527 in Experiment 54.

Mucic Acid Test (Optional). Prepare a hot water bath (above 90°C) for this experiment or use the one prepared for the Benedict's test. Place 0.1 g of the isolated lactose, 0.05 g of glucose (dextrose), and 0.05 g of galactose in three separate test tubes. Add 1 mL of water to each tube and dissolve the solids, with heating if neces-

---

[2] Dissolve 34.6 g of hydrated sodium citrate and 20.0 g of anhydrous sodium carbonate in 160 mL of distilled water by heating. Filter the solution, if necessary. Add to it a solution of 3.46 g of cupric sulfate $CuSO_4 \cdot 5H_2O$ dissolved in 20 mL of distilled water. Dilute the combined solutions to 200 mL.

sary. The lactose solution may be somewhat cloudy but will clear when the nitric acid is added. Add 1 mL of concentrated nitric acid to each tube. Heat the tubes in the hot-water bath for 1 hour in a hood (nitrogen oxide gases are evolved). Remove the tubes and allow them to cool slowly after the heating period. Scratch the test tubes with clean stirring rods to induce crystallization. After the test tubes are cooled to room temperature, place them in an ice bath. A fine precipitate of mucic acid should begin to form in the galactose and lactose tubes about 30 minutes after the tubes are removed from the water bath. Allow the test tubes to stand until the next laboratory period to complete the crystallization. Confirm the insolubility of the solid formed by adding about 1 mL of water and then shaking the resulting mixture. If the solid remains, it is mucic acid.

QUESTIONS

1. A student decided to determine the optical rotation of mucic acid. What should be expected as a value? Why?

2. Draw a mechanism for the acid-catalyzed hydrolysis of the acetal bond in lactose.

3. β-Lactose is present to a larger extent in an aqueous solution when the solution is at equilibrium. Why is this to be expected?

4. Very little of the free aldehyde form is present in an equilibrium mixture of lactose. However, a positive test is obtained with Benedict's reagent. Explain.

5. Outline a separation scheme for isolating casein, albumin, and lactose from milk. Use a flow-chart like that shown in the Advance Preparation and Laboratory Records section at the beginning of the book.

EXPERIMENT 50   ■

Mutarotation of Lactose

Polarimetry

In this experiment, you will study the mutarotation of lactose by polarimetry. The disaccharide α-lactose, made up of galactose and glucose, can be isolated from milk (Experiment 49). As you can see in the structures drawn in Experiment 49, the glucose unit can exist in one of two isomeric hemiacetal structures, α- and β-lactose. These isomers are diastereomers because they differ in configuration at one carbon atom. The glucose part can also exist in a free aldehyde form. This aldehyde form (open form in the equation below) is an intermediate in the equilibration of α- and β-lactose. Very little of this free aldehyde form exists in the equilibrium mixture.

Laboratory 1 - ISOLATION OF AN ANALGESIC
Experiment 9, page 71 of <u>Pavia</u>.

What is in the pill that you take when you have a headache or a fever? There is an analgesic such as aspirin (acetylsalicylic acid), ibuprofen or acetaminophen (structures on page 71 of <u>Pavia).</u> There are also a number of other compounds which make the pill more palatable. Usually there is some coating, there may be starch or a binder, sugar or a buffer such as sodium bicarbonate. Our goal in this lab will be to take an analgesic pill and to isolate the active ingredient. Fortunately the three analgesics listed above all have similar solubility properties and we can isolate each using the same set of procedures. Each student will isolate only one of the analgesics. Include the structures of the three analgesics and their melting points in your prelab.

WASTE DISPOSAL: Dispose of all organic waste including acetone in the waste containers under the hood. Use a plastic beaker in your hood to collect organic material during lab and then dispose of the waste properly after you are finished. Do not pour ANY organic solvents into the sink (that includes acetone)!

UPDATES:
1. Page 72–Use a regular glass pipet not a filter-tip pipet. Don't worry if the solution is slightly cloudy.
2. Be sure to record the amount of analgesic present in the pill you use.
3. On the back of this page is a sample grading key. The grading key is different for each lab since we don't do the same things each time, but certain components such as lab skills and understanding will always be present.   Next lab you will have a reaction.
4. Be sure to save a sample of your isolated analgesic for Experiment 2.

ISOLATION OF ANALGESIC   NAME_____

	Max	Grade
Pre-lab [30]		
Analgesic structures	15	_____
Procedure	15	_____
Lab skills [50]		
Overall lab performance	11	_____
Data & observations	14	_____
Product grading	5	_____
Cleanliness	5	_____
Safety	15	_____
Worksheet [20]		
Worksheet questions	20	_____
Subtotal	**100**	_____
Deductions	**(6)**	_____
Total	**100**	_____

LAB PERIOD 2 - INFORMATION SHEET
SYNTHESIS OF ACETAMINOPHEN (Exp 10B) AND TLC (Exp 11)

I. Relevant information

A. Write up the two experiments **separately**.

B. Prepare and run TLC plate 1- the knowns- while your acetaminophen reaction is running and cooling. This will save about 20 minutes.

C. The second TLC plate should be spotted with pre-made solutions of anacin and excedrin, a solution you make of your analgesic from week 1, a solution of your acetaminophen from week 2, an unknown which you will be given (be sure to record the number), and the reference mixture (6 spots). Use the 50% methylene chloride-50% ethanol mixture to dissolve the solids and use the ethyl acetate/acetic acid mixture as the developing solvent. If you do not have your week 1 analgesic, get some from another student. To check that the solutions which you prepare are concentrated enough look for the spot on the spotting line with the UV lamp before developing the plate. (ONLY 1 Unknown)

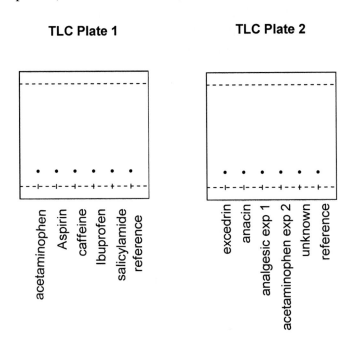

D. There will be no decolorization step in the acetaminophen synthesis and you do not have to take the melting point of your product.

E. Do not overheat your reaction. If you lose all of your solvent, add more water. No aluminum collars needed for heating.

ISOPENTYL ACETATE SYNTHESIS

We will be doing procedure **13B** on page 106 (not 13A). We will be preparing our reaction mixtures in a microwave vessel and microwaving the solutions for 5 minutes. You will only use 5 drops of sulfuric acid which your tf will add. We will not be refluxing the reaction mixture. (note- the dispensing pumps have a maximum volume of 2.0ml. Therefore to measure 2.5 ml, we will set the pump at 1.25 ml and dispense twice. Please do not change the pump to 2 and then 0.5 ml.)

To avoid irrevocable errors, keep your discarded layers in a clean container till you have product.

2. Be sure you have a stir bar in the microwave vessel. At the end of the experiment return the vessel to your tf who will check you for having the complete assembly.

3. After drying, weigh your crude product in a glass scintillation vial. Using a 3 ml reaction vial, distill 2 ml of the crude to get pure product. Remove and discard the first half ml of distillate and collect about 1mL more. Place it in a plastic sample vial and take the IR spectrum. Turn in both your crude and pure products to your TF.

4. You will use an aluminum block for heating during the distillation. Use the metal thermometer in the aluminum block (it fits in the little hole in the side of the block). Do **not** use a glass thermometer in the aluminum block – they explode. Use a glass thermometer in the Hickman head as shown in figure 14.7B page 710 and **record** the distillation temperature.

Diagram of Apparatus

5. Be sure you have one and only one "O" ring inserted between the ground glass joint of your condenser and the screw cap. Otherwise you will lose your product. You may need to insulate your vial with cotton or aluminum foil for the distillation.

POST-LAB QUESTIONS

1. Question 3, p 107 Why is the reaction mixture extracted with sodium bicarbonate? Give an equation and explain its relevance.

(2) What reagents would you place in the microwave tube if you wished to synthesize the ester ethyl butyrate ($CH_3CH_2CH_2CO_2CH_2CH_3$), which has the aroma of pineapple?

(3) The IR spectrum of isopentyl alcohol is shown below. Assign the peaks of diagnostic value above $1000\ cm^{-1}$.

(3) The IR spectrum of acetic acid is shown below. Assign the peaks of diagnostic value above $1000\ cm^{-1}$

INSTRUCTIONS FOR ANALYZING INFRARED (IR) SPECTRA

Infrared (IR) spectra provide information about the functional groups present in a molecule. You will use the IR spectrum to establish the identity and the purity of your product.

Consider the structure of the compound and consult a correlation table such as that on page 851 of your lab text, which lists the most important functional groups and where their corresponding IR peaks are likely to appear. Assign the peaks of diagnostic value above 1000 cm^{-1}, that is, state which functional group in your product gives rise to which peak.

Important: Write the assignment directly on your IR spectrum: do not make assignments in the text of your post-lab. You're encouraged to discuss the assignments in the text of your post-lab, but the assignments must appear on the IR spectrum that you submit.

Compare the IR spectrum of your product with that of an authentic sample. Such spectra can be found in the lab text and on the web. Some favorite on-line libraries of IR spectra can be found at

http://webbook.nist.gov/chemistry/
http://riodb01.ibase.aist.go.jp/sdbs/cgi-bin/cre_index.cgi?lang=eng

It's also a good idea to compare your spectrum with those of the starting materials and solvents employed in the reaction and purification process.

Some issues to entertain in your post-lab: Are the expected peaks present? Does your IR spectrum exhibit peaks that are not present in the spectrum of the authentic sample? What is causing the extra peaks (e.g., unreacted starting materials, residual solvent that you failed to remove during purification, etc.).

METHYL STEARATE

(1) You will be doing the bromine test at the end of the procedure.

(2) You will be taking an IR and preparing samples for both GC/MS and NMR.

(3) Be careful not to add the sulfuric acid too fast. Do not let the liquid level get higher than the sidearm of the flask (or into the tubing) or your reaction won't work.

(4) You will not monitor the reaction progress. Just stop the reaction at the designated time in the lab manual.

(5) Be sure to include an equation in your lab notebook for the reaction happening during the bromine test. (see prelab lecture slides)

Postlab Questions

(1) The IR spectrum of methyl oleate is shown below. Assign the peaks above 1500 cm$^-$^{1}.

(2) How does your IR spectrum of methyl stearate differ from that of methyl oleate?

Polystyrene (Exp 49C)

- Purify styrene by passing it through a plug of alumina. Take a short pasteur pipette and place a small piece of cotton on the bottom. Add a small amount of aluminum to the pipette about ¼ full. Add 3 mL to the plug slowly and pass it through the aluminum. You can speed this up by pushing the styrene through with a pipette bulb. Collect the filtrate in a small vial or beaker.

-Use the purified styrene for the reaction.

- Scale down the reaction. Use 2 mL of styrene and 50 mg of benzoyl peroxide. Set-up the reaction in a test tube.

- Heat the reaction mixture to 80-100 °C on an aluminum block. Once the solution begins to bubble (~5min), immediately take it off of the hotplate. (Be careful! It tends to splatter).

- Once the solution stops bubbling put it back on the hotplate. You will now heat it until it polymerizes. This will probably take at least take 30 minutes. You can set-up the benzoin reaction while you wait. Just make sure to check back regularly on the progress of your polymerization.

- Do not use your spatula to scrape your polystyrene. It sticks to everything and is hard to remove. You can use a disposable pipette if needed.

- Take an IR of your polymer. Assign the major peaks and discuss them in your lab report.

Postlab Questions:

1) Why do you pass the styrene through a plug of alumina (pipette with alumina in it) before you start the reaction?
2) What is the main difference in the IR between styrene and polystyrene?
3) Give an example of a possible termination step for the polymerization reaction..

INSTRUCTIONS FOR ANALYZING INFRARED (IR) SPECTRA

Infrared (IR) spectra provide information about the functional groups present in a molecule. You will use the IR spectrum to establish the identity and the purity of your product.

Consider the structure of the compound and consult a correlation table such as that on page 851 of your lab text, which lists the most important functional groups and where their corresponding IR peaks are likely to appear. Assign the peaks of diagnostic value above 1000 cm^{-1}, that is, state which functional group in your product gives rise to which peak.

Important: Write the assignment directly on your IR spectrum: do not make assignments in the text of your post-lab. You're encouraged to discuss the assignments in the text of your post-lab, but the assignments must appear on the IR spectrum that you submit.

Compare the IR spectrum of your product with that of an authentic sample. Such spectra can be found in the lab text and on the web. Some favorite on-line libraries of IR spectra can be found at

http://webbook.nist.gov/chemistry/
http://riodb01.ibase.aist.go.jp/sdbs/cgi-bin/cre_index.cgi?lang=eng

It's also a good idea to compare your spectrum with those of the starting materials and solvents employed in the reaction and purification process.

Some issues to entertain in your post-lab: Are the expected peaks present? Does your IR spectrum exhibit peaks that are not present in the spectrum of the authentic sample? What is causing the extra peaks (e.g., unreacted starting materials, residual solvent that you failed to remove during purification, etc.).

WILLIAMSON ETHER SYNTHESIS of Phenacetin

This experiment has been adapted from Miller, J., Neuzil, E. *Modern Experimental Organic Chemistry*, D.C. Heath and Co.: Lexington, MA 1982, pp228-231 and has undergone microwave enhancement by Danielle Falcone, class of '05 and R. Baar, M. R.; Falcone, D.; Gordon , C. *J. Chem. Educ.*, **2010**, *87*, pp 84–86.

BACKGROUND:

One way to synthesize aryl ethers is through a Williamson ether synthesis, which is the reaction of an alcohol (usually deprotonated) with an organohalide. The reaction proceeds through a S_N2 mechanism. The alcohol itself is not nucleophilic enough to undergo the reaction on its own so it needs to be deprotonated to make it a better nucleophile.

In this experiment you will be doing a Willamson ether synthesis starting with acetaminophen which is an analgesic you synthesized in a previous lab. You will be converting acetaminophen into another analgesic called phenacetin.

SAFETY NOTES
1) Iodoethane (ethyl iodide) is an irritant, toxic and readily absorbed through the skin. Wear gloves when handling and do not breathe vapors.
2) Assembly of the microwave rxn vessel is critical. The cap must be tight.

EXPERIMENTAL PROCEDURE:
Obtain a microwave reaction vessel with cap and stir bar from your TF.

Preparation of phenacetin:
Add acetaminophen (0.5 g) and postassium carbonate (1.1 equiv) directly into the microwave vessel containing a stirbar. Add 5 mL of acetone and iodoethane (1.2 equiv). Cap the reaction vessel (make sure to have both white Teflon plug and cap) and tighten the cap with the wrench. Label the top of your reaction vessel with your name on a piece tape. Make sure not to cover the hole on the top of the vessel. Your TF will microwave your reaction for 10 minutes at 130 °C at 1200 W power setting.

At the end of the heating period, recover your reaction vessel from the microwave turntable and let the reaction mixture cool. Spot a solution of the acetaminophen standard (you can do this while your reaction is in the microwave to save time) and spot your reaction mixture on a TLC plate (see TLC plate below).

Work-Up

Transfer the liquid in your microwave tube to a 25 mL Erlenmeyer leaving behind as much of the solid as possible. Rinse the remaining solid in your flask with CH_2Cl_2 (5 mL) and add it to the Erlenmeryer. Remove the solvent from the material in the Erlenmeyer by blowing a stream of air over it. Once the liquid has been removed, redissolve the solid obtained in CH_2Cl_2 (not all of the solid may dissolve) and transfer to a large falcon tube. Add 5% NaOH (10 mL) to the tube and shake well. Remove the top layer. Add saturated NaCl solution (10 mL) to the remaining organic layer in the falcon tube and shake. Remove the bottom layer, dry over sodium sulfate and filter to remove the sodium sulfate. Be sure to rinse the sodium sulfate with CH_2Cl_2 (2 mL) and filter. Evaporate the dichloromethane away by blowing air on the sample until a solid is obtained. Record the mass of your product obtained.

TLC

Dissolve a small amount of your product in acetone and spot it on your TLC plate from before. Run your TLC plate in ethyl acetate, which has been provided. Record your TLC plate in your notebook and calculate the R_f of your product and acetaminophen for your postlab.

Analysis

Obtain a mass of your purified product, TLC, LC/MS (sample diluted in CH_3OH) and NMR ($CDCl_3$).

TLC plate

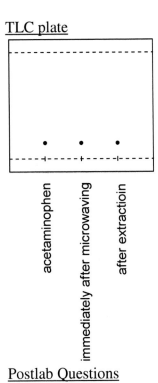

Postlab Questions

1) What should be the difference in the IR for acetaminophen and your product?

2) Why do you have to extract the reaction with 5% NaOH in water?

3) What would be the major difference between the NMR of the starting material and the product?

4) Why do you need to add base (K_2CO_3) to the reaction?

Methylcyclohexene

Procedure: Experiment 25A in lab manual.

DEVIATIONS FROM THE PROCEDURE IN THE LAB TEXT

Instead of using 4-methylcyclohexanol as a stating material you will be using 2-methylcyclohexanol.

Do not record the IR spectrum of the product, nor the boiling point, nor perform test for unsaturation.

Do perform TLC on the dehydration product: use CH_2Cl_2 as the developing solvent. Although the TLC result will not particularly pretty to look at, it may be informative.

Write out the mechanisms of how two possible products could be made in your lab notebook before lab.

Take a NMR and GC of the product.

POST-LAB REPORT
Some issues to entertain in your post-lab write-up include, but are not limited to: What is the product? How do you know what the product is? Is the product a single compound or a mixture? How do you know? If it is a mixture, why so? Is the product contaminated by impurities? If so, what are the impurities?

Much of what you say in the post-lab is guided by your NMR spectrum. Assign the peaks in your spectrum by: (1) drawing what you think the structure of the product is directly on your spectrum; (2) identifying the protons with code letters (e.g., "H$_a$", "H$_b$", "H$_c$", etc.), but grouping protons that give rise to the same signal under the same label; (3) writing "H$_a$", "H$_b$", "H$_c$", etc., near the appropriate peaks so that the assignment is clear; (4) identifying impurity peaks. The sketch at right shows the correct format applied to the NMR spectrum of 2-ethylanisole.

Benzoin and Benzil

BENZOIN Part (I, Exp 36A)
You only need to write up the first portion of the experiment on pg. 307 labeled reaction mixture.
- Set-up the reaction in a scintillation vial. Label the vial with your initials and 4 number code and give to your TF to store until the next lab.

BENZOIN Part (II)
At this lab session you will be completing the synthesis of benzoin (Exp 36A) and carrying out the oxidation of benzoin to benzil **following the procedure on page B9 in the rear of the lab text: do not use the procedure on page 309.**

Please keep the documents you submit for the Benzoin and Benzil experiments separate: they are two different experiments. Don't just staple everything together!

When you come to lab, immediately cool your vial of crude benzoin in an ice bath for 5 min to maximize the yield of benzoin. If no crystals form, use a glass rod to vigorously scratch the vial for 5 min. If after scratching no crystals form, add a few seed crystals of "store-bought" benzoin and continue scratching and cooling. Recrystallize benzoin in an Erlenmeyer flask from a minimum amount of hot 95% ethanol. Retain 0.03 g of your purified benzoin for NMR analysis.

You must have at least 0.30 g of purified benzoin to perform the oxidation of benzoin to benzil. If you don't have the required amount, make up the deficit by using "store-bought" benzoin.

BENZIL
Note the following deviations from the Benzil procedure in the lab text.
a. Initially heat the benzoin/Cu^{2+}/NH_4NO_3 solution at 150 °C (not at 135 °C as directed in the lab text) for 15 min.
b. If the reaction mixture does not turn a clear green color after 15 min at 150 °C, add another 0.5 mL of Cu^{2+}/NH_4NO_3 solution and continue heating at 150 °C.
c. If the reaction mixture does not turn a clear green color by 5 min after the addition of the extra Cu^{2+}/NH_4NO_3 solution, remove from the heat for 5 min.
d. Regardless of whether extra Cu^{2+}/NH_4NO_3 solution is added or not, decrease heat to 135 °C after the reaction mixture turns a clear green color.

Monitor the progress of the reaction by TLC so that you know when the reaction is complete. You should only use 2 TLC plates! The following procedure is suggested:

a. Spot a plate with standard benzoin solution, standard benzil solution (these standard solutions are already made up for you), and your reaction mixture before heating: call this the "time = 0 min plate". Spot the same TLC plate after 10 minutes and 20 minutes then develop the plate using CH_2Cl_2 as the developing solvent.

b. Repeat the spotting and development procedure on a second plate after 40 min of heating and run the plate. The reaction is complete when the spot corresponding to your reaction mixture consists only of benzil; this may take more than 20 min and you may have to run more than three plates. Whatever the TLC result, stop the reaction after about 50 min.

Recrystallize benzil from the minimum amount of hot 95% ethanol. The lab manual suggests using 7 mL of ethanol per gram of benzil, but this quantity is simply a rough guideline and in fact may be excessive.

Analyze the purified benzil by IR. Before recording the IR spectrum allow the purified benzil to air dry several minutes then put a small amount of benzil in a vial and place the vial in an oven for 10 minutes.

Analyze the purified benzil by LC/MS. Put a small amount of the solid (less than 1 mg) and dissolve in methanol. Take the vial to the instrument room where an instrument TF will help you set up the LC/MS. If your sample is yellow you have added too much.

In your post-labs analyze the NMR of benzoin and the IR and LC/MS of benzil, but remember that benzoin and benzil are separate experiments: keep all your documents relating to each experiment apart. If you failed to isolate benzoin, ask for a standard NMR to analyze.

POST-LAB REPORTS: SPECTRA

Much of what you say in the post-lab is guided by your NMR spectrum. Assign the peaks in your spectrum by: (1) drawing what you think the structure of the product is directly on your spectrum; (2) identifying the protons with code letters (e.g., "H$_a$", "H$_b$", "H$_c$", etc.), but grouping protons that give rise to the same signal under the same label; (3) writing "H$_a$", "H$_b$", "H$_c$", etc., near the appropriate peaks so that the assignment

is clear; (4) identifying impurity peaks. The sketch at right shows the correct format applied to the NMR spectrum of 2-ethylanisole.

You should discuss how you arrived at the assignments, but the assignments themselves must be written directly on the spectrum to be submitted with your post-lab.

On your IR spectrum draw the structure of the compound and write the assignments of the diagnostic peaks (e.g., N–H, O–H, etc.) directly on the spectrum.

Wittig reaction

Carry out the procedure for Exp 44B, p 362. You will NOT be preparing your own benzyltri-phenylphosphonim chloride (Wittig salt): you will use "store-bought" Wittig salt.

The second paragraph in the section "Separation of the isomers of 1,4-diphenyl-1,3-butadiene" (p 363) describes a method for removing traces of NaCl from the product. Because this procedure involves multiple transfers of the product from the Hirsch funnel to a beaker and then back to the Hirsch funnel, the amount of product lost during the transfers may be significant. It is recommended that you leave the product on the Hirsch funnel and simply wash the product with three 1-mL portions of water while applying suction. Allow the product to dry thoroughly by pulling air through after the washes with water.

You will be analyzing the product and a filtrate that contains a mixture of product and side-products as directed in the lab text ("Thin-Layer Chromatography", page 363): do not discard the filtrate until you are sure that you have a satisfactory TLC result. Use hexane as the developing solvent. Visualize the TLC plate using both the long- and short-wavelength settings of the UV lamp. The relevant R_f values are: *trans,trans*-product = 0.36, *cis,trans*-product = 0.41.

Do not determine the melting point of the product.

Be sure to record the NMR spectrum of your product and present an analysis (peak assignments, discussion of chemical shifts and splitting, indication of purity of the sample, etc.) of the spectrum in your lab report.

Take a GC/MS of your sample. Put a small amount of sample (less than 1 mg) in a GC vial and dissolve in hexanes.

Post-lab questions to be included with the lab report
(1) You did not prepare your own benzyltriphenylphosphonim chloride ($PhCH_2PPh_3Cl$, Wittig salt). Write a reaction showing how the Wittig salt is prepared from benzyl chloride ($PhCH_2Cl$).
(2a) Define the term "ylide".
(2b) You actually worked with an ylide in an earlier experiment this semester. Draw the structure of the ylide prepared in that earlier experiment.
(3) Write a sequence of reactions showing how the alkene at right could be synthesized by a Wittig reaction.
(4) Suppose you carried out a Wittig reaction that gave a mixture of *trans*- and *cis*-β-methyl-styrene (below) and were able to separate these two stereoisomers. What feature (aside from tiny chemical shift differences) in the NMR spectrum of these compounds would allow you to tell which was which?

trans-β-methylstyrene   *cis*-β-methylstyrene

<u>Luminol</u>

The "Aromatic Substitution" experiment originally scheduled in the syllabus is replaced by "The Synthesis of Luminol", Exp 52, p 437. Please read the Essay p 433. The experimental procedure you carry out starts at part B, p 440.

No mechanism for the formation of luminol is required in the pre-lab, but the reactions by which luminol produces luminescence are required. These were given at the pre-lab lecture and in the lab text.

Deviations from the procedure in the lab text

(1) The lab text instructs you to begin the synthesis of luminol by using "moist 5-nitrophthalhydrazide": this means 0.3 g of 5-nitrophthalhydrazide moistened with 3 drops of water. The reagent bottle may be labeled "3-nitrophthalhydrazide": this is an alternate name for the same compound.

(2) 0.65 g of $Na_2S_2O_4$ should be used instead of the 0.8 g as directed in the lab text.

(3) The lab text directs that the 5-nitrophthalhydrazide reaction mixture be heated in a 13x100 mm test tube: although this procedure is adequate, it requires careful monitoring on your part if a violent and dangerous ejection of hot material from the test tube is to be prevented. Instead, it is suggested that the reaction mixture be heated in a conical flask equipped with a spin vane and an air condenser.

(4) Do not perform the section in the lab text dealing with the quenching of luminescence by the addition of dyes.

(5) Take a LC/MS of your product by making a solution in methanol. Analyze your data in your lab report.

Post-lab questions to be included with the Luminol lab report

(1) Why is base (KOH) needed for the luminol to exhibit luminescence?
(2) Why does luminescence stop if the container of luminol, DMSO and KOH is kept closed?

EXPERIMENT 49rear

The chemistry of milk

You will start Experiment 49rear (Chemistry of milk) at lab session 5 and finish it at lab session 6. Submit a pre-lab concerning the whole experiment at the end of lab session 6; the post-lab report is due one week after lab session 6. The pre-lab does not require you to present any reaction mechanism, but do write out the reactions under study for Milk part II only.

Milk Part I

At lab session 5 you separate the components of milk following the procedure that starts at p B36 in the rear of lab text; stop after carrying out the "Precipitation of Lactose" section on p B38. The best recovery of casein is achieved if it is removed gently and the milk solution (not the hot water bath, but the actual milk solution) is at 40 °C when treated with acetic acid.

At lab session 6 you will perform several carbohydrate tests (carry out Benedict's test p B47, Barfoed's test p B47, and osazone formation p B47) on the lactose you isolated and on solutions of glucose and galactose for comparison.

Milk Part II

1) Isolate lactose and weigh your solid (B38). Record weights of your casein and albumins.
2) Perform Benedict (B47), Barfoed (B47) and phenyl hydrazine (B48) test on solutions of 5 different carbohydrates and an unknown (glucose, galactose, lactose, fructose and sucrose.) You should have 7 test tubes for each reaction. One for each carbohydrate, one for the unknown and a control.
3) Step 3: Hydrolyze your lactose (use the procedure found for sucrose B49) and test with a diastix strip. Use only 1 test strip. You TF will do one sample of lactose with the test strip whose results you should record.

Post-lab questions

(1) The osazone formation reaction involves a redox reaction: What is oxidized and what is reduced?

(2) Predict the result of Benedict's test on sucrose (see structure, p 146). Explain your answer in terms of the chemistry of the test.

(3) Draw the product that forms when lactose (below) reacts with Benedict's reagent.

lactose

(4) Explain why casein is soluble in milk but insoluble in dilute acetic acid.

(5) Cow's milk is a mixture of water, proteins, carbohydrates, fats, and minerals. On the average milk contains 87.1% by weight water and 4.9% by weight carbohydrate – proteins, fats, and minerals make up the remaining 8.0%. Assuming that all the carbohydrate in milk is lactose, calculate the mass of lactose in 4.0 g of dry milk powder.

The chemistry of the Clinitest strip

The strip has been impregnated with the enzymes glucose oxidase and peroxidase, as well as *ortho*-toluidine. Glucose is oxidized to gluconic acid and hydrogen peroxide by glucose oxidase:

glucose   gluconic acid

The hydrogen peroxide reacts with peroxidase to produce oxygen, which oxidizes the *ortho*-toluidine to give colored products:

$$2 \ H_2O_2 \quad \xrightarrow{\text{peroxidase}} \quad 2 \ H_2O \ + \ O_2$$

$\quad + \quad O_2 \quad \longrightarrow \quad$ colored products

ortho-toluidine

Preparation of an α,β-unsaturated ketone *via* Michael and Aldol reactions

Overview of the reactions

The carbon next to the carbonyl (C=O) carbon is called the α carbon and the carbon next to the α carbon is called the β carbon. An α,β-unsaturated carbonyl compound is a carbonyl compound (aldehyde, ketone, ester, etc.) that has a multiple (double or triple) bond between the α carbon and the β carbon.

trans-chalcone
an α,β-unsaturated ketone

In a Michael reaction, an α carbon attacks the β carbon of an α,β-unsaturated carbonyl compound to afford a 1,5-dicarbonyl compound, that is, the product has one carbonyl carbon at position 1 and another carbonyl carbon at position 5:

In an Aldol condensation, an α carbon attacks a carbonyl carbon to afford a β-hydroxy carbonyl compound, that is, the product has an OH group β to a carbonyl:

Under the reaction conditions you will be employing, the β-hydroxy carbonyl compound dehydrates to afford a new α,β-unsaturated carbonyl compound:

When the Michael–Aldol–dehydration sequence forms a ring, the overall reaction is called a Robinson annulation. This process is important in the laboratory preparation of steroids (see post-lab questions).

Deviations from the procedure and helpful hints

Carry out the procedure below instead of Exp 42, p 344 in your text. Background on the experiment can be found on pg. 344 of your lab manual.

Place 0.24 g chalcone, 0.15 mL ethyl acetoacetate, and 5 mL absolute ethanol in a microwave tube. Use a pipet pump and a graduated disposable pipet (not a syringe) to dispense the ethyl acetoacetate. Add a microwave tube stir bar (please don't lose it; this is not the spin vane in your kit). Swirl to dissolve; you may have to heat the tube gently in a hot water bath to get everything to go into solution. Add 0.25 mL 2.2 M NaOH. Seal the microwave tube with its stopper. Cover the microwave tube with its cap and click the cap shut using a block torque wrench. Label the top of your tube, but be careful not to cover the small hole at the top of the tube. Hand your microwave tube to the TF, who will insert it into a sleeve in the microwave wheel. The TF will take the wheel to the instrument room for microwave heating.

Try to submit your microwave tube to the TF as soon as you can: we want to microwave the whole section's samples in one go, so don't hold up the rest of the class. Be aware that one or two samples cannot be run in the microwave; there's no starting this lab over.

Cool the reaction mixture to room temperature and add 2 mL of water. Scratch the inside of the microwave tool with a glass stirring rod. Place the microwave tube in an ice–water bath until no more crystals appear to form. It's a good idea to scratch the microwave tube while it's sitting in the ice–water bath to induce crystallization. Vacuum filter the crystals on a Hirsch funnel, using 1 mL of ice-cold water to aid in the transfer. Then rinse the microwave tube with 1 mL of ice cold 95% ethanol to complete the transfer of the remaining solid from the microwave tube to the Hirsch funnel. Weigh the dry product. The solid contains sodium hydroxide and sodium carbonate which are removed in the next step. If you isolate very little product when you filter the crystals after the cooling period, but the filtrate is obviously cloudy with suspended material, try adding about 1 mL of ice-cold water to the filtrate and refiltering. This usually increases the amount of solid that collects on the filter disc.

Place your crude product in a centrifuge tube, add 1.5 mL of reagent-grade acetone, and centrifuge the tube. After centrifugation, withdraw the acetone solution to a *pre-weighed* small beaker. You are now ready to evaporate the acetone using gentle heat (place the small beaker in a hot–water bath) and slow stream of air. After the evaporation of the acetone, reweigh the small beaker to determine the yield of partially purified product.

Recrystallize the product after evaporating the acetone. But before doing so, carefully judge the amount of product you have at this point: **you need to have enough product to record its IR spectrum and to submit a sample for NMR analysis.** Depending on the amount of product you have and your recrystallization skills, it may be wise to submit your *partially purified product* for

Preparation of an α,β–unsaturated ketone via Michael and Aldol reactions

IR, LC/MS and NMR analysis. What if your recrystallization doesn't work out and you get nothing?

Crystallize the product in a 10 mL Erlenmeyer flask using a minimum amount of hot 95% ethanol (approximately 2 mL). After the solid has dissolved, allow the flask too cool slightly. Scratch the inside of the flask with a glass stirring rod until crystals appear. Allow the flask to sit undisturbed for a few minutes then place the flask in an ice-water bath for at least 15 minute.

Collect the crystals by vacuum filtration on a Hirsch funnel. Use two 0.5 mL portions of ice cold 95% ethanol to aid in the transfer. Allow the crystals to dry on the funnel. Weigh the solid you obtained.

Take a ^{1}H NMR, LC/MS and IR of your final product.

Post-lab

As part of your post-lab report, analyze your spectra. "Analyze" doesn't mean just assigning the peaks: it means assigning *and* discussing the basis of your assignments. For example, the IR of the product should exhibit two prominent peaks corresponding to carbon–oxygen double bond stretching, one belonging to the ester and the other to the ketone: How do you know which is which?

Post-lab questions

(1) In a Michael reaction, an α carbon attacks the β carbon of an α,β-unsaturated carbonyl compound to afford a 1,5-dicarbonyl compound. Ethyl acetoacetate has two α carbons: why does the α carbon sandwiched between the two carbonyls conduct the attack?

This forms...   ...not this: Why?

(2) In a Robinson annulation, an α,β-unsaturated carbonyl compound reacts with a carbonyl compound to afford a (new) cyclic α,β-unsaturated ketone by a Michael–Aldol–dehydration sequence. Draw the structure of the reactants that would combine to form the A ring of the steroid desoxy-19-nortestosterone (below) by a Robinson annulation.

desoxy-19-nortestosterone

Preparation of an α,β-unsaturated ketone via Michael and Aldol reactions

PREPARATION OF THE GRIGNARD REAGENT: PHENYLMAGNESIUM BROMIDE

bromobenzene + Mg $\xrightarrow{\text{ether}}$ phenylmagnesium bromide

Preparation of Glassware All glassware used in a Grignard reaction must be scrupulously dried. Surprisingly large amounts of water adhere to the wails of glassware, even glassware that is apparently dry. Dry all the pieces of glassware shown in the figure in an oven at 110 °C for at least 30 minutes. Prepare a drying tube with anhydrous calcium chloride and place it in the oven. In addition, dry the following: two 3-mL and one 5-mL conical vials, which will be needed for solutions and solvents, and a calibrated Pasteur pipet (0.5-mL and 1.0-mL calibration marks) for use in dispensing ether.

If there are visible signs of water in the apparatus, you must first dry the glassware and any plastic connectors by rinsing them with acetone. The glass pieces may then be placed in the oven.

Assemble the apparatus as shown in the figure as soon as the glassware has cooled somewhat. Obtain a 4.5-cm length of magnesium ribbon and scrape both sides of the ribbon with the side of a spatula to remove any oxide coating that may be present. Weigh the strip of magnesium and trim both ends until you have a weight of about 0.037 g (record the actual weight in your notebook). While holding the ribbon with tweezers, cut the strip into about 2-mm sections with sharp scissors, and allow the pieces to fall directly into a dry beaker. Remove the 5-mL conical vial from the apparatus and transfer the magnesium to the vial. Place a dry magnetic spin vane into the vial and reassemble the apparatus.

Formation of the Grignard Reagent Transfer about 4 mL of anhydrous diethyl ether into a dry 5-mL conical vial and cap the vial. Use this vial to store your dry ether during the course of this experiment. During the experiment, remove the ether from this vial with a dry calibrated Pasteur pipet.

Place 0.17 mL of bromobenzene (MW = 157.0) into a pre-weighed 3-mL conical vial and determine the weight of the material transferred. Add 1.0 mL of anhydrous ether to the vial. After the bromobenzene dissolves, draw this solution into the syringe and cap the vial that you used for the bromobenzene solution for later use. After inserting the syringe needle through the rubber septum, add 0.2 mL of the bromobenzene solution to the magnesium in the vial. Position the apparatus just above the hotplate and stir the mixture gently so as to avoid throwing the magnesium onto the side of the vial. You should begin to notice the evolution of bubbles from the surface of the metal, which signals that the reaction is starting. It will probably be necessary to heat the mixture using your hotplate to start the reaction. The hotplate should be adjusted to its lowest setting. Since ether has a low boiling point (35 °C), it may be sufficient to heat the vial by placing it just above the hotplate. Check to see if the bubbling action continues after the apparatus is lifted above the hotplate. The reaction should start, but if you experience difficulty, proceed to the next paragraph.

Optional Steps You may need to employ one or more of the following procedures if heating fails to start the reaction. If you are experiencing difficulty, remove the syringe and rubber septum. Place a dry glass stirring rod into the vial and gently twist the stirring rod so as to crush the magnesium against the glass surface. Reattach the rubber septum and heat the mixture again. Repeat the crushing procedure several times, if necessary, to start the reaction. If the crushing procedure fails to start the reaction, then add one small crystal of iodine to the vial. Again, heat the mixture gently. The most drastic action, other than starting the experiment over again, is to prepare a small sample of the Grignard reagent in a test tube. When this reaction starts, add it to the main reaction mixture in the vial.

Completing the Grignard Preparation When the reaction has started, you should observe the formation of a brownish-gray cloudy solution. Using a syringe, add the remaining solution of bromobenzene slowly over a period of 5 minutes. Be sure to hold the plunger of the syringe so that the entire solution is not added at one time. It may be necessary to heat the mixture occasionally with the hotplate during the addition. If the reaction becomes too vigorous, slow the addition of the bromobenzene solution and raise the apparatus higher above the hotplate. Ideally, the mixture will boil without the application of external heat. It is important that you heat the mixture if the reflux slows or stops. As the reaction proceeds, you should observe the gradual disintegration of the magnesium metal. When all the bromobenzene has been added, place 0.50 mL of anhydrous ether in the vial that originally contained the bromobenzene solution, draw it into the syringe, and add the ether to the reaction mixture. Remove the syringe after making this addition. You should add additional anhydrous ether to replace any that is lost during the reflux period. You should maintain the level of the reaction solvent so that it is no lower than the 1 mL mark of the conical vial. After a period of about 45 minutes from the beginning of the addition of bromobenzene, most or all of the magnesium metal should have reacted. Cool the mixture to room temperature.

PREPARATION OF TRIPHENYLMETHANOL

phenylmagnesium bromide   benzophenone

adduct   triphenylmethanol

Addition of Benzophenone While the phenylmagnesium bromide solution is being heated and stirred under reflux, make a solution of 0.273 g benzophenone in 0.50 mL of anhydrous ether in a 3-mL conical vial. Cap the vial until the reflux period is over. Once the Grignard reagent is cooled to room temperature, draw the benzophenone solution into the syringe. Add this solution as rapidly as possible to the stirred Grignard reagent, but at such a rate that the solution does not reflux too vigorously. Once the addition has been completed, cool the mixture to room temperature. The solution turns red and then gradually solidifies as the adduct ($Ph_3CO^-MgBr^+$) is formed. When stirring is no longer effective, remove the syringe and septum and stir the mixture with a spatula. Rinse the vial that contained the benzophenone solution with about 0.2 mL of anhydrous ether and add it to the mixture. Remove the reaction vial from the apparatus and cap it. Occasionally stir the contents of this vial. Recap the vial when it is standing to avoid contact with water vapor. The adduct should be fully formed after about 15 minutes. You may stop here.

Hydrolysis Add 1.5 mL of 6M hydrochloric acid (dropwise at first) to neutralize the reaction mixture, The acid converts the adduct to triphenylmethanol (Ph_3COH) and inorganic compounds ($MgBr_2$, $MgBr(OH)$). Eventually, you should obtain two distinct phases: the upper ether layer will contain triphenyl methanol; the lower aqueous hydrochloric acid layer will contain the inorganic compounds. Use a spatula to break up the solid during the addition of hydrochloric acid. You may need to cap the vial and shake it vigorously to dissolve the solid. Since the neutralization procedure evolves heat, some ether will be lost due to evaporation. You should add enough ether to maintain a 3-mL volume in the upper organic phase (use graduations on the vial for measurement). Make sure that you have two distinct liquid phases before separating the layers. More ether or hydrochloric acid may be added, if necessary, to dissolve any remaining solid. In some cases, it may be necessary to add more water instead of more hydrochloric acid.

If some material remains undissolved or if there are three layers, transfer all the liquids to your 10-mL falcon tube, Add more ether and hydrochloric acid to the conical vial, cap it, and shake it; then add the contents to the falcon tube. Continue adding small portions of ether and hydrochloric acid to the centrifuge tube and shake it until everything dissolves. At this point, you should have two clear layers.

Separation and Drying If a small amount of unreacted magnesium metal is present, you will observe bubbles of hydrogen being formed. You may remove the aqueous layer even though the magnesium is still producing hydrogen. Remove the magnetic spin vane with tweezers and rinse it with a little ether. Draw off the lower aqueous phase with a Pasteur pipet and place it in another conical vial. Remember to save the ether layer in the first vial because it contains the triphenylmethanol product. Reextract the aqueous phase in the second vial with 0.5 mL of ether. Remove the lower aqueous phase and discard it. Combine the remaining ether phase with the first ether extract. Transfer the combined ether layers to a dry 5-mL conical vial with a dry Pasteur pipet. Dry the ether solution with granular anhydrous sodium sulfate (two microspatulafuls measured in the V-grooved end).

Evaporation Remove the dried ether solution from the drying agent with a Pasteur pipet, transfer it to a small Erlenmeyer flask, and rinse the drying agent with more diethyl ether. Evaporate the ether solvent in a hood by heating the flask in a warm water bath. Evaporation will occur more quickly if a stream of nitrogen or air is directed into the flask, You should be left with a mixture that varies from a brown oil to a colored solid mixed with an oil. This crude mixture contains the desired triphenylmethanol and the by-product biphenyl. Most of the biphenyl can be removed by adding 1 mL of petroleum ether (bp 30-60 °C). Petroleum ether is a mixture of hydrocarbons that easily dissolves the hydrocarbon biphenyl and leaves behind the alcohol triphenylmethanol. Do not confuse this solvent with diethyl ether ("ether"). Heat the mixture slightly, stir it, and then cool the mixture to room temperature. Collect the triphenylmethanol by vacuum filtration on a Hirsch funnel and rinse it with small portions of petroleum ether. Air-dry the solid, weigh it, and calculate the percentage yield of the crude triphenylmethanol (MW = 260.3).

Crystallization Crystallize all of your product from hot isopropyl alcohol. Set the crystals aside to air-dry. Report the recovered yield in grams. Submit the sample to the instructor.

GRIGNARD REACTION: SYNTHESIS OF TRIPHENYLMETHANOL
Procedural changes and helpful hints for Grignard synthesis

Read pages 317-320 in the text, but use the procedure on the handout, which is a true microscale procedure.

1. Mg metal should be cut into pieces the width of a toothpick (small!). If possible bring your own scissors.

2. At the start of the lab you will receive a beaker of oven-dried equipment. Be sure to cap this equipment as soon as you get it. At the end of the lab you are to return to your TF a beaker with the following CLEAN equipment: two 5-mL vials, two 3-mL vials, 1 Claisen head, 1 drying tube with calcium chloride (use glass wool not cotton), 1 calibrated Pasteur pipette.

3. Use a 10-mL Erlemeyer to recrystallize your product.

4. Do TLC on the recrystallized product. Dissolve a spatula tip full of product in minimal ether in your 3-mL vial. Spot it on a small silica gel plate and use methylene chloride as your developing solvent. Use a 100-mL beaker and watch glass as a developing chamber. The R_f value of biphenyl is 0.9. The R_f value of triphenylmethanol is about 0.58. Visualize the plate with UV light.

5. Do IR on your product.

6. Dispose of all needles and syringes in the red sharps container. Do not put them in the garbage or glass waste.

7. Use only 3 syringes for the lab. One 5 mL and two 1 mL. You a calibrated Pasteur pipette for when you are transferring the dry ether to make solutions of your starting materials.

POST-LAB QUESTIONS

1. Why is the R_f value of biphenyl larger than that of triphenylmethanol?

2. Why does $Ph_3CO^-MgBr^+$ dissolve when HC1 is added? Write a chemical equation to describe what happens. Does it dissolve in the water layer or the ether layer? Is the final product, triphenylmethanol, soluble in ether or water? Explain your answer.

(3) What would be the difference in the NMR of triphenylmethanol and benzophenone?

Biginelli Reaction

Multicomponent reactions (MCRs) are important in organic and medicinal chemistry. In MCRs multiple starting materials react in one pot to yield (ideally) one product. The Biginelli reaction (discovered in the 1890s by Pietro Biginelli) is an MCR that can be used to prepare 3,4-dihydropyrimidinones, a class of compounds that exhibits pharmacological activity. The classical Biginelli reaction is an acid-catalyzed condensation of a β-dicarbonyl compound, an aromatic aldehyde, and urea:

β-dicarbonyl   aromatic aldehyde   urea   3,4-dihydropyrimidinone

By varying the identity of R_1, R_2, and Ar, pharmaceutical companies create a "chemical library" of 3,4-dihydropyrimidinones; each different compound is then screened for pharmacological activity, toxicity, severity of side effects, etc., with the hope of arriving at a commercially viable drug.

In this experiment the class will create a library of 3,4-dihydropyrimidinones, but each section will contribute only one compound to that library on the following basis:

Section	β-Dicarbonyl Compound	Aryl Aldehyde
Tuesday afternoon	ethyl acetoacetate	benzaldehyde
Tuesday night	ethyl acetoacetate	thiophene-2-carbaldehyde
Wednesday night	acetoacetamide	benzaldehyde
Thursday night	methyl acetoacetate	thiophene-2-carbaldehyde

Friday Afternoon	methyl acetoacetate	3,4,5-trimethoxybenzaldehyde

As part of your pre-lab preparation, you should look up the molecular weights of the compounds assigned to your section and whether they are liquids or solids. Everyone will use urea (MW = 60.06 g/mol) and ytterbium triflate monohydrate (Yb(OTf)$_3$·H$_2$O, MW = 620.25 g/mol) as a Lewis acid catalyst.

Ytterbium triflate catalyzed microwave procedure

To an Erlenmeyer flask add 4.0 mmol of urea and 0.40 mmol of Yb(OTf)$_3$·H$_2$O (separately weighed). Add next 0.4 mL ethanol and 4.0 mmol of the aldehyde. Lastly, add 1.2 mL of glacial acetic acid and 4.0 mmol of the β-dicarbonyl compound. Set the flask in a hot water bath and swirl periodically until all the solids dissolve. Transfer the solution to a microwave vessel. Be sure to add a small stir bar (please don't lose it or dump it down the drain!), cap the microwave tube and tighten the cap with the torque wrench. Label the top of the microwave tube with a small piece of tape with your name on it, being sure not to cover the vent hole. Give the tube to the TF, who will operate the microwave for ten minutes at 120 °C.

Cool the reaction mixture to room temperature, transfer to an Erlenmeyer flask, then place in an ice bath. The 3,4-dihydropyrimidinone should precipitate within about 20 minutes, but some may take significantly longer (maybe an hour): scratching the bottom of the Erlenmeyer may speed things along. Filter the solid using a Hirsch funnel; wash the product with **cold** ethanol. Record the mass of crude product.

Transfer your crude product to an Erlenmeyer flask or beaker. Dissolve your crude product in a minimal amount of hot ethanol. Allow the solution to cool fully to room temperature. Then place on ice and cool to 0 °C. Filter the solid using a Hirsch funnel, washing with **cold** ethanol. Weigh the purified compound.

You will record and analyze both the ^{1}H- and the ^{13}C-NMR spectrum of the purified product. You must prepare two separate tubes for ^{1}H- and ^{13}C-NMR analysis. Prepare the sample for ^{1}H-NMR analysis in the usual way, that is, about 25 mg of compound in three fingers of solvent. The sample for ^{13}C-NMR analysis must be much more concentrated, maybe 100 mg of compound in three fingers of solvent. Use deuterated dimethylsulfoxide (DMSO-d_6) as the solvent for both samples. Be sure to clearly label the NMR "ticket" as ^{1}H or ^{13}C as appropriate. You will also record an LC/MS by dissolving less than 1 mg of your sample in methanol in a LC/MS vial and submit it on the instrument.

Post-lab questions

(1) Find an example of a chemical library that has been constructed. Some synonyms of "chemical library" are "library synthesis" and "combinatorial synthesis". (See the bottom of the page for hints)

(a) Draw the structure of at least three compounds that were created as components of the library.

(b) Write a summary using chemical symbology (i.e., a chemical reaction showing starting materials, reaction conditions, and products; not a paragraph of text detailing the procedure) describing how the compounds were synthesized.

(c) Describe what physiological effect(s) the library compounds were intended to target (e.g., anti-tumor activity).

(d) Include a hard copy of the first page of the report you are citing or print out the first page of the web page you use as your reference. The source (journal or book reference, URL) of your example must be clear.

(2) What are the physiological effects of 3,4-dihydropyrimidinones? Look it up in a book or on the internet.

(3) Write a mechanism for the classical Biginelli reaction:

(4) What is the role of the ytterbium triflate ($Yb(OTf)_3$) in the reaction you conducted? Notice that $Yb(OTf)_3$ isn't in the classical Biginelli. Show at least one chemical equation that describes ytterbium triflate's function. (This can be found on the last page of the prelab slides)

How to find a library?

1) Google
2) Search on Journal of Medicinal Chemistry, an online journal:
   http://pubs.acs.org/journal/jmcmar
3) Use SciFinder (a scientific search engine) go to
   http://www.bu.edu/library/sel/research/scifinder/scifind/ set-up an account.
4) Use Web of Knowledge search:
   http://apps.webofknowledge.com.ezproxy.bu.edu/WOS_GeneralSearch_input.do?product
   =WOS&search_mode=GeneralSearch&SID=3EiboCLeCKJDBH3dbgP&preferencesSav
   ed=

Synthesis of Aspartame (Part I)

You should begin the synthesis of aspartame at the second lab period of the Aldol project.

The artificial sweetener aspartame (Nutrasweet®) was accidentally discovered in 1965 by James Schlatter when, in the course of synthesizing an antiulcer drug for the Searle pharmaceutical company, he licked his aspartame-contaminated fingers: aspartame was a side-product of the reaction Schlatter was conducting. We don't know exactly how aspartame is manufactured commercially because that is a corporate secret protected by patents. Your synthesis of aspartame will employ thermolysin, an enzyme isolated from the bacteria *Bacillus thermoproteolyticus*. Colonies of this microorganism are found growing in hot springs. The enzyme has a molecular weight of about 34,600 g/mol and consists of 316 amino acid residues.

If the laboratory synthesis of aspartame were simple, the carboxy (CO_2^-) group at the so-called α carbon of the naturally occurring amino acid L-aspartic acid would react with the amino (NH_3^+) group of the amino acid derivative L-phenylalanine methyl ester to create a new amide bond:

L-aspartic acid   L-phenylalanine methyl ester   aspartame

But life is not simple: it is very messy. L-Aspartic acid has two carboxy groups: what's to stop L-phenylalanine methyl ester from reacting with the carboxy group of L-aspartic acid that is not α (i.e., the wrong carboxy group) and what's to stop a carboxy group of L-aspartic acid from reacting with an amino group of another L-aspartic acid molecule?

We resort to two strategies to circumvent these unwanted side-reactions. First, we take advantage of the exquisite selectivity of thermolysin: only the carboxy group at the α carbon of L-aspartic acid reacts in the presence of the enzyme. Second, the amino group of L-aspartic acid is rendered unreactive by temporarily masking it with the carbobenzoxy group:

N-carbobenzoxy-
L-aspartic acid

N-carbobenzoxyaspartame

After the enzyme catalyzes the formation of the new amide bond, the carbobenzoxy protecting group is removed by treatment with ammonium formate (HCO_2NH_4) in the presence of carbon-supported palladium (Pd/C):

aspartame

In Part I of the synthesis of aspartame you carry out the thermolysin-catalyzed reaction.

Thermolysin-catalyzed synthesis of N-carbobenzoxyaspartame Weigh out 0.267 g (1 mmol) of N-carbobenzoxy-L-aspartic acid and 0.431 g (2 mmol) of L-phenylalanine methyl ester hydrochloride into a new centrifuge tube and suspend the powder mixture in 3 mL of distilled water. Add a clean spin vane to the tube: dirty spin vanes are contaminated with organic residue and acid or basic impurities that may deactivate enzyme. Using pH paper as your guide and with stirring, adjust the suspension to pH 7 by addition of 4 M NaOH. **This operation is a tricky patience-tester!** You are looking to turn the pH paper a definite mustard-yellow color: you are not looking for the color of merely wet pH paper (pH 6, not enough NaOH) and you are definitely not looking to turn the pH paper green or blue (pH 8 or 9, too much NaOH). About 0.7 mL of NaOH solution is required, but, if you overshoot the pH, you will have to start over. A good technique is to add about half the required amount of NaOH solution and then approach pH 7 by dropwise addition. The solution should be clear when pH 7 is reached. Be careful about how you withdraw the solution to spot the pH paper: remember that contaminated spatulas and glass rods may poison the enzyme. Add 0.2 mL of the thermolysin stock solution (0.05 g in 5 mL of distilled water). Don't worry if the enzyme solution is cloudy. Stir the solution for 5 min. Remove the spin vane using a magnetic extractor on the outside of the centrifuge tube -- don't put tweezers into the solution. Cap the tube, label it and leave it with the TF until the next laboratory period.

Synthesis of Aspartame (Part II)

In Part I of the synthesis of aspartame you should have conducted the thermolysin-catalyzed synthesis of *N*-carbobenzoxyaspartame:

| *N*-carbobenzoxy-
L-aspartic acid | L-phenylalanine
methyl ester | *N*-carbobenzoxyaspartame |

In the remaining lab periods devoted to the synthesis of aspartame, you will isolate *N*-carbobenzoxyaspartame, remove the carbobenzoxy protecting group by treatment with ammonium formate (HCO_2NH_4) in the presence of carbon-supported palladium (Pd/C), and analyze the final product. Several references to TLC are made in the procedure; see the section on TLC later in this handout.

Isolation of *N*-carbobenzoxyaspartame Break up the precipitate with a glass rod and filter through a Hirsch funnel. Wash the solid thoroughly using five 4-mL portions of distilled water. You are removing the enzyme and unreacted amino acids. When washing a solid on the Hirsch funnel disconnect the vacuum hose from the valve so that the wash liquid can be mixed well with the solid before being sucked through the filter. Save a very small sample (about 5 mg) for TLC.

At this point the solid is actually a salt in which one molecule of *N*-carbobenzoxyaspartame is ionically associated with one molecule of L-phenylalanine methyl ester:

We now wish to neutralize the *N*-carbobenzoxyaspartame by stripping away the L-phenylalanine methyl ester.

Transfer the solid to a centrifuge tube and place the tube in an ice–water bath. Add 3 mL of water and 1 mL of 1 M HCl. Stir the mixture very well with a glass rod, being sure that all of the solid (including whatever sticks to the sides of the tube) comes in contact with the HCl solution. After about 10 minutes the solid will change appearance and look more compact. The reaction that is taking place is

Filter the solid through a Hirsch funnel and wash with five 4-mL portions of ice-cold water. Save a small sample (about 5 mg) for TLC.

Removal of the carbobenzoxy protecting group Transfer the solid (which should still be moist) to a centrifuge tube. Add 0.126 g of ammonium formate (HCO_2NH_4), 2 mL of methanol, and a spin vane. Stir, but do not be concerned if all the solid fails to dissolve. Add 0.05 g of 5% Pd/C (the catalyst) to the centrifuge tube, washing down any catalyst particles that adhere to the sides of the tube with 0.5 mL of methanol.

> ☠ Use caution when handling the Pd/C catalyst: it may flash or spontaneously ignite. Do not scrape or grind the catalyst. Place combustible items (weighing boats, weighing paper, centrifuge tubes, filter discs, etc.) that have come into contact with the catalyst in a small beaker of water. At the end of the lab dispose of catalyst-contaminated items in the special Pd waste container.

Stir the suspension at room temperature in the open centrifuge tube until gas evolution ceases (about 20 min). If a precipitate forms, add water (no more than 1 mL) dropwise to dissolve the precipitate before going on to the next step. The reaction that is taking place is

Removal of the catalyst Centrifuge the tube. Be sure that there is no solid other than the catalyst before centrifugation. The product is in the supernate.

Although centrifugation separates out most of the catalyst, any residual catalyst suspended in the supernate is so fine that it must be removed by a special filtering technique. Place a filter disc in your Hirsh funnel and add a 1 cm layer of Celite (a mineral consisting of the fossilized remains of a hard-shelled algae). Then add about 1 mL of methanol to form a slurry and apply vacuum. You should produce a thin Celite "cake". Filter the supernate through the Celite cake by trickling it down the side of the Hirsch funnel using a pipet. If the supernate is added too rapidly, it will tunnel through the Celite and separation of the catalyst will not be achieved. Rinse the Celite with three 1-mL portions of methanol. Add water to the catalyst remaining in the centrifuge tube and dispose of it in the Pd waste container. The Celite cake should also be disposed of in the Pd waste.

Isolation of aspartame Transfer the filtrate to a 30-mL beaker. Apply a sample of the solution to a TLC plate (this solution should contain the crude aspartame) then evaporate the solvent by blowing a stream of air into the beaker while it is sitting in a hot-water bath. You are removing methanol and water so this operation may take some time. Recrystallize the product in a minimum amount (less than 5 mL) of hot methanol. Cool the solution in ice for at least 15 min to allow crystals to form. If you do not get product, reduce the volume to half by gentle heating and cool again.

Filter the product and let it dry on the filter. Be sure your filter flask is clean and dry before this final filtration. (If you have very little product, you can evaporate the filtrate to half its volume, cool, and collect additional product.) Weigh the product and save it for TLC and LC/MS (liquid chromatography/mass spectrometry) analysis.

TLC analysis Dissolve the two solid samples you saved from the "Isolation of *N*-carbobenzoxyaspartame" section and the recrystallized aspartame (about 5 mg each) in separate test tubes or vials in about 0.5 mL of methanol and spot each on the TLC plate on which you applied the crude aspartame solution. If the samples don't dissolve in the methanol, add a drop of water. Also spot a sample of authentic aspartame stock solution (if available) as a reference. Use a UV lamp to check your spots at the origin to be sure you can see them. Develop the plate using a 3:1:1 mixture of 1-butanol:acetic acid:water. This solvent moves slowly so the plate may take about 20 min to run. Visualize the plate with the UV lamp.

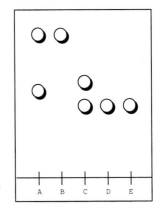

Ideally, your finished TLC plate should look like the figure at right. A = *N*-carbobenzoxyaspartame/L-phenylalanine methyl ester salt; B = *N*-carbobenzoxyaspartame; C = crude aspartame; D = recrystallized aspartame; E = authentic aspartame reference.

LC/MS analysis Dissolve about 0.005 g of the aspartame you synthesized in 1 mL of water in a test tube. You may have to heat it slightly in a hot water bath to get it to dissolve completely. Stuff a small ball of cotton down a Pasteur pipet and filter the aspartame solution directly into a special LC/MS vial. Rinse the cotton with 0.5 mL of water and add the rinse directly into the solution in the LC/MS vial. The TF will run the LC/MS samples.

<u>Aldol Reaction</u>

Your goals in this project-based experiment are (1) to identify an unknown aldehyde, (2) to identify an unknown ketone, and (3) to identify, purify, and characterize the product of a base-catalyzed aldol condensation with dehydration between the unknown aldehyde and ketone.

Two lab periods are devoted to the Aldol project: submit your pre-lab with your final report. **At the second Aldol lab period, begin the Synthesis of Aspartame experiment: you will prepare a reaction mixture that must sit for at least one day.**

Work plan
(1) You will be given a package containing two vials: one vial of unknown aldehyde and one vial of unknown ketone. **Record the code numbers of the vials in your notebook!** This is the only record of which unknowns you are given. If you need to replenish an unknown and you don't know what its code is, you'll have to start over with new unknowns -- and nobody wants that. The table on the next page lists the unknown aldehydes and ketones that are issued.

☠ The aldehydes and ketones are flammable and skin- and eye-irritants.

---

(2) Determine which vial contains the aldehyde and which the ketone. Submit samples from each vial for ^{1}H-NMR analysis. Try $CDCl_3$ as the solvent. If the unknown doesn't dissolve in $CDCl_3$, try DMSO-d_6 or methanol-d_3; in any case, **clearly indicate on the NMR "ticket" which solvent is used**. Because a spectrum is not recorded instantaneously (it takes 10–15 min to run), because there are 20 students in a section and we don't have 20 NMRs (an NMR costs about $300,000), and finally because the NMR instrument can be temperamental and rejects samples that are improperly prepared, expect delays in obtaining your NMR spectra. However, you need to know which is the aldehyde and which is the ketone before continuing: perform the chromic acid test (a qualitative way of identifying aldehydes). The NMR will confirm or contradict your qualitative test results.

Chromic Acid Test Aldehydes are oxidized to carboxylic acids by chromium trioxide (CrO_3) in acid solution:

$$3\,RCHO + 2\,CrO_3 + 6\,H^+ \rightarrow 3\,RCO_2H + 2\,Cr^{3+} + 3\,H_2O$$

Add 1 drop of unknown to 1 mL of HPLC- or reagent-grade acetone in a disposable test tube. (If there is any doubt about the purity of the acetone, test it beforehand with a drop of the chromic acid reagent.) Add 1 drop of the chromic acid reagent and swirl. The formation of a blue-green suspension due to insoluble salts of Cr^{3+} indicates a positive test. Most of the aldehydes issued in this experiment form the blue-green suspension in about 30-90 sec, but some may take longer so be flexible about interpreting the result. You are not looking to turn the entire solution blue-green: you are looking for the formation of blue-green particles in the solution.

☠ Sulfuric acid and the chromic acid reagent are corrosive. Chromium-containing compounds pose a special disposal concern. Rinse the test tubes in which you conduct the chromic acid test with wash acetone and dispose of the washes in the chromium-disposal container set up in the hood. Glassware and pipettes that come into contact with chromium should be disposed of in broken glassware boxes.

List of unknown aldehydes and ketones

Chemical Formula: C_7H_6O Molecular Weight: 106.12	Chemical Formula: C_5H_8O Molecular Weight: 84.12
Chemical Formula: C_8H_8O Molecular Weight: 120.15	Chemical Formula: $C_5H_{10}O$ Molecular Weight: 86.13
Chemical Formula: C_9H_8O Molecular Weight: 132.16	Chemical Formula: $C_6H_{10}O$ Molecular Weight: 98.14
Chemical Formula: $C_8H_8O_2$ Molecular Weight: 136.15	Chemical Formula: $C_7H_{14}O$ Molecular Weight: 114.19
Chemical Formula: $C_8H_8O_3$ Molecular Weight: 152.15	Chemical Formula: $C_7H_{12}O$ Molecular Weight: 112.17

(3) Once you have established which unknown is the aldehyde and which is the ketone, conduct the aldol condensation. The product of the reaction is called an α,β-unsaturated ketone or an enone:

ketone + aldehyde $\xrightarrow{OH^{\ominus}}$ α,β-unsaturated ketones (or enones) + H_2O

and/or

Notice that geometrical (*E,Z*) isomers of the product may result. Your job will be to determine whether a mixture of products is obtained and, if so, what is the major product. In some cases, the α,β-unsaturated ketones react further to afford dienones:

and/or $\xrightarrow{OH^{\ominus}}$ dienone + H_2O

The squiggly line in the dienone structure indicates that geometrical isomers may result.

In your report include the mechanism of the reaction that gave rise to the major product.

Aldol Condensation and Dehydration Measure 0.40 mL of unknown aldehyde and place it in a 5-mL conical vial. Measure 0.10 mL of unknown ketone and add it to the reaction vial. Add 2.0 mL of 95% ethanol and 1.5 mL of 2 M sodium hydroxide solution to the vial. Add a spin vane and stir for 15–30 min or longer if no precipitate forms. If the solution is only cloudy or very little precipitate has formed after 15 min, heat the reaction mixture in a beaker of boiling water for 10-15 minutes. Cool the vial to room temperature. The various possible condensation products form at different rates so be flexible about the reaction time. Be aware, however, that you may not see precipitate when the reaction flask is in the hot water bath because the product(s) may be soluble at that high temperature.

When precipitate seems to have stopped forming at room temperature, cool the flask further in an ice–water bath for 10 min. If the product is an oil, scratch the inside of the reaction vial with a glass rod during the cooling period. While the reaction mixture is cooling, chill 4 mL of 95% ethanol and 2 mL of a mixture of 4% acetic acid in 95% ethanol (v/v) in an ice bath.

Collect the product by vacuum filtration with a Hirsch funnel. Wash the product with 2 mL of the ice-cold ethanol, 2 mL of acetic acid in ethanol and finally 2 mL of ethanol. Each time disconnect the vacuum and thoroughly mix the solvent with the precipitate before allowing it to drain.

(4) Recrystallize the crude product; it is left up to you to determine an appropriate solvent for this purpose. See page 27 of the lab text for guidelines on solvent selection. Some possible choices are 95% ethanol, 9:1 (v/v) 95% ethanol/acetone and toluene. If you use toluene, you may have to add a few drops of hexane to promote crystallization. This is a "mixed solvent" technique; see pages 659 and 667 of the lab text.

(5) Characterize your purified product by IR, GC/MS, melting point and NMR. Check its purity by TLC, but again it is left up to you to find an appropriate developing solvent for that purpose (see page 785 of the lab text). A variety of solvents are available.

Aldol report

Submit your pre-lab along with your final report. The pre-lab should include a statement of the objective and procedure. The specific reaction and mechanism that gave rise to the major product can be left for the final report. As usual, record observations as you perform the experiment. Calculate a percent yield of your crude and purified aldol condensation product.

You should summarize the reasoning that led you to the identification of all compounds. Your report should include analyses of all spectra and a summary of the chemical tests you carried out. Be sure to explain peak locations (IR and NMR), splitting and integration (NMR). Note the presence of any impurities. Draw the structure of the pertinent compound and make peak assignments directly on the spectra. Include drawings of TLC plates.